PLANT BIOCHEMISTRY

Botanical Monographs

Edited by

W. O. JAMES F.R.S.

Professor of Botany
Imperial College, London, England

VOLUME THREE
PLANT BIOCHEMISTY

PLANT
BIOCHEMISTRY

D. D. DAVIES
B.Sc. Ph.D.
Reader in Biology
University of East Anglia

J. GIOVANELLI
B.Sc.Agr. Ph.D.
Plant Physiology Unit, C.S.I.R.O.,
Division of Food Preservation and School of
Biological Sciences, University of Sydney,
(Sydney, N.S.W., Australia)

T. AP REES
M.A. D.Phil.
Plant Physiology Unit, C.S.I.R.O.,
Division of Food Preservation and School of
Biological Sciences, University of Sydney,
(Sydney, N.S.W. Australia)

BLACKWELL
SCIENTIFIC PUBLICATIONS
OXFORD

FIRST PUBLISHED 1964

Printed in Great Britain by
ADLARD & SON LTD, THE BARTHOLOMEW PRESS, DORKING
and bound by
THE KEMP HALL BINDERY, OXFORD

CONTENTS

PREFACE

This book is intended for students of plant physiology and assumes a background of chemistry. There is no sharp boundary between plant physiology and biochemistry. Nevertheless textbooks of physiology are more numerous than textbooks of biochemistry. We have attempted to write a book which supplements existing texts of plant physiology, by paying rather more attention to chemical aspects. For example we have given a general account of enzyme kinetics rather than the application of Michaelis-Menten type kinetics to problems in plant physiology.

To keep the book reasonably short we have made many decisions about length. For example the length of the chapter on photosynthesis is conditioned by the fact that a book on this subject is being prepared in this series. We have tried to reflect current research interest by paying special attention to expanding subjects. On the other hand, we have not tried to incorporate the very latest research material and this decision is reflected in references at the end of each chapter. Literature citations are limited to cases where appeals to authority are needed and where references have some special significance. The reading list is intended to encourage wider reading and could be used as an entry into the relevant literature. However we advise our young readers to use *Chemical Abstracts* and *Biological Abstracts*. A list of journals and books of special interest to plant biochemists is given at the end of this preface.

We wish to thank Professor W. O. James F.R.S., for his invitation to write this book and for his advice on the general outline. We would also like to thank our colleagues in C.S.I.R.O. Division of Food Preservation, and in the University of Sydney, particularly Drs D. K. Dougall and D. Graham for helpful criticism of some chapters, and also Miss Penny Harpur for her skill in deciphering our handwriting. Our wives have gracefully accepted the existence of this book and we hope that it will be of some use to some students.

DAVID DAVIES *University of East Anglia*
JOHN GIOVANELLI *Sydney, N.S.W.*
TOM AP REES

REVIEW JOURNALS

1. *Annual Review of Plant Physiology*
2. *Annual Review of Biochemistry*
3. *Advances in Enzymology*
4. *Physiological Reviews*
5. *Biological Reviews*

NOMENCLATURE

The following list is not exhaustive. It includes only those abbreviations and symbols used commonly in the text.

AMP, ADP, ATP ⎫
CMP, CDP, CTP ⎪ Mono-, di-, and triphosphates of adenosine,
GMP, GDP, GTP ⎬ cytidine, guanosine and uridine, respectively
UMP, UDP, UTP ⎭

ADPG	Adenosine diphosphoglucose
CMU	p-Chlorophenyl dimethylurea
CoA	Coenzyme A
CMP.PC	Cytidine diphosphate choline
DNA	Deoxyribonucleic acid
DNP	2,4-Dinitrophenol
DPT	Diphosphothiamine
E ⎱ Enz ⎰	Enzyme
EMP pathway	Embden-Meyerhof-Parnas pathway
ES	Enzyme-substrate complex
exp	Exponential function, e.g. $\exp x = e^x$
FAD	Flavin adenine dinucleotide
FMN	Flavin mononucleotide
.FP	Flavoprotein
GSH	Glutathione
IAA	Indoleacetic acid
NAD	Nicotinamide adenine dinucleotide
$NADH_2$	Reduced form of nicotinamide adenine dinucleotide
NADP	Nicotinamide adenine dinucleotide phosphate

ix

NADPH$_2$	Reduced form of nicotinamide adenine dinucleotide phosphate
OD	Optical density
PGA	3-Phosphoglyceric acid
PMS	Phenazine methosulphate
P	Product
P$_i$	Inorganic phosphate
PP	Inorganic pyrophosphate
PPNR	Photosynthetic pyridine nucleoiide reductase
RNA	Ribonucleic acid
s-RNA	Soluble ribonucleic acid
S	Substrate
THFA	Tetrahydrofolic acid
TTP	Thymidine triphosphate
UDPG	Uridine diphosphoglucose

PHYSICAL CONSTANTS

E_h	Oxidation reduction potential
E_0	Standard oxidation reduction potential
E_0'	"Standard" oxidation reduction potential at pH 7
F	Faraday constant
ΔG	Free energy change
ΔG_o	Standard free energy change
$\Delta G'$	"Standard" free energy change at pH 7
k	Rate constant
K	Equilibrium constant
Ka	Dissociation constant of an acid
pKa	-Log Ka
Km	Michaelis constant
v	Velocity
V_{max}	Apparent maximum velocity
V_{app}	Maximum velocity

ACKNOWLEDGEMENTS

We wish to thank the following for permission to publish the following figures: Dr. C. R. Anfinsen and the publishers J. Wiley & Sons Inc., New York, for Figure 1.4; the American Chemical Society for Figures 1.5 and 1.20; the Academic Press Inc. for Figure 1.6 and the American Society of Biological Chemists for Figure 1.8.

CHAPTER 1

PROTEINS AND ENZYMES

In presenting an account of plant biochemistry it would seem reasonable to begin at the beginning. However, the study of biochemistry is largely the study of integrated cycles and to find the beginning is like posing the riddle of childhood 'which came first the chicken or the egg?' It can be argued that on the basis of evolutionary theory, the riddle may be answered in favour of the egg. A somewhat more sophisticated question 'which came first the gene or the cytoplasm?' is more difficult to answer. Whichever viewpoint is held, it is clear that nucleic acid (gene or virus) requires the presence of cytoplasm to manifest itself, whilst cytoplasm may, in the absence of nucleic acid, contract or perform various metabolic processes. Cytoplasm makes itself apparent by reason of its proteins and in particular by the association of catalytic properties with certain proteins called enzymes. Much of what follows in this book is an account of complex patterns of enzyme catalysis and so we begin by discussing proteins and the catalytic properties of the enzymes.

It is now widely accepted that enzymes are proteins and the converse statement, that proteins are enzymes, has been made by the Finnish biochemist A. I. Virtanen. Whilst the second statement is an overstatement, the first has no known exceptions, though it is true that protein fragments may have catalytic activity. The first evidence to support the view that enzymes are proteins was the isolation in 1926 of the enzyme urease in pure and crystalline form and the demonstration that it was a globulin protein. These results obtained by Sumner in America were opposed to the views of the distinguished German chemist Richard Willstätter. Willstätter had, in one sense, been unlucky to work with the enzyme peroxidase which is an extremely active catalyst. During purification, active preparations of peroxidase were obtained, containing no detectable nitrogen and in certain cases no detectable carbon or nitrogen. Following the isolation of crystalline urease, Willstätter argued that protein was a non-specific carrier of the labile and catalytically active group. Sumner did not capitulate but set about the difficult task of prov-

1

ing that catalytic activity was a property of the protein itself. As an example of his work we mention the purification of a specific antibody, antiurease, and the demonstration that following partial digestion of urease the amount of enzyme activity remaining corresponded to the amount of material that could be precipitated with antiurease. Following Sumner's work, numerous enzymes have been crystallized and the view that enzymes are proteins has become axiomatic.

The Classification of Proteins and Enzymes

There is no satisfactory classification of proteins, but following proposals by the British and American Physiological Societies (1907–8) and the publication of Osborne's book on *The Vegetable Proteins* (1919), the 'simple' proteins have been classified as follows.

(1) Albumins   Soluble in water and salt solutions.
(2) Globulins   Sparingly soluble in water, soluble in salt solutions.
(3) Prolamins   Insoluble in water and absolute ethanol, soluble in 70–80 per cent ethanol.
(4) Glutelins   Insoluble in all the above, soluble in acids and alkali.

There is an almost continuous spectrum of solubilities between the albumins and the globulins and since both show increased solubility as the salt concentration is increased, there can be no sharp division between these two groups. A number of globulins which occur in certain seeds as storage proteins, have been isolated as crystalline proteins, e.g. edestin from hemp seed, excelsin from Brazil nuts, arachin and conarachin from peanuts. Albumins are probably not storage proteins, and all globulins are not storage proteins. Thus the β-amylase present in barley is an albumin whereas the α-amylase is a globulin. The main storage proteins of the cereals are prolamins and glutelins. Because of their economic importance, the proteins of wheat have been extensively investigated. The prolamin of wheat is known as gliadin and together with α- and β-glutelin constitutes glutein, which is the residue remaining when starch is removed from flour. Flour with a high protein content is desirable for bread making, but a low protein content is required in flour used for biscuits.

SIMPLE PROTEINS

Simple proteins consist entirely of amino acids joined by peptide bonds to form one or more polypeptides chains having at one end an N-terminal group (i.e. a free amino group) and at the other end a terminal carboxyl group.

CONJUGATED PROTEINS

Conjugated proteins are associated with non-amino acid components. Thus the glycoproteins are highly viscous compounds in which the protein is linked to a polysaccharide. Whilst the nature of the bond is uncertain, it is probable that free amino groups on proteins react with carbohydrates in the way that amino acids and glucose react to give glucosylamines, which undergo the Amadori arrangement to yield fructosylamines. Lipoproteins are of wide distribution, being associated with membranes (see p. 260). The link between protein and lipid is weak and can be split by ethanol. Many preparations of lipoproteins from plants are coloured due to their content of carotenoids. Chlorophyll can be considered as a lipid and a green protein chlorophyll complex called chloroplastin has been isolated from a number of leaves. However, attempts to isolate chloroplastin of a definite composition have been unsuccessful. Crystalline preparations of chloroplastin have been obtained, but available evidence indicates that the protein is loosely adsorbed to crystalline chlorophyll. Flavoproteins and iron porphyrin proteins are important in respiration and are discussed in Chapter 5. The term nucleoprotein is often given to loose complexes of protein and nucleic acid, many of which are probably artifacts of isolation. There is an intimate association between nucleic acid and protein in certain organelles such as the microsomes, but a chemical association has not been established.

Enzymes are usually named by adding the suffix -ase to the name of the substrate or to the type of reaction catalysed. Thus fumarase is the enzyme which catalyses the hydration of fumarate and malic dehydrogenase is the enzyme which catalyses the removal of hydrogen from L-malate. The nomenclature and classification of enzymes is being revised by a commission established by the International Union of Biochemistry. Rules for a rational nomenclature will be put forward and rational names will be used for indexing and abstracting. Trivial names are to be recommended where the rational name is too long. Until this classification is available we list the following groups.

HYDROLYTIC ENZYMES

Enzymes acting by the introduction of the elements of water. For example, alkaline and acid phosphatases hydrolyse phosphate esters under alkaline and acid conditions respectively.

Oxidizing Enzymes

Enzymes removing hydrogen from a substrate but not reacting with oxygen are known as dehydrogenases. Thus malic dehydrogenase transfers hydrogen from malate to a coenzyme. Enzymes reacting directly with oxygen are known as oxidases. Thus glycolic acid oxidase transfers hydrogen from glycolate to oxygen. The term reductase is sometimes used in place of dehydrogenase if it is thought that the reaction proceeds, under physiological conditions, in the direction of substrate reduction. Thus the enzyme which catalyses the reduction of glyoxylate to glycolate in the presence of a coenzyme, has been named glyoxylic reductase rather than glycolic dehydrogenase, because the equilibrium favours substrate reduction and this is the postulated direction of the reaction within the cell.

Transferases

The first two groups are examples of transferring enzymes, but are excluded by defining transferases as 'those enzymes which transfer part of a donor molecule, except hydrogen or electrons, to an acceptor molecule, and neither donor nor acceptor may be water'. This is a very large group and includes the phosphotransferases more usually known as the kinases which transfer phosphate from one compound to another. Thus hexokinase transfers the terminal phosphate of adenosine triphosphate to glucose to form glucose-6-phosphate. The transaminases which transfer the amino group from an α-amino acid to an α-keto acid. A review of the transferases has recently been written by Hoffmann-Ostenhof (1960).

Decarboxylases

For example pyruvic decarboxylase which produces acetaldehyde and carbon dioxide from pyruvate.

Isomerases

For example phosphohexose isomerase catalyses the interconversion of glucose-6-phosphate and fructose-6-phosphate.

Protein Purity

The term protein has thus far been used in the generic sense, but it is difficult to define an individual protein. It has been widely held that for every gene there is an enzyme and we might argue that an individual protein or enzyme is the product of a single gene. Thus a particular enzyme, say malic dehydrogenase, could be regarded as an individual protein. However, in recent years, evidence has accumulated for the existence within the same organism of distinct molecular species of malic dehydrogenase. The name isozyme has been proposed for such divisions of the functional unit or enzyme. Theoretically it should be possible to isolate these individual proteins to characterize them, but technically this is frequently very difficult.

Purification of Proteins

The following are the most frequently used methods of purifying proteins.

SALT FRACTIONATION

Whilst albumins and globulins can be salted into solution, high concentrations of salt cause precipitation and it is possible to separate proteins with low solubility in salt solution from proteins with a higher solubility. The salt may be added in increments and the precipitates collected in a centrifuge before the addition of more salt. Alternatively, the proteins may be precipitated and serially extracted at different concentrations of salt. The salt most commonly used is ammonium sulphate, but ammonium citrate and ammonium phosphate have also been used.

ETHANOL OR ACETONE FRACTIONATION

Proteins may be fractionally precipitated by increasing the concentration of apolar solvents such as ethanol and acetone. It is necessary to keep the temperature close to the freezing point of the mixture during fractionation. A refrigerated centrifuge is essential for alcohol fractionation. Since the heat of solution of ethanol occurs mainly in diluting from absolute to 90 per cent, it is advisable to use 90 per cent ethanol for fractionation.

SELECTIVE PRECIPITATION

Certain proteins may be precipitated by lowering the pH or by gently heating a solution. Particular enzymes can sometimes be protected by carrying out the precipitation in the presence of the substrate.

ADSORPTION ON GELS

Certain proteins can be adsorbed on gels of calcium phosphate or aluminium hydroxide. Adsorption is generally most efficient at low pH and low ionic strength. The protein may be eluted by increasing the pH or the ionic strength. Proteins not adsorbed by the gel can sometimes be purified by adsorbing other proteins — such a process has been given the illogical name of negative adsorption.

Ion-exchange Chromatography

Recently, substituted celluloses have been extensively used — diethyl-aminoethylcellulose which is weakly basic and carboxymethylcellulose which is weakly acidic have proved most effective.

Gel Filtration

This technique has recently been introduced and is based on the separation of proteins according to their molecular weight by means of a commercial preparation called Sephadex. Sephadex is an insoluble but hydrophilic cross-linked dextran which functions as a molecular sieve to separate proteins on the basis of their size.

Special Methods

It is sometimes possible to make use of special properties of enzymes to purify them. For example, the enzyme enolase has a high affinity for Mg^{++} and can be purified by chromatography on Mg^{++} sulphoxy-methyl cellulose columns.

Criteria of Purity

For some years the hallmark of protein purity was taken to be crystallinity, but the existence of mixed crystals and the polydisperse nature of many crystalline preparations have shown crystallinity to be no sure guarantee of purity. A number of tests to detect the presence of impurities can be applied.

The Ultracentrifuge

The ultracentrifuge was developed by Svedberg to produce centrifugal forces of the order 500,000 times gravity. The relative centrifugal force is proportional to the radius from the axis of rotation and to the square of the speed of rotation. By applying very large centrifugal forces to a protein solution, the process of sedimentation is much more rapid than that of diffusion. Initially the protein molecules are evenly distributed through the solvent, but on applying a centrifugal force, the protein molecules migrate away from the axis of rotation and a fairly sharp boundary is formed between the water and the protein solution. The refractive index changes markedly at the boundary and various optical systems have been devised to follow the movement of the boundary during centrifugation. If a single molecular species is being examined a single boundary will be observed. If two proteins are present and they are sufficiently different in size, two boundaries will be observed. The rate at which a boundary moves is:

$$\frac{dx}{dt} = sw^2x$$

where x is the distance from the axis of rotation, w is the angular velocity in radians per second and s is a constant — the sedimentation constant. The value of s for proteins lies between 1 and 200×10^{-13} sec. A value of 1×10^{-13} is taken as one Svedberg unit (S).

ELECTROPHORESIS

Proteins carry positive and negative charges due to the presence of a number of ionizable groups in the molecule (see p. 11). When the pH of the medium is increased the protein tends to acquire a net negative charge due to reactions of the following type:

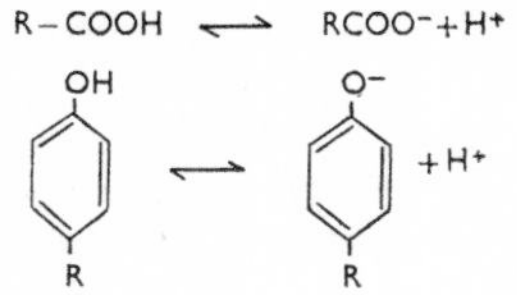

When the pH of the medium is decreased the protein tends to acquire a net positive charge due to reactions of the following type

$$H_2N—R + H^+ \rightleftharpoons NH_3^+—R$$

Thus if a mixture of proteins is placed in an electric field, proteins with a net negative charge will move to the anode, proteins with a positive charge will move to the cathode and proteins at their isoelectric point (i.e. with zero net charge) will remain stationary. Separations may be achieved on filter paper soaked in buffer, on buffered starch columns or in the refined electrophoretic apparatus designed by Tiselius. The student is referred to two articles by Alberty (1948) for an authoritative account of the principles involved in the use of the Tiselius apparatus.

ION-EXCHANGE CHROMATOGRAPHY

The production of celluloses substituted with ionic groups has led to the rapid development of methods for separating proteins. When a protein solution is passed through a column of the weakly basic diethylaminoethylcellulose, many proteins are bound and may be subsequently eluted from the column by increasing concentrations of salt. This method has been widely used as a preparative method but could well be used to check protein purity.

SOLUBILITY

When a pure substance is dissolved, the amount in solution is directly proportional to the amount of substance added to the solvent until saturation is reached. After saturation no more will go into solution and the solubility curve has the form shown in Fig. 1.1A. If two proteins are present, the more soluble protein will continue to go into solution after the less soluble protein has reached saturation and the solubility curve will have the form shown in Fig. 1.1B. The presence of more than one inflection point thus indicates the presence of more than one protein. Though a number of plant proteins have been highly purified and crystallized, in no case has a preparation been shown to be homogeneous by all the above tests.

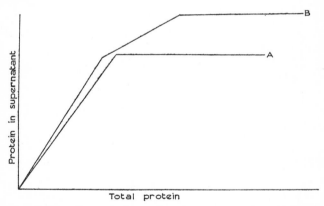

FIG. 1.1. Solubility curves: A, 1 compound; B, mixture of two compounds.

Protein Structure

Hydrolysis of proteins in strong hydrochloric acid leads to the production of free amino acids. The amino acids can be regarded as the building units from which proteins are constructed. Twenty-two amino acids have been conclusively demonstrated as constituents of plant proteins and

TABLE 1.1

The amino acids of proteins

Amino acid	Notes
Alanine $CH_3CH(NH_2)COOH$	First isolated from silk.
Arginine $HN=C(NH_2)NH(CH_2)_3CH(NH_2)COOH$	First isolated from lupine seedlings. Gives a red colour with α-napthol and sodium hypochlorite (Sakaguchi test).
Asparagine $H_2NOCCH_2CH(NH_2)COOH$	First isolated from asparagus. In 1933 proved to be a constituent of edestin — the seed protein of hemp. Subsequently found to be generally present in protein.
Aspartic acid $HOOCCH_2CH(NH_2)COOH$	First known as a hydrolysis product of asparagine.
Cysteine $HSCH_2CH(NH_2)COOH$	Readily oxidized to cystine. Acid hydrolysis of proteins yields cystine.
Cystine $HOOC\ CH(NH_2)CH_2SSCH_2CH(NH_2)COOH$	Probably the most important unit in determining the tertiary structure of proteins.
Glutamic acid $COOH(CH_2)_2CH(NH_2)COOH$	First isolated from wheat gluten. When boiled in aqueous solution gives rise to pyrrolidone carboxylic acid. $O=C-CH_2-CH_2-CHCOOH$ $\quad\vert\_\_\_\_\_NH\_\_\_\_\_\vert$
Glutamine $H_2NOC(CH_2)_2CH(NH_2)COOH$	First isolated from beet juice. Its presence in protein first established in edestin.
Glycine $CH_2(NH_2)COOH$	Also known as glycocoll. The N-methyl derivative–sarcosine– has been reported as a constituent of protein from peanuts.
Histidine 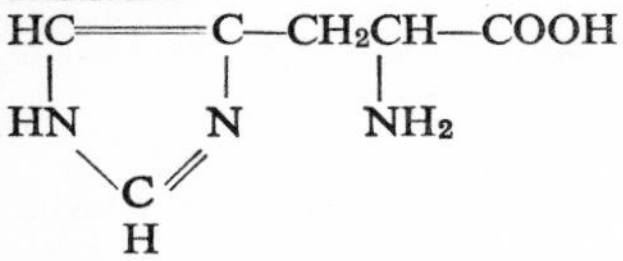 $HC\!=\!\!=\!\!=C-CH_2CH-COOH$ $\ \ \vert\qquad\ \vert\qquad\ \ \vert$ $HN\qquad N\qquad NH_2$ $\quad\diagdown C\diagup$ $\qquad H$	On coupling with diazotized sulphanilic acid in alkaline solution gives a red colour (Pauly reaction).

Amino acid	Notes
Hydroxyproline 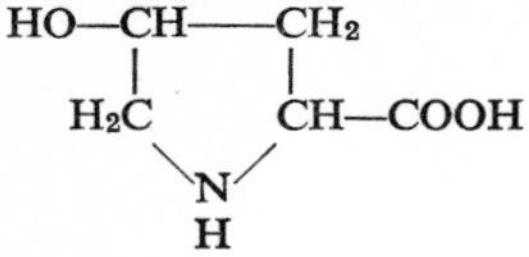 HO—CH——CH$_2$ 　|　　　　| H$_2$C　　　CH—COOH 　　＼N／ 　　　H	Strictly an imino acid not generally found in proteins. In plants present in protein associated with the cell wall. In animals a constituent of collagen.
Isoleucine 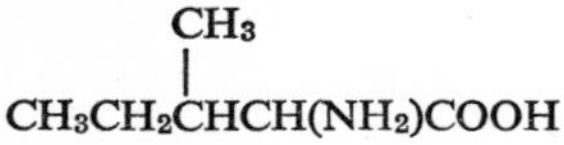 　　CH$_3$ 　　| CH$_3$CH$_2$CHCH(NH$_2$)COOH	First isolated from beet sugar molasses.
Leucine (CH$_3$)$_2$CHCH$_2$CH(NH$_2$)COOH	First isolated from cheese.
Lysine H$_2$N(CH$_2$)$_4$CH(NH$_2$)COOH	Certain plant proteins (e.g. zein and gliadin) may lack or contain only small amounts of lysine.
Methionine CH$_3$S(CH$_2$)$_2$CH(NH$_2$)COOH	The source of alkali stable sulphur of proteins. Readily oxidized to the sulphoxide
Phenylalanine 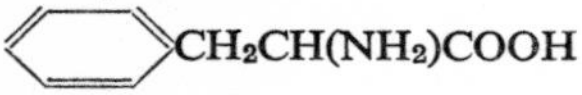 ⟨benzene ring⟩CH$_2$CH(NH$_2$)COOH	First isolated from lupine sprouts
Proline 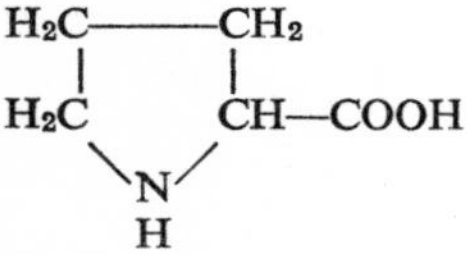 H$_2$C———CH$_2$ 　|　　　　| H$_2$C　　　CH—COOH 　　＼N／ 　　　H	An imino acid soluble in alcohol. Gives a yellow colour with ninhydrin.
Serine HOCH$_2$CH(NH$_2$)COOH	Phosphoserine is also present in certain proteins.
Threonine CH$_3$CH(OH)CH(NH$_2$)COOH	May be present in certain proteins as a phosphate ester.
Tryptophane 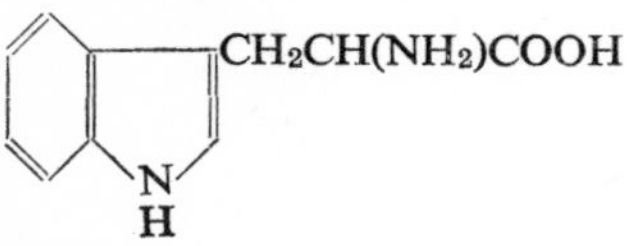 ⟨indole ring⟩CH$_2$CH(NH$_2$)COOH	Present in proteins in relatively small amounts.
Tyrosine HO⟨benzene ring⟩CH$_2$CH(NH$_2$)COOH 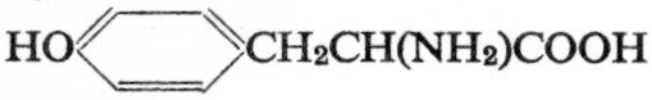	Has very low solubility in water.
Valine (CH$_3$)$_2$CHCH(NH$_2$)COOH	Present in proteins in relatively small amounts.

these are listed in Table 1.1. The sequence of amino acids in proteins is probably determined by a code present in nucleic acid (see p. 437). Current theories of coding can account for twenty amino acids; hence it is necessary to assume that hydroxyproline is alternative to proline as one of the 'magic twenty' and that cysteine but not cystine is coded.

General Properties of the Amino Acids

IONIZATION

Amino acids exist in aqueous solution as dipolar ions or zwitterions. For example, under acid conditions glycine will be in the form $CH_2(NH_3)^+COOH$ and under alkaline conditions $CH_2(NH_2)COO^-$, but at the isoelectric point there is no net charge on the molecule which can be written $CH_2(NH_3)^+COO^-$. Glycine carries charges on the α-amino group and the carboxyl group. Most amino acids have only these two groups but a number of amino acids have other ionizable groups. Thus dicarboxylic amino acids (e.g. aspartic acid) have a distal carboxyl group and diaminocarboxylic acids (e.g. lysine) have a distal amino group.

Other ionizable groups are

(1) The imidazole ring of histidine

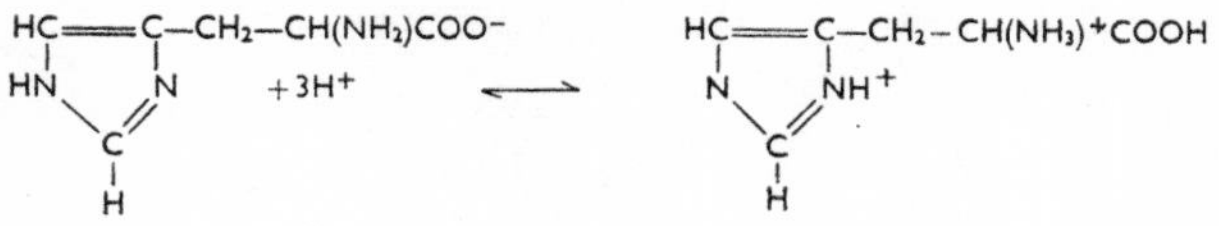

(2) The phenolic hydroxyl of tyrosine

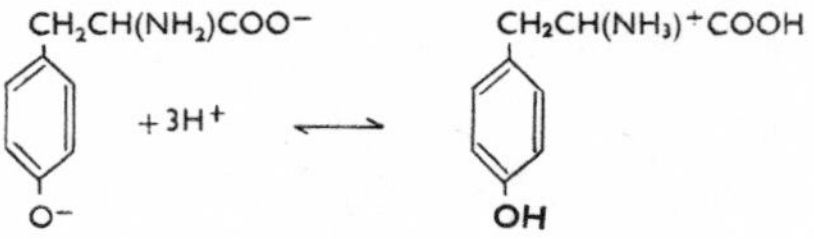

(3) The sulphydryl of cysteine

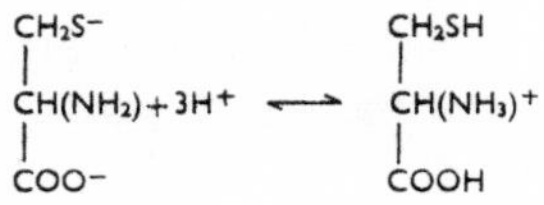

and (4). The guanidino group of arginine

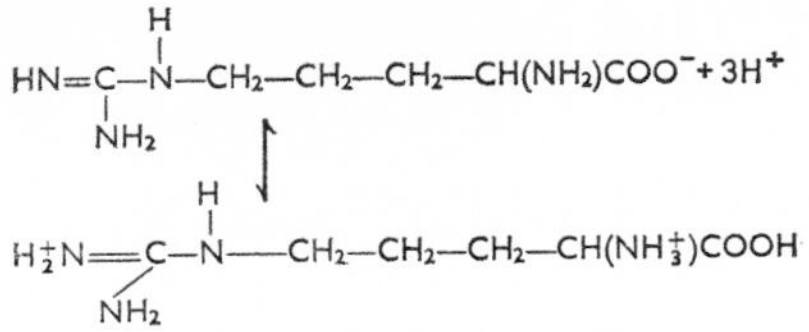

$$HN{=}C{-}N{-}CH_2{-}CH_2{-}CH_2{-}CH(NH_2)COO^- + 3H^+$$

(with H on the N and NH$_2$ below)

$$H_2^+N{=}C{-}N{-}CH_2{-}CH_2{-}CH_2{-}CH(NH_3^+)COOH$$

(with H on the N and NH$_2$ below)

The ionization of these various groups is of importance in the effect of pH on enzyme activity (see p. 56).

Consider the ionization of a carboxyl group:

$$R{-}COOH \rightleftharpoons H^+ + RCOO^-$$

At equilibrium, the dissociation constant

$$Ka = \frac{(H^+)(RCOO^-)}{(RCOOH)}$$

$$H^+ = Ka\,\frac{(RCOOH)}{(RCOO^-)}$$

$$-\log H^+ = -\log Ka - \log \frac{(RCOOH)}{(RCOO^-)}$$

Just as the abbreviation for $-\log H^+$ is pH, the abbreviation for $-\log$ Ka is pKa.

$$pH = pKa - \log \frac{(RCOOH)}{(RCOO^-)}$$

$$= pKa + \log \frac{(RCOO^-)}{(RCOOH)}$$

which is known as the Henderson-Hasselbalch equation. When

$$\frac{(RCOOH)}{(RCOO^-)} = 1$$

(i.e. when the acid is half neutralized)

$$pH = pKa$$

The student frequently finds it confusing to learn that the amino group behaves like an acid and that the relationship pH = pKa is valid.

The ionization of an amino group may be represented:

$$R{-}(NH_3)^+ \rightleftharpoons R\,(NH)_2 + H^+$$

Here following the Brønsted concept of a base as one with a tendency to gain a proton, the dissociation of the amino group is written from the acidic form.

Thus

$$Ka = \frac{(R(NH_2))(H^+)}{(R(NH_3^+))}$$

$$pH = pKa - \log\frac{(R(NH_3^+))}{(R(NH_2))}$$

$$= pKa + \log\frac{(R(NH_2))}{(R(NH_3)^+)}$$

When the amino group (in the acid form) is half neutralized

$$pH = pKa$$

Thus when glycine is titrated (Fig. 1.2) with HCl the carboxyl group is first neutralized (at half neutralization $pH = pKa_1 = 2\cdot3$). Titration with NaOH leads to the neutralization of the amino group (when $0\cdot5$ equivalents of NaOH have been added $pH = pKa_2 = 9\cdot6$).

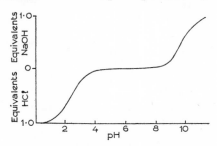

FIG. 1.2. Titration curve of glycine.

When amino acids contain other ionizable groups it becomes difficult to decide the ionization sequence. However, a large number of investigations have given the following results.

TABLE 1.2

pKa values for ionizable groups in proteins

Group	Range of pKa values
α-Carboxyl	1·8–2·2
Distal carboxyl	3·9–4·3
Imidazole	6·1
α-Amino	8·3–9·8
Tyrosine OH	10·1
Distal NH₂	10·5
Guanidino	10·8

The ionization of cysteine is a matter of some controversy, but the pKa for the α-carboxyl group is 2·0 and the other pKa's are at 8·3 and 10·4.

OPTICAL ACTIVITY

With the exception of glycine, which lacks an asymmetric carbon atom, all amino acids are optically active and all the amino acids found in proteins have the L-configuration around the α-carbon atom. The capital letter L denotes the configuration and not the direction of polarization of light, which may be dextro- or laevorotatory and is denoted by the signs (+) or (−) respectively or alternatively by the italicized letters d or l. The configuration about the α-carbon atom can be chemically determined *relative* to an allied optically active compound. For example, L-serine can be converted to L-alanine or L-cysteine, by the following reactions:

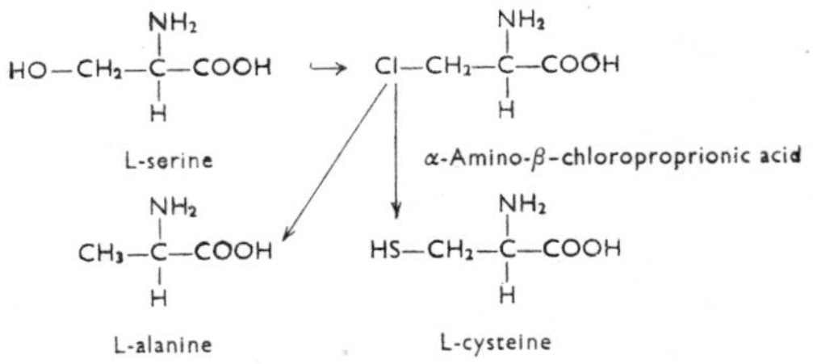

$$HO-CH_2-\underset{\underset{H}{|}}{\overset{\overset{NH_2}{|}}{C}}-COOH \longrightarrow Cl-CH_2-\underset{\underset{H}{|}}{\overset{\overset{NH_2}{|}}{C}}-COOH$$

L-serine   α-Amino-β-chloroproprionic acid

$$CH_3-\underset{\underset{H}{|}}{\overset{\overset{NH_2}{|}}{C}}-COOH \qquad HS-CH_2-\underset{\underset{H}{|}}{\overset{\overset{NH_2}{|}}{C}}-COOH$$

L-alanine   L-cysteine

Since the reactions do not involve the α-carbon atom the three amino acids must have the same configuration.

In cases involving a change of substituents at an asymmetric carbon atom, the substitution may be associated with an inversion of configuration (Walden inversion) and an alternative method of determining the relative configuration is necessary. For example, the determination of the configuration of (+) alanine and (−) alanine relative to (+) lactic acid involves the substitution of NH_2 for OH and the direct substitution involves a Walden inversion. However the configuration may be determined by effecting a chemical change in one of the substituents bound to the asymmetric carbon atom: corresponding configurations should bring about analogous changes of rotation.

Table 1.3 shows that (+) alanine has the same configuration as (+) lactic acid.

In order to facilitate the expression of these relationships Emil Fischer arbitrarily assigned the prefix D to an α-substituted carboxylic acid

TABLE 1.3
Optical activity of derivatives of lactic acid and alanine

Derivative	(+) Lactic acid	(+) Alanine	(−) Alanine
Amide of the benzoyl compound	+120°	+70°	−70°
Ethyl ester of the benzoyl compound	+49°	+12°	−12°
Methyl ester of the benzoyl compound	+35°	+4°	−4°
Ethyl ester of the acetyl compound	−76°	−74°	+74°
Ethyl ester of the toluene sulphonyl compound	−129°	−78°	+78°

when the α-substituted group points to the right, when the COOH group is at the top and R points backwards.

D-glyceraldehyde is the accepted standard of reference for the carbohydrate series and L-serine is the reference standard for the amino acids. That these standards are in agreement has been shown by the following reactions

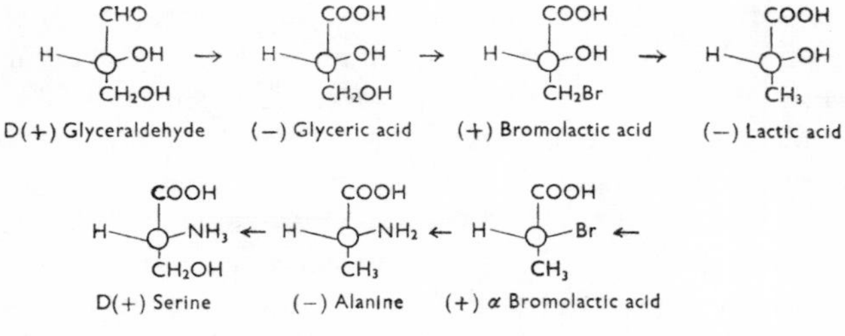

The original choice of configuration by Fischer had obviously a 50:50 chance of being correct and recent X-ray analysis has shown that his choice represented the true situation.

The Primary Structure of Proteins

Emil Fischer and Franz Hofmeister independently proposed that proteins may be considered as complex polypeptides in which the amino acids are joined by amide links called peptide bonds. Thus glycine and alanine may condend to give the peptide glycyl alanine

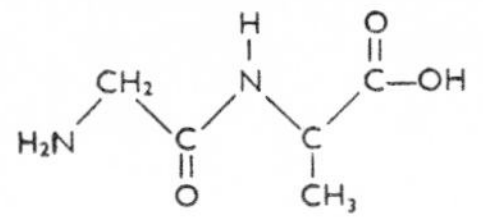

or alanyl glycine

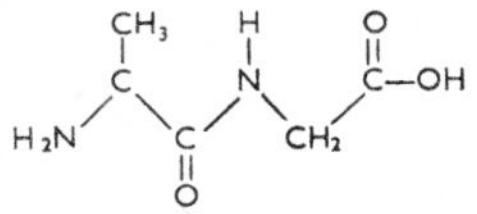

The convention of naming peptides is to consider them as acylated derivatives of the amino acid with the free carboxyl group.

The C—N bond is a partial double bond so that the planar peptide bond can exist in two forms:

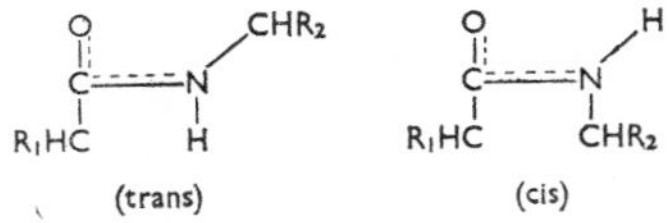

(trans)   (cis)

However the *cis* form is not likely to be of wide occurrence in proteins because of steric hindrance. The number and sequence of amino acids linked together by peptide bonds constitutes the primary structure of the protein. Proteins range in size from a molecular weight of 6000 for insulin to molecular weights in excess of a million. Insulin is an extremely small protein, but contains fifty-one amino acid residues; a protein of molecular weight 100,000 would contain approximately 900 amino acid residues. The task of determining the primary structure of a protein is thus formidable, but did not deter Sanger, who at the end of the second world war started a series of investigations which culminated in 1954 when the complete primary structure of insulin was announced. The success of Sanger and his co-workers was due to the development by Sanger of a method for amino end group analyses and the development by Martin and Synge of methods for the isolation of compounds by partition chromatography on filter paper.

FILTER PAPER CHROMATOGRAPHY

The partitioning of a solute between two immiscible solvents has been known for many years. Martin and Synge conceived the idea of using filter paper to hold a polar phase stationary whilst allowing the apolar mobile phase to move over the surface of the paper. Solutes applied to the paper would thus partition between the phases and the rate at which the solute moved down the paper relative to the solvent front, would depend on the partition coefficient of the solute between the polar phase (usually water) and the mobile phase. By the appropriate choice of solvents, it is possible to separate many compounds. Further resolution can be achieved by two-dimensional chromatography. In this technique the solvent is allowed to run in one direction, the paper dried and a different solvent then allowed to travel along the paper at right angles to the original direction. Sensitive colour tests are necessary to detect the separated compounds — for example α-amino acids may be detected by means of the following reactions:

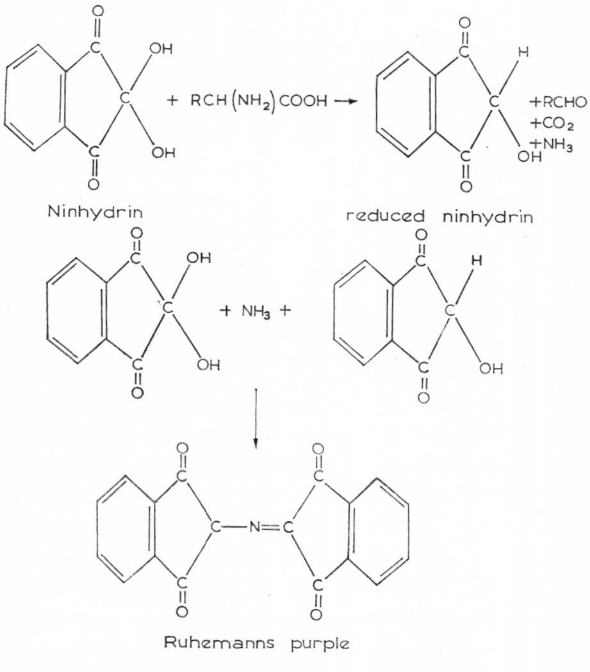

Ninhydrin

reduced ninhydrin

$$+ NH_3 +$$

Ruhemanns purple

An alcoholic solution of ninhydrin is sprayed over the dried paper chromatogram which is then heated in an oven. The position of the amino acid can be seen by the formation of purple spots.

If the compounds are radioactive they may be detected by placing X-ray film over the chromatogram.

2

Amino End Group Analyses

The N-terminal residue of a polypeptide chain bears a free amino group and may be distinguished from other amino acids by chemical reactions involving the free amino group. The first attack on the structure of insulin was to identify the N-terminal residues. 1,2,4-fluorodinitrobenzene reacts with amino groups to form yellow DNP (dinitrophenyl) compounds.

Hydrolysis of the DNP protein yields the DNP derivatives of those amino acids which were present as N-terminal residues. Thus in a hydrolysate of DNP-insulin, Sanger detected DNP-glycine and DNP-phenylalanine, thereby indicating the presence of two polypeptide chains — a glycyl chain and a phenylalanyl chain. The weakest point in this method is the destruction of the N-terminal DNP-amino acid which occurs during acid hydrolysis. In certain cases enzymes may be used to hydrolyse the DNP proteins. N-terminal proline is best determined by the phenylisothiocyanate method (see p. 19).

Determination of the Sequence of Amino Acids

(a) The Fluorodinitrobenzene Method

Amino acid residues close to the N-terminal position can be determined by an extension of the DNP method. Complete hydrolysis of a DNP polypeptide will give the DNP derivative of the N-terminal residue; partial hydrolysis will give a mixture of DNP peptides which may be separated, hydrolysed and the amino acids identified. For example, Sanger was able to oxidize insulin with performic acid and isolate two fractions — one of which (fraction B) possessed a phenylalanine N-terminal residue. Partial hydrolysis of the DNP phenylalanyl chain gave a number of DNP peptides, four of which were isolated and hydrolysed and their hydrolysis products identified (Table 1.4).

From the composition of these peptides and the fact that peptide B_4 on partial hydrolysis gives rise to the smaller peptides (B_2, B_3) it is clear that the N-terminal sequence is Phenylalanine-Valine-Aspartate-Glutamate.

TABLE 1.4
DNP-phenylalanyl peptides from insulin

Peptide	Hydrolysis products
B_1	DNP-Phenylalanine
B_2	DNP-Phenylalanine, Valine
B_3	DNP-Phenylalanine, Valine and Aspartate
B_4	DNP-Phenylalanine, Valine, Aspartate, Glutamate

(b) THE PHENYLISOTHIOCYANATE METHOD

This method introduced by Edman is based on the finding that with acid catalysis, the phenylthiocarbamates of peptides rearrange to give the phenylthiohydantoins of the N-terminal amino acid, and the shortened peptide. Phenylthiocarbamates of peptides are readily formed at 40° and pH 8–9 by the reaction

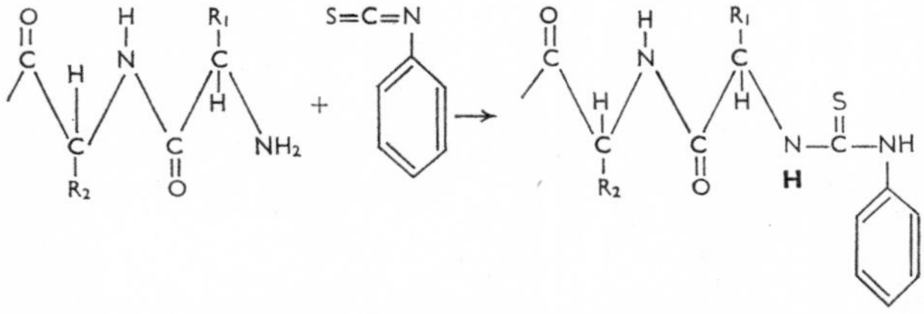

The release of the terminal amino acid in the form of the phenylthiohydantoin may be carried out under anhydrous conditions (nitromethane saturated with hydrochloric acid gas) or in 3N hydrochloric acid.

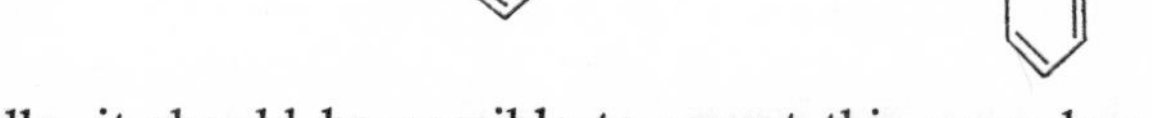

Theoretically, it should be possible to repeat this procedure until the complete sequence of amino acids has been determined. However, the repeated cleavage of the terminal amino acid residues causes cumulative damage to the rest of the peptide chain and usually it is possible to split off a maximum number of six or seven residues. The obvious method to determine the amino acid sequence would be to identify the phenylthiohydantoins produced by the stepwise degradation. The identification and estimation of the phenylthiohydantoins is sometimes difficult and the alternative 'subtractive' method must be used, as for example in the determination of the structure of ribonuclease. After removal of the N-terminal amino acid as a phenylthiohydantoin, the remaining peptide is hydrolysed and analysed. The sequence of amino acids in the peptide is deduced from the residues remaining after each step.

THE DETERMINATION OF C-TERMINAL AMINO ACIDS

There is no satisfactory chemical method for the determination of C-terminal amino acids, but the enzyme carboxypeptidase can be used in certain cases. Carboxypeptidase specifically attacks C-terminal peptide bonds of polypeptides.

Point of cleavage by carboxypeptidase

Thus it is to be expected that the enzyme will release amino acids, one by one, along the polypeptide chain. By identifying and estimating these amino acids it is possible to determine the sequence of amino acids. Thus, for example, when α-corticotropin was treated with carboxypeptidase three amino acids were released and the relative rates at which they were released (phenylalanine > glutamate > leucine) indicated that the sequence of amino acids was phenylalanine, glutamate and leucine.

It should be noted that the substrate specificity of carboxypeptidase is largely determined by the nature of the C-terminal residue, the most effective substrates have aromatic C-terminal residues, whilst a terminal proline blocks the peptide from attack by carboxypeptidase. In the case of α-corticotropin, only three amino acids are released because the fourth amino acid is proline.

THE PRIMARY STRUCTURE OF PARTICULAR PROTEINS

Following the successful eludication of the structure of insulin, a number of investigators have initiated programmes to determine the structure of other proteins. The primary structure of ribonuclease is almost completely known, but there are a number of uncertainties. The structure of the protein moiety of tobacco mosaic virus has recently been announced. The structures proposed for insulin, ribonuclease and tobacco mosaic

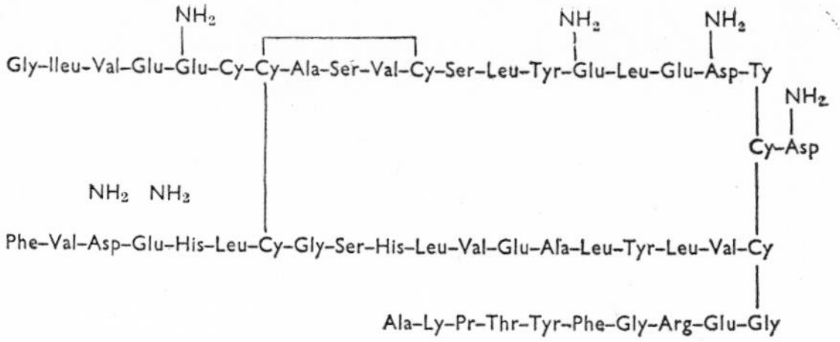

NH₂   NH₂   NH₂

Gly–Ileu–Val–Glu–Glu–Cy–Cy–Ala–Ser–Val–Cy–Ser–Leu–Tyr–Glu–Leu–Glu–Asp–Ty

NH₂

Cy–Asp

NH₂ NH₂

Phe–Val–Asp–Glu–His–Leu–Cy–Gly–Ser–His–Leu–Val–Glu–Ala–Leu–Tyr–Leu–Val–Cy

Ala–Ly–Pr–Thr–Tyr–Phe–Gly–Arg–Glu–Gly

Bovine Insulin

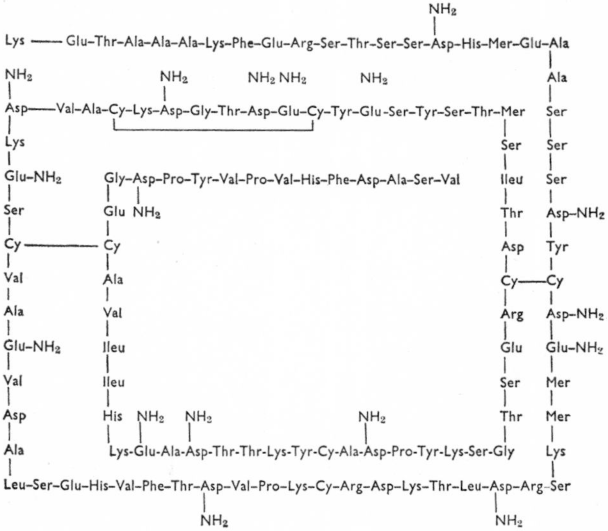

NH₂

Lys ——— Glu–Thr–Ala–Ala–Ala–Lys–Phe–Glu–Arg–Ser–Thr–Ser–Ser–Asp–His–Mer–Glu–Ala

| NH₂ | | NH₂ | NH₂ NH₂ | NH₂ | | Ala |
Asp——Val–Ala–Cy–Lys–Asp–Gly–Thr–Asp–Glu–Cy–Tyr–Glu–Ser–Tyr–Ser–Thr–Mer   Ser

Lys   Ser   Ser

Glu–NH₂   Gly–Asp–Pro–Tyr–Val–Pro–Val–His–Phe–Asp–Ala–Ser–Val   Ileu   Ser

Ser   Glu NH₂   Thr   Asp–NH₂

Cy——— Cy   Asp   Tyr

Val   Ala   Cy——Cy

Ala   Val   Arg   Asp–NH₂

Glu–NH₂   Ileu   Glu   Glu–NH₂

Val   Ileu   Ser   Mer

Asp   His NH₂ NH₂   NH₂   Thr   Mer

Ala   Lys–Glu–Ala–Asp–Thr–Thr–Lys–Tyr–Cy–Ala–Asp–Pro–Tyr–Lys–Ser–Gly   Lys

Leu–Ser–Glu–His–Val–Phe–Thr–Asp–Val–Pro–Lys–Cy–Arg–Asp–Lys–Thr–Leu–Asp–Arg–Ser

NH₂   NH₂

Bovine Pancreatic Ribonuclease

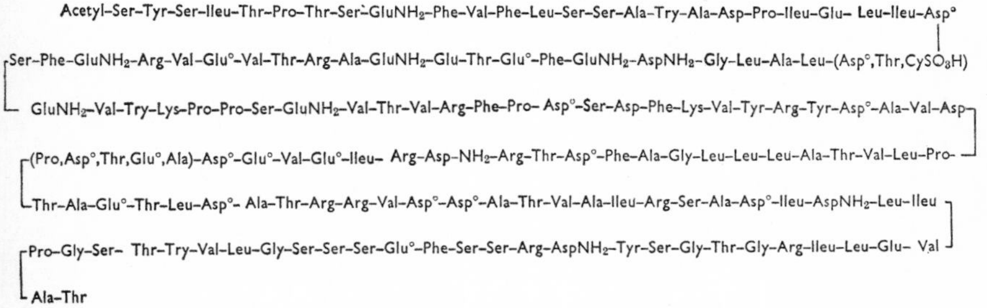

Acetyl–Ser–Tyr–Ser–Ileu–Thr–Pro–Thr–Ser–GluNH₂–Phe–Val–Phe–Leu–Ser–Ser–Ala–Try–Ala–Asp–Pro–Ileu–Glu– Leu–Ileu–Aspº

Ser–Phe–GluNH₂–Arg–Val–Gluº–Val–Thr–Arg–Ala–GluNH₂–Glu–Thr–Gluº–Phe–GluNH₂–AspNH₂–Gly–Leu–Ala–Leu–(Aspº,Thr,CySO₃H)

GluNH₂–Val–Try–Lys–Pro–Pro–Ser–GluNH₂–Val–Thr–Val–Arg–Phe–Pro– Aspº–Ser–Asp–Phe–Lys–Val–Tyr–Arg–Tyr–Aspº–Ala–Val–Asp

(Pro,Aspº,Thr,Gluº,Ala)–Aspº–Gluº–Val–Gluº–Ileu– Arg–Asp–NH₂–Arg–Thr–Aspº–Phe–Ala–Gly–Leu–Leu–Leu–Ala–Thr–Val–Leu–Pro–

Thr–Ala–Gluº–Thr–Leu–Aspº– Ala–Thr–Arg–Arg–Val–Aspº–Aspº–Ala–Thr–Val–Ala–Ileu–Arg–Ser–Ala–Aspº–Ileu–AspNH₂–Leu–Ileu

Pro–Gly–Ser– Thr–Try–Val–Leu–Gly–Ser–Ser–Ser–Gluº–Phe–Ser–Ser–Arg–AspNH₂–Tyr–Ser–Gly–Thr–Gly–Arg–Ileu–Leu–Glu– Val

Ala–Thr

Aspº = Asp or AspNH₂; Gluº = Glu or GluNH₂

FIG. 1.3. **Proposed structure for bovine insulin, bovine pancreatic ribonuclease, and protein moiety of tobacco mosaic virus.**

virus protein are shown in Fig. 1.3. The only plant enzyme which has been extensively investigated is papain. Papain has a single peptide chain with an N-terminal isoleucine and 180 amino acid residues. There are six cysteine residues, one of which is highly reactive, but there are no disulphide bridges.

The Secondary Structure of Proteins

The term secondary structure relates to the main factors determining the structure of the individual peptide chains. In a peptide chain, free rotation is possible around the bonds of the α-carbon atoms. Consequently in neutral and alkaline solutions, the synthetic polypeptide poly-L-glutamic acid exists as a random coil. However, on acidifying the medium, polyglutamate assumes a tight helical configuration in which the carboxyl and amino groups are held together by means of hydrogen bonds. This particular configuration known as the α-helix was first clearly defined by Pauling and Corey. The key to the helical structure is the formation of strong hydrogen bonds between particular carboxyl and amino groups. A strong hydrogen bond is one in which the $O - - - - - H—N$ distance is approximately $2 \cdot 79 \pm 0 \cdot 12 \text{Å}$. Strong hydrogen bonding takes place when the chain takes the form of a helix in which there are $3 \cdot 6$ residues per turn, that is when eighteen residues form five turns and so place the first amino acid residue in the same plane as the eighteenth residue. One complete turn of the helix may be represented as:

hydrogen bond

in which thirteen atoms form a hydrogen bonded loop. A more detailed diagram of the α-helix is shown in Fig. 1.4. The α-helix has two types of repeat (a) the distance between successive turns of the spiral ($5 \cdot 55 \text{Å}$), (b) the spacing along the chain of successive amino acid residues ($1 \cdot 5 \text{Å}$). By means of X-ray analysis, evidence has been obtained by Perutz showing the presence of the $1 \cdot 5 \text{Å}$ spacing in poly-γ-benzyl-L-glutamate, horse hair, muscle fibres and methaemoglobin.

A number of other helical structures have been described, but they are generally less stable than the α-configuration. However, there is good evidence that proteins can change their shape and a number of forms other than the random coil and the α-helix may be expected. Experimental evidence for the existence of the α-helix is not particularly good. The model proposed by Pauling and Corey is intellectually satisfying

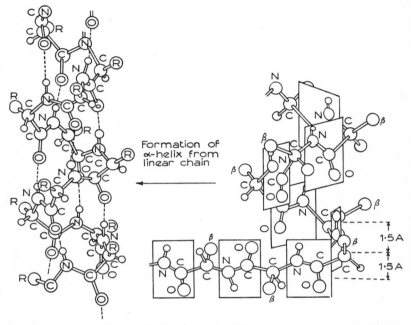

Formation of
α-helix from
linear chain

FIG. 1.4. Structure of the α-helix of proteins (after ANFINSEN, C. R. (1959) *The Molecular Basis of Evolution.* John Wiley & Sons Inc, New York).

but the X-ray analysis of globulins has not revealed helical structures and the conclusion of some crystallographers is that if helical structures exist they are short and interspersed with structurally amorphous regions.

The Tertiary Structure of Proteins

The way in which the peptide chains are bound together constitutes the tertiary structure of proteins. The most important bonds are hydrogen bonds and disulphide bonds.

As noted in the previous section, the α-helix is stabilized by the formation of strong hydrogen bonds when CO and NH groups are appropriately positioned. When peptide chains are in the extended β-form (Fig. 1·5) steric hindrance between opposing side chains tends to prevent the formation of hydrogen bonds. There are however two structures in which the peptide chain is not quite fully extended and there is adequate

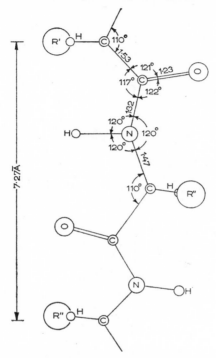

FIG. 1.5. Extended form of polypeptide chain (after COREY, R. B. & DONAHUE, J. (1950) *J. Am. Chem. Soc.* **72**, 2899).

'packing space' for the side-chain groups so that hydrogen bonds can be formed between peptide chains. The unit residue repeat in this structure is 3·34 Å as compared to the 3·5 Å repeat in the extended chain and the chains may be parallel or antiparallel — giving rise to the so-called pleated sheet structure (Fig. 1.6).

In addition to the C=O – – – H—N bond there is evidence for an ionic hydrogen bond — the carboxylate tyrosine bond:

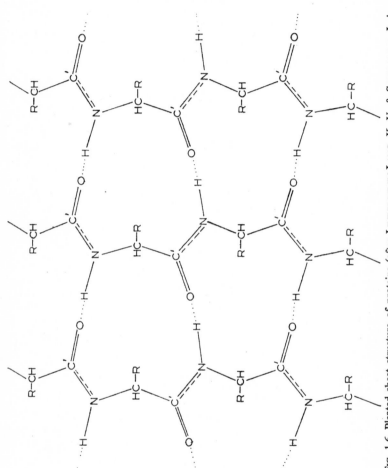

FIG. 1.6. Pleated sheet structure of proteins (after LINDERSTRØM-LANG, K. V. & SCHELLMAN, J. A, (1959) in *The Enzymes, Vol.* 1, ed. BOYER, P. D., LARDY, H. & MYRBACK, K. Academic Press Inc New York).

Disulphide bonds may link two different peptide chains together or two half cystine residues in the same chain, thereby creating a loop in that chain.

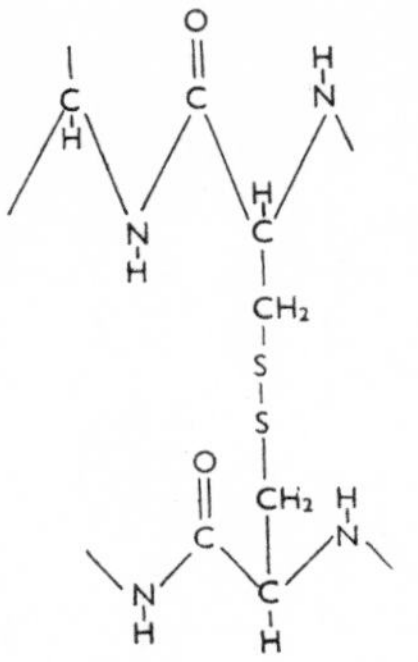

Rotation about the S—S bond is very restricted and the formation of S—S bonds tends to produce a semi-rigid tertiary structure. However there is extensive if inconclusive evidence that the interconversion of SH and S—S groups may play an important role in biological control mechanisms.

Before concluding this section, it is necessary to stress the fact that many more factors are probably involved in the tertiary structure of proteins. For example, papain has no disulphide bonds and enolase lacks cysteine or cystine residues, yet both maintain the globular form. Chibnall has proposed the existence of thiol esters in proteins and recently it has been suggested that a thiol ester type bond occurs at the active site of papain.

The Mechanism of Enzyme Action

Early attempts to explain enzyme action assumed that the enzyme acted on a substrate merely by its presence. For example, Barendrecht (1904) suggested that radiation from the enzyme was absorbed by the substrate molecules which were thereby activated to give products. The majority of workers consider that union between enzyme and substrate is essential for catalytic activity. Historically, the concept of a combination between enzyme and substrate was developed to explain the finding that enzymes show a high degree of stereospecificity for their substrates. The specificity of enzymes led Fischer (1894) to propose a 'lock and key' model for the steric relations at the active site, but the kinetic implications of such a model were first noted by Brown (1902). According to the law of mass action, the velocity of a chemical reaction is proportional to the active masses of the reacting substances, the molecular concentration of a substance being taken as a measure of its active mass. Thus the rate of a chemical reaction is a linear function of the substrate concentration (Fig. 1.7A). The rate of an enzyme catalysed reaction is however nearly always related to the substrate concentration by a curve of the form shown in Fig. 1.7B. This apparent deviation from the law of mass action was explained by Brown in terms of an enzyme substrate compound which represents the 'effective active mass' of the reaction.

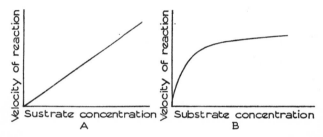

FIG. 1.7. Effect of substrate concentration on reaction velocity. A, chemical reaction; B, enzyme catalyzed reaction.

Kinetics of Enzyme Action

The kinetic analysis of a process requires that the postulated reaction mechanism be put in simple mathematical terms permitting the derivation of a rate equation. The validity of the postulate may then be tested by comparing the rate equation with experimental results.

In the following pages a number of rate equations are derived and methods of determining kinetic constants are discussed.

THE EQUILIBRIUM ASSUMPTION

The ideas of Brown led Henri (1904) and Michaelis & Menten (1913) to the formulation of a rate equation based on an irreversible mechanism which may be represented as

$$E+S \underset{k_2}{\overset{k_1}{\rightleftharpoons}} ES \overset{k_3}{\rightarrow} E+P \tag{1.1}$$

ES represents the enzyme substrate complex, E the free enzyme, S the substrate and P the product. The effective active mass is thus ES and the velocity of P formation (v) is $k_3(ES)$. On the assumption that ES is in equilibrium with E and S (i.e. k_3 is the rate constant of the slow step) we may derive an expression for ES.

Putting the total enzyme $E_T = E + ES$, at equilibrium

$$k_2\,(ES) = k_1\,(E_T - ES)\,(S) \tag{1.2}$$

$$k_2\,(ES) + k_1\,(ES)\,(S) = k_1\,(E_T)\,(S)$$

$$(ES) = \frac{(E_T)\,(S)}{k_2/k_1 + (S)}$$

Maximum velocity (V_{max}) will be attained when all enzyme sites are occupied i.e. when $(E_T) = (ES)$

$$V_{max} = k_3 E_T$$

$$v = \frac{V_{max}(S)}{k_2/k_1 + (S)}$$

The ratio k_2/k_1 is the dissociation constant for ES and we may write:

$$v = \frac{V_{max}(S)}{Km + (S)} \tag{1.3}$$

The term Km called the Michaelis constant has the meaning of a dissociation constant in this particular example. However, in other cases the relationship between Km and the velocity constants may become very complex (see Table 1.5) Consequently in this book Km is defined as the concentration of substrate which gives half maximum velocity.

When

$$V_{max/v} = 2 \qquad Km = (S)$$

THE STEADY STATE ASSUMPTION

From the mechanism expressed in eqn (1.1) we note that the rate of disappearance of S is:

$$-\,dS/dt = k_1(E_T - ES)(S) - k_2(ES)$$

The equilibrium assumption employed in the previous derivation requires that:

$$k_1(E_T - ES)(S) = k_2(ES) \tag{1.2}$$

Thus $dS/dt = 0$, i.e. the substrate is not transformed. The pseudo-derivation of Michaelis and Menten was replaced by a steady state treatment of enzyme kinetics which was introduced in a short note by Briggs & Haldane (1925).

Consider eqn (1.1). When E and S are mixed, there will be a rapid removal of free enzyme as it combines with S. This is called the transient state which leads to a steady state in which the rate of removal of S equals the rate of production of P and the concentration of the enzyme substrate complex is constant.

$$\mathrm{d}ES/\mathrm{d}t = k_1(ES) - k_2(ES) - k_3(ES) = 0 \qquad (1.4)$$

Finally comes a phase in which the steady state disappears and eventually leads into equilibrium. The steady state, sometimes called the stationary state, may be defined as that period in which the rate of for-

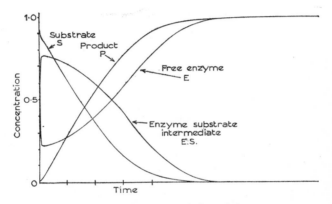

FIG. 1.8. Digital computer solution of the system

$$E + S \underset{k_2}{\overset{k_1}{\longleftrightarrow}} ES \overset{k_2}{\longrightarrow} E + P$$

(after Chance 1960).

mation of product and the concentration of all intermediates remain constant. The duration of the steady state may be short except at high substrate concentration and it is of interest to note that by measuring product formation it may be difficult to detect deviation from a zero order reaction. This is clearly seen in Fig. 1.8 which is the digital computer solution of the Michaelis-Menten system. The trace of product formation appears to follow zero order kinetics long after the trace for the intermediate compound shows the deviation from the steady state.

From the steady state eqn (1.4) and putting $E_T = E + ES$

$$ES = \frac{k_1(E_T)(S)}{k_1(S) + k_2 + k_3}$$

$$= \frac{(E_T)(S)}{(S) + [(k_2 + k_3)/k_1]}$$

Since

$$v = k_3(ES) \text{ and } V_{max} = k_3(E_T)$$

$$v = \frac{V_{max}(S)}{(S) + [(k_2 + k_3)/k_1]}$$

Putting

$$(k_2 + k_3)/k_1 = Km^1$$

$$v = \frac{V_{max}(S)}{(S) + Km^1} \tag{1.5}$$

Km^1 is not a true dissociation constant but is equal to S when $V_{max}/v = 2$.

It is appropriate at this point to warn the student about confusion in the nomenclature of the Michaelis-Menten constant. The essentially practical definition of the Michaelis constant employed in this book follows the example of Haldane (1930), Alberty (1956) and Dixon & Webb (1958). Reiner (1959), on the other hand, considers this usage to be wrong and restricts the use of Km to the special case when it is a true dissociation constant of the enzyme substrate complex. Laidler (1958) points out that in the Michaelis-Menten equation Km is the dissociation constant of ES:

$$E + S \underset{k_2}{\overset{k_1}{\rightleftharpoons}} ES$$

$$Km = \frac{k_2}{k_1} = \frac{(E)(S)}{(ES)}$$

The modern convention is, however, to express equilibrium constants with the products in the numerator and Laidler consequently uses

$$K = \frac{k_1}{k_2} = \frac{(ES)}{(E)(S)}$$

The constant used by Laidler is thus an affinity constant and is equal to $1/Km$.

Kinetics of the Reversible Michaelis-Menten System

$$E + S \underset{k_2}{\overset{k_1}{\rightleftharpoons}} ES \underset{k_4}{\overset{k_3}{\rightleftharpoons}} E + P \tag{1.6}$$

The reaction $S \to P$ may go nearly to completion and in the 'irreversible' system of Michaelis and Menten (eqn 1.1), this case is treated by putting $k_4 = 0$. This approximation is not necessarily valid, since k_4 need not be small. As shown below

$$\frac{(P)}{(S)} = \frac{k_1 k_3}{k_2 k_4} \tag{1.7}$$

Thus the condition for $(P) \gg (S)$ is that $k_1 k_3 \gg k_2 k_4$. The assumption in the Michaelis-Menten system that k_4 is very small is only one possibility.

Accordingly we derive the rate law as follows: Putting $E_T = ES + E$

$$\frac{dES}{dt} = k_1(E_T - ES)S + k_4(E_T - ES)P - k_2(ES) - k_3(ES) = 0$$

$$(ES) = \frac{(E_T)[k_1(S) + k_4(P)]}{k_1(S) + k_4(P) + k_2 + k_3}$$

The observed velocity $v =$

$$k_3(ES) - k_4(E_T - ES)(P)$$

Substituting for (ES)

$$v = \frac{k_3(E_T)k_1(S) - k_2 k_4(E_T)(P)}{k_1(S) + k_4(P) + k_2 + k_3} \tag{1.8}$$

At equilibrium $v = 0$

$$k_3(E_T)k_1(S) = k_2 k_4(E_T)(P)$$

and

$$\frac{(P)}{(S)} = \frac{k_1 k_3}{k_2 k_4} \tag{1.7}$$

Maximum velocity in the direction $S \to P = V_f = k_3(E_T)$
Maximum velocity in the direction $P \to S = V_r = k_2(E_T)$
Substituting in (1.8)

$$v = \frac{k_1 V_f(S) - k_4 V_r(P)}{k_1(S) + k_4(P) + k_2 + k_3} \tag{1.9}$$

(1.9) reduces to a simple form when $P = 0$

$$v_f = \frac{k_1 V_f(S)}{k_1(S) + k_2 + k_3} = \frac{V_f(S)}{(S) + [(k_2 + k_3)/k_1]} = \frac{V_f(S)}{(S) + K_S}$$

where

$$K_S = \frac{k_2 + k_3}{k_1}$$

similarly

$$K_P = \frac{k_2 + k_3}{k_4}$$

From eqn (1.8) we may derive a relationship between the equilibrium constant (K_{app}) and the kinetic constants.

Dividing (1.8) by $k_2 + k_3$

$$v = \frac{[k_1(S)V_f/(k_2+k_3)] - [k_4(P)V_r/(k_2+k_3)]}{[k_1(S)/(k_2+k_3)] + [k_4(P)/(k_2+k_3)] + [k_2/(k_2+k_3)] + [k_3/(k_2+k_3)]}$$

$$= \frac{[(S)V_f/K_S] - [(P)V_r/K_P]}{(S)/K_S + (P)/K_P + 1}$$

At equilibrium $v = 0$

$$\frac{(S)V_f}{K_S} = \frac{(P)V_r}{K_P}$$

$$\frac{(P)}{(S)} = K_{app} = \frac{K_P V_f}{K_S V_r} \tag{1.10}$$

This relationship was first deduced by Haldane. The relationship is valid for the mechanism illustrated in eqn (1.6), but other mechanisms may give different Haldane relationships. Many of these have been deduced by Alberty and are presented in Table 1.5.

The usefulness of these relationships is that they provide a test of the validity of a postulated reaction mechanism. A kinetic study of an enzyme reaction can never prove that a particular mechanism is correct. However, such studies are useful as a means of eliminating certain postulated mechanisms. Thus, if the measured kinetic constants do not show the relationship to the equilibrium constant, deduced for a particular mechanism, then that particular mechanism can be eliminated.

THE ESTIMATION OF KINETIC CONSTANTS

The effect of substrate concentration on the velocity of an enzyme catalysed reaction can usually be related to the Michaelis-Menten equation.

3

TABLE 1.5

Rate laws and the Haldane relationship for particular mechanisms of enzyme action

	Mechanism	Rate law	Haldane relationship
1.	$E+S \rightleftharpoons ES \rightleftharpoons E+P$	$v=\frac{V_{max}(S)}{K_m+(S)}$	$K_{app}=\frac{(P)}{(S)}=\frac{V_S K_P}{V_P K_S}$
2.	$E+A \rightleftharpoons EA$ $EA+B \rightleftharpoons EC+D$ $EC \rightleftharpoons E+C$	$v=\frac{V_{max}}{1+K_A/(A)+K_B/(B)+K_{AB}/(A)(B)}$	$K_{app}=\frac{(C)(D)}{(A)(B)}=\frac{V_f^3 K_C K_D}{V_r^3 K_A K_B}$
3.	$E+A \rightleftharpoons EA$ $EA+B \rightleftharpoons EAB \rightleftharpoons EC+D$ $EC \rightleftharpoons E+C$	$v=\frac{V_{max}}{1+K_A/(A)+K_B/(B)+K_{AB}/(A)(B)}$	$K_{app}=\frac{(C)(D)}{(A)(B)}=\frac{V_f K_C K_D}{V_r K_A K_B}$
4.	$E+A \rightleftharpoons EA$ $ECD \rightleftharpoons EC+D$ $E+B \rightleftharpoons EB$ $ECD \rightleftharpoons ED+C$ $EA+B \rightleftharpoons EAB$ $EC \rightleftharpoons E+C$ $EB+A \rightleftharpoons EAB$ $ED \rightleftharpoons E+D$ $EAB \rightleftharpoons ECD$	Rate law non-linear in $(1/v)(1/S)$. However if $EAB \rightarrow ECD$ is rate determining $v=\frac{V_{max}}{1+K_A/(A)+K_B/(B)+K_{AB}/(A)(B)}$ If the affinity of the enzyme for one substrate is not affected by the other $v=\frac{V_{max}}{1+K_A/(A) \quad 1+K_B/(B)}$	$K_{app}=\frac{(C)(D)}{(A)(B)}=\frac{V_f K_{(CD)}}{V_r K_{(AB)}}$ $K_{app}=\frac{(C)(D)}{(A)(B)}=\frac{V_f K_C K_D}{V_r K_A K_B}$
5.	$E+A \rightleftharpoons EA \rightleftharpoons E'+C$ $E'+B \rightleftharpoons E'B \rightleftharpoons E+D$	$v=\frac{V_{max}}{1+K_A/(A)+K_B/(B)}$	$K_{app}=\frac{V_f^2 K_C K_D}{V_r^2 K_A K_B}$

The curve of this equation is asymptotic, that is, the maximum velocity is only attained at an infinite concentration of substrate (Fig. 1.7b). Accurate extrapolation of experimental data to obtain V_{max} can be achieved by converting the Michaelis-Menten equation into a linear form. This device appears to have been first adopted by Woolf but was not widely used until the publication of the paper by Lineweaver & Burk (1934) which gave the following linear equation:

$$\frac{1}{v} = \frac{1}{V_{max}} + \frac{K_m}{V_{max}} \cdot \frac{1}{(S)} \tag{1.11}$$

$1/v$ is thus a linear function of $1/S$ (Fig. 1.9a).

Alternative linear equations are:

$$v = V_{max} - K_m \, v/(S) \tag{1.12}$$

(v is a linear function of v/S)

and

$$\frac{(S)}{v} = \frac{K_m}{V_{max}} + \frac{1}{V_{max}} \cdot (S) \tag{1.13}$$

(S/v is a linear function of (S))

The lines obtained from these equations are shown in Fig. 1.9b and c.

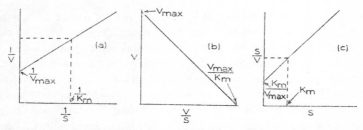

Fig. 1.9. Relationship between velocity and enzyme concentration.

Plots based on eqn (1.12) are considered superior by Hofstee (1959) though Dixon & Webb (1959) have expressed a slight preference for the double reciprocal plot of eqn (1.11).

THE MEASUREMENT OF INITIAL VELOCITIES

The determination of substrate concentration is generally easy and accurate but the determination of velocity is frequently difficult. The derivation of the rate laws is based on the assumption of truly *initial* velocities which are particularly difficult to obtain at low substrate concentration. Certain methods used in elementary classes are obviously not valid procedures; for example, the rate of starch hydrolysis is sometimes measured by the time taken for a solution to no longer give a blue colour with iodine. This method gives the average velocity of the reaction but clearly does not give the initial velocity. When studying the effect of temperature on the rate of hydrolysis, a high temperature may give a high initial velocity but because of thermal denaturation of the enzyme the rate may slow down to give an average velocity slower than that obtained at a lower temperature (Fig. 1.10).

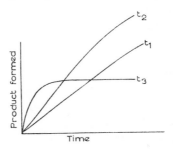

FIG. 1.10. Effect of temperature on the rate of an enzyme reaction ($t_1 < t_2 < t_3$).

Whilst the error is obvious in such cases, it may not be as apparent when refined instruments are used to measure the velocity. The most widely used method to obtain the true initial velocity is to make the maximum possible number of determinations of substrate or product concentration during a short period after mixing the enzyme and substrate. At high substrate concentrations, and when the equilibrium of the reaction is favourable, the steady state is maintained sufficiently long to give a linear rate and the initial rate is then determined with accuracy. As the substrate concentration is lowered, the period of linearity becomes shorter and eventually cannot be detected and errors may be expected in the evaluation of the initial velocity. It is thus important to know the degree of error associated with such rate determinations.

Consider the reaction

$$A \underset{k_2}{\overset{k_1}{\rightleftharpoons}} B$$

At low substrate concentration the reaction may be considered first order and the first order rate equation is:

$$dB/dt = k_1(A_0 - B) - k_2 B = k_1 A_0 - k_1 B - k_2 B$$
$$= k_1[A_0 - (1 + k_2/k_1)B]$$

where A_0 is the initial substrate concentration, B is the concentration of product at any time and k_1 and k_2 are the velocity constants ($k_1/k_2 = K$ equilibrium).

Integration gives the concentration B at time t:

$$B = \frac{A_0\{1 - \exp[-k_1 t(1 + k_2/k_1)]\}}{1 + k_2/k_1} \qquad (1.14)$$

The initial velocity may be measured as the amount of product formed in time t, i.e. (B/t), whereas the 'true' initial velocity is $dB/dt = k_1 A_0$. For these two values to agree within 5 per cent, $B/k_1 A_0 t$ must be greater than 0·95. Thus

$$0{\cdot}95 < \frac{1 - \exp[-k_1 t(1 + k_2/k_1)]}{(1 + k_2/k_1)\,k_1 t}$$

In the case of the enzyme fumarase which has been studied by Alberty, K equilibrium $= k_1/k_2 = 4{\cdot}5$, and the value of $k_1 t$ for which the ratio is 0·95 is 0·1. Substitution for $k_1 t = 0{\cdot}1$ into eqn (1.14) leads to the conclusion that if the measured initial velocity of formation of malate is to be obtained with an error of less than 5 per cent, the extent of the reaction must not be measured beyond 7·8 per cent. With malate as the substrate (K equilibrium $= 1/4{\cdot}5$) a similar calculation shows that only the first 1·7 per cent of the reaction may be used because of the unfavourable equilibrium.

ORDER OF REACTION DURING ENZYME CATALYSIS

It has been assumed that the student is familiar with the concept of orders of reaction, but its application to enzyme kinetics will be briefly discussed here.

Since according to the law of mass action, the rate of a chemical change is proportional to the concentration of the reacting substances, it is clear that the rate of a reaction must decrease with time as the reactants are consumed. The order of the reaction is the number of molecules whose concentrations determine the rate of the reaction.

FIRST ORDER CHEMICAL REACTION

For a first order reaction it can readily be shown that the rate of product formation decreases in a logarithmic manner so that the plot of the logarithm of the substrate concentration against time is linear. The initial rate of a reaction

$$A \xrightarrow{k} B$$

is given by:

$$-dA/dt = kA_0$$

The rate at any time is:

$$dB/dt = k(A_0 - B)$$

Rearranging for integration gives:

$$\frac{dB}{(A_0 - B)} = kdt$$

which integrates to give:

$$k = \frac{1}{t} \ln \frac{A_0}{(A_0 - B)}$$

$$= \frac{2 \cdot 303}{t} \log \frac{A_0}{(A_0 - B)}$$

Rearranging gives:

$$t = \frac{2 \cdot 303}{k} \log \frac{A_0}{(A_0 - B)}$$

$$= \frac{2 \cdot 303}{k} \log A_0 - \frac{2 \cdot 303}{k} \log (A_0 - B)$$

Since $2 \cdot 303/k \log A_0$ is a constant it follows that a plot of $\log (A_0 - B)$ against t should be linear with slope equal to $-2 \cdot 303/k$.

ENZYME REACTIONS APPROXIMATING TO FIRST ORDER

In the case of enzymic reactions this method can be used to evaluate the initial rate of reaction ($dA/dt = A_0 k$) but is only valid at low substrate concentrations.

The velocity of most enzymic reactions is given by the Michaelis-Menten equation:

$$v = \frac{V_{max}(S)}{K_m + (S)}$$

At low substrate concentrations $S \ll K_m$. The Michaelis-Menten equation reduces to:

$$v = \frac{V_{max}(S)}{K_m}$$

Since V_{max} and K_m are constants the reaction rate is proportional to the substrate concentration and first order kinetics are applicable. At high substrate concentrations where $S \gg K_m$

$$v = V_{max}$$

Thus at high concentrations of substrate the velocity is independent of concentration and zero order kinetics apply. At intermediate substrate concentrations the order of the reaction will lie between 1 and 0.

Kinetics of Two Substrate Reactions

The first order treatment of enzyme kinetics developed by Michaelis and Menten is applicable to hydrolytic reactions because the concentration of water is effectively constant so that the reactions are pseudounimolecular.

Because of the difficulty of varying the water concentration, relatively little is known about the role of water in hydrolytic reactions. An ingenious approach to this problem has been developed by Koshland & Herr (1957) who set out to determine whether or not water acts from a specific water site on the surface of the enzyme.

Phosphate esters undergo hydrolysis in water and methanolysis in methanol.

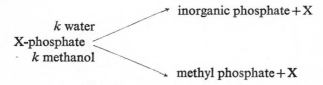

The ratio of the two bimolecular velocity constants was determined in concentrated (12·5 M) methanol-water solutions and by means of a sensitive isotopic method employing ^{14}C-labelled methanol in dilute (10^{-5} M) methanol–water solutions. It was argued that, if water acts freely from solution, the ratio $k$water/$k$methanol should be approximately the same in the presence and absence of the enzyme. However, if water occupies a specific site on an enzyme, the ratio should be greater in the presence of the enzyme. Experimentally, it was found that in the case of adenosine triphosphate the ratio $k$water/$k$methanol was 2·5 in the absence of an enzyme, but in the presence of an enzyme from muscle which hydrolyses ATP, the ratio was between 300 and 1000. It can therefore be concluded that there is a specific water site on the enzyme.

Most enzyme reactions are bimolecular and the Michaelis-Menten treatment requires extension. Consider a reaction of the type:

$$A + B \rightleftharpoons C + D$$

A number of possible reaction mechanisms must be considered and for each mechanism a rate law can be derived. As in the case of the pseudo-unimolecular reactions the derivation may be based on the equilibrium assumption or the steady state assumption.

In general, the equilibrium assumption leads to simple algebraic equations which are readily solved. The steady state assumption, on the other hand, requires the solution of a number of simultaneous equations and the algebra can become tedious.

Consider the mechanism in which the enzyme may combine with either substrate to form binary complexes and with both substrates to form a ternary complex which is catalytically active and breaks down to form free enzyme and products.

$$E + A \underset{k_2}{\overset{k_1}{\rightleftharpoons}} EA$$

$$E + B \underset{k_4}{\overset{k_3}{\rightleftharpoons}} EB$$

$$EB + A \underset{k_6}{\overset{k_5}{\rightleftharpoons}} EAB \overset{k_9}{\rightarrow} E + \text{products}$$

$$EA + B \underset{k_8}{\overset{k_7}{\rightleftharpoons}} EAB \overset{k_9}{\rightarrow} E + \text{products}$$

The equilibrium assumption requires that the rate at which EAB breaks down to products be the rate determining step and that all enzyme substrate complexes are at equilibrium. We derive the rate law as follows:

Defining the four equilibria:

$$(E) + (A) \underset{k_2}{\overset{k_1}{\rightleftharpoons}} (EA); \quad (EA) = \frac{k_1}{k_2}(E)(A) = \frac{(E)(A)}{K_A}$$

$$(E) + (B) \underset{k_4}{\overset{k_3}{\rightleftharpoons}} (EB)$$

$$(EB)+(A)\underset{k_6}{\overset{k_5}{\rightleftharpoons}}(EAB); \quad (EB)=\frac{k_6}{k_5}\frac{(EAB)}{(A)}=\frac{(EAB)K_{BA}}{(A)}$$

$$(EA)+(B)\underset{k_8}{\overset{k_7}{\rightleftharpoons}}(EAB); \quad (EA)=\frac{(EAB)K_{AB}}{(B)}$$

$$(EAB)\overset{k_9}{\rightarrow}(E)+(C)+(D)$$

$$E=\frac{(EA)K_A}{(A)}=\frac{(EAB)(K_{AB})(K_A)}{(B)(A)}$$

The conservation equation is:

$$(E_T)=(EAB)+(EA)+(EB)+(E)$$

$$(E_T)=(EAB)+\frac{(EAB)(K_{AB})}{(B)}+\frac{(EAB)(K_{BA})}{(A)}+\frac{(EAB)(K_{AB})(K_A)}{(A)(B)}$$

$$(EAB)=\frac{(E_T)}{1+K_{AB}/(B)+K_{BA}/(A)+[(K_{AB})(K_A)/(A)(B)]}$$

$$v=k_9(EAB)$$

$$=\frac{k_9(E_T)}{1+K_{AB}/(B)+K_{BA}/(A)+[(K_{AB})(K_A)/(A)(B)]} \tag{1.15}$$

If one of the reactants, say B, is maintained at a very high concentration, (1.15) reduces to:

$$v=\frac{k_9(E_T)}{1+K_{BA}/(A)}$$

If $k_9(E_T)=V_{max}$ the above equation is identical with the Michaelis-Menten equation:

$$v=\frac{V_{max}(A)}{1+K_{BA}}$$

If we make the restrictive assumption that the affinity of the enzyme for one substrate is not affected by the presence of the second substrate, i.e.

$$K_A=K_{BA} \text{ and } K_B=K_{AB}$$

From (1.15) we obtain

$$v=\frac{k_9(E_T)}{1+K_B/(B)+K_A/(A)+[(K_A)(K_B)/(A)(B)]}$$

$$=\frac{k_9(E_T)}{[1+K_A/(A)][1+K_B/(B)]} \tag{1.16}$$

so that when B is maintained at a high concentration

$$v = \frac{V_{max}(A)}{1 + K_A}$$

The steady state treatment of this reaction mechanism requires the solution of four simultaneous equations

$$dEA/db = 0 = k_1(E)(A) + k_8(EAB) - k_2(EA) - k_7(EA)(B)$$
$$dEB/db = 0 = k_3(E)(B) + k_6(EAB) - k_4(EB) - k_5(EB)(A)$$
$$dE/dt = 0 = k_2(EA) + k_4(EB) - k_1(E)(A) - k_3(E)(B)$$
$$dEAB/dt = 0 = k_5(EB)(A) + k_7(EA)(B) - k_6(EAB) - k_8(EAB) - k_9(EAB)$$

and leads to an equation of some complexity. The solution provided by Dixon and Webb does not give a linear reciprocal plot except for two special cases — (1) when the rate determining step is

$$EAB \xrightarrow{k_9} E + \text{products}$$

i.e. when the equilibrium assumption is valid and (2) when the enzyme always combines with one substrate before the other, i.e. only one binary complex is formed.

The rate laws for a number of mechanisms are collected in Table 1.5, together with the Haldane relationship discussed on p. 31.

The Determination of Kinetic Constants of Two Substrate Reactions

$$A + B \rightleftharpoons C + D$$

It will be noted for all the mechanisms listed in Table 1.5 that when B is held at a high and constant concentration $(B \gg K_B)$ the rate laws reduce to:

$$v = \frac{V_{max}}{1 + K_A/(A)} = \frac{V_{max}(A)}{(A) + K_A}$$

Thus the kinetic constants can be determined by holding one substrate at a concentration approaching saturation and varying the concentration of the second substrate. The results can then be plotted and the kinetic constants determined graphically as described on p. 33. A few special cases must, however, be considered.

(a) Effect of Varying A and B Simultaneously

Some workers study the effect of substrate concentration on enzyme activity by simultaneously varying the concentration of A and B whilst maintaining the concentrations $A = B$. The physical meaning of the value of substrate giving half maximum velocity, then depends on the reaction mechanism.

Consider mechanism 5, Table 1.5. Here E and E' represent two forms of the free enzyme; for example in the case of a transaminase (see p. 361) the two forms could be enzyme pyridoxal phosphate and enzyme pyridoxamine phosphate.

The rate law is:

$$v = \frac{V_{max}}{1 + K_A/(A) + K_B/(B)}$$

when $A = B$

$$\frac{1}{v} = \frac{1 + (K_A + K_B)/(A)}{V_{max}}$$

which gives a linear plot of $(1/v)/(1/A)$.

$$\frac{V_{max}}{v} = 1 + [K_A + K_B]/(A)$$

when $V_{max}/v = 2$

$$(A) = K_A + K_B$$

The value of A giving half maximum velocity is thus the sum of the two Michaelis constants K_A and K_B. With the exception of mechanism 2 all other mechanisms give linear plots of $(1/v)/(1/A)$ and

$$(A) = K_A + K_B + \tfrac{1}{2}K_{AB}$$

Mechanism 2 conforms to the rate law

$$v = \frac{V_{max}}{[1 + K_A/(A)][1 + K_B/(B)]}$$

when $A = B$

$$\frac{1}{v} = \frac{[1 + K_A/(A)][1 + K_B/(A)]}{V_{max}}$$

which does not give a linear plot of $(1/v)/(1/A)$

when $V_{max}/v = 2$

$$2 = 1 + \frac{K_A}{(A)} + \frac{K_B}{(A)} + \frac{K_A K_B}{(A^2)}$$

$$(A) = \frac{K_A + K_B + \sqrt{[(K_A)^2 + 6K_A K_B + (K_B)^2]}}{2}$$

(b) Determination of the Kinetic Constant K_{AB}

If A is held constant at A_0 (which is of the order of magnitude of K_A) and the concentration of B varied, the apparent maximum velocity is then:

$$V_{app} = \frac{V_{max}}{1 + K_A/(A_0)}$$

and the rate law is

$$v = \frac{V_{app}[1 + K_A/(A_0)]}{1 + K_A/(A_0) + K_B/(B) + K_{AB}/(A_0)(B)} \tag{1.17}$$

Let the concentration of B giving

$$\frac{V_{app}}{v_1} = 2 = K_{B,\,1}$$

Then

$$v_1 = \frac{V_{app}[1 + K_A/(A_0)]}{1 + K_A/(A_0) + K_B/K_{B,\,1} + K_{AB}/(A_0)K_{B,\,1}}$$

$$\frac{V_{app}}{v_1} = 2 = \frac{1 + K_A/(A_0) + K_B/K_{B,\,1} + K_{AB}/(A_0)K_{B,\,1}}{1 + K_A/(A_0)}$$

$$1 + \frac{K_A}{(A_0)} = \frac{K_B}{K_{B,\,1}} + \frac{K_{AB}}{(A_0)K_{B,\,1}}$$

$$K_{AB} = (A_0)K_B + K_A K_{B,\,1} - K_B(A_0)$$

$$= (A_0)(K_{B,\,1} - K_B) + K_A K_{B,\,1} \tag{1.18}$$

$K_{B,\,1}$ is determined by keeping A at A_0.
K_B is determined by keeping A at A_{max}.
K_A is determined by keeping B at B_{max}.
K_{AB} is determined by substitution in eqn (1.18).

(c) Determination of Kinetic Constants when One Substrate Cannot be Held at High Concentration

As previously pointed out the Michaelis constant for one substrate can be determined by keeping the second substrate at a high and constant concentration, so that the rate law reduces to the rate law for a single substrate. However, there are a number of cases when the second substrate cannot be held at a saturating concentration. Thus a substrate may not be sufficiently soluble to give a concentration which will saturate the enzyme, or high concentrations may activate or inhibit an enzyme. Substrate inhibition is immediately apparent during an experiment and substrate activation becomes apparent when the experimental results are plotted as in Fig. 1.11. Under these conditions the evaluation of kinetic constants becomes difficult and they can only be obtained by assuming that a particular law is valid. Consider cases where the con-

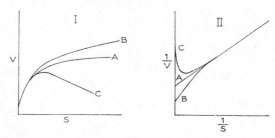

FIG. 1.11. Substrate activation or inhibition of an enzyme reaction. A, normal kinetics; B, substrate activation; C, substrate inhibition.

centration of A cannot be increased until it saturates the enzyme. K_A can be measured directly by keeping the concentration of B close to saturation. The evaluation of K_B follows:

Case A. The rate law is

$$v = \frac{V_{max}}{1 + K_A/(A) + K_B/(B) + K_{AB}/[(A)(B)]}$$

If $K_{B,1}$ and $K_{B,2}$ are determined when the concentration of A is A_1 and A_2 respectively it follows from eqn (1.18) that

$$(A_1)(K_{B,1} - K_B) + K_{B,1}K_A = (A_2)(K_{B,2} - K_B) + K_{B,2}K_A$$

$$K_B = \frac{K_{B,2}[(A_2) + K_A] - K_{B,1}[(A_1) + K_A]}{A_2 - A_1}$$

All values on the right-hand side can be measured.

Case B. The rate law is

$$v = \frac{V_{max}}{1 + K_A/(A) + K_B/(B)}$$

Let $K_{B,1}$ be determined when the concentration of A is held at A_1.
Then the apparent maximum velocity

$$V_{app} = \frac{V_{max}}{1 + K_A/(A_1)}, \qquad V_{max} = V_{app}[1 + K_A/(A_1)]$$

$K_{B,1}$ is the concentration of B giving $V_{app}/v = 2$.

Then

$$v = \frac{V_{app}[1 + K_A/(A_1)]}{1 + K_A/(A_1) + K_B/K_{B,1}}$$

$$\frac{V_{app}}{v} = \frac{1 + K_A/(A_1) + K_B/K_{B,1}}{1 + K_A/(A_1)} = 2$$

$$K_B = K_{B,1} + \frac{K_{B,1}K_A}{(A_1)}$$

Case C. The rate law is

$$v = \frac{V_{max}}{[1 + K_A/(A)][1 + K_B/(B)]}$$

In this case K_B is independent of the concentration of A.

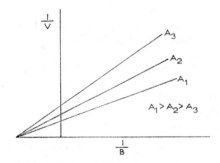

This statement may be proved as follows.
As in the previous case:

$$V_{app} = \frac{V_{max}}{1 + K_A/(A_1)}$$

and $K_{B,1}$ is the concentration of B giving $V_{app}/v = 2$

$$v = \frac{V_{app}[1 + K_A/(A_1)]}{[1 + K_A/(A_1)][1 + K_B/(K_{B,1})]}$$

$$\frac{V_{app}}{v} = \frac{[1 + K_A/(A_1)][1 + K_B/(K_{B,1})]}{(1 + K_A/A_1)} = 2$$

$$K_B = K_{B,1}$$

Enzyme Substrate Compounds

The idea of an enzyme substrate compound was developed to explain the kinetic relationship between the velocity of a reaction and the substrate concentration. More recently, the observation that the uptake of cations by plant tissues shows Michaelis-Menten type kinetics has been taken as evidence for the existence of cation carrier complexes (Epstein, 1952). It is important to emphasize that the methodology of kinetic analysis is one of elimination. If the kinetic consequences of a postulated reaction mechanism are at variance with experimental results, we can eliminate the postulate. However, a number of possible reaction mechanisms may lead to the same rate law and consequently it is impossible to distinguish between these mechanisms. For example, whilst the observation of Michaelis-Menten type kinetics is compatible with an enzyme substrate complex, other mechanisms are possible and Medwedew (1937) has proposed a theory of enzyme action in which a complex between enzyme and substrate is catalytically inactive. Medwedew proposed that the rate of an enzyme reaction is proportional to the concentration of enzyme molecules *engaged* in inelastic collisions, i.e. collisions in which there is a transfer of kinetic energy.

Thus

$$v = k_1 E_C \tag{1.19}$$

The rate of change of E_C with respect to substrate concentration is

$$dE_C/dS = k_2 E_f \tag{1.20}$$

Where E_f is the concentration of enzyme molecules *available* for inelastic collisions

$$E_T = E_f + E_C$$

The solution of (1.20) putting $E_C = 0$ and $S = 0$ is:

$$E_C = E_T[1 - 1/\exp(k_2 S)]$$

$$v = k_1 E_T[1 - 1/\exp(k_2 S)]$$

Maximum velocity is given when all the enzyme molecules are engaged in inelastic collisions.

$$V_{max} = k_1 E_T$$

$$v = V_{max}[1 - 1/\exp(k_2 S)]$$

This equation gives a curve of the same form as the Michaelis-Menten curve. Consequently the observation of kinetics of the Michaelis-Menten type cannot be taken as proof of the existence of an enzyme substrate complex or a carrier cation complex or an auxin receptor complex. It is worth noting the conclusion drawn by Ogston (1955) 'no deductions about the manner of combination can be drawn from kinetic studies alone without the use of additional considerations such as chemical reactivities, direct demonstration of chemical change and comparisons of stereochemical structures'.

Fortunately there is good evidence for the existence of enzyme substrate compounds, but before discussing this evidence it is necessary to outline the chemistry of certain special substrates called coenzymes.

Coenzymes and Prosthetic Groups

Many enzymic reactions are of the type

$$A + B \leftrightarrow C + B'$$

where A and B represent substrates. A large number of reactions share a common substrate. For example, the above reaction and the reaction

$$B' + D \leftrightarrow B + E$$

share the reactants B and B', which function catalytically so that the sum of the two reactions is

$$A + D \leftrightarrow C + E$$

B and B' can be regarded as part of the enzymic mechanism and are called coenzymes. The distinction between a coenzyme and a substrate is not rigid. The examples listed in Table 1.6 have fairly complicated

TABLE 1.6

Examples of coenzymes

Name	Page on which formula is given	Function
Nicotinamide-adenine dinucleotide	179	Hydrogen transfer.
Coenzyme A	159	Acyl transfer.
Adenosine diphosphate	71	Phosphate transfer.
Uridine diphosphoglucose	123	Glycosyl transfer.
Tetrahydrofolic acid	370	Active C_1 transfer.

structures, in a number of cases being related to vitamins, and are widely recognized as coenzymes. However, there are a number of cases in which a substrate acts catalytically in the transfer of a group from one compound to another, but such substrates are not termed coenzymes, partly because they have relatively simple structures and partly because they participate in other reactions where they do not have a catalytic role.

For example, glutamate and α-ketoglutarate play an important role in the transfer of amino groups:

$$\alpha\text{-ketoglutarate} + NADH_2 + NH_3 \rightleftharpoons \text{glutamate} + NAD + H_2O$$
$$\text{glutamate} + \text{oxaloacetate} \rightleftharpoons \alpha\text{-ketoglutarate} + \text{aspartate}$$

The sum of the two reactions is

$$\text{oxaloacetate} + NADH_2 + NH_3 \rightleftharpoons \text{aspartate} + NAD + H_2O$$

Glutamate and α-ketoglutarate function catalytically but also participate as substrates in a number of other reactions.

Whilst most enzymes analyse as though consisting entirely of amino acid residues, a number of enzymes possess non-amino acid groups which are active in transferring groups. Such enzymes can be regarded as consisting of two parts — a protein apoenzyme and a non-protein prosthetic group. The prosthetic group differs from a coenzyme in that the coenzyme readily dissociates from the enzyme, but the distinction is quantitative rather than qualitative. Thus, for example, the enzyme triose phosphate dehydrogenase can be crystallized from muscle with 3 to 4 moles of NAD per mole enzyme. The coenzyme is not appreciably removed by dialysis but can be removed by treatment with charcoal. The dissociation constant of the complex is less than 10^{-7}. The coenzyme would probably be considered as a prosthetic group if its coenzyme nature was not established for other enzymes. Dixon and Webb have suggested that a distinction may be made between prosthetic groups and coenzymes, in that prosthetic groups undergo their whole catalytic cycle while attached to the protein whilst carriers like NAD must migrate from one protein to another. However, there is evidence (see p. 203) that in the case of triosephosphate dehydrogenase, the coenzyme may undergo a complete catalytic cycle whilst attached to the protein. A list of prosthetic groups is shown in Table 1.7.

A most important property of certain coenzymes is their ability to

TABLE 1.7

Examples of prosthetic groups

Name	Page on which formula is given	Function
Cytochrome	186	Electron transport.
Flavin adenine dinucleotide	182	Hydrogen transfer.
Pyridoxal phosphate	362	Various reactions involving amino transfer.
Diphosphothiamine	109	Various decarboxylases; transfers aldehydes.

be reversibly reduced. Warburg established that it is the nicotinamide ring of nicotinamide-adenine dinucleotide which undergoes reduction. The reduction of NAD and NADP leads to a marked change in the absorption spectrum (Fig. 5.1, p. 180). These changes were first observed by Warburg and similar spectral changes are observed when NAD undergoes addition reactions. Thus cyanide reacts with NAD to give a compound with an absorption peak at 327 mμ which may be compared with the 340 mμ peak of reduced NAD. Dihydroxyacetone reacts with NAD to give a compound absorbing at 340 mμ. The nicotinamide ring can exist as a resonating system with the positive charge distributed as shown below.

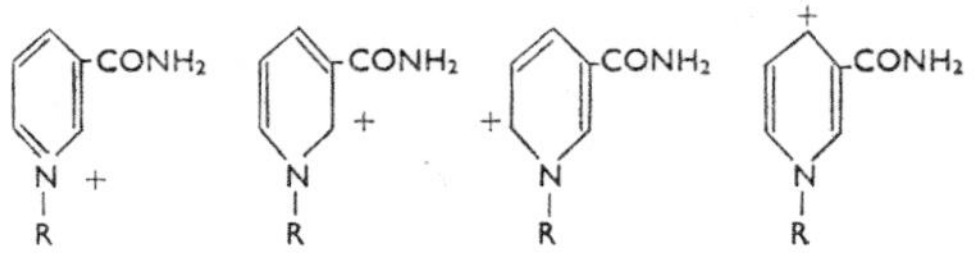

The last structure is the dominant resonance form so that addition reactions and reduction lead to the same change in ring structure and hence similar absorption spectra.

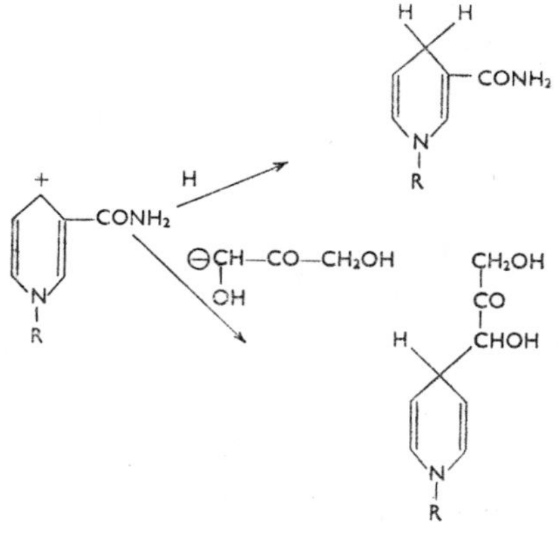

Evidence for the Existence of Enzyme-substrate Compounds

Spectroscopic Evidence

Flavin mononucleotide and flavin adenine dinucleotide can be separated from certain apoenzymes by treatment with ammonium sulphate at acid pH. When the flavins are added to solutions of their appropriate apoenzymes, they combine and in so doing the absorption maximum of the free flavins (445–450 mμ) is displaced towards longer wavelengths — in the case of old yellow enzyme to 465 mμ. This fact led Theorell & Bonnichsen (1951) to look for an analogous shift in the absorption spectrum of NADH$_2$ when it combines with liver alcohol dehydrogenase.

When stoichiometric amounts of alcohol dehydrogenase and NADH$_2$ were mixed, the absorption spectrum showed a peak at 325 mμ (Fig. 1.12). By increasing the amount of enzyme added to a constant amount of NADH$_2$ and measuring the increase in optical density at 310 mμ, it was found that 2 moles of NADH$_2$ were bound per mole of enzyme (Fig. 1.13).

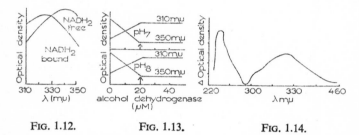

FIG. 1.12.   FIG. 1.13.   FIG. 1.14.

FIG. 1.12. Absorption spectrum of free and alcohol dehydrogenase bound NADH$_2$ (after Theorell & Bonnichsen 1951).

FIG. 1.13. Determination of a number of molecules of NADH$_2$ bound per mole of alcohol dehydrogenase. Optical densities are measured when varying concentrations of alcohol dehydrogenase are mixed with NADH$_2$ (40 μM) (after Theorell & Bonnichsen 1951).

FIG. 1.14. Difference spectrum of the NAD-triosophosphate dehydrogenase compound—obtained by splitting with H$_2$O$_2$ (after Chance 1954).

A more general method of studying the absorption spectra of these compounds is to add excess NAD or NADH$_2$ to the enzyme and record the spectrum. An agent which attacks SH groups is then added to split off bound coenzyme and the spectrum recorded. The difference spectrum gives the absorption spectrum of the complex. Racker used iodoacetate to split the compound formed between mammalian triosephosphate dehydrogenase and NAD. However, this reagent absorbs in the ultraviolet region and a more satisfactory reagent is hydrogen peroxide which has little absorption at wavelengths over 230 mμ. The absorption spectrum of the compound formed between triosephosphate dehydrogenase and NAD is shown in Fig. 1.14.

Lactic dehydrogenase from heart muscle forms a complex with NADH₂ which can be observed by the absorption peak at 330 mμ.

The search for other spectroscopically distinct enzyme-coenzyme compounds has not been too successful, but there is evidence of fluorescence changes when NADH₂ is added to a number of enzymes including yeast alcohol dehydrogenase and liver glutamic dehydrogenase.

Evidence for a stable compound formed between one of the enzymes of the fatty acid oxidation system (see p. 270) and its substrate has been presented by Beinert & Crane (1956). When acyl dehydrogenase is reduced with a chemical reducing agent such as sodium dithionite ($Na_2S_2O_4$) the spectrum typical of a reduced flavoprotein appears (Fig. 1.15A) and the reduced flavoprotein is autoxidizable. When the same enzyme acts upon its substrate octanoyl CoA there is an increase

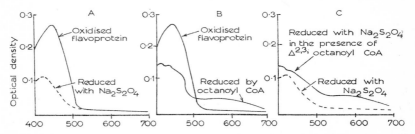

Fig. 1.15. Evidence for the formation of a stable enzyme product intermediate, in the oxidation of octanoyl CoA by an acyl dehydrogenase of pig liver.

in optical density between 500 and 650 mμ (Fig. 1.15B) due to the formation of a flavin free radical (p. 204). Formation of this free radical is also observed when the enzyme is chemically reduced in the presence of the product of octanoyl CoA oxidation, α, β-unsaturated octanoyl CoA (Fig. 1.15C). In both cases, the free radical formed is relatively stable, and the reduced flavoprotein is not readily autoxidized. These results suggest that the enzyme when reduced forms a flavin free radical which is stabilized in the presence of its reaction product. The reduced enzyme can be re-oxidized only in the presence of a specific 'electron transferring flavoprotein' (p. 271).

EVIDENCE FROM TRACER EXPERIMENTS

The enzyme phosphoglucomutase catalyses the interconversion of glucose-1-phosphate and glucose-6-phosphate. The reaction mechanism may be written:

$$Enz-P + G-1-P \leftrightharpoons E + G-1, 6-P_2$$

$$E + G-1, 6-P_2 \leftrightharpoons E-P + G-6-P$$

If ^{32}P labelled glucose-1-phosphate is used as a substrate, ^{32}P is incorporated into the enzyme and on acid degradation it has been shown that the phosphate is attached to a serine residue (see p. 57). An essentially similar series of reactions takes place with the enzyme phosphoglyceromutase.

EVIDENCE BY ULTRACENTRIFUGAL SEPARATION

Enzymes and enzyme substrate compounds can be sedimented under conditions which produce only small concentration gradients with the free substrate.

When yeast alcohol dehydrogenase is added to a solution of NAD, the free enzyme and the enzyme-NAD complex can be sedimented in the ultracentrifuge and the concentration of free NAD can be measured in the supernatant. From such data the dissociation constant can be calculated (Table 1.8).

TABLE 1.8

Binding of NAD by yeast triose phosphate dehydrogenase
(after Velick, 1954)

Initial concentration				Moles NAD bound	K
		NAD		Moles Enz.	
Enzyme	NAD	Free	Bound		
	(moles/litre) $\times 10^4$				(moles/litre) $\times 10^5$
0·15	0·145	0·064	0·081	0·54	1·7
0·15	0·29	0·122	0·168	1·12	0·96
0·15	0·58	0·298	0·282	1·88	0·19

The Relationship Between K_m and a Dissociation Constant

The fact that certain enzyme substrate compounds have characteristic absorption spectra makes it possible to measure the dissociation constant of ES and compare it with the K_m value determined from the overall kinetics, i.e. by the formation of the product.

Consider the spectra of free $NADH_2$ and $NADH_2$ bound to alcohol dehydrogenase (Fig. 1.12). There is no single wavelength at which the formation of the complex can be measured without interference from

$NADH_2$. However, at 328 mμ and 354 mμ the molar extinction coefficient of $NADH_2$ is nearly the same, whilst there is a considerable difference for the complex at these wavelengths.

Britton Chance has developed a spectrophotometric method in which flickering light at 328 mμ and 354 mμ is passed through a solution and thence to a photocell. This produces an alternating current whose amplitude is proportional to the difference in light absorption at the two wavelengths. When $NADH_2$ is added to the solution, there is no difference in the light absorbed at 328 mμ and 354 mμ.

However, the instrument also records the optical density, i.e. the extinction coefficient, at 328 mμ and so measures the amount of $NADH_2$ added. If alcohol dehydrogenase is present, the complex Enz. $NADH_2$ will be formed and the optical density at 354 mμ will fall. Since $NADH_2$ and Enz. $NADH_2$ are isosbestic, i.e. have the same molar extinction coefficient, at 328 mμ, the optical density ratio increment (E 328–E 354) will increase and produce an alternating current, the amplitude being recorded by the spectrophotometer.

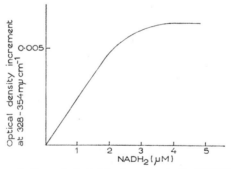

FIG. 1.16. Titration of dilute alcohol dehydrogenase with $NADH_2$ at pH 7·0 (concentration alcohol dehydrogenase=1·17 μM) (after Theorell & Chance 1951).

The result of such a titration is shown in Fig. 1.16.

The value of $NADH_2$ giving half maximum binding of enzyme is approx. 1·5 μM. The concentration free enzyme = bound enzyme = 0·585 μM. Concentration free $NADH_2$ = 1·5 − 2 × 0·585 μM.

Then

$$K = \frac{(NADH_2)^2 \, (Enz.)}{(Enz. \, [NADH_2]_2)}$$

$$= 10^{-7} \text{ at pH 7·0}$$

This value may be compared with $K_m = 1.5 \times 10^{-5}$ obtained by steady state kinetics.

The Active Site

The active site is that part of the enzyme which combines with the substrate. Following Koshland (1960) we define the active site as consisting of those amino acids making contact with the substrate and those 'auxiliary' amino acids which have a definite role to play in the enzyme action.

Three main methods of studying the active site have been developed.

INHIBITION BY GROUP SPECIFIC COMPOUNDS

A substance may inhibit an enzyme by combining at the active site and thereby preventing the substrate from gaining access to the active site; such inhibition is said to be competitive. Alternatively a substance may inhibit by reacting with the enzyme in such a way as to reduce the catalytic activity whilst not preventing the formation of the enzyme substrate complex. The steady state analysis of enzyme inhibition is complex, but a general analysis based on the equilibrium assumption has been provided by Friedenwald & Maengwyn Davies (1954). Representing inhibitor as I, the various equilibria may be written:

$$E + S \rightleftharpoons ES \qquad E = (ES).K_m/(S) \tag{1.21}$$

$$E + I \rightleftharpoons EI \qquad (EI) = (E).I/K_I = (ES).(I)K_m/(S)K_I \tag{1.22}$$

$$EI + S \rightleftharpoons EIS \qquad (EIS) = (S)/aK_m = (ES).I/aK_I \tag{1.23}$$

$$ES + I \rightleftharpoons EIS \qquad (EIS) = ES(I)/aK_1 \tag{1.24}$$

$$E_m = E + ES + EI + EIS$$

$$= \frac{K_m(ES)}{(S)} + (ES) + \frac{(ES)(I)K_m}{(S)K_I} + \frac{(ES)(I)}{aK_I}$$

For the Michaelis-Menten mechanism (eqn 1.1)

$$v = k_3(ES)$$

$$= \frac{k_3(E_T)}{K_m/(S) + 1 + (I)K_m/(S)K_I + (I)/aK_I}$$

$$V_{max} = k_3(E_T)$$

$$v = \frac{V_{max}}{1 + K_m/(S) + (I)K_m/(S)K_I + (I)/aK_I} \tag{1.25}$$

This solution is general and we are frequently interested in two special cases.

(a) COMPETITIVE INHIBITION

If I and S compete for the active site, the complex EIS cannot exist. This is equivalent to putting $a = \infty$.

Consequently (1.25) reduces to

$$v = \frac{V_{max}}{1 + K_m/(S) + (I)K_m/(S)K_I}$$

$$= \frac{V_{max}(S)}{K_m[1 + (I)K_I] + (S)} \qquad (1.26)$$

In the reciprocal form (1.26) becomes

$$\frac{1}{v} = \frac{1}{V_{max}} + \frac{K_m(1 + (I)/K_I)}{V_{max}(S)}$$

Thus $1/v$ is a linear function of $1/s$. When S is very large

$$\frac{1}{v} = \frac{1}{V_{max}}$$

Thus the maximum velocity is unaffected by the presence of I as shown in Fig. 1.17.

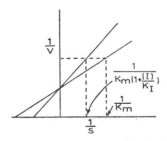

FIG. 1.17. Competitive inhibition of an enzyme reaction.

(b) NON-COMPETITIVE INHIBITION

If I combines with the enzyme so as to inhibit the catalytic step (i.e. reduces k_3), but does not interfere with the affinity of the enzyme for S.

Then $a = 1$ and eqn (1.25) reduces to

$$v = \frac{V_{max}}{1 + K_m/S + (I)K_m/(S)K_I + (I)/K_I}$$

$$= \frac{V_{max}}{[1 + (I)/K_I][1 + K_m/(S)]}$$

It should be noted that V_{max} is the maximum velocity in the absence of inhibitor. In the presence of I, $V_{max}{}^I$ is the lesser quantity.

$$\frac{V_{max}}{1 + (I)/K_I}$$

The substrate concentration giving half this value is v_I.

$$\frac{v^I}{V_{max}{}^I} = \frac{1}{2} = \frac{V_{max}(S)}{[1 + (I)/K_I]/[K_m + (S)]} \cdot \frac{1 + (I)/K_I}{V_{max}}$$

$$\therefore \quad K_m = S$$

A non-competitive inhibitor thus reduces V_{max} but does not alter the apparent K_m as shown in Fig. 1.18.

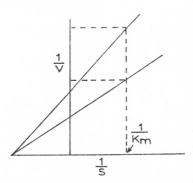

FIG. 1.18. Non-competitive inhibition of an enzyme reaction.

Competitive and non-competitive inhibitions can be experimentally recognized by measuring (in the presence and absence of inhibitor) the effect of substrate concentration on reaction velocity. It must be remembered that these two forms of inhibition are special cases and frequently results do not fit either of the extremes. Thus whilst I may not combine at the active site, the affinity of EI for S may not be the same as that of E for S, so that $a \neq 1$. In the case where S and I compete for the active site, they may also combine with E at another site and affect the affinity of E for I and/or S. Thus EIS is not a forbidden species and $a \neq \infty$.

In the case of simple competitive inhibition it is usually sufficient to establish that the substrate protects the enzyme from the inhibitor. For example Vallee (1958) has shown that yeast alcohol dehydrogenase which crystallizes with four zinc atoms per mole is inhibited by the metal chelating agent 1,10-phenanthroline. The inhibition is competitive with respect to $NADH_2$ or NAD, but non-competitive with respect to alcohol and acetaldehyde, thus suggesting that the coenzyme is bound to the active site by a zinc atom.

pH DEPENDENCE

This method stems from the suggestion of Michaelis & Pechstein (1914) that the bell-shaped curve of enzyme activity against pH, is a result of ionization of groups on the enzyme. In many cases the Michaelis constant or the maximum velocity is dependent on pH in a manner resembling a titration curve. Calculations (see Dixon & Webb, 1958) permit the determination of a pK for the group involved, and in certain cases the tentative identification of the group (see Table 1.2). The pH dependence of the maximum velocity may be unlike the pH dependence of the Michaelis constant. In such cases it may be argued that different groups are involved in the binding and decomposition of the enzyme substrate complex.

COVALENT LABELLING

A major breakthrough in the study of the active site occurred when it was found that the nerve gas di*iso*propylphosphorofluoridate (DFP) reacts stoichiometrically with certain enzymes to give a stable phosphorylated enzyme (Balls & Jansen, 1952). The parallelism between the stoichiometry of the reaction

$$(C_3H_7O)_2 \, POF + Enz. \, H \rightleftharpoons Enz. - PO(OC_3H_7)_2 + HF$$

and enzyme inactivation, together with substrate protection suggests that phosphorylation occurs at the active site. The treatment of purified enzymes with ^{32}P-labelled DFP, followed by enzymatic or acid hydrolysis led to the finding that the hydroxyl group of serine bears the phosphoryl group. The short-range sequence of amino acids surrounding the DFP seryl residue has been found to be common to a number of enzymes including chymotrypsin, trypsin, pancreatic elastase, thrombin and somewhat surprisingly the same sequence occurs around the serine of phosphoglucomutase which combines with the substrate. This sequence is:

aspartate-serine-glycine

The sequence,

glutamate-serine-alanine

is present in liver aliesterase, pseudocholinesterase and phosphoglyceromutase.

The recurring sequence of three similar amino acids at the active site of eight enzymes is not likely to be coincidence. The wide differences in substrate specificity between the eight enzymes makes it unlikely that these residues are involved in binding the substrate but suggests that they are involved in bond breaking. In this connection it is of interest that treatment of phosphoglucomutase with cysteine produces proteolytic activity.

Theories of Enzyme Action

It is reasonably certain that the formation of an enzyme substrate complex is an essential of enzyme catalysis. One of the earliest theories of enzyme action proposed that the frequency of collisions between two substrates is increased by the formation of a ternary complex between enzyme and substrates.

This theory has been treated quantitatively by Koshland who has shown that it cannot play a quantitatively significant part in catalysis (Table 1.9); nevertheless the proposed mechanism is an essential feature of catalysis.

TABLE 1.9

Comparison of observed enzymic rates with those calculated by the collision frequency theory (after Koshland, 1956)

Enzyme	Ratio $\dfrac{\text{Velocity of enzymic reaction}}{\text{Velocity of non-enzymic reaction}}$	
	A. Calculated	B. Observed
Hexokinase	1·8	7×10^9
Phosphorylase	2·5	$1·4 \times 10^{11}$
Alcohol dehydrogenase	0·5	9×10^8

ACTIVATION ENERGY

Most chemical reactions proceed more rapidly at higher temperatures and Arrhenius found that when the logarithm of a velocity constant was plotted against the reciprocal of the absolute temperature, a straight line relationship was obtained. The integrated form of the Arrhenius equation which gives this linear relationship is

$$\ln k = \text{Constant} - E/RT \text{ or } k = \text{Constant} \times \frac{1}{\exp(E/RT)}$$

(where k is a velocity constant

R is the gas constant

and T the absolute temperature).

To explain this relationship Arrhenius proposed that an equilibrium exists between inactive and active molecules and that only the latter participate in chemical reactions. In the Arrhenius equation, E is the energy difference between the two forms and is termed the energy of activation. It follows from the Maxwell-Boltzmann distribution law that the fractional number of molecules with energies equal to or greater than the activation energy E is given by

$$\frac{N^*}{N} = \frac{1}{\exp(E/RT)}$$

where N^* is the number of molecules with energies $\geqq E$

N is the total number of molecules.

From this equation it can be seen that a small decrease in the energy of activation produces a large increase in the number of molecules with energies equal to or greater than E (Table 1.10).

These relationships form the theoretical basis for the widely held view that enzymes function by lowering the activation energy. This concept may be illustrated diagrammatically (Fig. 1.19).

TABLE 1.10

Calculated relationship between activation energy (E) and the fractional number of molecules with energy equal to or greater than E.

Energy of activation E (k cal/mole)	$\dfrac{N^*}{N} = \dfrac{1}{\exp(E/RT)}$ $T = 25°C$
1·0	0·185
2·0	$3 \cdot 42 \times 10^{-2}$
10·0	$4 \cdot 71 \times 10^{-8}$
20·0	$2 \cdot 33 \times 10^{-15}$

It will be immediately apparent to the student that this is not an explanation of catalysis but merely poses the question in different terms; it is necessary to explain how an enzyme reduces energy of activation.

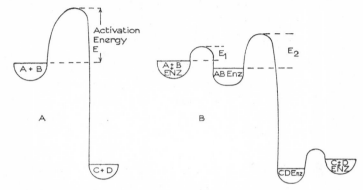

FIG. 1.19. Energy profile for: A, an uncatalysed reaction; B, a catalysed reaction.

ENERGY TRANSFER THEORY

This theory is sometimes termed the 'strain theory' or 'the rack' and has been postulated for hydrolytic enzymes. It proposes that when a substrate is bound to an enzyme the substrate is strained. The enzyme is assumed to hold a substrate at two or more points so that movements of the tertiary structure of the protein may compress or stretch the substrate and thereby 'activate' it. There is no simple quantitative basis for this theory, but the theory can be put to a simple test.

Consider a group of compounds represented by the formula ROQ and which are hydrolysed according to the equation

$$R—O—Q + H_2O \leftrightharpoons ROH + QOH$$

By keeping R constant and varying Q it is possible to obtain a series of compounds in which the Q—O bond is weaker than, equal to, or stronger than the R—O bond. If the enzyme simply provides energy to ROQ, the weakest bond would be expected to break. Fortunately it is possible to determine which bond is broken by carrying out the reaction in water enriched with ^{18}O. If the R—O bond is broken the isotope would be expected to appear in $R^{18}OH$.

$$R—O—Q + H_2^{18}O \leftrightharpoons R^{18}OH + QOH$$

Similarly, rupture of the Q—O bond would produce $Q^{18}OH$.

$$R—O—Q + H_2^{18}O \leftrightharpoons ROH + Q^{18}OH$$

The following phosphate esters are substrates for the enzyme alkaline phosphatase and have varying bond strengths so that the point of cleavage predicted by the theory can be tested. In glucose-1-phosphate the glucosyl—O bond is weaker than the P—O bond and on the basis of the strain theory hydrolysis should give ^{18}O glucose. In butyl phosphate the butyl—O bond and P—O bond are of approximately the same strength and ^{18}O could appear in either butanol or phosphate. In phenyl phosphate the phenyl—O bond is stronger than the P—O bond and ^{18}O would be expected in the phosphate. The experimental results (Table 1.11) show that the position of bond cleavage (P—O) is independent of the bond strength suggesting that the strain theory is invalid at least in the case of alkaline phosphatase.

TABLE 1.11

Cleavage point in hydrolyses catalysed by alkaline phosphatase
(after Koshland, 1956)

| Phosphate ester | ^{18}O content of water | ^{18}O content of inorganic phosphate liberated | | Observed |
		Calculated for C—O cleavage	Calculated for P—O cleavage	
Glucosyl	0·939	0·00	0·24	0·25
Butyl	1·23	0·00	0·30	0·25
Phenyl	1·37	0·00	0·34	0·34

THE MECHANISM OF GROUP TRANSFER REACTIONS

Many reactions are of the type

$$B—X + Y \rightleftharpoons B—Y + X$$

From organic chemistry there is ample evidence that the replacement of X by Y at a primary or secondary carbon atom can take place by the following mechanism.

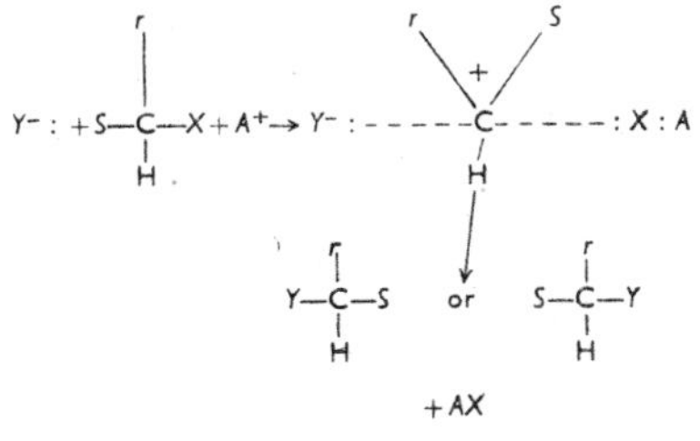

The reagent Y^- with its unshared pair of electrons is said to make a nucleophilic attack on the C-atom and the reagent A^+ is said to make an electrophilic attack. Group A^+ attracts the electrons of X weakening the C—X bond while the group Y^- shares its electrons with the C-atom and thus helps to push out the X-group. If the rate determining step is the formation of the carbonium ion

the carbonium ion can react with Y, which can approach from either side, to give a racemic mixture. However, if the attack of Y is the rate determining step and is virtually simultaneous with the departure of X, the bonds are inverted by the attack, 'like the vanes of an umbrella in a high wind'.

$$Y^- + S - C - X \quad Y^- - - - C - - - X^- \rightarrow Y - C - S + X^-$$

ENZYME REACTIONS WITH A CHANGE OF CONFIGURATION

Few enzyme reactions fall into this category, but β-amylase is one example, the α-glycosidic link being hydrolysed to give β maltose. It is reasonable to assume a single displacement mechanism in which there is a direct attack by water on the maltosyl carbon atom. A basic group (B) on the enzyme that would attract a proton and partially convert water to OH^- would probably increase the rate of the reaction. Likewise an acidic group (A) which would attract electrons from the maltosyl oxygen atom and hence weaken the C—O bond would also accelerate the reaction. However these groups must be very precisely placed and this has in general been explained by the lock and key model of the enzyme substrate complex proposed by Fischer. Recently, however, it has been suggested that in some cases the substrate induces the enzyme to fold around it.

THE INDUCED-FIT THEORY

In the case of β-amylase, only terminal maltose residues are attacked, that is only maltose units with an unsubstituted OH group at C-4 can be attacked. The lock and key model readily explains this by assuming either a specific bond between the hydroxyl and the enzyme, or a small cavity to accommodate the hydroxyl group. Cycloamylose has no terminal maltose units but is, nevertheless, a competitive inhibitor of β-amylase and kinetic studies have indicated that the internal maltose units of amylose act as competitive inhibitors (Thoma & Koshland, 1960). This competitive inhibition can be explained by the induced fit theory as shown in Fig. 1.20.

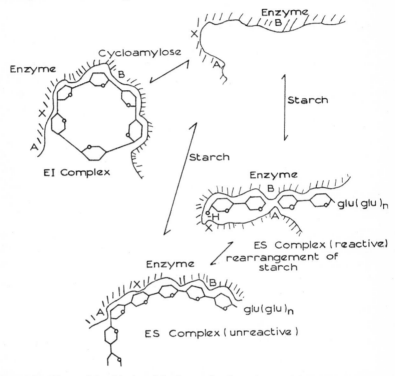

FIG. 1.20. Illustration of induced fit theory for β-amylase activity (Thoma & Koshland 1960).

READING LIST

McELROY W. D. & GLASS B.(Ed.) (1954) *A Symposium on the Mechanism of Enzyme Action*. Johns Hopkins Press, Baltimore

ALBERTY R. A. (1956) Enzyme Kinetics. *Adv. Enz.* **17**, 1

SANGER F. (1956) The Structure of Insulin. In *Currents in Biochemical Research* Ed. Green D. E. Interscience Pub., New York

DIXON M. & WEBB E. C. (1958) *Enzymes*. Longmans Green & Co., London

BOYER P.D., LARDY H. & MYRBÄCK K. (Ed.) (1958) *The Enzymes*, **1**. Acad. Press, New York

SHIFRIN S. & KAPLAN N. O. (1960) Coenzyme Binding. *Adv. Enz.* **22**, 337
KOSHLAND D. E. (1960) The Active Site and Enzyme Action. *Adv. Enz.* **22**, 45

LITERATURE CITED

ALBERTY R. A. (1948) *J. Chem. Educ.* **25**, 426, 619
ALBERTY R. A. (1956) *Adv. Enz.* **17**, 1
BALLS A. K. & JANSEN E. F. (1952) *Adv. Enz.* **13**, 321
BARENDRECHT H. P. (1904) *Z. Physik. Chem.* **49**, 456
BEINERT H. & CRANE F. L. (1956) in *Symposium on Inorganic Nitrogen Metabolism*, p. 601. Ed. McElroy W. D. & Glass B. Johns Hopkins Press, Baltimore
BRIGGS G. E. & HALDANE J. B. S. (1925) *Biochem. J.* **19**, 338
BROWN A. (1902) *J. Chem. Soc.* **81**, 373
CHANCE B. (1954) *A Symposium on the Mechanism of Enzyme Action.* Ed. McElroy W. D. & Glass B. Johns Hopkins Press, Baltimore.
CHANCE B. (1960) *J. Biol. Chem.* **235**, 2440
DIXON M. & WEBB E. C. (1958) *Enzymes.* Longmans Green & Co., London
DIXON M. & WEBB E. C. (1959) *Nature* **184**, 1298
EPSTEIN E. & HAGEN C. E. (1952) *Pl. Physiol.* **27**, 457
FISCHER E. (1894) *Ber deut Chem. Ges.* **27**, 2985
FRIEDENWALD J. S. & MAENGWYN-DAVIES G. D. (1954) in *Symposium on the Mechanism of Enzyme Action*, p. 154. Ed. McElroy W. D. & Glass B. Johns Hopkins Press, Baltimore
HALDANE J. B. S. (1930) *Enzymes.* Longmans Green & Co., London
HENRI V. (1904) *Archivio di Fisiologia* **1**, 299.
HOFFMANN-OSTENHOF O. (1960) *Ann. Rev. Biochem.* **29**, 73.
HOFSTEE B. H. J. (1959) *Nature* **184**, 1296
KOSHLAND D. E. (1956) *J. Cell. & Comp. Physiol.* Supp. 1, p. 217
KOSHLAND D. E. (1960) *Adv. Enz.* **22**, 45
KOSHLAND D. E. & HERR E. B. (1957) *J. Biol. Chem.* **228**, 1021
LAIDLER K. J. (1958) *The Chemical Kinetics of Enzyme Action.* Clarendon Press, Oxford
LINEWEAVER H. & BURK D. (1934) *J. Am. Chem. Soc.* **56**, 658
MEDWEDEW G. (1937) *Enzymologia* **2**, 1, 31, 53
MICHAELIS L. & MENTEN M. L. (1913) *Biochem. Z.* **49**, 333
MICHAELIS L. & PECHSTEIN H. (1914) *Biochem. Z.* **60**, 79
OGSTON A. G. (1955) *Disc. Faraday Soc.* **20**, 161
OSBORNE T. B. (1919) *The Vegetable Proteins.* Longmans Green & Co., London
REINER J. M. (1959) *Behaviour of Enzyme Systems.* Burgess Publishing Co. Minneapolis
THEORELL H. & BONNICHSEN R. (1951) *Acta Chim. Scand.* **5**, 379
THEORELL H. & CHANCE B. (1951) *Acta. Chim. Scand.* **5**, 1127
THOMA J. A. & KOSHLAND D. E. (1960) *J. Am. Chem. Soc.* **82**, 3329
VALLEE B. L. (1958) *Proc. Fourth Int. Cong. of Biochem.* **8**, 138, Pergamon Press
VELICK S. F. (1954) *A Symposium on the Mechanism of Enzyme Action.* Ed. McElroy W. D. & Glass B. Johns Hopkins Press, Baltimore.

CHAPTER 2

BIOENERGETICS

Heat Production in Plants

A comparison between respiration and burning frequently forms the basis on which the elementary student is introduced to the subject of bioenergetics. Historically, this approach dates back to Lavoisier who, in 1780, concluded that 'respiration is combustion'. The danger of this approach is that of any argument based on analogy; in this particular case made dangerous by the plausability of certain false analogies. A number of possible misconceptions can be avoided by stating the obvious — a living organism is not a heat engine and does not convert heat into any other form of energy.

Most elementary text-books of plant physiology describe methods for demonstrating the production of heat during respiration, the simplest method being to record the increase in temperature which takes place when seeds are germinated in a thermos flask. This experiment was reported by Peirce in 1912 and his paper clearly shows his dilemma. He notes that respiration is associated with the production of heat and states that 'heat thus liberated must either be converted into work or given off', but in the last paragraph he wrote — 'In this study I have been occupied with an unessential, although inevitable feature of the process of respiration'.

There appears to be a fairly widely held belief that energy transfer during plant respiration is a relatively efficient process, that is, a considerable portion of the energy made available by the oxidation of carbohydrate is conserved rather than dissipated as heat. This belief stems from the finding that muscular contraction has an overall efficiency of about 20 per cent and certain theoretical considerations (see p. 215) indicate that the transfer of energy to adenosine triphosphate during the oxidation of glucose may be as high as 40 per cent. There is very little experimental evidence to support this belief. Rodewald (1887) measured the total energy of plant material as heat of combustion and found that stems of *Brassica oleracea* var. *kohlrabi* dissipate 97 per cent of the total energy as heat. In the case of apples 99·2 per cent appears as heat. It can be concluded that little mechanical work is performed by these tissues. This experimental approach does not determine the amount of energy conserved by the plant, because any conserved energy is estimated in the heat of combustion. To measure the amount of energy conserved it is necessary to calculate the maximum amount of heat which could be produced by respiration and to compare it with the measured production of heat. For example, if a plant oxidizes a mole of glucose to 6 moles of carbon dioxide, the maximum amount of heat which can be produced is 682 kcal. The difference between 682 kcal and the measured production of heat is the amount of energy conserved.

Experiments with wheat seedlings conducted by Doyer (1915) indicated that 2 days after germination 83 per cent of the energy of respiration was conserved, and after 6 days 50 per cent of the energy was conserved. However, Wohl & James (1942) have shown that there is reason to doubt the accuracy of Doyer's results. Estimates of heat losses from apples indicate that the conservation of energy is less than 10 per cent. In view of the limited experimental evidence for higher plants, we note that when yeast is growing on glucose, ethanol or acetic acid, the conservation of energy has been estimated as 29·2, 36·6 and 22·6 per cent respectively. It may be argued that green plants have abundant energy available in the form of sunlight and thermodynamic efficiency is thus of little importance. However, seedlings have only the chemical energy of food reserves and it seems reasonable to expect, on evolutionary grounds, that all plants should be thermodynamically efficient. The limited amount of thermochemical data for plants is disappointing. Many predictions concerning the energetics of plants can be made from studies with cell free systems but it is important to check these predictions experimentally. For example, the ripening of fruit is associated with a rapid rise in respiration called the climacteric, and it has been suggested that the climacteric represents the breakdown of cellular organization and control. Evidence that the climacteric is associated with a lowered conservation of energy has not been obtained.

Heat Production in an Enzymic Reaction

Consider the reaction

$$A + B \rightleftharpoons C + D \tag{2.1}$$

Suppose all participants are present at 1 molal activity and enzyme is added; the reaction will then proceed to an equilibrium such that

$$K_{(equil)} = [(C)(D)]/[(A)(B)]$$

and heat (ΔH) will be generated. The heat generated has two components.

$$\Delta H° = \Delta G° + T\Delta S$$

FREE ENERGY

ΔG is the difference between the total free energy of all participants at the beginning of the reaction and at equilibrium; it represents energy which can be used to perform work and corresponds to the forces which hold atoms together. In the absence of a system to utilize this free energy it is dissipated as heat. Quantitatively ΔG is expressed as calories per mole of reaction.

The value of ΔG for a reaction is a function of the concentration of the reactants. Thus, the higher the concentration of the substrates, the greater is the change in free energy. To facilitate the calculation of free energy changes it is necessary to know the free energy change for standard conditions ($\Delta G°$). These conditions are taken as a temperature of 25°C, gases at a pressure of 1 atmosphere, and solutes at a concentration of 1 molal activity. The standard for water is taken as unity rather than 55·5 which is the molar activity of water for dilute solutions. An alternative standard ($\Delta G'$) is frequently used in biochemistry; in the alternative standard the standard condition of the hydrogen ion is taken as that of pH 7 rather than 1 molal activity (pH = 0).

Reference to compilations of thermodynamic data (e.g. Burton & Krebs, 1953) gives the standard free energy change for many reactions of biochemical interest, thus

fructose-6-phosphate + ATP ⇌ fructose-1, 6-diphosphate + ADP
$$(\Delta G' = -4\cdot2 \text{ kcal}) \qquad (2.2)$$

fructose-1, 6-diphosphate ⇌ phosphoglyceraldehyde +
dihydroxyacetonephosphate ($\Delta G' = +5\cdot5$ kcal) (2.3)

Under standard conditions reaction (2.2) will move from left to right until equilibrium is reached and the free energy loss will be 4·2 kcal. The reaction is said to be exergonic and the loss of free energy is recorded by giving $\Delta G'$ a negative sign. Reaction (2.3) is said to be endergonic and $\Delta G'$ is given a positive sign. It will be appreciated that this terminology is completely artificial. Under standard conditions reaction (2.3) cannot move from left to right, but will move from right to left with a loss of free energy amounting to 5·5 kcal. A chemical reaction can only proceed in the direction of loss of free energy and the concept of an endergonic reaction can be misleading.

The free energy change for particular conditions may be calculated from the equation

$$\Delta G = \Delta G^\circ + RT \ln [(C)(D)]/[(A)(B)] \qquad (2.4)$$

ΔG° is a constant related to the equilibrium constant by the equation

$$\Delta G^\circ = -RT \ln K \qquad (2.5)$$

The remaining term in eqn (2.4) is the concentration term and is responsible for an apparent anomaly. If the reaction is started by mixing pure A and B, then at time t_0, C and $D = 0$ and the concentration term

$$\Delta G \text{ (conc.)} = -RT \ln [(C)(D)]/[(A)(B)] \qquad (2.6)$$

becomes infinity. Thus eqn (2.4) predicts that in the absence of products ΔG will be negative and infinitely large. Considered from the point of view that ΔG is a measure of disequilibrium, this result is meaningful. From the point of view of energetics its meaning is not immediately apparent. To resolve the anomaly, we must look more closely at the meaning of ΔG.

Let the total energy of A and B be G. When an infinitesimally small amount of reaction (dn moles) has taken place $\Delta G = dG/dn$. It is thus apparent that ΔG is a differential quantity and if the *total* energy change is needed it is necessary to integrate eqn (2.6).

If 1 mole of A is mixed with 1 mole of B and enzyme added, the degree of advancement of the reaction may be denoted as n moles and will vary between 0 (pure A and B) and 1·0 (pure C and D). Eqn (2.6) may be written:

$$\Delta G \text{ (conc.)} = \frac{dG \text{ (conc.)}}{dn} = RT \ln \frac{(1-n)^2}{n^2} = 2RT \ln \frac{(1-n)}{n}$$

Integrating gives

$$G \text{ (conc.)} = 2RT[(n-1) \ln (1-n) - n \ln n]_0^n \qquad (2.7)$$

The total free energy change due to the concentration term will thus be maximum when $n = 0·5$ and will amount to 830 calories. For a reaction where $K = 1$ ($\Delta G^\circ = 0$) A and B will be in equilibrium with their products when $n = 0·5$. On mixing pure A and B and starting the reaction, $-\Delta G$ will decrease as the reaction proceeds, becoming zero at equilibrium. When ΔG for the reaction is zero, the total free energy ($-G$) will be at its maximum of 830 calories. The general equation for the total free energy of a reaction relative to the degree of advancement is given by (2.8)

$$G = n\Delta G^\circ + 2RT[(n-1) \ln (1-n) - n \ln n]_0^n \qquad (2.8)$$

The relationships between the *total* free energy, the *change* of free energy and the degree of advancement of the reaction are shown in Fig. 2.1.

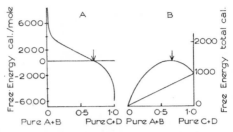

FIG. 2.1. The variation in free energy with the degree of advancement of a chemical reaction

$$A + B \rightleftharpoons C + D \ (\Delta G° = -1000 \text{ cal}).$$

The arrows indicate equilibrium point. A, variation of $\Delta G(-dG/dn)$ with degree of advancement; B, variation of total free energy G with degree of advancement (modified from Wilkie 1960).

ENTROPY

The entropy value (S) of a compound at a given temperature, corresponds to the energy levels of intramolecular vibrations, rotations and translations. These motions have quantized energy levels and the larger the number of energy levels available to a molecule, the more probable is that particular molecular structure and the greater is its entropy. The relationship between entropy and probability is given by the equation

$$S = k \ln W$$

where k is the gas constant per molecule (i.e. the gas constant R divided by Avogadro's number), and W is the number of energy levels available to the molecule without changing the total energy. If a compound is heated, more energy levels become available and entropy increases. When the compound is cooled W decreases and at absolute zero becomes 1 so that the entropy is zero.

Entropy is the capacity factor of heat and if the free energy of a system is dissipated as heat there is a *creation* of entropy, which represents the inefficiency of energy conservation. The *creation* of entropy must be distinguished from the exchange of entropy which is the difference between the entropy values of the reactants at the beginning and end of the reaction.

Consider the hydrolysis of adenosine triphosphate

$$ATP + H_2O \rightarrow ADP + H_3PO_4$$

Under standard conditions, except that the temperature was 37°C and the pH = 7·0, the following values were obtained; $\Delta G = -7·7$ kcal, $\Delta H = -4·8$ kcal, $T\Delta S = +2·9$ kcal. These values are related by the expression

$$\Delta G = \Delta H - T\Delta S$$

Thus for every mole of ATP which is hydrolysed 7·7 kcal are available for work. If work is not performed there will be a *creation* of entropy and 4·8 kcal of heat will be generated. The difference between ΔG and ΔH is the entropy term $T\Delta S = 2·9$ kcal so that the *exchange* of entropy in the system amounts to $2900/310 = 9·45$ entropy units (calories/mole/°K). If work could be performed with 100 per cent efficiency there would be no *creation* of entropy and 2·9 kcal of heat would be *absorbed* from the environment.

In the application of thermodynamics to intermediary metabolism, changes of entropy are not usually as important as changes in free energy, but they should not be forgotten or minimized. For example, early estimates of ΔH for the hydrolysis of ATP gave values of about 12 kcal. It was assumed that the entropy term was small and the free energy change was therefore thought to be 12 kcal. Recent investigations have given values of about 5 kcal for the ΔH for hydrolysis of ATP and the entropy term of about 3 kcal is quantitatively important.

Schroedinger (1944) emphasized the importance of entropy in the statement 'living organisms feed on negative entropy'. The complex molecules of cells have less freedom and are, in general, less random than the molecules from which they are formed so that their synthesis involves a decrease in entropy. Current thought tends to emphasize the role of free energy in biosynthesis but consideration of the entropy function is becoming of importance in relation to the amount of information which a cell can store, with particular reference to genetic information.

The Measurement of Thermochemical Data

Three methods are widely used.

(a) Calorimetry

Calorimetry measures the heat exchange during a chemical reaction and is most widely used to determine heats of combustion. A special application of the method has been developed by Benzinger (1956) which enables ΔH, $\Delta G°$ and ΔS to be calculated from two calorimetric determinations. Consider the reaction

$$A + B \rightleftharpoons C + D$$

Starting with pure A and B in dilute solution (less than 10^{-2} M) the heat exchange (Q_1) in reaching equilibrium is measured in a microcalorimeter. The heat exchange for the reverse reaction (Q_2) is similarly measured. Benzinger has shown that:

$$\Delta H = Q_1 - Q_2$$
$$\Delta G° = -RT \ln (Q_1/Q_2)^2$$
$$\Delta S = (\Delta H - \Delta G°)/T$$

(b) Equilibrium Measurements

The standard free energy change of a reaction is related to the equilibrium constant by the equation

$$\Delta G° = -RT \ln K$$

K can be determined with greatest accuracy when it approaches unity, but the use of refined analytical methods such as spectrophotometry permit the evaluation of K when it is of the order 10^5, though in such cases there may be uncertainty about the attainment of equilibrium.

(c) Oxidation-Reduction Potentials

The conventions used by physical chemists and biochemists differ in the sign given to the potential. The convention employed by biochemists defines the system with the more positive oxidation reduction potential as the stronger oxidant. At constant pH, the oxidation reduction potential of a system is given by the equation

$$E_h = E_0 + RT/nF \times \ln (\text{oxidant/reductant})$$

The relationship between the oxidation reduction potential and free energy is given by

$$\Delta G' = -nFE_h$$

where F is the Faraday constant (23 068 cal per volt equivalent) and n is the number of electrons involved.

Energy Conservation

When glucose is combusted, the free energy is dissipated as heat. Plants oxidize glucose by mechanisms which avoid the complete dissipation of free energy as heat. The energy conserving reactions involve the formation of anhydrous high energy compounds and the coupling of oxidative reactions to reductive biosynthetic reactions by means of coenzymes.

ANHYDROUS COMPOUNDS OF METABOLISM

In 1905 Harden and Young observed that the fermentation of glucose by yeast extracts was associated with the disappearance of inorganic phosphate. Subsequent work has shown that the esterification of inorganic phosphate is a fundamental mechanism of energy conservation in which the key compounds are adenosine triphosphate (ATP) and adenosine diphosphate (ADP)

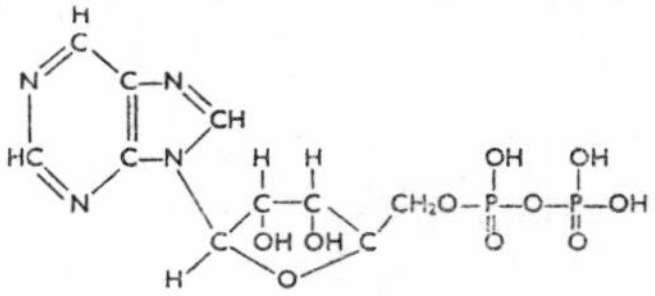

Adenosine diphosphate

Available evidence indicates that during the oxidation of a mole of glucose 32 moles of inorganic orthophosphate become the terminal phosphate group of ATP. The combustion and biological oxidation of glucose may be compared:

Combustion

$$C_6H_{12}O_6 + 6O_2 \rightarrow 6CO_2 + 6H_2O \quad (\Delta G' = -686 \cdot 5 \text{ kcal})$$

Biological oxidative phosphorylation

$$C_6H_{12}O_6 + 32P_i + 32ADP + 6O_2 \rightarrow 6CO_2 + 38H_2O + 32ATP$$
$$(\Delta G' = -400 \text{ kcal})$$

The mechanism of oxidative phosphorylation is discussed in Chapter 5, but whatever mechanism is involved, it is clear that a considerable fraction of the energy has been conserved by the formation of ATP.

Consider the oxidation of phosphoglyceraldehyde. Leaves contain three dehydrogenases active with this substrate, one of which catalyses the reaction

3-phosphoglyceraldehyde + NADP + H_2O →
$$\text{3-phosphoglycerate} + NADPH_2 \quad (\Delta G' = -13 \cdot 4 \text{ kcal})$$

The other two dehydrogenases, which differ in their coenzyme specificity, catalyse reactions which involve the formation of a carboxyl phosphate group:

3-phosphoglyceraldehyde + $\begin{matrix} \text{NAD} \\ \text{or} \\ \text{NADP} \end{matrix}$ + $P_i \rightarrow$

1,3-diphosphoglycerate + $\begin{matrix} \text{NADH}_2 \\ \text{or} \\ \text{NADPH}_2 \end{matrix}$ $(\Delta G' = +1 \cdot 5 \text{ kcal})$

The oxidation of an aldehyde to a carboxyl group involves a large change in free energy and the reaction is irreversible. Diphosphoglycerate has a higher energy level than 3-phosphoglycerate so that part of the free energy change associated with the oxidation of an aldehyde is conserved. The phosphate of the carboxyl phosphate may be transferred to ADP and subsequently to another phosphate acceptor, e. g. glucose

1,3 diphosphoglycerate		ADP		glucose-6-phosphate
Reaction 1 $\Delta G' = -4\cdot7$ kcal				Reaction 2 $\Delta G' = +5\cdot1$ kcal
3-phosphoglycerate		ATP		glucose

Here we see the further role of ATP as a coupling agent. Reaction 1 tends to produce a high ratio of ATP/ADP so that reaction 2 proceeds in the direction of glucose esterification. The two reactions are coupled by the reactants which are common — ATP and ADP. The dual roles of ATP are interrelated but are conveniently discussed separately.

ADENOSINE TRIPHOSPHATE AND HIGH ENERGY COMPOUNDS

In 1941 Lipmann proposed that in certain reactions, the anticipated free energy difference between reactants and products did not appear and was retained in the phosphate bonds of the product. He proposed that these phosphate bonds be termed 'energy rich' and written $\sim$P. In the absence of reliable thermodynamic data he estimated that the average energy present in an energy rich bond was about 9000 to 11 000 cal, compared to an ester phosphate linkage where the energy was estimated to be about 3000 cal. Four types of energy rich links were envisaged.

(1) Enolphosphate, e.g. phosphoenolpyruvate

$$CH_2\!=\!C\!-\!O\!\sim\!PO_3H_2$$
$$|$$
$$COOH$$

(2) Carboxyl phosphate, e.g. 1,3-diphosphoglycerate

$$\overset{\displaystyle O}{\underset{\displaystyle \parallel}{}}$$
$$H_2O_3POCH_2\!-\!CHOH\!-\!C\!-\!O\!\sim\!PO_3H_2$$

(3) Amine phosphate, e.g. creatine phosphate

$$\overset{\displaystyle NH}{\underset{\displaystyle \parallel}{}}$$
$$HN\!-\!C\!-\!N\!-\!CH_2\!-\!COOH$$
$$\wr \quad\quad |$$
$$PO_3H_2 \quad CH_3$$

(4) Pyrophosphate, e.g. adenosine triphosphate

$$\text{Adenosine—}\overset{\displaystyle \overset{O}{\|}}{\underset{\displaystyle \underset{OH}{|}}{P}}\text{—O}\sim\overset{\displaystyle \overset{O}{\|}}{\underset{\displaystyle \underset{OH}{|}}{P}}\text{—O}\sim\overset{\displaystyle \overset{O}{\|}}{\underset{\displaystyle \underset{OH}{|}}{P}}\text{—OH}$$

Consideration of the thermodynamic data makes it clear that 1,3-di-phosphoglyceric acid is a high energy compound compared with 3-phos-phoglyceric acid. Lipmann specifically located this 'extra' energy in the carboxyl phosphate bond — which may or may not be correct. His use of the term high energy bond conflicts with physico-chemical usage, where bond energy is defined with reference to the heat of formation from gaseous elements. Thus a high energy bond would require a large amount of energy to break it. In contrast, Lipmann used the term to designate a bond which released a large amount of energy on splitting. It would thus seem advisable to replace the expression high energy bond by high energy compound, where the concept of high energy is bio-chemical rather than physicochemical.

The biochemical approach to metabolism started with investigations of catabolism and in particular respiration and oxidation. Thus the biochemical convention for oxidation-reduction potentials records the oxidizing potential as $+$ve whereas in physicochemical usage the oxidizing potential is recorded as $-$ve. Similarly in thermodynamics, the biochemist is interested in the heats of combustion of compounds and takes the products of complete combustion (carbon dioxide and water) as a reference state. The physico-chemical reference state is that of elements in their standard state. Thus high energy compounds have relatively large heats of combustion but relatively low heats of formation. In this sense it is evident that fats and carbohydrates are high energy compounds, but Lipmann restricted the concept to cases where there was a large free energy change on hydrolysis. Whilst it is true that recent determinations have given lower values for the free energy of hydrolysis, the concept focuses attention on the importance of anhydrides. The problem of anabolism is in large measure the problem of forming anhydrous links in the aqueous environment of the cell. The process of oxidative phosphorylation whereby ATP is formed from ADP and P_i is discussed in Chapter 5, but here we note the possible significance of the association of oxidative phosphorylation with the lipid membranes of the mitochondria.

ADENOSINE TRIPHOSPHATE AS A COUPLING AGENT

ATP participates in a wide range of reactions which are conveniently classified by reference to the point at which ATP is cleaved — the point of cleavage being determined by specific enzymes. This facility makes ATP a versatile carrier of chemical energy.

The points at which ATP is cleaved are shown below:

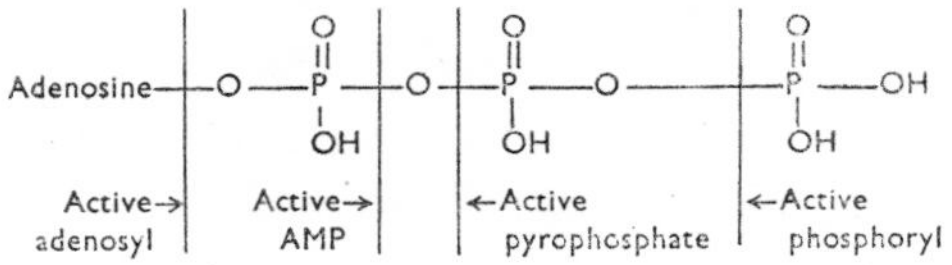

(a) ACTIVE PHOSPHORYL CLEAVAGE

The transfer of the terminal phosphate of ATP to various acceptors is catalysed by specific enzymes termed kinases. The mechanism of the reaction may be considered as a nucleophilic attack on the terminal phosphorus of ATP. Substrates providing the electronegative group R—O—H may be classified as follows.

(i) *Alcohols*

e.g. glucose + ATP $\rightleftharpoons$ glucose-6-phosphate + ADP

(ii) *Enols*

e.g. pyruvate + ATP $\rightleftharpoons$ phosphoenolpyruvate + ADP

(iii) *Acids*

e.g. 3-phosphoglycerate + ATP $\rightleftharpoons$ 1,3-diphosphoglycerate + ADP

(iv) *Phosphates*

e.g. adenosine monophosphate (AMP) + ATP $\rightleftharpoons$ 2 ADP

The last reaction, catalysed by the enzyme adenylate kinase, plays an important role in bioenergetics. The substrate for oxidative phosphorylation is ADP, but AMP is formed from ATP by a variety of reactions. Adenylate kinase catalyses the phosphorylation of AMP and so provides the substrate for oxidative phosphorylation.

(b) ACTIVE PYROPHOSPHATE CLEAVAGE

In this type of attack on ATP, AMP is split out and the attacking group is pyrophosphorylated — hence the enzymes are termed pryophosphokinases. The best documented example is 5-phosphoribose pyrophosphokinase which catalyses the reaction

ribose-5-phosphate + ATP ⇌ 5-phosphoribosylpyrophosphate + AMP

This enzyme has been demonstrated in mitochondria isolated from arti-
choke and germinating corn, but the mechanism of the reaction has not
been studied with the plant enzyme. A direct pyrophosphate transfer is
indicated by studies employing ATP labelled in specific positions with
^{32}P. These studies have shown that the terminal and middle phosphate
groups of ATP are transferred to ribose-5-phosphate.

Phosphoribosylpyrophosphate is involved in nucleotide synthesis:

base + phosphoribosylpyrophosphate ⇌ nucleotide + pyrophosphate

and also in the biosynthesis of purine bases (see Chapter 11).

(c) ACTIVE AMP CLEAVAGE

There are many examples of this type of cleavage which may be classified by the nature of the substrates making the nucleophilic attack on
ATP.

(i) *Phosphates*

e.g. pantetheine-4-phosphate + ATP ⇌ dephospho-coenzyme A + PP

Dephospho-coenzyme A is the substrate for a specific phosphokinase:

dephospho-coenzyme A + ATP ⇌ coenzyme A + ADP

The product of the reaction–coenzyme A–plays an important role in
metabolism (see p. 159 and Chapter 7).

(ii) *Fatty acids*

e.g. acetate + ATP + CoA ⇌ acetyl CoA + AMP + PP

Studies with ^{18}O-labelled acetate have shown that the reaction takes
place in the following stages.

(1) Acetate makes a nucleophilic attack on the innermost phosphorus
atom; pyrophosphate is split off and the active AMP reacts with
acetate to form adenylacetate:

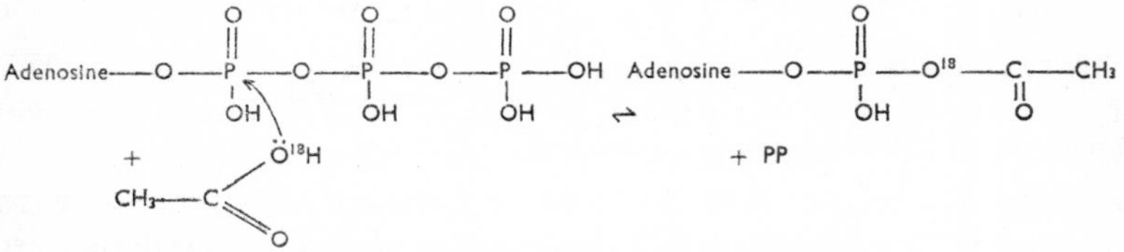

(2) Coenzyme A which has a free SH group then makes a nucleo-

philic attack on the carbonyl carbon atom of adenylacetate; AMP is split off and the active acetate reacts with coenzyme A to form acetyl coenzyme A.

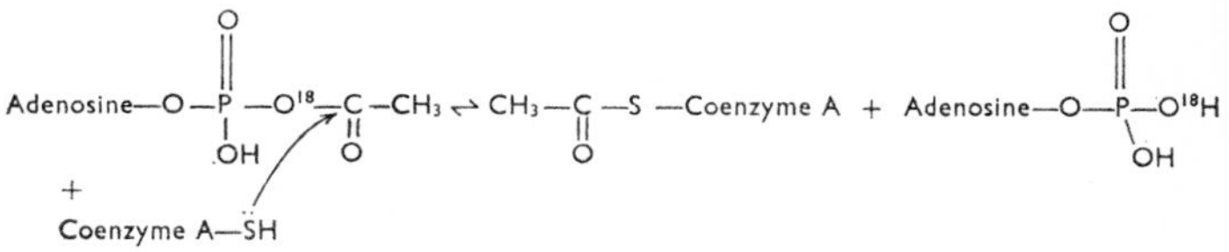

$$\text{Adenosine—O—P—O}^{18}\text{—C—CH}_3 \rightleftharpoons \text{CH}_3\text{—C—S—Coenzyme A} + \text{Adenosine—O—P—O}^{18}\text{H}$$

Coenzyme A—SH

(iii) *Amino acids*

A large number of amino acid activating enzymes have been observed in various preparations from plants. The reaction may be represented

$$\text{amino acid} + \text{ATP} \rightleftharpoons \text{aminoacyl AMP} + \text{PP}$$

Available evidence strongly implicates aminoacyl adenylates in protein synthesis.

(iv) *Sulphate*

$$\text{ATP} + \text{sulphate} \rightleftharpoons \text{adenosine-5'-phosphosulphate} + \text{PP}$$

The equilibrium constant for this reaction is approximately 10^{-8}. However, a specific kinase phosphorylates adenosine-5'-phosphosulphate at the 3-position of ribose:

adenosine-5'-phosphosulphate + ATP →
$$\text{3'-phosphoadenosine-5'-phosphosulphate} + \text{ADP}$$

The equilibrium of the second reaction lies far to the right and the Michaelis constant for adenosine-5'-phosphosulphate is very small so that a net synthesis of 3'-phosphoadenosine-5'-phosphosulphate can occur.

(d) ACTIVE ADENOSYL CLEAVAGE

e.g. L-methionine + ATP → S-adenosyl-L-methionine + PP + P

This reaction is of importance in biological methylation (see p. 374). It involves the complete dephosphorylation of ATP and studies with ^{32}P-labelled ATP have shown that the terminal phosphate emerges as inorganic phosphate while the remaining phosphates emerge as pyrophosphate. Experiments with $H_2^{18}O$ in the medium showed that ^{18}O entered phosphate but not pyrophosphate. We may conclude that during the activation of methionine ATP is split as shown below:

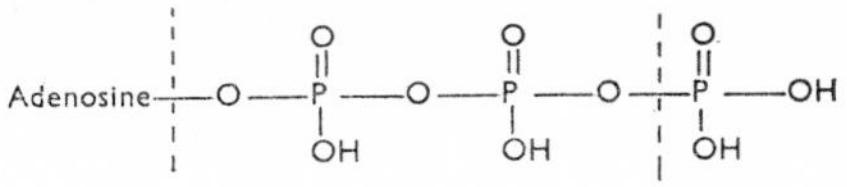

COMPARISON OF PYROPHOSPHATE AND ORTHOPHOSPHATE SPLITTING OF ATP

According to the concept of high energy bonds introduced by Lipmann ATP would be represented as

$$adenosine\text{-}phos \sim phos \sim phos$$

This formulation implies that the pyrophosphate split giving AMP is thermodynamically similar to the orthophosphate split giving ADP. However $\Delta G°$ for the pyrophosphate split is $-12\cdot1$ kcal compared with $-8\cdot9$ kcal for the orthophosphate split. The difference between these two values stems from the fact that pyrophosphate is not a high energy compound. If the free energy of hydrolysis was a simple function of the pyrophosphate bond, cleavage of ATP to give ortho- or pyrophosphate would be expected to involve the same free energy change and inorganic pyrophosphate would be expected to be a high energy compound. The standard free energy of hydrolysis of pyrophosphate is only $-3\cdot8$ kcal. The consequences of the thermodynamic differences between ortho- and pyrophosphate cleavage of ATP can be seen by comparing the synthesis of synthetic polyribonucleotides and deoxyribonucleic acid (DNA). The formation of synthetic polyribonucleotides involves an orthophosphate split of a nucleoside diphosphate and the reaction is readily reversible. The synthesis of DNA involves a pyrophosphate split of a deoxy-nucleoside triphosphate and the reaction is not readily reversed.

THE CENTRAL ROLE OF ATP IN BIOENERGETICS

The reactivity of ATP in various enzymic reactions is largely due to the electron-attracting properties of the phosphorus atom in the phosphate group. The attack of a nucleophilic agent on ATP requires specific enzymes and usually divalent cations; it is probable that the conversion of the thermodynamically active ATP into a kinetically active form involves some change of structure at the enzyme site which may involve chelation. However, these properties are found in other compounds and we must consider the role of other high energy compounds.

Nucleoside Polyphosphates

Mono, di- and triphosphates of uridine, guanosine, cytidine and inosine participate in metabolism. A number of transphosphorylations take place between these compounds, though it is not yet clear how many of the numerous reactions are catalysed by specific enzymes. The following reactions are examples:

(1) ATP + uridine monophosphate (UMP) $\rightleftharpoons$ ADP + uridine
$$\text{diphosphate (UDP)}$$

(2) Uridine triphosphate (UTP) + AMP $\rightleftharpoons$ UDP + ADP

(3) UDP + ATP $\rightleftharpoons$ UTP + ADP

The presence of these enzymes makes it difficult to establish the nucleotide specificity of kinases. However, all the evidence suggests that ATP dependent kinases play the dominant role in metabolism. The main role of the other nucleotides seems to lie in the formation of acid anhydrides in which the terminal phosphate is replaced by some other group. In the case of UTP and GTP, various sugars and sugar derivatives replace the phosphate (see Chapter 3) and in CTP the phosphate may be replaced by an alcohol, choline, ethanolamine or glycerol (see Chapter 7).

The various reactions involving these compounds are discussed on other pages but their role as high energy compounds can be illustrated by the following example.

The bacterial enzyme sucrose phosphorylase catalyses the reaction

glucose-1-phosphate + fructose $\rightleftharpoons$ sucrose + P_i ($\Delta G° = +700$ cal)

Sucrose synthesis in plants occurs by the reaction

UDP − glucose + fructose $\rightleftharpoons$ sucrose + UDP ($\Delta G° = -1000$ cal)

The difference in free energy (1700 cal) corresponds to the difference between the free energy of hydrolysis of the sugar phosphate linkage of UDP glucose and glucose-1-phosphate.

Thioesters of Coenzyme A

The various intermediates of carbohydrate metabolism are phosphate-containing compounds whilst the intermediates of fatty acid metabolism are thioesters of coenzyme A (CoA). The properties of CoA are discussed in Chapter 7, but here we note that CoA is a sulphydryl compound (often written CoASH) and forms fatty acyl CoA derivatives in which the acyl mercaptan bond can be compared with the acyl phosphate bond. Thus the large free energy change associated with the oxidation of an aldehyde to an acid is partly conserved in the formation of a carboxyl phosphate.

phosphoglyceraldehyde $+ P_i + NAD \leftrightarrow$
$$1,3\text{-diphosphoglycerate} + NADH_2$$

Similarly energy is conserved in the formation of acetyl CoA from acetaldehyde

acetaldehyde $+ CoASH + NAD \leftrightarrow acetyl\ S\ CoA + NADH_2$

and thioesters of coenzyme A are thus high energy compounds.

ONIUM COMPOUNDS

Onium compounds have been defined as 'substances formed by an addition reaction, in the course of which some atom increases its valence by one unit and so increases its formal charge algebraically by one unit'. For example, the methylation of dimethylethanolamine yields choline which is a quarternary ammonium compound.

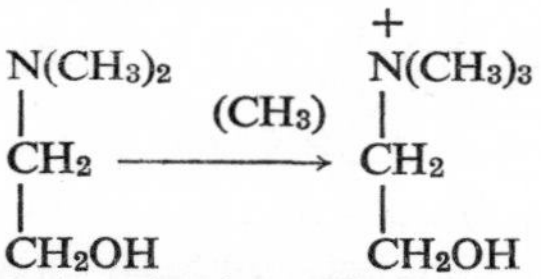

Dimethylethanolamine   Choline

The concept of onium compounds as high energy compounds was independently advanced by Cantoni (1952) and Woolley (1953). Cantoni noted that compounds acting as methyl donors were methyl-onium compounds. Woolley noted that a number of bases could exchange with the thiazolium moiety of thiamine:

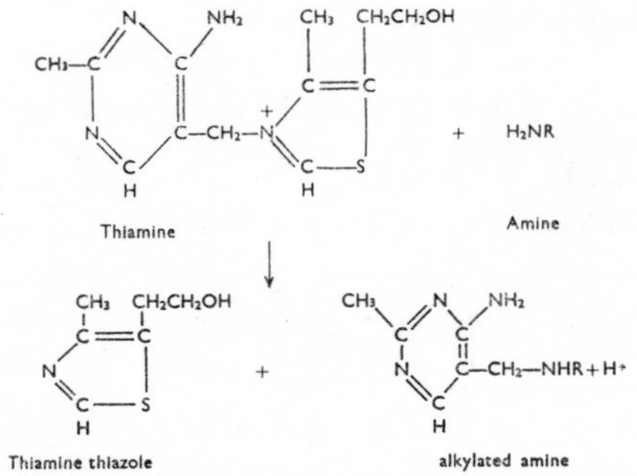

Thiamine   Amine

Thiamine thiazole   alkylated amine

He suggested that onium compounds were high energy compounds and

6

that the reduction of a quaternary nitrogen made the energy available for synthesis.

REDUCING POTENTIAL AND COUPLED REACTIONS

When one reactant in a bimolecular reaction undergoes oxidation, the other reactant undergoes reduction and the reduced product may participate in a reductive biosynthetic reaction. Consider the fixation of carbon dioxide by pyruvic acid. The equilibrium of the reaction

$$\text{pyruvate} + CO_2 \rightleftharpoons \text{oxaloacetate}$$

strongly favours decarboxylation. The reductive carboxylation of pyruvate is by contrast readily reversible.

$$\text{pyruvate} + CO_2 + NADPH_2 \rightleftharpoons \text{malate} + NADP \ (\Delta G' = -0.3 \text{ kcal})$$

The sustained production of malate requires some mechanism for regenerating $NADPH_2$ from NADP. For example, glucose-6-phosphate may reduce NADP:

$$\text{glucose-6-phosphate} + NADP \rightarrow \text{6-phosphogluconate} + NADPH_2$$

The reducing potential of $NADPH_2$ drives the carboxylation reaction. The sustained carboxylation of pyruvate is possible because the equilibrium for glucose-6-phosphate oxidation favours NADP reduction and so maintains a high $NADPH_2/NADP$ ratio which by mass action results in the synthesis of malate from pyruvate and carbon dioxide: NADP and $NADPH_2$ act as coupling agents linking the oxidation of glucose-6-phosphate to the reductive carboxylation of pyruvate.

'Push-pull' reactions in biosynthesis

The term push-pull is borrowed from electronics and is here applied to reactions which involve consecutive oxidations and reductions. Consider the fixation of carbon dioxide in the following reaction:

$$\text{pyruvate} + CO_2 + NADPH_2 \rightleftharpoons \text{malate} + NADP$$
$$\text{malate} + NAD \rightleftharpoons \text{oxaloacetate} + NADH_2$$

Sum: $\text{pyruvate} + CO_2 + NAD + NADPH_2 \rightleftharpoons \text{oxaloacetate} + NADP + NADH_2$

The equilibrium constant of the reaction $NAD + NADPH_2 \rightleftharpoons NADP + NADH_2$ is approximately unity so that the equilibrium constant of the overall reaction is approximately equal to the unfavourable equilibrium for direct carboxylation.

$$\text{pyruvate} + CO_2 \rightleftharpoons \text{oxaloacetate}$$

However, a large fixation of carbon dioxide can occur if the ratios $NAD/NADH_2$ and $NADPH_2/NADP$ are maintained at a high level.

The biological significance of this mechanism is made clear by considering a reaction involving an oxido-reduction but only one coenzyme. The enzyme uridine diphosphate galactose 4-epimerase catalyses the interconversion of uridine diphosphate glucose and uridine diphosphate galactose. Epimerization at C-4 of the hexose involves the reactions

In this case the coenzyme has a catalytic role and cannot affect the equilibrium ratio which is 3 : 1 in favour of the glucose nucleotide. It follows that the functioning of a push-pull mechanism requires different coenzymes and this duality is an essential feature of the organization of synthetic reactions.

The simultaneous production of high energy anhydrides and reducing potential ($NADPH_2$) is possible because cells possess two pyridine nucleotide coenzymes and two sets of enzymes for the oxidation of carbohydrates. The reactions of the Krebs cycle can be considered as a mechanism for providing $NADH_2$ as a substrate for oxidative phosphorylation. Outside the mitochondria, and thereby separated from the hydrogen transporting system, are the enzymes of the pentose phosphate pathway which can be written as the overall reaction

$$C_6H_{12}O_6 + 12NADP + 6H_2O \rightarrow 6CO_2 + 12NADPH_2$$

and thus produce the reducing potential necessary for biosynthesis.

The Duality of Pathways for Catabolism and Anabolism

Many catabolic reactions are hydrolytic, e.g. the hydrolysis of sucrose catalysed by invertase:

$$\text{sucrose} + H_2O \rightarrow \text{glucose} + \text{fructose}$$

The reaction is shown as irreversible and the equilibrium lies far to the right. Nevertheless, the possibility that sucrose synthesis occurs by a reversal of the invertase reaction was considered by early workers. It was obvious that the equilibrium position was dominated by the concentration of water and it was suggested that at interfaces the concentration of water may be sufficiently low for sucrose synthesis to occur. Experimental evidence does not support this view and it is widely believed that with few exceptions anabolism is not the reversal of catabolism. A few examples will illustrate the background leading to current views on the duality of pathways.

The possibility that plants can effect a reversal of the reactions of glycolysis has long been entertained by plant physiologists. Following the demonstration by Calvin and his associates (see p. 246) that the path of carbon in photosynthesis was via the intermediates of glycolysis, it was tempting to argue that the reactions of glycolysis were reversed due to the high reducing potential and the high ratio of ATP/ADP. However, whilst the intermediates are common to glycolysis and photosynthesis the mechanisms are different. For example, fructose-1,6-diphosphate is formed according to the reaction

$$\text{fructose-6-phosphate} + \text{ATP} \rightleftharpoons \text{fructose-1,6-diphosphate} + \text{ADP}$$

However, the high ratio of ATP/ADP associated with photosynthesis is unfavourable for dephosphorylation and plants contain a specific phosphatase which catalyses the reaction

$$\text{fructose-1,6-diphosphate} \rightarrow \text{fructose-6-phosphate} + P_i$$

Following the demonstration that amylose is formed by the reaction

$$\text{glucose-1-phosphate} \rightleftharpoons \text{amylose} + P_i$$

which is catalysed by phosphorylase, it was thought that phosphorylase was an enzyme of anabolism and amylase an enzyme of catabolism. However, the equilibrium constant of the phosphorylase reaction is small and sensitive to changes in pH. Thus the equilibrium ratio of glucose-1-phosphate to phosphate is 0·09 at pH 5·0 and 0·32 at pH 7·0 — the amylose concentration being taken as constant. Thus a high pH favours starch breakdown and it has been suggested that phosphorylase plays a part in stomatal movement where it is considered to catalyse synthesis and degradation of starch according to the pH of the cell sap (Williams, 1954). Similarly it has been suggested (Edelman, 1956) that amylase, which is highly active in plant extracts, does not exert its hydrolytic properties in the living cell so that phosphorylase could have a catabolic and anabolic function. The discovery of an almost irreversible synthesis of amylose form uridine diphosphate glucose (see p. 141) casts doubt on the anabolic function of phosphorylase.

READING LIST

KREBS H. A. & KORNBERG H. L. (1957) *Energy Transformations in Living Matter.* Springer-Verlag

KLOTZ I. M. (1957) *Some Principles of Energetics in Biochemical Reactions.* Acad. Press, New York

GEORGE P. & RUTMAN R. J. (1960) The 'High Energy Phosphate Bond' Concept. *Prog. in Biophys.* **10**, 1

JOHNSON M. (1960) Enzymic Equilibria and Thermodynamics. In *The Enzymes*, Vol. 3, Chapter 21. Ed. Boyer P. D., Lardy H. & Myrbäck K. Acad. Press, New York

WILKIE D. R. (1960) Thermodynamics and the Interpretation of Biological Heat Measurements. *Prog. in Biophys.* **10**, 260

DAVIES D. D. (1961) *Intermediary Metabolism in Plants.* Cambridge Univ. Press

LITERATURE CITED

BENZINGER T. H. & HEMS R. (1956) *Proc. Natl. Acad. Sci. U.S.* **42**, 896

BURTON K. & KREBS H. A. (1953) *Biochem. J.* **54**, 94

CANTONI G. L. (1952) In *Phosphorus Metabolism*, 2, Vol. 2, p. 129. Johns Hopkins University Press, Baltimore, Maryland

DOYER L. C. (1915) *Rec. Trav. Bot. Neerland.* **12**, 369

EDELMAN J. (1956) *Adv. Enz.* **17**, 189

LIPMANN F. (1941) *Adv. Enz.* **1**, 99

PEIRCE G. J. (1912) *Bot. Gaz.* **53**, 89

RODEWALD H. (1887) *Jb. Wiss. Bot.* **18**, 263

SCHROEDINGER E. (1944) *What is Life.* Cambridge Univ. Press

WILKIE D. R. (1960) *Prog. in Biophys.* **10**, 260

WILLIAMS W. T. (1954) *J. Expt. Bot.* **5**, 343

WOHL K. & JAMES W. O. (1942) *New Phyt.* **41**, 230

WOOLEY D. W. (1953) *Nature* **171**, 323

CHAPTER 3

THE CARBOHYDRATES

°The term carbohydrate was originally given to substances with the empirical formula of $Cx(H_2O)x$. This has been widened to include a number of closely related compounds which differ from $Cx(H_2O)x$ either in their empirical formula, e.g. the deoxy sugars, or in their composition, e.g. the amino sugars which contain nitrogen. Carbohydrates may be regarded as polyhydroxy aldehydes or ketones together with their simple derivatives and polymers. Three main classes are recognized. The monosaccharides or simple sugars are characterized by the fact that they cannot be hydrolysed to yield simpler carbohydrates. The monosaccharides are the units which are joined together to form the more complex carbohydrates. These latter compounds are divided into two groups, the oligosaccharides containing relatively few monosaccharide units, and the polysaccharides containing many units. Examples of oligosaccharides are sucrose, trehalose and raffinose: polysaccharides are represented by starch and cellulose. The simpler carbohydrates tend to be sweet, soluble, crystalline substances of constant molecular weight. The more complex carbohydrates are less clearly defined in that their molecular weight varies with the source and method of preparation.

MONOSACCHARIDES
Structure and Occurrence

The monosaccharides will be taken to include the sugars, deoxy sugars, amino sugars, the sugar alcohols and the sugar acids. Only a small proportion of the monosaccharides have been found in plants. A number of these play, at the most, only a minor role in metabolism and attention will be concentrated upon those of known importance. It should be appreciated that further study may reveal that hitherto neglected compounds are also important.

SUGARS

The monosaccharide sugars are polyhydroxy aldehydes or ketones. They may be classified according to the number of carbon atoms which they contain; three, four, five, six and seven carbon sugars are known as triose, tetrose, pentose, hexose and heptose, respectively. Sugars with an aldehyde group — the aldoses, are distinguished from those with a keto group — the ketoses. There is a tendency to confine the suffix -ose to the aldoses and to use the suffix -ulose for ketoses. Monosaccharides with fewer than five carbon atoms show a progressive lack of those properties normally associated with the group as a whole and the pentoses and hexoses may be considered the basic carbohydrates.

(a) STRUCTURE

The empirical formulae of the pentoses and hexoses are $C_5H_{10}O_5$ and $C_6H_{12}O_6$ respectively. The members of these groups which are known to be of biochemical importance have been shown to be straight chain carbon compounds with the carbonyl group at one end. Glucose may be represented as

$$\overset{}{(HO)H_2C} - \overset{*}{CH(OH)} - \overset{*}{CH(OH)} - \overset{*}{CH(OH)} - \overset{*}{CH(OH)} - CHO$$
$$\quad 6 \quad\quad 5 \quad\quad\quad 4 \quad\quad\quad 3 \quad\quad\quad 2 \quad\quad\quad 1$$

This, in fact, is one of the earliest formulae given to glucose and serves to illustrate two important facts. Firstly, the need of an unambiguous way of referring to the individual carbon atoms. The accepted numbering system for the aldoses refers to the carbonyl carbon as number one; in the ketoses, represented below by fructose,

$$\overset{}{(HO)H_2C} - \overset{*}{CH(OH)} - \overset{*}{CH(OH)} - \overset{*}{CH(OH)} - CO - CH_2(OH)$$
$$\quad 6 \quad\quad 5 \quad\quad\quad 4 \quad\quad\quad 3 \quad\quad\quad 2 \quad\quad\quad 1$$

the carbonyl carbon is number 2. Secondly, it is clear that in the above formulae those carbons marked with an asterisk are asymmetric. Consequently there will be sixteen stereoisomers of the aldohexoses and eight of the ketohexoses. The number of stereoisomers is given by 2^n where n is the number of asymmetric carbon atoms. The ability of enzymes to distinguish between stereoisomers and the consequent importance of the steric configuration of substrate molecules make it imperative to pay careful attention to the exact shape of carbohydrate molecules. In 1891 Fischer demonstrated that naturally occurring dextrorotatory glucose could be represented as in Fig. 3.1B. Asymmetric carbon atoms lie in the centre of a regular tetrahedron and therefore Fig. 3.1B is a conventional representation of the tetrahedral formula shown in Fig. 3.1A. The rules which must be followed in this representation form the first Fischer convention. If the two formulae are compared it will be seen that in the Fischer convention the groups lying at the ends of the vertical lines lie in the plane of the paper but the groups at the ends of the horizontal lines, the corners of the tetrahedron made by the —H and —OH groups, lie above the plane of the paper.

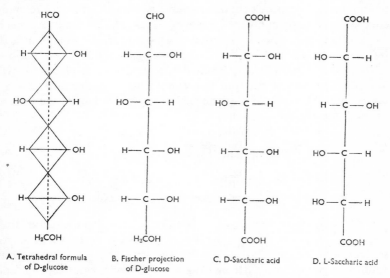

A. Tetrahedral formula of D-glucose   B. Fischer projection of D-glucose   C. D-Saccharic acid   D. L-Saccharic acid

FIG. 3.1. Formulae of glucose and saccharic acid.

It is stressed that the formula in Fig. 3.1B is a projection of the tetrahedral formula and therefore may not be rotated except in the plane of the paper.

There are sixteen stereoisomers of the formula represented in Fig. 3.1B. These may be divided into eight pairs or two series of compounds which are mirror images (enantiomorphs) of each other. The members of these pairs are given the same specific name but are distinguished according to which series they belong. Even today there is no entirely satisfactory method of determining the absolute configuration of sugar molecules, but it is fairly simple to determine their configuration relative to each other. Clearly, one of the prime requirements is a satisfactory reference compound to which all the others may be related. This procedure was followed by Fischer and forms the basis of his second convention. He assigned, quite arbitrarily, a particular configuration to one of the two enantiomorphs of saccharic acid. The most obvious difference between these enantiomorphs was the direction in which they rotated the plane of polarized light. Fischer called the compound represented by Fig. 3.1C D-saccharic acid and that represented by Fig. 3.1D L-saccharic acid.

The carbohydrates were then designated D or L according to whether they were derived from D- or L-saccharic acid. The choice of a compound containing more than one asymmetric carbon atom as a reference compound led to a number of inconsistencies. These were overcome by Rosanoff in 1906 when he suggested that glyceraldehyde be chosen as the reference compound. This choice is accepted today and the configuration of the monosaccharides is determined by their relation to glyceraldehyde. All the sugars derivable from D-glyceraldehyde are assigned to the D series, all the compounds derivable from L-glyceraldehyde are assigned to the L series.

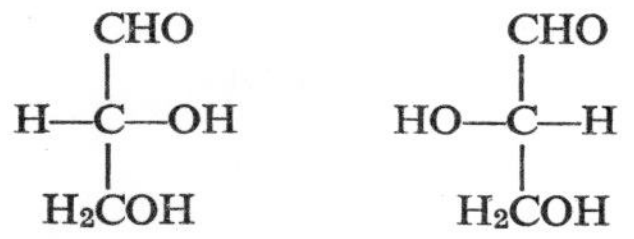

$$
\begin{array}{cc}
\text{CHO} & \text{CHO} \\
| & | \\
\text{H---C---OH} & \text{HO---C---H} \\
| & | \\
\text{H}_2\text{COH} & \text{H}_2\text{COH}
\end{array}
$$

D-Glyceraldehyde   L-Glyceraldehyde

It is not difficult to discover whether an individual sugar is related to D- or to L-glyceraldehyde since the higher sugars can be synthesized from glyceraldehyde by successive cyanohydrin syntheses. A good general rule for the assignment of a particular sugar to the D or L series depends upon the position of the H and OH groups of the asymmetric carbon atom which is furthest from the reference group (CO or CHO). When the carbon chain is arranged with the reference group uppermost the D series of compounds have the OH group on the last asymmetric carbon to the right: in the L series this OH group is to the left. This rule is illustrated below by D- and L-glucose.

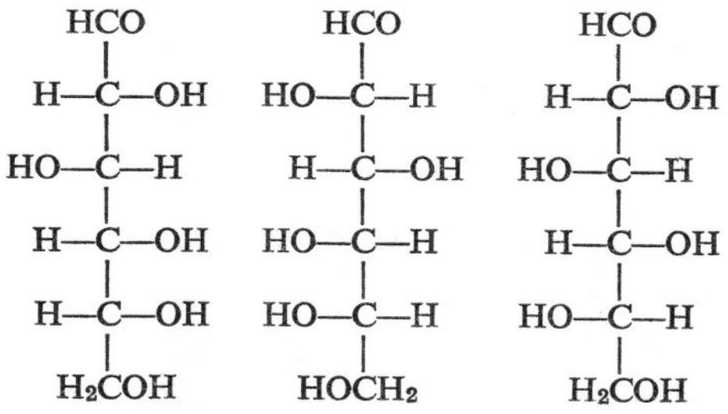

$$
\begin{array}{ccc}
\text{HCO} & \text{HCO} & \text{HCO} \\
| & | & | \\
\text{H---C---OH} & \text{HO---C---H} & \text{H---C---OH} \\
| & | & | \\
\text{HO---C---H} & \text{H---C---OH} & \text{HO---C---H} \\
| & | & | \\
\text{H---C---OH} & \text{HO---C---H} & \text{H---C---OH} \\
| & | & | \\
\text{H---C---OH} & \text{HO---C---H} & \text{HO---C---H} \\
| & | & | \\
\text{H}_2\text{COH} & \text{HOCH}_2 & \text{H}_2\text{COH}
\end{array}
$$

D-Glucose   L-Glucose   L-Idose

It is important to realize that the difference between D- and L-glucose is not merely the configuration about carbon 5. The two molecules are mirror images and the configuration about carbon 5 is a guide to their classification. Simply changing the H and OH about carbon 5 of D-glucose would give rise to a compound quite different from L-glucose, i.e. L-idose.

The designation of a sugar as D or L refers only to its geometrical configuration: it does not refer to the direction in which the sugar rotates the plane of polarized light. The initial assignment of the terms D and L to the two forms of glyceraldehyde was a guess. We now know that this guess was correct and that D-glyceraldehyde is dextrorotatory. This does not mean that all the D sugars are dextrorotatory; many are laevorotatory. To avoid confusion the symbols D and L should be applied only to the configuration of a molecule. The direction in which that molecule rotates the plane of polarized light should be indicated by + for clockwise or dextrorotatory and − for laevorotatory e.g. D(+)glucose or D(−)ribose.

The properties of D-glucose show that, for at least some of the time, the molecule must exist in a ring form. For example, it is not always possible to demonstrate the aldehyde properties of glucose. This is because of the formation of a hemi-acetal bond between the aldehyde group and one of the OH groups. Hemi-acetal and acetal bonds are formed between aldehydes and alcohols.

$$R-CHO + R^1OH \longrightarrow R-\underset{\underset{\displaystyle OH}{|}}{\overset{\overset{\displaystyle OR_1}{|}}{CH}}$$

Hemi-acetal

$$R-\underset{\underset{\displaystyle OH}{|}}{\overset{\overset{\displaystyle OR_1}{|}}{CH}} + R^1OH \longrightarrow R-\underset{\underset{\displaystyle OR_1}{|}}{\overset{\overset{\displaystyle OR_1}{|}}{CH}}$$

Acetal

The hemi-acetal bond in glucose may be formed between the aldehyde group and the OH group of carbon 4 or 5. Such structures are related to furane and pyrane respectively and their Fischer formulae are:

Pyranose form of
D-glucose

Furanose form of
D-glucose

The naturally occurring monosaccharides exist mostly in the pyranose form but there are important instances in which some, the ketoses in particular, exist in the furanose form.

Ring formation in monosaccharides makes the number one carbon atom asymmetric and gives rise to another pair of stereoisomers. These stereoisomers which differ only in the configuration about carbon 1 are called anomers and are referred to as the α- or β-forms of a sugar. A convention has been adopted for the designation of anomers. In the D series the more dextrorotatory form is the α-anomer and is written with the OH on the right of carbon atom number 1.

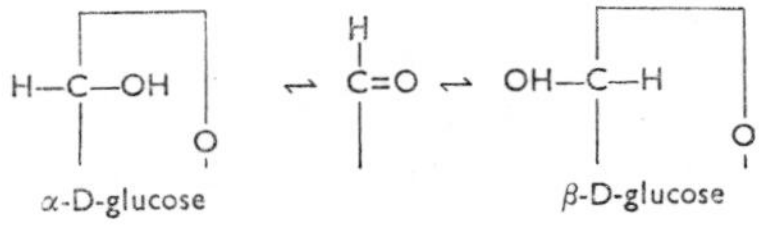

α-D-glucose   β-D-glucose

The interrelationship between the various stereoisomers of D-glucose is shown below:

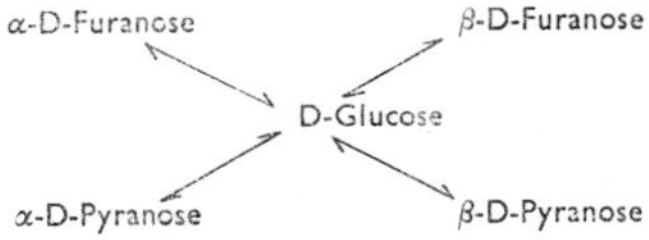

α-D-Furanose   β-D-Furanose

D-Glucose

α-D-Pyranose   β-D-Pyranose

The Fischer formulae do not portray accurately the steric arrangements of the molecule in the ring form. For example, in the ring form of α-D-glucopyranose the Fischer projection does not show that C6 and its attached groups are *trans* with respect to the hydroxyl groups on carbons 1, 2 and 4; nor does it show the proximity of carbons 1 and 5. Both these points are evident in the Haworth perspective formulae. In these, five and six membered rings are drawn as derivatives of furane and pyrane respectively, e.g. Fig. 3.2.

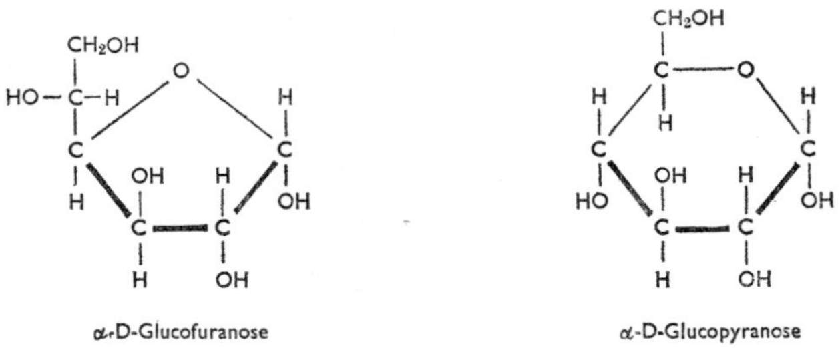

α-D-Glucofuranose   α-D-Glucopyranose

FIG. 3.2. Haworth perspective formulae of α-D-glucose.

In the Haworth perspective the ring is regarded as an almost regular hexagon set in one plane. It is drawn with that plane at right angles to the paper and with the three darker lines of the hexagon nearest the reader. Groups lying to the left of the carbon chain in Fischer's formula are arranged above the plane of the hexagon, those on the right are below. The relation between the two types of formulae is shown for α-D-glucose in Fig. 3.3.

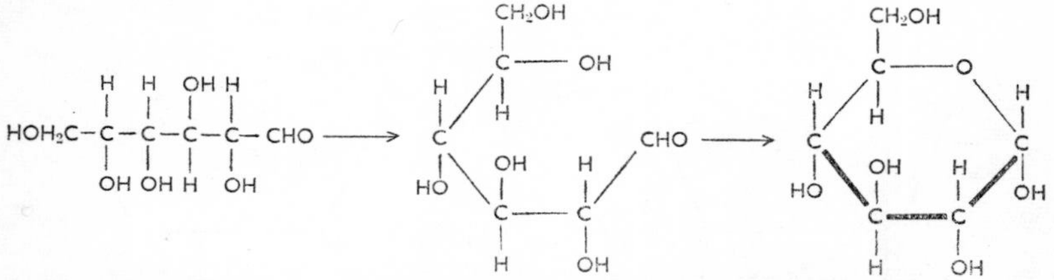

FIG. 3.3. Relationship between Fischer projection and Haworth perspective of α-D-glucose.

Even the Haworth formulae fail to give a completely satisfactory picture of some sugar molecules. The assumption that all the members of the rings lie in the same plane may be applied to the five-membered rings but not to the six-membered rings. The pyranose ring is not in a single plane since its atoms are arranged so that there is a minimum distortion of the carbon bonds from a regular tetrahedron. Such an arrangement results in two of the atoms of the ring being in a different plane from the rest. Eight such strainless ring forms of the pyranose ring are possible. These are shown in Fig. 3.4. Two general arrangements exist, that in C1 and 1C, or the chair forms and that in the remaining models or the boat forms. If the models C1, B1, B2 and B3 are compared with 1C, 1B, 2B and 3B respectively it will be seen that the two series differ in their arrangement of the carbon hydrogen bonds. Bonds which are axial in C1, B1, B2 and B3 are equatorial in the series 1C, 1B, 2B and 3B.

Pyranose rings are thought to exist preferentially in one or other of the two chair forms. However, there is evidence that the boat form may be adopted under certain conditions.

From our knowledge of the stereoisomers of glucose it is possible to deduce the different configurations of the other sugars. The interrelationship between the aldoses and ketoses is shown in Fig. 3.5. Both the hexoses and the pentoses are capable of forming furanose and pyranose rings and therefore can exist not only as α and β forms, but also in the different boat and chair forms.

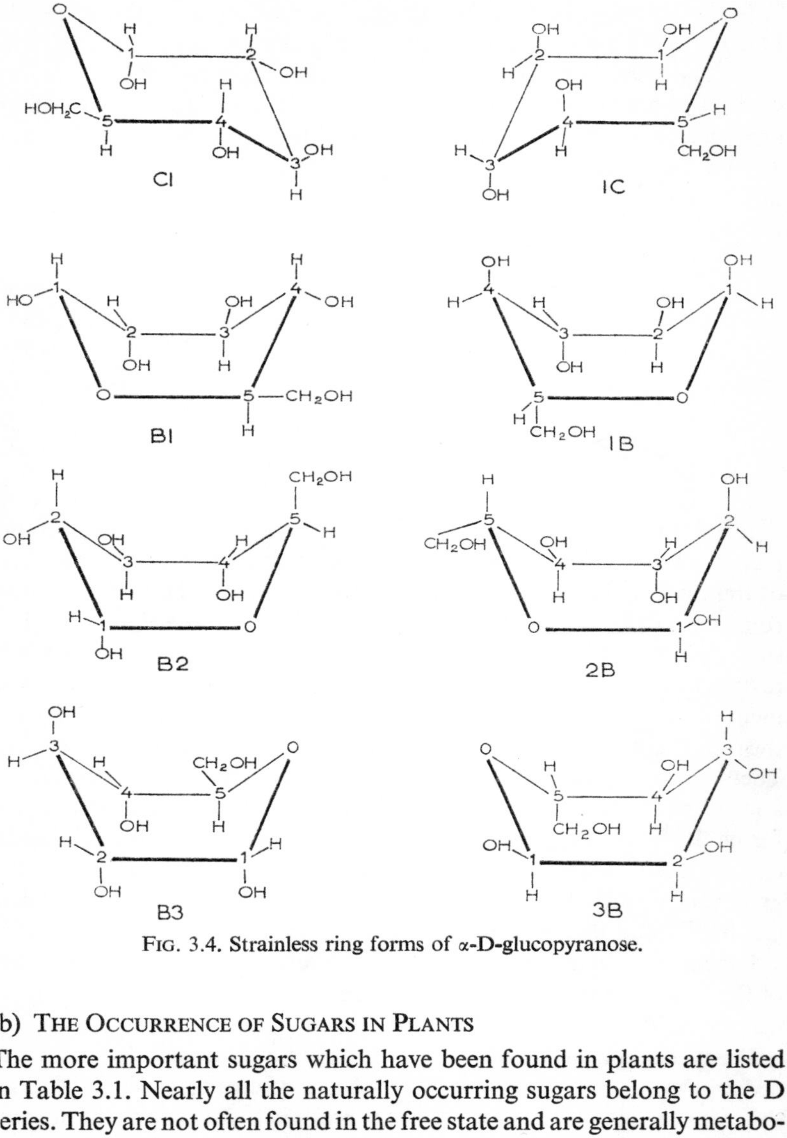

FIG. 3.4. Strainless ring forms of α-D-glucopyranose.

(b) THE OCCURRENCE OF SUGARS IN PLANTS

The more important sugars which have been found in plants are listed in Table 3.1. Nearly all the naturally occurring sugars belong to the D series. They are not often found in the free state and are generally metabolized as their phosphate esters which are present in very small amounts. Other combined forms of sugars include the homopolymers like starch and cellulose the heteropolymers like gums and mucilages and the

```
        CHO
         |
    H – C – OH
         |
       CH₂OH

   Glyceraldehyde
```

```
      CHO                CH₂OH                 CHO
       |                   |                    |
  H – C – OH            C = O             HO – C – H
       |                   |                    |
  H – C – OH          H – C – OH           H – C – OH
       |                   |                    |
     CH₂OH               CH₂OH                CH₂OH

   Erythrose          Erythrulose           Threose
```

```
   CHO          CH₂OH          CHO          CHO          CH₂OH          CHO
    |             |             |            |             |             |
H – C – OH      C = O      HO – C – H    H – C – OH      C = O      HO – C – H
    |             |             |            |             |             |
H – C – OH   H – C – OH    H – C – OH   HO – C – H    HO – C – H   HO – C – H
    |             |             |            |             |             |
H – C – OH   H – C – OH    H – C – OH    H – C – OH    H – C – OH    H – C – OH
    |             |             |            |             |             |
  CH₂OH         CH₂OH         CH₂OH        CH₂OH         CH₂OH         CH₂OH

  Ribose       Ribulose      Arabinose     Xylose       Xylulose      Lyxose
```

```
  CHO          CHO          CHO          CHO          CHO          CHO          CHO          CHO
   |            |            |            |            |            |            |            |
H–C–OH     HO–C–H       H–C–OH      HO–C–H       H–C–OH      HO–C–H       H–C–OH      HO–C–H
   |            |            |            |            |            |            |            |
H–C–OH      H–C–OH      HO–C–H       HO–C–H       H–C–OH      H–C–OH      HO–C–H       HO–C–H
   |            |            |            |            |            |            |            |
H–C–OH      H–C–OH       H–C–OH       H–C–OH      HO–C–H      HO–C–H       HO–C–H       HO–C–H
   |            |            |            |            |            |            |            |
H–C–OH      H–C–OH       H–C–OH       H–C–OH       H–C–OH      H–C–OH       H–C–OH       H–C–OH
   |            |            |            |            |            |            |            |
 CH₂OH        CH₂OH        CH₂OH        CH₂OH        CH₂OH        CH₂OH        CH₂OH        CH₂OH

 Allose      Altrose      Glucose      Mannose      Gulose       Idose      Galactose      Talose
```

```
   CH₂OH              CH₂OH              CH₂OH                     CH₂OH
     |                  |                  |                         |
   C = O              C = O              C = O                     C = O
     |                  |                  |                         |
 H – C – OH        HO – C – H         H – C – OH                HO – C – H
     |                  |                  |                         |
 H – C – OH        H – C – OH         HO – C – H                HO – C – H
     |                  |                  |                         |
 H – C – OH        H – C – OH         H – C – OH                H – C – OH
     |                  |                  |                         |
   CH₂OH              CH₂OH              CH₂OH                     CH₂OH

  Allulose           Fructose           Sorbose                  Tagatose
```

FIG. 3.5. D series of aldoses and ketoses.

TABLE 3.1

Monosaccharide sugars of biological importance

For convenience the Fischer projections have been turned so that groups normally shown on the right of the carbon chain now appear below.

Sugar	Formula	Occurrence
Triose D-Glyceraldehyde	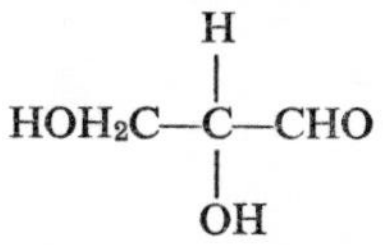 $\overset{\displaystyle H}{\underset{\displaystyle OH}{HOH_2C-C-CHO}}$	3-Phosphate ester
Dihydroxyacetone	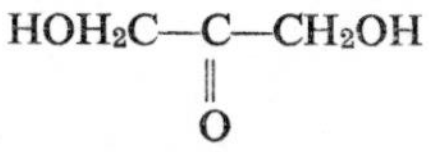 $\underset{\displaystyle O}{HOH_2C-C-CH_2OH}$	Monophosphate ester
Tetrose D-Erythrose	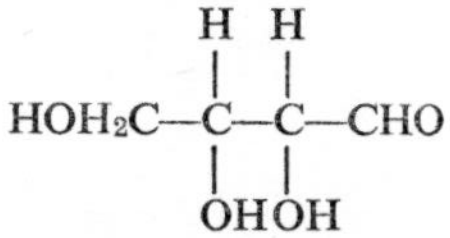 $\overset{\displaystyle H\ \ H}{\underset{\displaystyle OH\,OH}{HOH_2C-C-C-CHO}}$	4-Phosphate ester
Aldopentoses D-Ribose	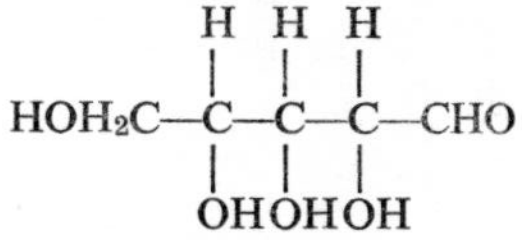 $\overset{\displaystyle H\ \ H\ \ H}{\underset{\displaystyle OH\,OH\,OH}{HOH_2C-C-C-C-CHO}}$	The 5-phosphate ester is an intermediary metabolite. Found in furanose form as component of ribonucleic acid and certain coenzymes.
D-Xylose	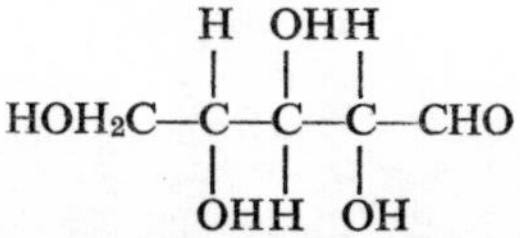 $\overset{\displaystyle H\ \ OH\,H}{\underset{\displaystyle OH\,H\ \ OH}{HOH_2C-C-C-C-CHO}}$	Widely distributed as α-D-xylopyranose in xylans.

Intermediary metabolites. (bracket spanning the first three Occurrence entries)

	Structure	Notes
L-Arabinose	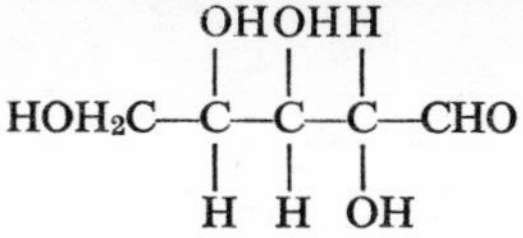 HOH₂C—C—C—C—CHO (OH OH H H / H H OH)	Found as free sugar in coniferous wood and as component of gums and hemicellulose.
Ketopentoses **D-Ribulose** or **D-Erythro-pentulose**	HOH₂C—C—C—C—CH₂OH (H H / OH OH O)	5-Phosphate ester is intermediary metabolite.
D-Xylulose or **D-Threo-pentulose**	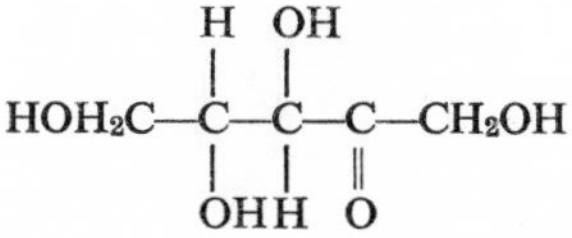 HOH₂C—C—C—C—CH₂OH (H OH / OH H O)	5-Phosphate ester is intermediary metabolite.
Aldohexoses **D-Glucose**	HOH₂C—C—C—C—C—CHO (H H OH H / OH OH H OH)	The most widely distributed sugar. Found free in fruit juices, as phosphate esters, as component of polysaccharides and in glycosides. Occurs only in pyranose form.
D-Galactose	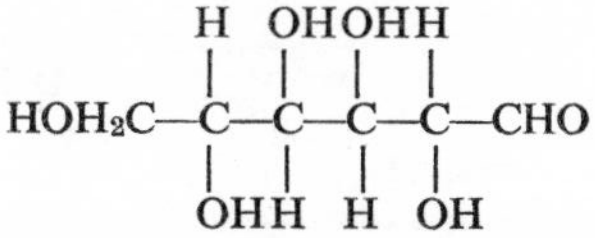 HOH₂C—C—C—C—C—CHO (H OH OH H / OH H H OH)	Reported present as free sugar in ivy berries. Frequently found in polysaccharides and glycosides.
L-Galactose	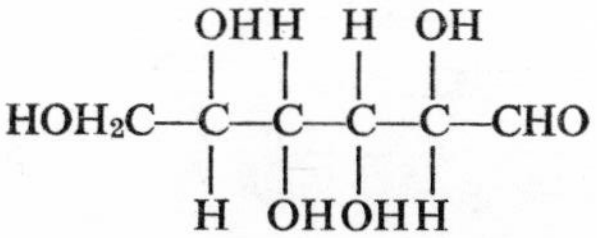 HOH₂C—C—C—C—C—CHO (OH H OH H / H OH OH H)	Found in the pyranose form in some polysaccharides, e.g. chagual gum and agar.

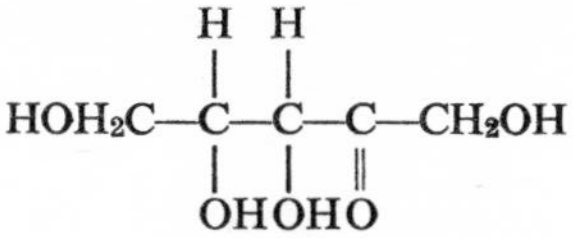

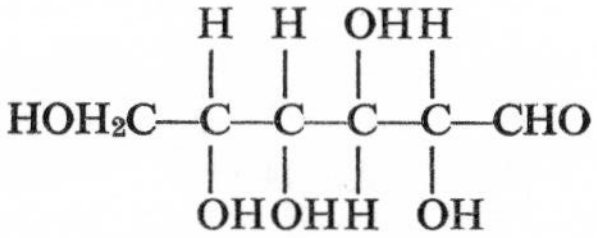

7

TABLE 3.1—*contd.*

Sugar	Formula	Occurrence
D-Mannose	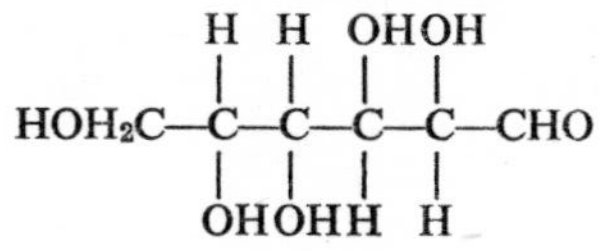 $HOH_2C-\overset{H}{\underset{OH}{C}}-\overset{H}{\underset{OH}{C}}-\overset{OH}{\underset{H}{C}}-\overset{OH}{\underset{H}{C}}-CHO$	Not reported as free sugar but occurs widely in gums and mannans.
Ketohexose D-Fructose	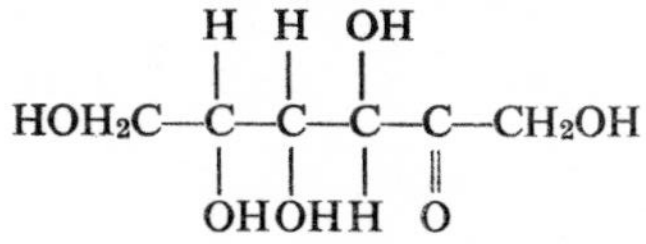 $HOH_2C-\overset{H}{\underset{OH}{C}}-\overset{H}{\underset{OH}{C}}-\overset{OH}{\underset{H}{C}}-\overset{}{\underset{O}{C}}=-CH_2OH$	The only ketohexose commonly found in plants. Occurs free in fruit juices. Widely distributed as the disaccharide sucrose and occurs as polymers. The phosphate esters are important metabolites.
Heptuloses D-Sedoheptulose or D-Altro-heptulose	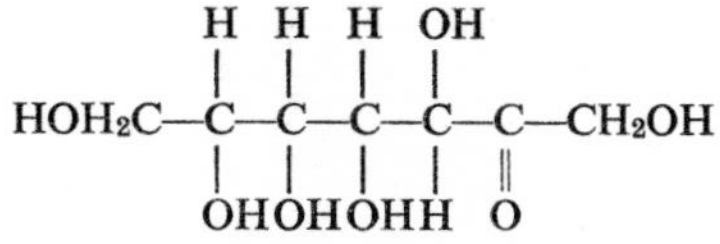 $HOH_2C-\overset{H}{\underset{OH}{C}}-\overset{H}{\underset{OH}{C}}-\overset{H}{\underset{OH}{C}}-\overset{OH}{\underset{H}{C}}-\overset{}{\underset{O}{C}}=-CH_2OH$	Found free in the leaves of Crassulacean plants. The phosphate esters are metabolites.
D-Manno-heptulose	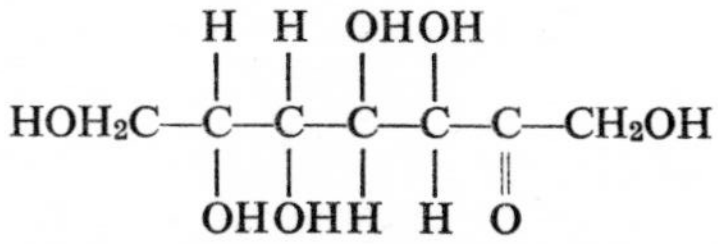 $HOH_2C-\overset{H}{\underset{OH}{C}}-\overset{H}{\underset{OH}{C}}-\overset{OH}{\underset{H}{C}}-\overset{OH}{\underset{H}{C}}-\overset{}{\underset{O}{C}}=-CH_2OH$	Found free in avocado pears.

glycosides in which the sugar is joined to some non-carbohydrate compound by a glycosidic link. The non-sugar moiety of glycosides may be any of a wide range of compounds and is called the aglycone.

DEOXY SUGARS

These sugars are deoxy in the sense that they have lost an oxygen through the replacement of an hydroxyl group by hydrogen. The most important deoxy sugar is deoxyribose which is the sugar component of the hereditary material deoxyribonucleic acid. The relationship of deoxyribose to ribose is shown below:

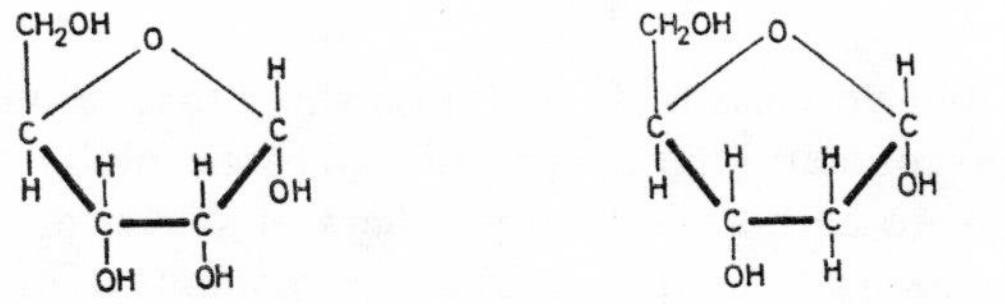

α–D–Ribofuranose   α-D-2-Deoxy-D-Ribofuranose

Deoxyribose in the combined form is found only in the furanose configuration. A number of deoxy hexoses are found in plants. 6-Deoxy-L-mannose or rhamnose occurs free and as a component of glycosides and polysaccharides of gums and mucilages. 6-Deoxy-L-galactose or L-fucose is found in the cell walls of certain marine algae and 6-deoxy-D-glucose or D-quinovose is found in some glycosides.

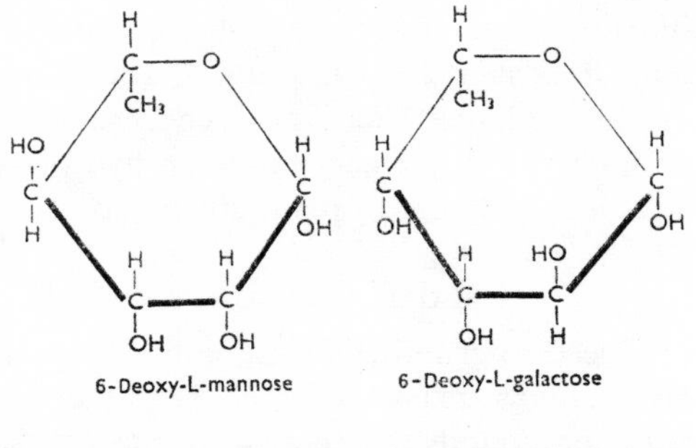

6-Deoxy-L-mannose   6-Deoxy-L-galactose

The fact that it is the terminal group which is deoxy has led to the designation of these deoxy hexoses as methyl pentoses or methyloses. This is perhaps inadvisable since it wrongly implies that deoxy sugars are formed by methylation. This point is exemplified by the rare branched sugar L-cladinose which is deoxy at carbon 6 and has methyl and methoxyl groups attached to carbon 3.

$$
\begin{array}{c}
\text{CHO} \\
| \\
\text{CH}_2 \\
| \\
\text{CH}_3-\text{C}-\text{O}-\text{CH}_3 \\
| \\
\text{HO}-\text{C}-\text{H} \\
| \\
\text{HO}-\text{C}-\text{H} \\
| \\
\text{CH}_3
\end{array}
$$

L-Cladinose

Studies of the biosynthesis of L-cladinose show that radioactivity from the methyl group of methionine is transferred to the methyl and methoxyl carbons but not to carbon 6. Methyl ethers of sugars are fairly widely distributed in plants where they occur as components of many gums and mucilages.

AMINO SUGARS

The amino sugars are characterized by the replacement of an hydroxyl group of the sugar by an amino group. The amino sugars of greatest importance are glucosamine and galactosamine which are widely distributed in animals and micro-organisms in the form of polymers and muco-substances. Chitin, which is the main polysaccharide of the hyphal walls of most fungi, is a polymer of N-acetyl glucosamine. The unequivocal demonstration of small amounts of amino sugars in tissue extracts is exceptionally difficult. Amino sugars are generally considered to be absent from higher plants. Recent evidence indicates that they may be present in small amounts in some plants. There is evidence that pollen grains contain a polymer which yields D-glucosamine on hydrolysis and that the same compound is a component of plant glycolipids.

SUGAR ALCOHOLS

Sugars may be reduced to give the corresponding sugar alcohols. These acyclic polyhydric alcohols are best considered together with the inositols. The two groups of compounds together constitute the polyols.

All but three of the theoretically possible sugar alcohols containing four, five, six and seven carbon atoms are known and many of them have been found in plants. The sugar alcohol which is most commonly found in plants is sorbitol. Sorbitol is reported only from plants, where it is found quite commonly in fruits. D-mannitol is also widely reported from higher plants whilst galactitol has a widespread distribution ranging from red algae to the mannans of higher plants.

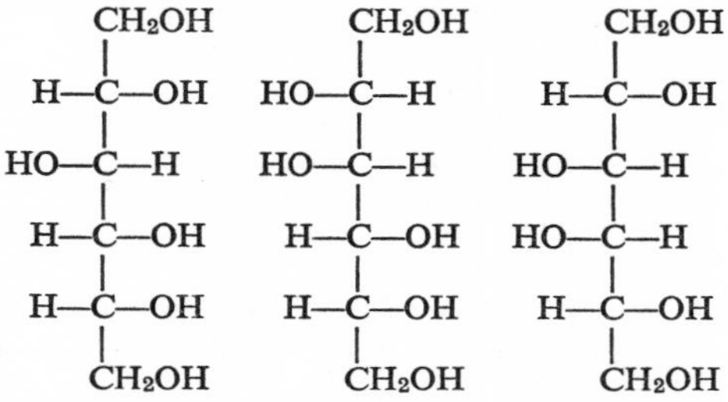

| CH₂OH | CH₂OH | CH₂OH |
| Sorbitol | Mannitol | Galactitol |

The alicyclic polyhydric alcohols or inositols are very widely distributed in plants. Perhaps the most important inositol is *meso*-inositol. Apart from *meso*-inositol, D-, L-, DL- and *scyllo*-inositol are all commonly found in plants. D-inositol may constitute several per cent of the dry weight of coniferous heartwood. *Meso*-inositol is found generally as phytin and is common in the phosphatides of higher plants (see p. 259). The inositols exist as strainless non-planar rings and show a conformational isomerism in the same way as hexose sugars. *Meso*-inositol is thought to exist in a chair form with five hydroxyl groups disposed equatorially and one axially:

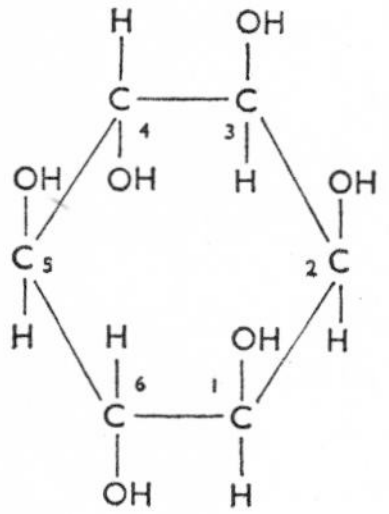

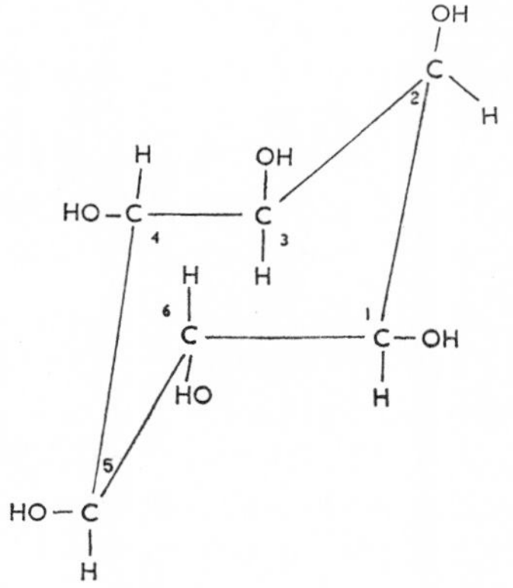

SUGAR ACIDS

Sugars can be oxidized to give sugar acids. Three types of sugar acid are of general importance. These are the aldonic acids in which the carbonyl group is oxidized to COOH, the uronic acids in which the primary alcoholic group is oxidized to COOH and the saccharic acids in which both the primary alcoholic group and the carbonyl group are oxidized.

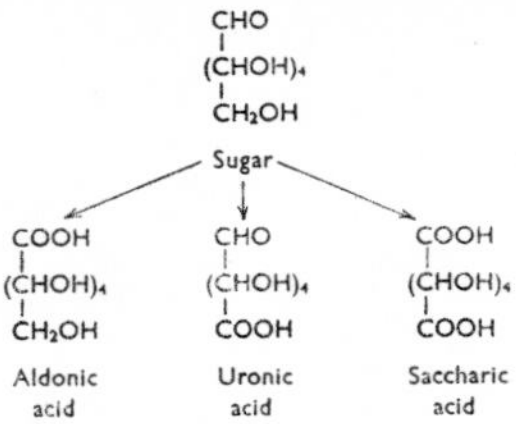

In solution these acids are able to form 'inner esters' or lactones. Two types of lactone may be distinguished — the γ-lactone and the δ-lactone.

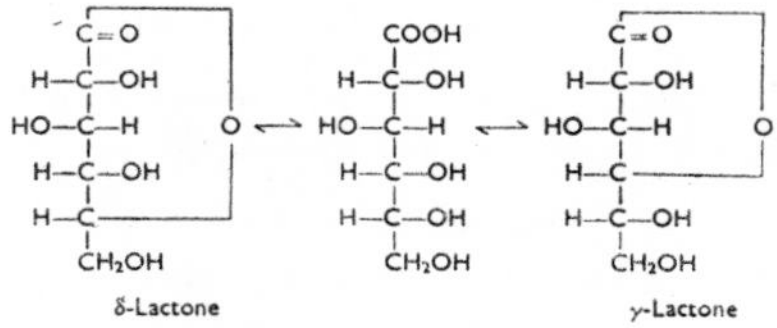

The sugar acids of known biochemical importance are the aldonic acid ester, phosphogluconic acid which is a respiratory intermediate, and the uronic acids — D-glucuronic acid, D-galacturonic acid and D-mannuronic acid.

D-Glucuronic Acid   D-Mannuronic Acid   D-Galacturonic Acid

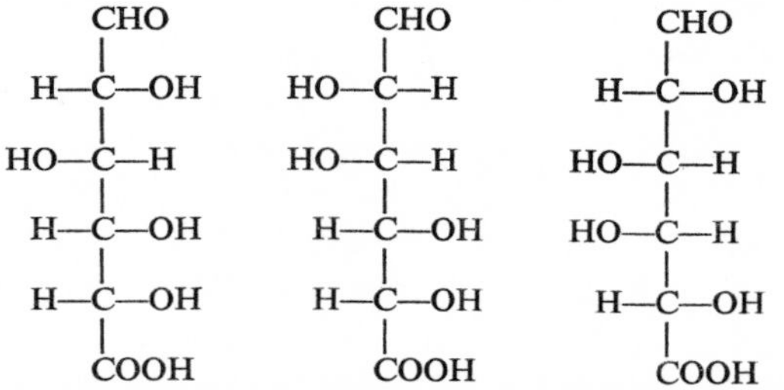

Glucuronic and galacturonic acids are widely distributed throughout the plant kingdom as components of gums and cell walls. Mannuronic acid is found in the cell walls of certain algae.

Ascorbic acid or vitamin C is probably of universal occurrence in plant tissues. Ascorbic acid is a six carbon γ-lactone which exists in solution as in equilibrium with the 3-keto acid.

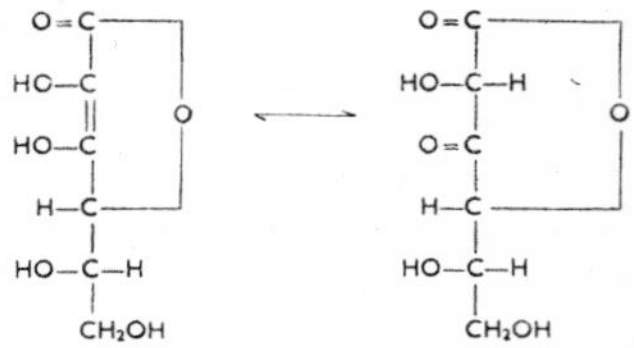

Although ascorbic acid is readily

oxidized to dehydroascorbic acid by plant tissues, most of the naturally occurring acid is in the reduced form.

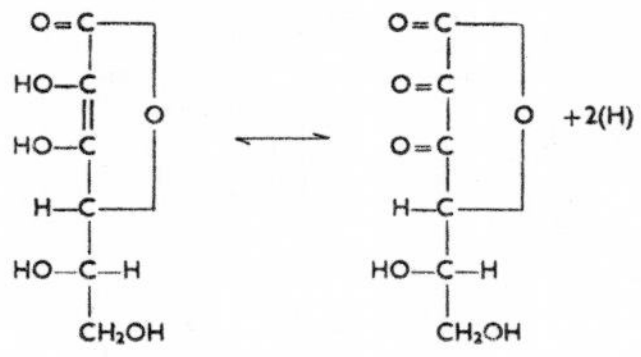

L-Ascorbic acid → Dehydroascorbic acid + 2(H)

Oxidation

THE EMBDEN-MEYERHOF-PARNAS (EMP) PATHWAY

Study of the intermediary metabolism of carbohydrates began almost by accident in 1897 when Buchner, who was experimenting to see whether sugar would preserve a yeast extract, found that the cell free extract fermented sugar. About this time the concept of enzymes as catalysts of metabolism was gaining acceptance and the ferment was named zymase. Several years later, Harden and Young showed that a boiled yeast extract contained at least two factors necessary for zymase activity. One was a dialysable co-factor which they called co-zymase, the other was inorganic phosphate. They demonstrated that the phosphate disappeared during fermentation, isolated a sugar phosphate ester and concluded that the ester was formed during fermentation. The isolation of this Harden and Young ester, later shown to be fructose-1,6-diphosphate, was the first indication of the important role of sugar phosphate esters in metabolism. This was followed by the isolation of the Robison ester (glucose-6-phosphate) and the Neuberg ester (fructose-6-phosphate).

In the 1930's a series of brilliant investigations into the pathways of muscle glycolysis and yeast fermentation led to the elucidation of the scheme shown in Fig. 3.6.

The principle upon which these investigations were based has been stated by Gowland Hopkins — 'the fact that the body, though the seat of a myriad reactions and capable perhaps of learning, to a limited extent and under stress of circumstances, is in general able to deal only with what is customary to it'. The phenomenon of adaptive enzyme formation is contrary to the above principle but this complication only became apparent many years later.

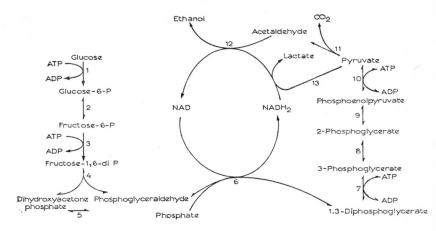

FIG. 3.6. Reactions of EMP pathway.

1. Hexokinase
2. Phosphohexoisomerase
3. Phosphofructokinase
4. Aldolase
5. Triosephosphate isomerase
6. Phosphoglyceraldehyde dehydrogenase

7. Phosphoglyceryl kinase
8. Phosphoglyceromutase
9. Enolase
10. Pyruvic kinase
11. Pyruvic decarboxylase
12. Alcohol dehydrogenase
13. Lactic dehydrogenase

The methodology used may be illustrated by the following example.

The inhibition of fermentation by fluoride was first demonstrated by Embden in 1924. In 1930 Nilsson isolated a phosphate ester from fluoride poisoned yeast extracts and in 1933 Embden demonstrated that Nilsson ester was metabolized by muscle extracts with the production of pyruvate and phosphate. In the same year Neuberg demonstrated that synthetic 3-phosphoglycerate was similarly metabolized and in the following year Embden identified the Nilsson ester as 3-phosphoglycerate. Further study of the metabolism of 3-phosphoglycerate led to the isolation of 2-phosphoglycerate and phosphoenolpyruvate. Meyerhof and Kiessling found that the formation of 2-phosphoglycerate from 3-phosphoglycerate was not inhibited by fluoride, whilst the formation of phosphoenolpyruvate from 3-phosphoglycerate was inhibited. It follows that the sequence of reactions is 3-phosphoglycerate→2-phosphoglycerate→ phosphoenolpyruvate and that the last reaction is the site of fluoride inhibition.

During the elucidation of this pathway it became apparent that the reactions were not restricted to the rather special cases of anaerobiosis studied and that the steps up to the formation of pyruvate constituted a general route of carbohydrate oxidation. This led to a certain amount of confusion in nomenclature. We shall describe those oxidations in which molecular oxygen is finally reduced as respiration and use fermentation to refer to oxidations in which some compound other than oxygen is finally reduced. The pathway outlined above will be referred to as the Embden-Meyerhof-Parnas or EMP pathway.

It is now accepted that plants oxidize carbohydrate via the EMP pathway, the pyruvate produced being metabolized via the tricarboxylic acid cycle (see p. 157). Under certain conditions pyruvate is fermented, generally to ethanol and CO_2, but in a number of plants lactate has been shown to be formed. The evidence for the operation of the EMP pathway in plants may be summarized:

(1) All the intermediates have been isolated.

(2) Iodoacetate and fluoride, which inhibit triose phosphate dehydrogenase and enolase respectively, inhibit fermentation and respiration of tissues and extracts.

(3) A number of tissues and extracts have been shown to metabolize substrates in a manner consistent with the operation of the EMP pathway. For example, acetone powders of pea seeds quantitatively convert glucose-6-phosphate to ethanol and CO_2. Specifically labelled glucose oxidized through the EMP pathway would be expected to label ethanol and CO_2 as shown in Table 3.2.

TABLE 3.2

Distribution of glucose carbons in ethanol and CO_2 after oxidation via EMP pathway

| | | Glucose carbons | | | | | |
		1	2	3	4	5	6
Ethanol	Methyl C	+	−	−	−	−	+
	Hydroxymethyl C	−	+	−	−	+	−
CO_2		−	−	+	+	−	−

These expectations were confirmed with corn roots under anaerobic conditions.

(4) All the enzymes of the EMP pathway have been demonstrated in plants: a number of them have been purified. This evidence is expanded on the following pages:

Hexokinase

$$\text{hexose} + \text{ATP} \rightarrow \text{hexose-6-phosphate} + \text{ADP}$$

$$\text{At pH } 6\cdot0 \; K = \frac{(\text{glucose-6-PO}_4)(\text{ADP})}{(\text{glucose})(\text{ATP})} = 1\cdot6 \times 10^2$$

The reaction catalysed by hexokinase may be regarded as irreversible. Hexokinase appears to be specific towards ATP but hexokinase from plants shows activity with glucose, fructose, mannose and glucosamine. This broad specificity is comparable to that reported for hexokinase from yeast and is not thought to be due to the presence of a complex mixture of hexokinases. Nevertheless, peas do contain two hexokinases, one which will react with glucose and fructose and another which is specific for fructose. Hexokinase requires magnesium and studies with the yeast enzyme show that, like other kinases, it breaks P—O and not C—O bonds. In plants hexokinase activity has been found in both the soluble and particulate fractions of the cell.

Phosphoglucomutase

glucose-1-phosphate + phospho-enzyme⇌

glucose-1,6-diphosphate + dephospho-enzyme
$$K = 4\cdot56$$

glucose-1,6-diphosphate + dephospho-enzyme⇌

glucose-6-phosphate + phospho-enzyme
$$K = 3\cdot76$$

This enzyme has been crystallized from muscle and highly purified from potato and *Phaseolus radiatus*. Glucose-1,6-diphosphate is the coenzyme. The isolated enzyme requires magnesium and, with the exception of that from *Phaseolus*, is activated by cysteine. At equilibrium at 30°C 5·5 per cent of the glucose-1-phosphate is present.

Phosphohexoisomerase

$$
\begin{array}{ccc}
\overset{\times}{\text{H}}-\text{C}=\text{O} & \overset{\times}{\text{H}}-\text{C}-\text{OH} & \overset{\bullet}{\text{H}}\;\;\text{C}=\text{O} \\
\text{HO}-\text{C}-\text{H} & \text{C}=\text{O} & \text{H}-\text{C}-\text{OH} \\
\text{HO}-\text{C}-\text{H} \rightleftharpoons & \text{HO}-\text{C}-\text{H} \rightleftharpoons & \text{HO}-\text{C}-\text{H} \\
\text{H}-\text{C}-\text{OH} & \text{H}-\text{C}-\text{OH} & \text{H}-\text{C}-\text{OH} \\
\text{H}-\text{C}-\text{OH} & \text{H}-\text{C}-\text{OH} & \text{H}-\text{C}-\text{OH} \\
\text{CH}_2\text{O}\textcircled{P} & \text{CH}_2\text{O}\textcircled{P} & \text{CH}_2\text{O}\textcircled{P}
\end{array}
$$

| Mannose-6-phosphate | Fructose-6-phosphate | Glucose-6-phosphate |

Two phosphohexoisomerases have been isolated from animals. Phosphoglucose isomerase catalyses the interconversion of glucose-6-phosphate and fructose-6-phosphate, and phosphomannose isomerase acts on mannose-6-phosphate and fructose-6-phosphate. These enzymes have been shown to activate different hydrogens on carbon-1 of fructose-6-phosphate as shown in the equation. The phosphoglucose enzyme also differs from the phosphomannose enzyme in having no requirement for divalent cations.

Although there have been relatively few direct demonstrations of phosphoglucose isomerase activity in plants, the role of this enzyme in the EMP pathway and the evidence for the oxidation of hexose via this pathway leave little doubt that the enzyme is widely distributed in plants. Phosphoglucose isomerase has been purified from *Phaseolus radiatus*. At equilibrium the ratio of glucose-6-phosphate to fructose-6-phosphate was 1·5. However, more recent determinations indicate a higher ratio ranging from 2·76 at 38° to 3·85 at 20°.

Phosphofructokinase

D-fructose-6-phosphate + ATP → D-fructose-1,6-diphosphate + ADP

$$K = \frac{(\text{fructose-1,6-diphosphate})(\text{ADP})}{(\text{fructose-6-phosphate})(\text{ATP})} = 1\cdot8 \times 10^2$$

This is a very specific enzyme, it requires magnesium and may be regarded as irreversible.

Aldolase

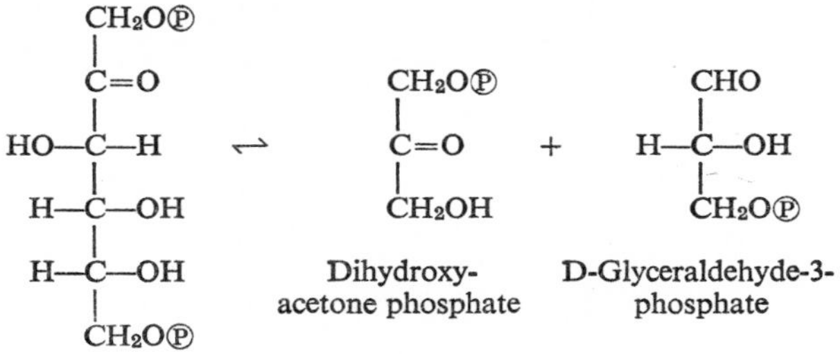

$$
\begin{array}{cccc}
\text{CH}_2\text{O}\textcircled{P} & & \text{CH}_2\text{O}\textcircled{P} & \text{CHO} \\
| & & | & | \\
\text{C=O} & & \text{C=O} & \text{H—C—OH} \\
| & & | & | \\
\text{HO—C—H} \;\;\rightleftharpoons & & \text{CH}_2\text{OH} \;\;+\;\; & \text{CH}_2\text{O}\textcircled{P} \\
| & & & \\
\text{H—C—OH} & & \text{Dihydroxy-} & \text{D-Glyceraldehyde-3-} \\
| & & \text{acetone phosphate} & \text{phosphate} \\
\text{H—C—OH} & & & \\
| & & & \\
\text{CH}_2\text{O}\textcircled{P} & & & \\
\end{array}
$$

D-Fructose-1,6-
diphosphate

$K(31°\text{C, pH } 8\cdot5)$

$$= \frac{\text{(dihydroxyacetone phosphate)(D-glyceraldehyde-3-phosphate)}}{\text{(D-fructose-1,6-diphosphate)}}$$

$$= 1\cdot15 \times 10^{-4}$$

The aldolase reaction is an aldol type condensation. Aldolase appears to be completely specific for dihydroxyacetone phosphate but will function with a number of aldehydes, e.g. D- and L-phosphoglyceraldehyde and D-erythrose phosphate. This relative specificity could lead to the re-synthesis of unsymmetrically labelled hexose. Aldolase generally acts upon a sugar phosphate in which carbons 3 and 4 have OH groups in the *trans* position. The plant aldolase differs from that of muscle in that it is not inhibited by heavy metals, and from that of yeast in that it is not inhibited by cysteine.

Triosephosphate Isomerase

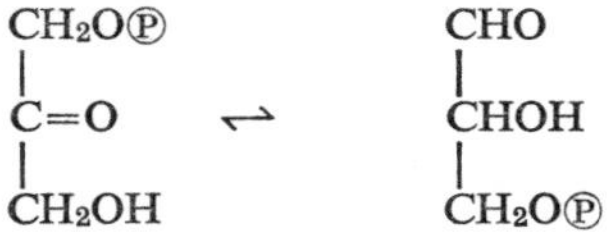

$$
\begin{array}{cc}
\text{CH}_2\text{O}\textcircled{P} & \text{CHO} \\
| & | \\
\text{C=O} \;\;\rightleftharpoons & \text{CHOH} \\
| & | \\
\text{CH}_2\text{OH} & \text{CH}_2\text{O}\textcircled{P} \\
\end{array}
$$

Dihydroxyacetone   D-Glyceraldehyde-3-
phosphate   phosphate

$$K = \frac{\text{(dihydroxyacetone phosphate)}}{\text{(D-glyceraldehyde-3-phosphate)}} = 22$$

Note the preponderance of the ketose at equilibrium.

Phosphoglyceraldehyde Dehydrogenase

$$\begin{array}{l} \text{CHO} \\ | \\ \text{CHOH} + \text{NAD} + \text{H}_3\text{PO}_4 \\ | \\ \text{CH}_2\text{O}\circledP \end{array} \quad \rightleftharpoons \quad \begin{array}{l} \text{COO}\circledP \\ | \\ \text{CHOH} + \text{NADH}_2 \\ | \\ \text{CH}_2\text{O}\circledP \end{array}$$

D-Glyceraldehyde-3-phosphate   1,3-Diphosphoglyceric acid

$$K = \frac{(\text{1,3-diphosphoglyceric acid})(\text{NADH}_2)(\text{H}^+)}{(\text{D-glyceraldehyde-3-phosphate})(\text{NAD})(\text{H}_3\text{PO}_4)} = 1$$

Three different enzymes capable of catalysing the oxidation of 3-phosphoglyceraldehyde have been isolated from plants. It appears that the enzyme concerned in the EMP pathway is specific for NAD, requires phosphate and is similar to the much studied enzyme from yeast and muscle. At equilibrium only a relatively small proportion of the aldehyde is oxidized. The oxidation will be greatly favoured if the reaction is coupled to one which will oxidize $NADH_2$. Alchohol dehydrogenase or lactic dehydrogenase fulfil this role and form the following oxidation and reduction couple:

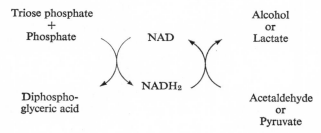

Triose phosphate + Phosphate   NAD   Alcohol or Lactate

NADH₂

Diphospho-glyceric acid   Acetaldehyde or Pyruvate

This dehydrogenase, which is very sensitive to sulphydryl reagents, contains 3 to 4 moles of tightly-bound NAD per mole of enzyme. The NAD is removed by sulphydryl reagents and it has been suggested that it is bound to the enzyme by the sulphydryl groups of glutathione. The mechanism of action of this enzyme is discussed on p. 213.

Two other phosphoglyceraldehyde dehydrogenases occur in leaves. One is similar to that already described except that it is specific for NADP. Recently this enzyme has also been found in castor beans. The third enzyme is also specific for NADP but shows no requirement for phosphate and catalyses the direct conversion of 3-phosphoglyceraldehyde to 3-phosphoglyceric acid. This reaction is not reversible. A possible role for the NADP dependent enzyme which requires phosphate is discussed on p. 248.

Phosphoglyceryl Kinase

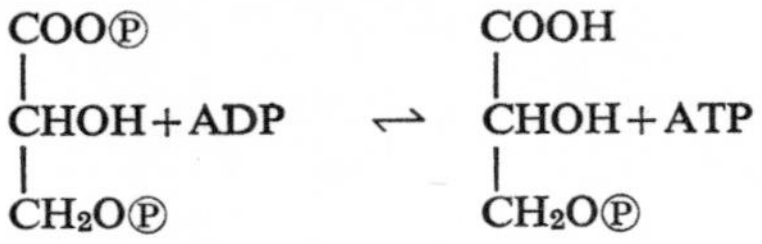

$$
\begin{array}{ccc}
\underset{\text{acid}}{\underset{\text{1,3-Diphosphoglyceric}}{\begin{array}{c} \text{COO}\circledP \\ | \\ \text{CHOH + ADP} \\ | \\ \text{CH}_2\text{O}\circledP \end{array}}}
& \rightleftharpoons &
\underset{\text{acid}}{\underset{\text{3-Phosphoglyceric}}{\begin{array}{c} \text{COOH} \\ | \\ \text{CHOH + ATP} \\ | \\ \text{CH}_2\text{O}\circledP \end{array}}}
\end{array}
$$

$$K = \frac{(\text{ATP})(\text{3-phosphoglyceric acid})}{(\text{ADP})(\text{1,3-diphosphoglyceric acid})} = 3 \cdot 3 \times 10^3$$

It has been known for a long time that the oxidation of phosphoglyceraldehyde to phosphoglyceric acid could result in the formation of ATP. It is now clear that two reactions are involved and that the second is catalysed by phosphoglyceryl kinase.

Phosphoglyceromutase

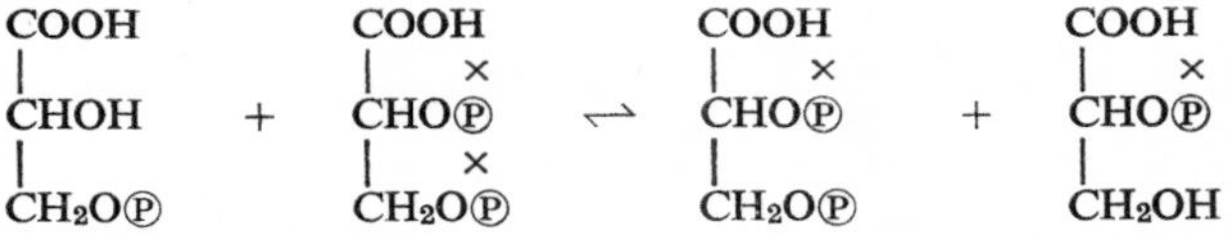

$$
\underset{\substack{\text{3-Phospho-}\\\text{glyceric acid}}}{\begin{array}{c} \text{COOH} \\ | \\ \text{CHOH} \\ | \\ \text{CH}_2\text{O}\circledP \end{array}}
+
\underset{\substack{\text{2,3-Diphospho-}\\\text{glyceric acid}}}{\begin{array}{c} \text{COOH} \\ | \quad \times \\ \text{CHO}\circledP \\ | \quad \times \\ \text{CH}_2\text{O}\circledP \end{array}}
\rightleftharpoons
\underset{\substack{\text{2,3-Diphospho-}\\\text{glyceric acid}}}{\begin{array}{c} \text{COOH} \\ | \quad \times \\ \text{CHO}\circledP \\ | \\ \text{CH}_2\text{O}\circledP \end{array}}
+
\underset{\substack{\text{2-Phospho-}\\\text{glyceric acid}}}{\begin{array}{c} \text{COOH} \\ | \quad \times \\ \text{CHO}\circledP \\ | \\ \text{CH}_2\text{OH} \end{array}}
$$

$$K = \frac{(\text{2-phosphoglyceric acid})}{(\text{3-phosphoglyceric acid})} = 0 \cdot 22$$

An enzyme catalysing the above reaction has been demonstrated in plants. The need for 2,3-diphosphoglycerate as a coenzyme indicates an analogy with phosphoglucomutase. However the phospho-enzyme has not yet been detected and work with the purified enzyme from rabbit muscle has not revealed a requirement for metal ions. Evidence has been presented that some plant tissues, possibly only seeds, contain a phosphoglyceromutase which has no requirement for 2,3-diphosphoglycerate and which catalyses the direct conversion of 3-phosphoglycerate to 2-phosphoglycerate.

Enolase

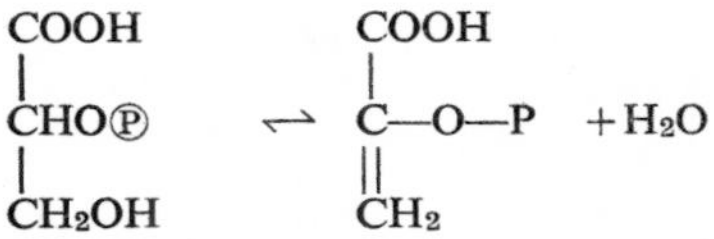

$$
\underset{\substack{\text{2-Phosphoglyceric}\\\text{acid}}}{\begin{array}{c} \text{COOH} \\ | \\ \text{CHO}\circledP \\ | \\ \text{CH}_2\text{OH} \end{array}}
\rightleftharpoons
\underset{\text{Phosphoenolpyruvate}}{\begin{array}{c} \text{COOH} \\ | \\ \text{C---O---P} \\ || \\ \text{CH}_2 \end{array}}
+ \text{H}_2\text{O}
$$

$$K = \frac{\text{(phosphoenolpyruvate)}}{\text{(2-phosphoglycerate)}} = 6\cdot3$$

Enolase catalyses the dehydration of 2-phosphoglyceric acid, this reaction converts a low energy phosphate ester into a high energy compound. The purified enzyme from peas requires magnesium and is sensitive to fluoride. Studies with enolase purified from an animal source indicate that it is a single peptide chain which contains neither cysteine nor cystine.

Pyruvic Kinase

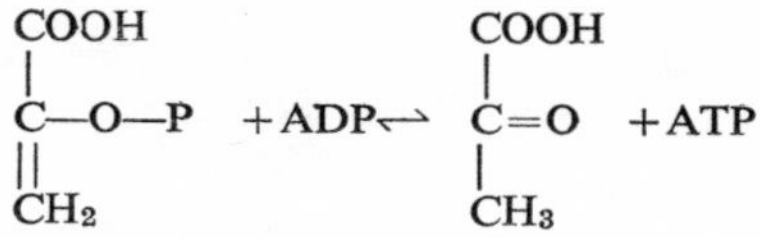

$$
\begin{array}{ccc}
\text{COOH} & & \text{COOH} \\
| & & | \\
\text{C—O—P} & +\text{ADP} \rightleftharpoons & \text{C=O} \quad +\text{ATP} \\
|| & & | \\
\text{CH}_2 & & \text{CH}_3 \\
\end{array}
$$

Phosphoenolpyruvate   Pyruvic acid

$$K = \frac{\text{(pyruvate)(ATP)}}{\text{(phosphoenolpyruvate)(ADP)(H}^+)} = 1\cdot15 \times 10^8$$

This kinase is a transphosphorylase which requires magnesium and a monovalent ion such as potassium or rubidium. Provided that these ions are present the reaction may be reversed but the equilibrium strongly favours the formation of pyruvate.

Pyruvic Decarboxylase

$$CH_3 . CO . COOH \rightarrow CH_3 . CHO + CO_2$$

Since this reaction is practically irreversible the enzyme is best regarded as a decarboxylase. This enzyme has been found in appreciable amounts in many plant tissues but the activities reported for leaves are often very low. The co-factor, diphosphothiamine (thiamine pyrophosphate, co-carboxylase, see Fig. 3.7) is probably bound to the apoenzyme by magnesium ions.

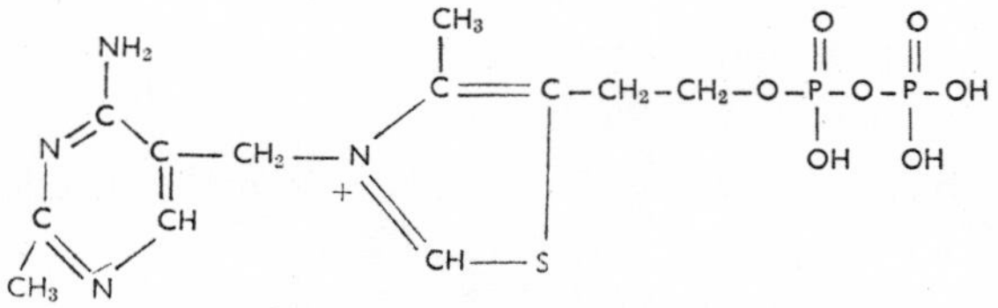

FIG. 3.7. Formula of diphosphothiamine (DPT).

DPT is the coenzyme for all enzymes known to decarboxylate α-keto acids. The first step in these reactions appears to be the cleavage of the keto acid to give CO_2 and an 'active aldehyde' bound to the coenzyme. There is good evidence that in the decarboxylation of pyruvate the active acetaldehyde is linked to C-2 of the thiazolium ring to give a compound which is a 2-hydroxyethyl derivative of thiamine. The proposed reactions are:

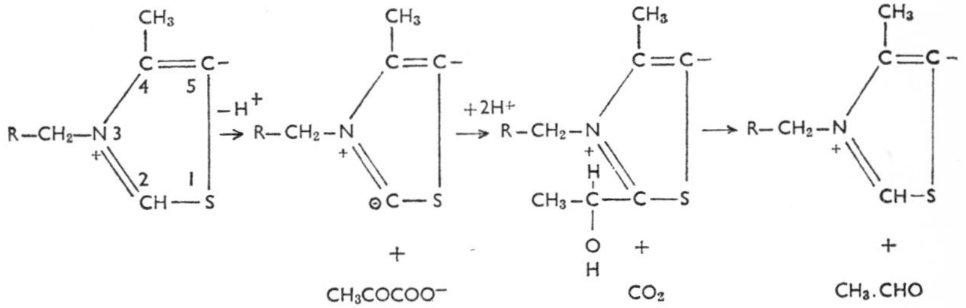

It has been shown that this derivative is formed during the decarboxylation of pyruvate and during oxidation by pyruvic oxidase in yeast. These two reactions are catalysed by different enzymes. The decarboxylase produces acetaldehyde, and the oxidase transfers the active aldehyde to lipoic acid (p. 164). Pyruvic decarboxylase also catalyses the formation of acetoin from pyruvate and acetaldehyde, or from acetaldehyde alone (carboligase reaction). In the presence of a suitable hydrogen acceptor, pyruvic decarboxylase behaves as an oxidase and pyruvate is oxidatively decarboxylated to acetate and CO_2.

Studies with mutant forms of tomato and *Arabidopsis* indicate that plants make thiamine by joining the separately synthesized pyrimidine and thiazole moieties. The steps involved in the synthesis of DPT have not been studied in plants but evidence for the reactions shown opposite has been obtained in yeast.

Alcohol Dehydrogenase

$$CH_3CHO + NADH_2 \rightleftharpoons NAD + CH_3CH_2OH$$

$$\text{At } 25°C \; K = \frac{(CH_3CHO)(NADH_2)(H^+)}{(CH_3CH_2OH)(NAD)} = 1 \times 10^{-11}$$

Although this enzyme occurs widely in plants its mode of action has been studied with crystalline preparations from yeast or horse liver. In addition to this enzyme an alcohol dehydrogenase requiring NADP has also been found in plants.

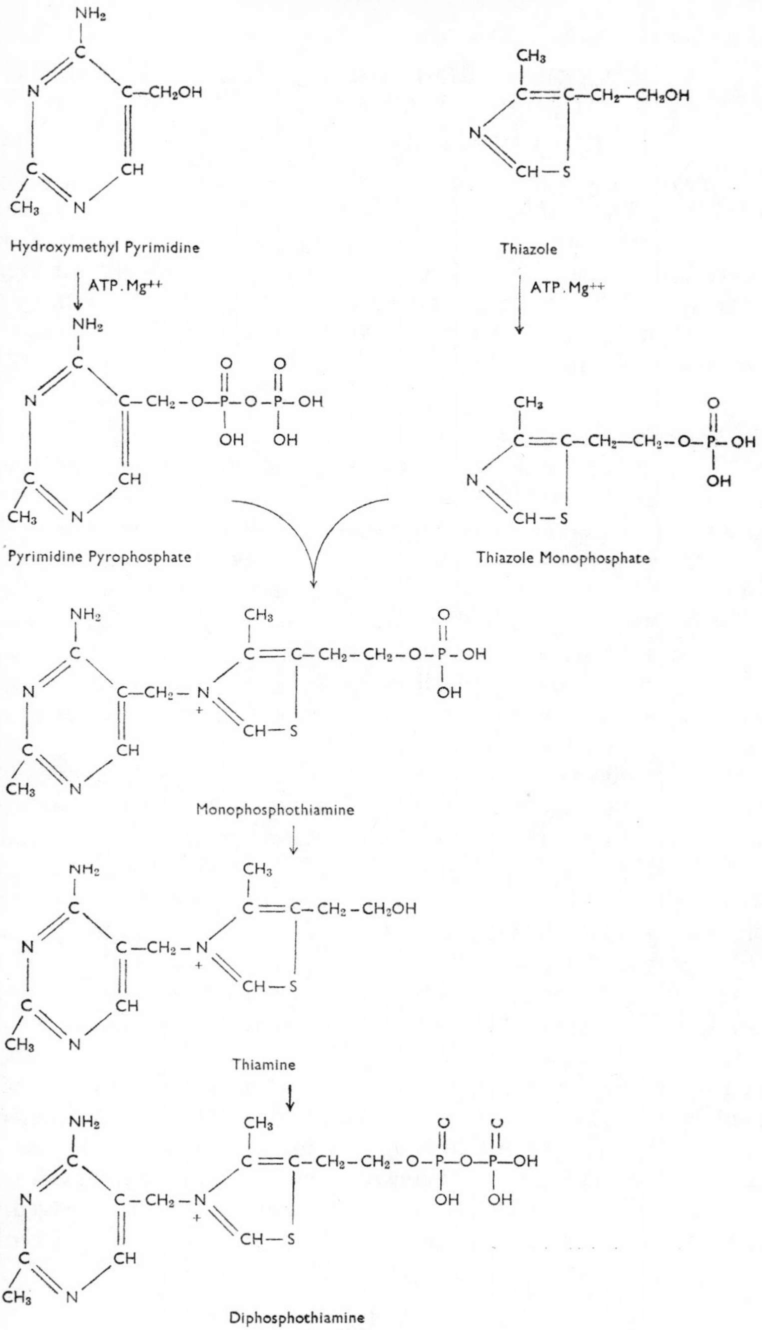
Hydroxymethyl Pyrimidine
Thiazole
ATP.Mg++
ATP.Mg++
Pyrimidine Pyrophosphate
Thiazole Monophosphate
Monophosphothiamine
Thiamine
Diphosphothiamine

Biosynthesis of DPT.

Lactic Dehydrogenase

$$CH_3COCOOH + NADH_2 \rightarrow CH_3CHOH\ COOH + NAD$$
$$K = \frac{(CH_3CO\ COOH)(NADH_2)(H^+)}{(CH_3CHOH\ COOH)(NAD)} = 2 \cdot 76 \times 10^{-12}$$

This enzyme has been found in a number of plants but is not widely distributed. Lactic dehydrogenase from plants resembles that from muscle in being specific for L-lactic acid, although the enzyme from *Chlorella* produces D-lactic acid. The enzyme from animals functions with either NAD or NADP, but the plant enzyme has only been shown to function with NAD. The enzyme from yeast is linked directly to the cytochrome system.

THE PENTOSE PHOSPHATE PATHWAY

The apparent universality of the EMP pathway must not be taken to imply that it is the only way in which carbohydrates can be oxidized. It is now known that there are a number of other routes. In contrast to the time taken to establish the EMP sequence much of the evidence for the other pathways has been obtained in the last decade. This is testimony not only to the excellent foundation laid during the study of the EMP pathway, but also to the advantages gained by the use of radioactive substrates and chromatography. One of these more recently discovered pathways appears to be widely distributed in plants; it has been variously named the direct oxidation pathway, the hexose monophosphate shunt and the pentose phosphate pathway.

The first indication that glucose could be oxidized by reactions other than those of the EMP pathway was the demonstration in Warburg's laboratory that red blood cells and yeast contained an enzyme which oxidized glucose-6-phosphate to 6-phosphogluconate in the presence of a coenzyme which was identified as NADP. In 1936 both Warburg and Dickens showed that 6-phosphogluconate could be oxidized further. Although both Dickens and Lipmann correctly suggested that pentose was formed in this oxidation they were unable to demonstrate it. Dickens did, however, show that yeast could convert ribose-5-phosphate to triose phosphate and pyruvate. After the war it was shown that ribulose-5-phosphate was formed by the oxidation of 6-phosphogluconate and a number of enzymes were isolated which would catalyse the interconversion of sugar phosphates containing three, four, five, six and seven carbons. These enzymes could convert pentose phosphate to hexose and together with the NADP-linked dehydrogenases could be arranged so as to account for the complete oxidation of glucose. The enzymes specially associated with the pentose phosphate pathway are discussed below.

Glucose-6-phosphate Dehydrogenase

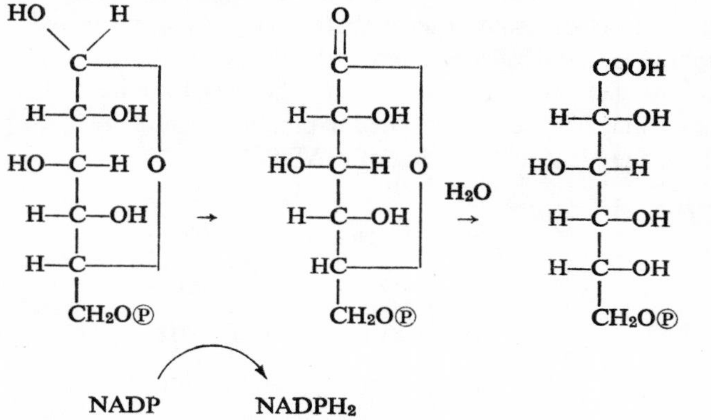

D-Glucose-6- phosphate	D-Gluconolactone- 6-phosphate	D-6-Phosphogluconic acid

The oxidation of glucose-6-phosphate takes place in two steps, the equilibria of which strongly favour the formation of 6-phosphogluconate. $\triangle G°$ has been calculated as being about $-6\cdot5$ kcal. Glucose-6-phosphate dehydrogenase catalyses the formation of the δ-lactone of phosphogluconic acid. This enzyme is widely distributed in plants and is specific for NADP, transferring hydrogen to the B-side of the ring. The lactone can hydrolyse spontaneously to phosphogluconic acid. Nevertheless, a lactonase catalysing this reaction has been isolated from *Azotobacter vinelandii* and is probably present in plants.

6-Phosphogluconic Dehydrogenase

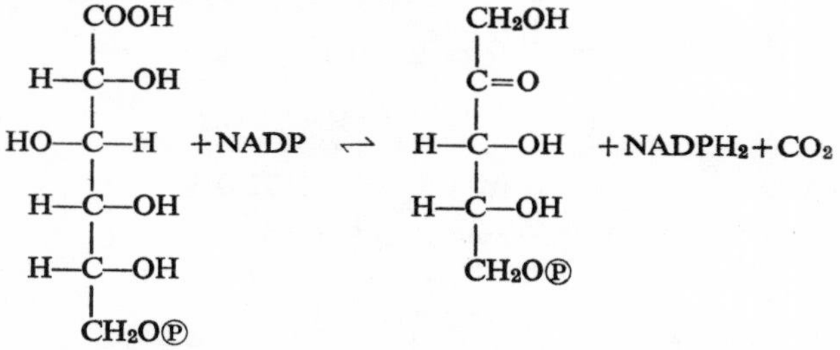

D-6-Phosphogluconate	D-Ribulose-5-phosphate

$$K = \frac{(\text{ribulose-5-phosphate})(\text{NADPH}_2)(\text{H}^+)(\text{CO}_2)}{(\text{6-phosphogluconate})(\text{NADP})} = 1\cdot3$$

The mechanism of this reaction in which C-1 of the hexose is released as CO_2 is unknown but it is clear that ribulose-5-phosphate is the final product. Two different intermediates have been proposed, 3-keto-6-phosphogluconate by Horecker and the 2,3-enediol of 6-phosphogluconate by Dickens and Glock; but neither has been demonstrated. The enzyme which is widely distributed in plants transfers the hydrogen to the B-side of the nicotinamide ring of NADP.

Phosphoriboisomerase

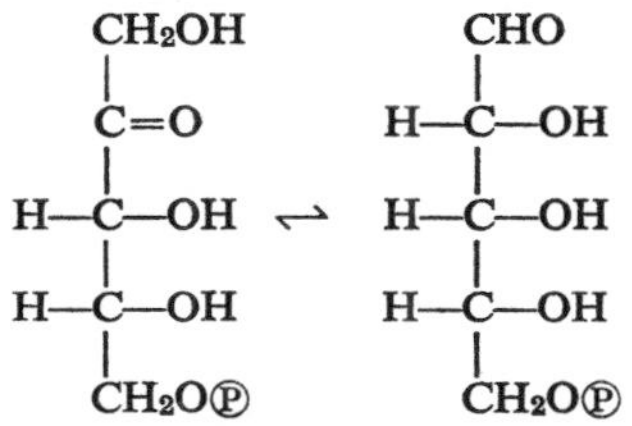

D-Ribulose-5-phosphate   D-Ribose-5-phosphate

$$K = \frac{(\text{ribose-5-phosphate})}{(\text{ribulose-5-phosphate})} = 3\cdot2 \text{ at } 37°C$$

$$3\cdot8 \text{ at } 25°C$$
$$6\cdot1 \text{ at } 0°C$$

Phosphoriboisomerase is widely distributed in plants and has been purified from *Medicago sativa*. The reaction is readily reversible but the equilibrium is markedly dependent upon the temperature.

Ribulose-5-phosphate Epimerase

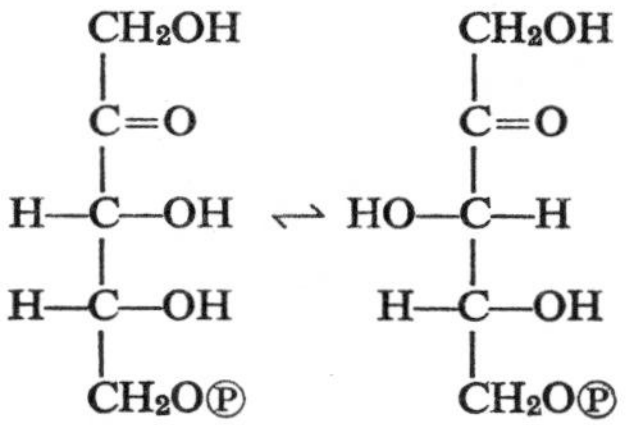

D-Ribulose-5-phosphate   D-Xylulose-5-phosphate

$$K = \frac{(\text{xylulose-5-phosphate})}{(\text{ribulose-5-phosphate})} = 1\cdot5 \text{ at } 25°C$$

For some time it was thought that ribulose-5-phosphate was the sub-strate for transketolase. However, with the discovery of ribulose-5-phosphate epimerase it was realized that ribulose-5-phosphate is first converted to xylulose-5-phosphate. Sugars which differ only in the con-figuration about a single carbon are called epimers and enzymes which catalyse their interconversion are termed epimerases.

Transketolase

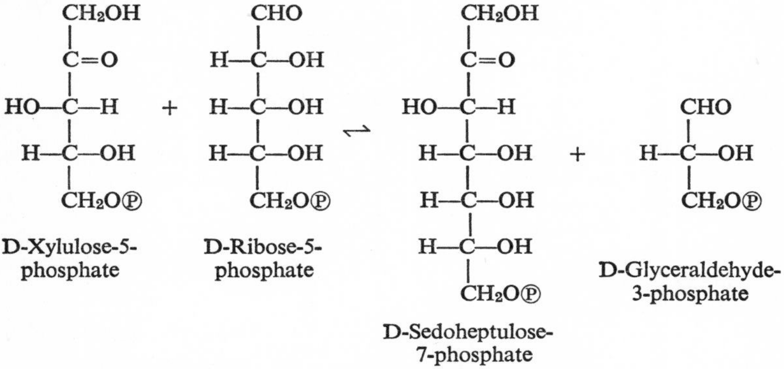

D-Xylulose-5-phosphate

D-Ribose-5-phosphate

D-Sedoheptulose-7-phosphate

D-Glyceraldehyde-3-phosphate

$$K = \frac{(\text{sedoheptulose-7-phosphate})(\text{glyceraldehyde-3-phosphate})}{(\text{xylulose-5-phosphate})(\text{ribose-5-phosphate})} = 1 \cdot 2$$

Transketolase has been purified from spinach and shown to require both magnesium and diphosphothiamine. The two-carbon moiety trans-ferred during the reaction is not found free but occurs as an enzyme bound active glycolaldehyde which is formed by the splitting of a ketol group

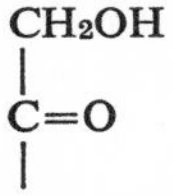

$$\begin{array}{c} CH_2OH \\ | \\ C=O \\ | \end{array}$$

from the donor substrate. In a transketolase reaction the acceptor must be an aldehyde and the donor must have the configuration

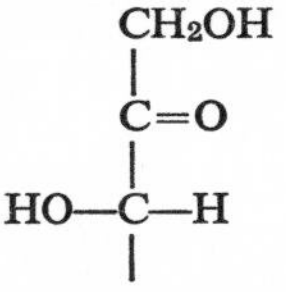

$$\begin{array}{c} CH_2OH \\ | \\ C=O \\ | \\ HO-C-H \\ | \end{array}$$

Within these limits there is a very broad specificity for both acceptors and donors. This is shown in Table 3.3. Transketolase reactions are readily reversible.

TABLE 3.3

Substrates for transketolase

Donors	Acceptors
Hydroxypyruvate	Formaldehyde
L-Erythrulose	Glycolaldehyde
D-Xylulose-5-phosphate	DL-Glyceraldehyde
D-Xylulose	D-Glyceraldehyde-3-phosphate
D-Fructose-6-phosphate	D-Erythrose-4-phosphate
D-Sedoheptulose-7-phosphate	D-Ribose-5-phosphate
D-Octulose-8-phosphate	D-Deoxyribose-5-phosphate
	D-Arabinose-5-phosphate
	D-Glucose-6-phosphate

Substrates for transaldolase

Donors	Acceptors
D-Octulose-8-phosphate	D-Glyceraldehyde-3-phosphate
D-Sedoheptulose-7-phosphate	L-Glyceraldehyde-3-phosphate
D-Fructose-6-phosphate	Glyceraldehyde
Sorbose-6-phosphate	D-Ribose-5-phosphate
D-Fructose	

Transaldolase

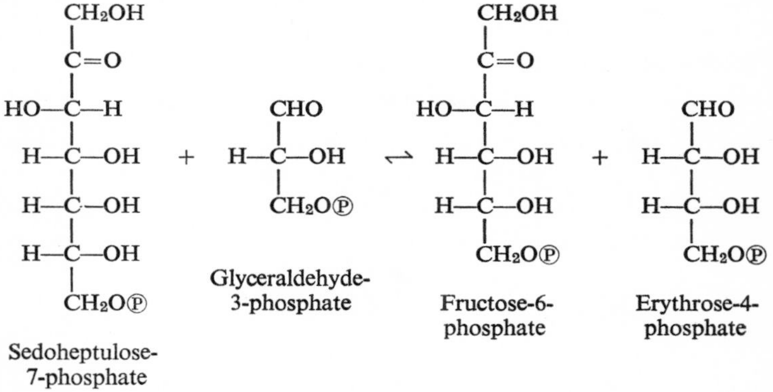

Sedoheptulose-7-phosphate + Glyceraldehyde-3-phosphate ⇌ Fructose-6-phosphate + Erythrose-4-phosphate

$$K = \frac{(\text{fructose-6-phosphate})(\text{erythrose-4-phosphate})}{(\text{sedoheptulose-7-phosphate})(\text{glyceraldehyde-3-phosphate})} = 1 \cdot 0$$

The following reaction mechanism has been established for yeast transaldolase:

donor (keto sugar) + enzyme ⇌ dihydroxyacetone-enzyme + aldehyde

dihydroxyacetone-enzyme + acceptor aldehyde ⇌ product (keto sugar) + enzyme

The dihydroxyacetone group is firmly bound to the enzyme. Transaldolase shows no requirement for cofactors and has a broad specificity for donors and acceptors (Table 3.3). Highest activity is shown with D-fructose-6-phosphate or D-sedoheptulose-7-phosphate as donors and D-glyceraldehyde-3-phosphate and D-erythrose-4-phosphate as acceptors. Transaldolase reactions are readily reversible.

Fructose-1,6-diphosphatase

The phosphatases are a group of enzymes which hydrolyse phosphate esters by breaking P—O bonds and transferring the phosphoryl group to water. Plants contain phosphatases capable of hydrolysing a large number of phosphate esters. Apart from a few exceptions, e.g. fructose-1,6-diphosphatase (p. 249), the physiological significance of phosphatases is obscure. Phosphatases also catalyse the transfer of a phosphoryl group to acceptors other than water, e.g.

phenyl phosphate + glucose⇌phenol + glucose-6-phosphate

In contrast to the hydrolytic reaction the energy of the phosphate bond is conserved in this transphosphorylase reaction. However very high concentrations of alternative acceptor are necessary for effective competition with water. It is thus unlikely that the transphosphorylase reaction plays any important role in metabolism.

The phosphatases may be divided into three main classes according to the type of substrate which they attack.

Phosphomonoesterase   Phosphodiesterase

Polyphosphatase

Plants contain at least two enzymes which catalyse the reaction

fructose-1,6-diphosphate + H_2O → fructose-6-phosphate + H_3PO_4

A specific fructose-1,6-diphosphatase, which requires Mg^+, has been isolated and shown to have optimum activity at pH 8·5 and none at pH 7·0. The second enzyme has an optimum at pH 7·0, does not require magnesium and appears to be associated with the chloroplasts in spinach leaves. A crude preparation of this enzyme removed the phosphate from carbon 1 of both fructose-1,6-diphosphate and sedoheptulose-1,7-diphosphate.

A system consisting of purified enzymes of carbohydrate metabolism has been shown to catalyse the conversion of 1 mole of glucose to 6 moles of CO_2. The pathway of this oxidation is usually written as in Fig. 3.8.

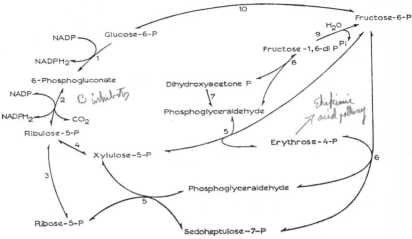

1. Glucose-6-phosphate dehydrogenase
2. 6-Phosphogluconic dehydrogenase
3. Phosphoriboisomerase
4. Ribulose-5-phosphate epimerase
5. Transketolase
6. Transaldolase
7. Triosephosphate isomerase
8. Aldolase
9. Fructose-1,6-diphosphatase
10. Phosphohexoisomerase

FIG. 3.8. Alternate reactions of pentose phosphate pathway.

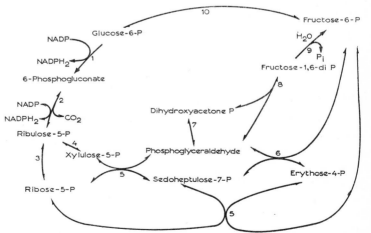

FIG. 3.9. Alternate reactions of pentose phosphate pathway.
The enzymes are numbered as in Fig. 3.8.

The broad specificity of transketolase makes it possible to draw the different but equally valid scheme shown in Fig. 3.9. In both schemes the oxidation is complete, does not involve the direct synthesis of ATP and specifically reduces NADP not NAD. The complete oxidation is made possible through the action of the transferring enzymes which eventually bring all the carbons of the initial glucose into position one from which they are released as CO_2. Figs. 3.10 and 3.11 show that the oxidation of

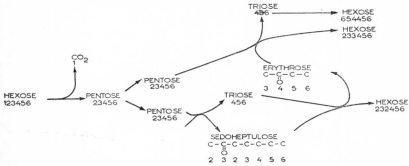

FIG. 3.10. Distribution of glucose carbons in conventional scheme for pentose phosphate pathway.

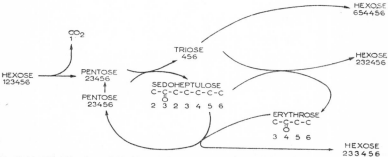

FIG. 3.11. Distribution of glucose carbons in alternate scheme for pentose phosphate pathway.

glucose through either of the two proposed schemes results in the same distribution of carbon atoms. At present there is no definitive evidence in favour of one scheme or the other. This fact focuses attention upon the question of whether it is correct to regard the pentose phosphate pathway as a rigid formal sequence. The organization of enzymes into such a sequence requires either high specificity of the enzymes or their spatial separation. All the enzymes of the pentose phosphate pathway appear to be soluble and the key enzymes — transketolase, transaldolase and aldolase, have very broad specificities. With the exception of glucose-6-phosphate dehydrogenase all the enzymes catalyse readily reversible reactions. If these enyzmes are soluble to the extent that substrates may diffuse freely amongst them, then their lack of specificity makes it very difficult to see how they could operate in a fixed sequence. There is at present no conclusive experimental evidence for a definite and fixed pentose phosphate pathway. Until such evidence is available the pentose phosphate pathway may be regarded as a pool of substrates in dynamic equilibrium and capable of adjusting to a new equilibrium value when any of the substrates are withdrawn from the pool. If a fixed sequence is eventually established it would indicate a high degree of spatial organization, possibly a mosaic of soluble enzymes, which is far more sophisticated than that indicated by present studies.

EVIDENCE FOR THE OPERATION OF THE PENTOSE PHOSPHATE PATHWAY

1. All the enzymes and substrates have been found in plants.
2. When ^{14}C ribose, xylose, sedoheptulose and gluconate are fed to plants the label appears in the respiratory CO_2.
3. Labelling patterns consistent with the operation of the pathway have been obtained in:

   a. Hexose after feeding with pentose and sedoheptulose.
   b. Alcohol and CO_2 after feeding xylose, ribose, sedoheptulose and gluconate.
   c. Respiratory CO_2 after supplying specifically labelled glucose.

C_6/C_1 Ratios

The most commonly sought evidence for the operation of the pentose phosphate pathway is a C_6/C_1 ratio of less than unity. This ratio represents:

$$\frac{\text{Percentage yield of }^{14}CO_2 \text{ from glucose-6-}^{14}C}{\text{Percentage yield of }^{14}CO_2 \text{ from glucose-1-}^{14}C}$$

Glucose passing through the EMP pathway is cleaved by aldolase and the products are equilibrated by triosephosphate isomerase. Consequently C_6 is equivalent to C_1 and the EMP pathway produces a C_6/C_1 ratio of unity. Glucose passing through the pentose phosphate pathway loses C_1 as CO_2 in the reaction

$$6\text{-phosphogluconate} + NADP \rightleftharpoons$$
$$ribulose\text{-}5\text{-phosphate} + NADPH_2 + CO_2$$

and would thus give a C_6/C_1 ratio less than unity immediately after feeding the labelled glucose, though subsequent equilibration would bring the ratio back to unity.

Initially, attempts were made to use the C_6/C_1 ratio to obtain quantitative estimates of the relative amount of glucose entering the two pathways. However, for the following reasons, it is now generally considered that this simple approach is not valid.

(1) The rate at which $^{14}CO_2$ appears will in part be determined by the pool sizes of the various intermediates. For example, the presence of large pools of Krebs cycle acids would dilute the radioactivity of carbon entering the Krebs cycle and so give a low yield of $^{14}CO_2$. Glucose passing through the pentose phosphate pathway would (assuming a small pool of hexose phosphates), release C_1 with relatively little dilution. This effect tends to overestimate the participation of the pentose phosphate pathway.

(2) Reversibility of the aldolase reaction in association with rapid triose phosphate isomerization would tend to equilibrate C_6 and C_1 and so underestimate the pentose phosphate pathway.

(3) Feeding glucose may increase the steady state concentration of glucose-6-phosphate within the cell and thereby change the rate at which the simultaneous reactions proceed.

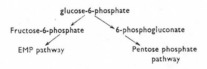

(4) There is evidence in leaves (see p. 252) that pentoses yield glycolate and thus CO_2. If this reaction is general it could invalidate the widely held view that a C_6/C_1 ratio differing significantly from unity is presumptive evidence for the operation of the pentose phosphate pathway.

(5) Recycling (if the pentose phosphate pathway is considered as a cycle) or shuttling (if it is considered as a dynamic pool), would affect the pattern of $^{14}CO_2$ released. The effect of recycling upon the release of glucose carbons as $^{14}CO_2$ has been considered in detail by Katz & Wood (1960). These authors concluded that it was improbable that the contributions of the different pathways could be evaluated from the rates at which individual glucose carbons appeared as $^{14}CO_2$ even if the

yield from all six carbons were known. However, insufficient data is available to decide whether recycling of hexose through the pentose phosphate pathway occurs in plants.

A modification of the C_6/C_1 ratio has been proposed by Wang, who expressed the difference between the yields of $^{14}CO_2$ from carbons 1 and 6 of glucose as a percentage of the yield from glucose-3,4-^{14}C plus the difference between the yield from 1- and 6-labelled glucose, i.e.

G_t = amount of added glucose engaged in catabolic functions

G_1, G_6, $G_{3(4)}$ = percentage recovery of ^{14}C as $^{14}CO_2$ from specifically labelled glucose

$$G_t = (G_1 - G_6) + G_{3(4)}$$

$$\text{Contribution of PPP} = \frac{G_1 - G_6}{G_t}$$

This type of calculation is open to the same criticism applied to the simple C_6/C_1 ratio.

It is probable that the oxidative decarboxylation of hexose to pentose via the pentose phosphate pathway occurs generally in plants and that the pentose so formed can be converted to hexose by other enzymes of the pathway. Present evidence indicates that the pentose need not necessarily be converted to hexose. If the pathway is a pool of substrates in dynamic equilibrium then intermediates may be withdrawn without stopping the pathway. Thus the pentose phosphate pathway may be not only a route of glucose oxidation but also a source of pentose for synthesis of nucleic acids, and erythrose for synthesis of aromatic compounds. Another important function of this pathway may be the production of $NADPH_2$ required for reductive biosynthesis (p. 80).

Although the EMP and pentose phosphate pathways are the only routes of carbohydrate oxidation known in plants, a number of other pathways have been described in animals and micro-organisms. In animals there is evidence for the operation of a cyclic pathway of glucose oxidation which has been called the glucuronic acid cycle (Holzer, 1959). In micro-organisms there are a number of fermentative pathways. In plants fermentation implies the formation of either ethanol and CO_2 or lactate via the EMP pathway. In micro-organisms the term is applied to any process in which an intermediate metabolite, rather than oxygen, is finally reduced.

Interconversion of Monosaccharides

The naturally occurring monosaccharides are derived from the common hexoses, glucose and fructose. The reactions involved in the interconversion of the more important monosaccharides are discussed below. Sugar nucleotides play a central role in these reactions. A sugar nucleotide is a sugar or sugar derivative in which the glycosidic OH group is esterified with the second phosphate group of a nucleoside-5-phosphate, e.g. uridine diphosphoglucose (UDPG):

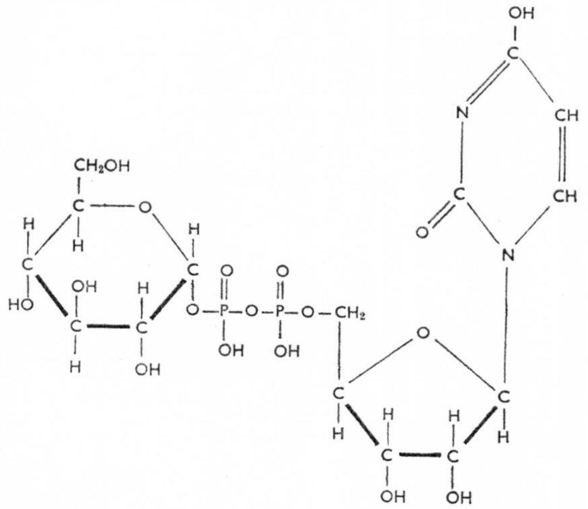

A wide range of sugar nucleotides has been demonstrated in plants. The commonest sugar nucleotides contain uridine but those containing guanosine, cytidine and thymidine have also been isolated. The sugar may be an aldohexose, aldopentose, uronic acid, sugar alcohol or an amino-sugar.

Sugar nucleotides are synthesized from the nucleoside triphosphate and the sugar phosphate.

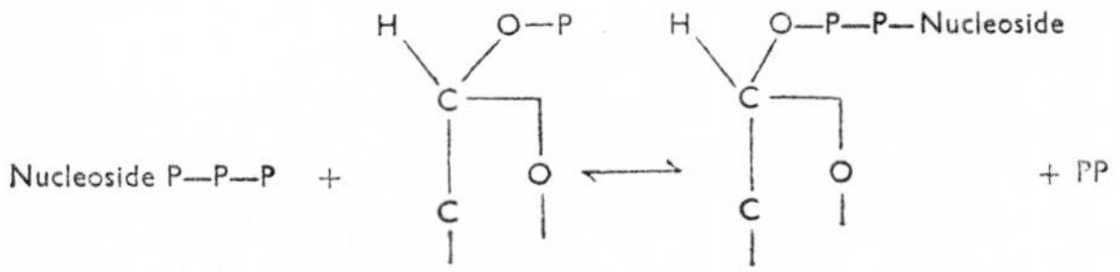

The liberated pyrophosphate all comes from the nucleoside triphosphate and the enzymes are called pyrophosphorylases. The equilibrium constant appears to be near unity. Despite this, considerable synthesis of sugar nucleotides would occur if, as is probable, the reaction were coupled to inorganic pyrophosphatase. Both alkaline and acid pyrophosphatases have been shown to be generally distributed in plants. The equilibrium of this reaction strongly favours hydrolysis.

$$\text{HO} \overset{\overset{O}{\|}}{\underset{\underset{OH}{|}}{P}} \text{—O—} \overset{\overset{O}{\|}}{\underset{\underset{OH}{|}}{P}} \text{—OH} \quad + H_2O \;\rightarrow\; 2\ \text{HO} \overset{\overset{O}{\|}}{\underset{\underset{OH}{|}}{P}} \text{—OH}$$

The nucleoside diphosphosugar pyrophosphorylases require a divalent cation. Studies with partially purified extracts of mung bean seedlings showed that there is no exchange of ^{32}P between UTP and pyrophosphate unless the sugar phosphate is present. It would appear that a free uridyl enzyme intermediate is not formed and the following mechanism has been proposed.

$$\text{Nucleoside} - \overset{}{P} \overset{x}{P} \overset{x}{P} + P - \text{sugar} + \text{Enzyme} \;\rightleftharpoons$$

$$\text{Enzyme} \left[\text{Nucleoside} - P \underset{P-\text{Sugar}}{\overset{\overset{x\ x}{P\ P}}{\diagup}} \right] \;\rightleftharpoons$$

$$\text{Enzyme} + \text{Nucleoside} - \text{PP} - \text{sugar} + \overset{x\ x}{P\ P}$$

The pyrophosphorylases are specific for sugars with a configuration about carbon-1 similar to that of the α-D-anomer of hexose-1-phosphate. The individual enzymes are discussed in the metabolism of the appropriate monosaccharides. It will also be seen that sugar nucleotides can be formed from other sugar nucleotides and that the presence of a pyrophosphorylase is not essential for synthesis.

GALACTOSE

Galactose and glucose-1-phosphate are interconverted as follows:

galactokinase

[1]   galactose + ATP $\longleftarrow\!\!\!\longrightarrow$ galactose-1-phosphate + ADP

$$K = 26 \pm 3 (\text{pH } 7 \cdot 0, \text{ at } 25°\text{C})$$

UDP-glucose pyrophosphorylase

[2] α-D-glucose-1-phosphate + UTP $\longleftarrow\!\!\!\longrightarrow$ UDP-glucose + PP

$$K = 1 \cdot 0$$

galactose-1-phosphate uridyl transferase

[3] galactose-1-phosphate + UDP-glucose⇌

glucose-1-phosphate + UDP-galactose

$$K = 1 \cdot 1$$

UDP-glucose-4-epimerase

[4]   UDP-galactose⇌UDP-glucose

$$K = 0 \cdot 3$$

Sum of 3 + 4   galactose-1-phosphate⇌glucose-1-phosphate

Evidence that this represents the pathway between the two hexoses in plants is:

(i) Wheat leaves convert galactose to glucose without cleavage of the carbon chain.

(ii) The presence of the necessary intermediates and enzymes has been demonstrated in plants.

Galactokinase has been demonstrated in particulate preparations from mung beans and in contrast to the hexokinase discussed on p. 104 catalyses the phosphorylation of the aldehydic oxygen on carbon 1. UDP-glucose pyrophosphorylase has been partially purified from mung bean seedlings and appears to be specific for glucose-1-phosphate. There is evidence that in corn coleoptiles much of the activity of this enzyme is associated with the cell walls. Galactose-1-phosphate uridyl transferase catalyses the readily reversible transfer of the uridyl group between glucose-1-phosphate and galactose-1-phosphate. The enzyme has been isolated from animals and micro-organisms and recently evidence of its occurrence in soya bean shoots has been presented. UDP-glucose-4-epimerase has been found in mung beans and intensively studied with preparations from yeast and liver. In the presence of either T_2O or $H_2{}^{18}O$ label does not appear in either of the nucleotides. These observations, together with the requirement for NAD, are consistent with an oxidoreduction mechanism. However, it has not been possible to isolate a uridine diphospho-4-keto hexose which would be the expected intermediate.

The interconversion of glucose-1-phosphate and galactose-1-phosphate was initially thought to be due to the activity of a single enzyme which was called galactowaldenase. This name is sometimes given to the epimerase. Epimerase is preferable since the reaction does not appear to proceed through the mechanism of a Walden inversion.

There is evidence that plants also contain a uridine diphosphogalactose pyrophosphorylase:

$$UTP + galactose\text{-}1\text{-}phosphate \rightarrow UDP\text{-}galactose + PP$$

It is difficult to be certain that this activity is due to a single enzyme.

MANNOSE

Since plant hexokinase catalyses the formation of mannose-6-phosphate, this enzyme and phosphomannoisomerase probably provide the links between mannose and the main pathways of carbohydrate oxidation. The presence of guanosine diphosphomannose has been reported in plants. The following enzymes, isolated from yeast but not from plants, catalyse the formation of guanosine diphosphomannose.

phosphomannomutase

mannose-6-phosphate $\longleftarrow$ $\longrightarrow$ mannose-1-phosphate

mannose pyrophosphorylase

mannose-1-phosphate + GTP $\longleftarrow$ $\longrightarrow$ GDP-mannose + PP

DEOXY SUGARS

Little data on the metabolism of deoxy sugars is available, most of which has been obtained from bacteria and animals.

Despite the importance of DNA the synthesis of deoxyribose has not been elucidated. Deoxyribose aldolase, found in animals and bacteria, catalyses the reversible reaction:

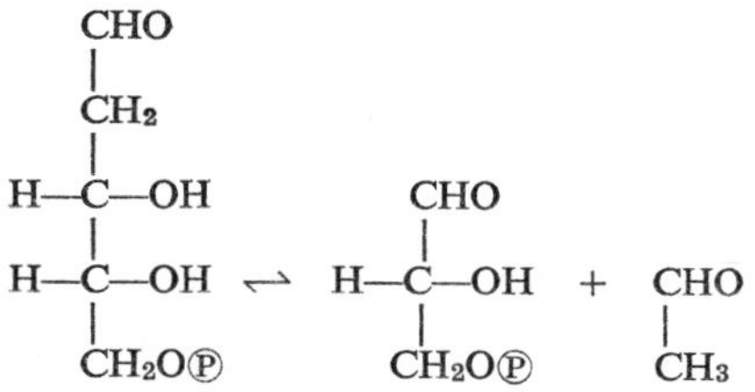

```
        CHO
         |
        CH₂
         |
    H—C—OH          CHO
         |            |
    H—C—OH  ⇌   H—C—OH   +   CHO
         |            |            |
    CH₂O℗        CH₂O℗        CH₃
```

When specifically labelled glucose was supplied to both *E. coli* and Ascites cells the distribution of label in ribose and deoxyribose was inconsistent with a mechanism involving deoxyribose aldolase but consistent with the view that ribose and deoxyribose have a common precursor. There is evidence from bacteria and animals that the ribose of nucleosides and nucleotides is converted to deoxyribose without cleavage of the carbon chain. For example, cell free extracts of *E. coli* convert cytidine-5-phosphate to deoxycytidine-5-phosphate. The conversion requires Mg, ATP and $NADH_2$.

Studies with a number of bacteria indicate that L-rhamnose is formed from glucose by epimerization about glucose carbons 3 and 4 and reduction of the primary alcoholic group. Extracts of *Pseudomonas aeruginosa* catalyse the multistep reaction

thymidine diphosphoglucose $+ NADPH_2 \rightleftharpoons$
thymidine diphosphorhamnose $+ NADP + H_2O$

The conversion apparently requires NAD as well, although its reduction has not been demonstrated. An enzyme catalysing the following reaction has been demonstrated in soya beans and lucerne and has been partially purified from *Pseudomonas aeruginosa*:

glucose-1-phosphate $+$ thymidine triphosphate $\rightleftharpoons$
thymidine diphosphoglucose $+$ pyrophosphate

These reactions may represent the route by which plants metabolize rhamnose. Further knowledge of rhamnose metabolism in plants is restricted to the observation that a number of seedlings convert it to rhamnonic acid.

Studies with bacteria and animals indicate that L-fucose may be metabolized in a manner analogous to that described for L-rhamnose. An extract of *Aerobacter aerogenes* catalyses the reaction:

GDP-D-mannose $+ NADPH_2 \rightleftharpoons$ GDP-L-fucose $+ NADP$

AMINO SUGARS

A pyrophosphorylase for UDP-N-acetyl glucosamine has been demonstrated in extracts of mung bean seedlings.

UTP $+$ N-acetyl-α-D-glucosamine-1-phosphate $\rightleftharpoons$
UDP-N-acetyl-D-glucosamine $+ PP$

Work with animals and micro-organisms has revealed the following enzymes which could represent the pathway from hexose to N-acetyl-α-D-glucosamine-1-phosphate.

(1) fructose-6-phosphate $+$ glutamine $\rightleftharpoons$
glutamic acid $+$ glucosamine-6-phosphate

(2) acetyl CoA $+$ glucosamine-6-phosphate $\rightleftharpoons$
N-acetyl-glucosamine-6-phosphate $+ CoA$

(3) N-acetyl-glucosamine-6-phosphate $\rightleftharpoons$ N-acetyl-glucosamine-1-

phosphate

9

UDP-N-acetyl-D-glucosamine might be expected to act as a donor of acetyl-N-glucosamine in the synthesis of polymers.

SUGAR ALCOHOLS

There is evidence that certain polyols act as reserve carbohydrates in fruits. During photosynthesis large amounts of activity from $^{14}CO_2$ appear rapidly in mannitol in *Fucus vesiculosus* and in sorbitol in plum leaves. In plum leaves the sorbitol appears to turn over quickly indicating rapid metabolism. It is likely that sugar alcohols and sugars in plants are interconverted by enzymes similar to the polyol dehydrogenases reported in micro-organisms. These dehydrogenases catalyse a wide range of such interconversions. Generally they are specific for either an aldose or a ketose and are linked to either NAD or NADP. Most of the known polyol dehydrogenases act upon the free sugar although mannitol dehydrogenase oxidizes D-mannitol-1-phosphate to fructose-1-phosphate. An individual sugar alcohol may be the substrate for two dehydrogenases. Thus xylose and xylulose may be interconverted by the push-pull mechanism discussed on p. 80.

$$NADPH_2 \qquad\qquad NAD$$
$$D\text{-xylose} \longleftarrow \longrightarrow \text{xylitol} \longleftarrow \longrightarrow D\text{-xylulose}$$

Another example is the interconversion of L-sorbose and D-fructose:

$$NADPH_2 \qquad\qquad NAD$$
$$L\text{-sorbose} \longleftarrow \longrightarrow D\text{-sorbitol} \longleftarrow \longrightarrow D\text{-fructose}$$

Feeding experiments indicate that plants form inositol by cyclization of hexose. Strawberries and parsley leaves metabolize *meso*-inositol-^{14}C readily and convert it primarily to the D-galacturonosyl residues of pectic substances. The first step in this conversion is probably an oxidative cleavage of inositol to glucuronic acid.

SUGAR ACIDS

Aldonic acids are formed via their δ-lactones by the oxidation of aldoses at carbon 1. The major oxidation of this type which has been demonstrated in plants is the formation of 6-phosphogluconic acid described on p. 113.

The uronic acids appear to be formed either by the oxidation of the corresponding sugar or by epimerization of another uronic acid. Both routes involve sugar nucleotides.

The presence in plants of a UDPG dehydrogenase and a UDP-D-glucuronic acid pyrophosphorylase makes it likely that glucuronic acid is formed as follows:

glucose-1-phosphate		UDP-glucose	2NAD
+	$\rightleftharpoons$	+	
UTP		PP	

glucuronic acid-1-phosphate		UDP-glucuronic acid	$2NADH_2$
+	$\rightleftharpoons$	+	
UTP		PP	

UDP-glucose dehydrogenase catalyses a two-step oxidation.

$$UDPG + 2NAD + H_2O \leftrightharpoons UDP\text{-glucuronic acid} + 2NADH_2$$

Studies with the purified enzyme from peas failed to separate the two steps and it was not possible to demonstrate an intermediate. The purified enzyme did not react with UDP-galactose.

UDP-glucuronic acid pyrophosphorylase has been demonstrated in particulate preparations of mung bean.

$$UTP + \text{glucuronic acid-1-phosphate} \leftrightharpoons UDP\text{-glucuronic acid} + PP$$

The crude preparation is active with UDP-galacturonic acid and also contains a D-glucuronic acid kinase:

$$\overset{Mg}{\alpha\text{-D-glucuronic acid} + ATP \leftrightharpoons ADP + \alpha\text{-D-glucuronic acid-1-phosphate}}$$

Plant tissues metabolize both D-glucuronic acid and its γ-lactone. Experiments with labelled glucuronic acid and its lactone indicate that, whilst much of the acid is converted to galacturonic acid and thence to pectin, a significant proportion is decarboxylated at carbon 6 to give pentose which is incorporated into cell wall hemicelluloses. A decarboxylase has been isolated from mung beans and shown to catalyse the reaction

$$UDP\text{-D-glucuronic acid} \rightarrow UDP\text{-D-xylose} + CO_2$$

This enzyme is specific for UDP-D-glucuronic acid and has an equilibrium far towards decarboxylation.

A UDP-galactose dehydrogenase has not been demonstrated and the only known route for the synthesis of galacturonic acid is via UDP-glucuronic acid epimerase. Particulate preparations of mung beans catalyse the reaction:

$$UDP\text{-D-glucuronic acid} \leftrightharpoons UDP\text{-D-galacturonic acid}$$

$$K = 1 \cdot 1$$

The same preparations also catalyse the epimerization of UDP-D-xylose:

$$\text{UDP-D-xylose} \rightleftharpoons \text{UDP-L-arabinose}$$
$$K = 1 \cdot 0$$

Treatment of the particles with digitonin differentiated between the two activities suggesting the existence of specific enzymes. When galacturonic acid-^{14}C is supplied to plants the overall distribution of label is similar to that found with glucuronic acid-[14]C. However, galacturonic acid makes a greater contribution to pectin and a smaller contribution to the hemiculloses. The following reactions have been demonstrated for glucuronic and galacturonic acids in plants: the metabolism of mannuronic acid does not appear to have been studied.

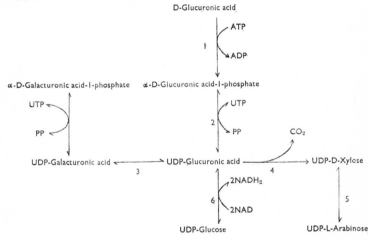

(1) D-Glucuronic acid kinase	(4) UDP-glucuronic decarboxylase
(2) UDP-glucuronic pyrophosphorylase	(5) UDP-D-Xylose epimerase
(3) UDP-glucuronic acid epimerase	(6) UDP-glucose dehydrogenase

Little is known of the metabolism of the saccharic acids in plants. These acids appear to be formed by the oxidation of the corresponding uronic acid, as label from glucuronic acid-^{14}C and galacturonic acid-^{14}C supplied to mung bean seedlings appears in glucaric and galactaric acids respectively.

ASCORBIC ACID

This section will deal only with the synthesis of ascorbic acid; its oxidation is discussed on p. 206. Present evidence strongly indicates that in plants ascorbate is formed from hexose without cleavage of the carbon chain and that D-glucose and D-galactose are the only sugars which can act as precursors. The conversion of these D-sugars to L-ascorbic acid must involve either an inversion of the groups around C5 or reduction at C1 accompanied by oxidation at C6 so that C6 becomes the reference carbon. In the latter case the conventional representation of the molecule will be completely inverted and C6 will become C1. Mapson (1960) has presented evidence for the operation of the following pathways in plants.

D-Galactose	Methyl D-Galacturonate	L-Galactono γ-Lactone	L-Ascorbic acid	L-Gulono γ-Lactone	D-Glucurono γ-Lactone	D-Glucose
CHO	CHO	$\overset{O}{\overset{\|}{C}}$	$\overset{O}{\overset{\|}{C}}$	$\overset{O}{\overset{\|}{C}}$	CHO	CHO
H—C—OH	H—C—OH	HO—C—H	HO—C	HO—C—H	H—C—OH	H—C—OH
HO—C—H	HO—C—H	H—C—OH	HO—C	HO—C—H	—CH	HO—C—H
HO—C—H	HO—C—H	H—C	H—C	H—C	H—C—OH	H—C—OH
H—C—OH	H—C—OH	HO—C—H	HO—C—H	HO—C—H	H—C—OH	H—C—OH
CH₂OH	COOCH₃	CH₂OH	CH₂OH	CH₂OH	CO	CH₂OH

Note that the conversion of the uronic acid to the corresponding aldonic acid makes C6 the reference carbon and that the conventional representation of the molecule is inverted to give L-isomers.

Studies with cell free systems from peas support this scheme. The soluble fraction contains an enzyme which catalyses the reduction of esters of D-galacturonic acid in the presence of $NADPH_2$. L-galactono-γ-lactone appears as the first stable product but the presence in animals of an aldonolactonase suggests that the free acid may be formed first.

$$\begin{array}{ccc} \text{D-galacturonic acid} + NADPH_2 & \rightleftharpoons & NADP \\ \text{esters} & & + \\ & & \text{L-galactonic acid} \\ & & \text{derivatives} \\ & & \downarrow \\ & & \text{L-galactono-γ-lactone} \end{array}$$

This preparation also catalyses the reduction of D-glucurono-γ-lactone but at one-third of the rate measured for esters of galacturonic acid. Particulate preparations from peas contain an L-galactono-γ-lactone dehydrogenase which converts L-galactono-γ-lactone to L-ascorbic acid. Only one-twentieth of this activity was found when L-gulono-γ-lactone was supplied. A similar enzyme from cauliflower was shown to be specific for L-galactono-γ-lactone. The specificity of these enzymes favours the pathway in which ascorbate is formed via D-galacturonate and L-galactono-γ-lactone.

Feeding experiments give some support to Mapson's scheme but the ready interconversion of glucose and galactose makes it difficult to decide whether ascorbate is synthesized via the galactono- or the gulono-γ-lactone pathways, or both. Plants will convert D-galacturonic methyl ester and the γ-lactones of L-galactonic, L-gulonic and D-glucuronic acids to L-ascorbate. Activity from 1- and 6-labelled glucurono-lactone fed to ripening strawberries appeared respectively in C1 and 6 of galacturonic acid of pectic substances and C6 and 1 of L-gulonic acid and L-ascorbic acid. This distribution of label is consistent with the inversion of the hexose molecule required by Mapson's scheme. Similar experiments carried out by Loewus with specifically labelled glucose and galactose supplied to the same material showed that much of the glucose and some of the galactose was converted to ascorbate without inversion of the carbon chain. Apart from evidence that glucose-6-phosphate is involved, the reaction sequence and the enzymes are unknown. A suggested route is the formation of 6-phosphogluconate followed by oxidation at C3 to give the corresponding keto acid and then inversion of the configuration at C5.

At present it appears that plants can convert galactose to ascorbate through its uronic and aldonic acids and that a similar route exists for glucose. In addition there is a completely different pathway from hexose to ascorbate in which the change from the D to the L configuration is achieved by an inversion at carbon 5. In this respect plants differ from animals in which the main, if not, the only route of ascorbate synthesis is:

D-glucose→D-glucuronate→L-gulonic acid→L-gulono-lactone→
2 keto-L-gulono-lactone→L-ascorbic acid.

OLIGOSACCHARIDES

Structure and Occurrence

Oligosaccharides are composed of relatively few monosaccharide sugars linked together by glycosidic bonds. A glycoside is formed by the exchange of an organic radical (R) with the hydrogen of the hemi-acetal hydroxyl group of an aldose or a ketose.

Another monosaccharide can act as the alcohol in this reaction.

These glycosidic bonds may be formed with any of the free OH groups of the second monosaccharide. When both hemi-acetal OH groups are involved the product has no reducing properties. Since an anomeric carbon is always involved in the formation of glycosides both α and β stereoisomers exist.

A wide range of oligosaccharides may be formed from the relatively few common monosaccharides by different combinations of the following variables: type and ring form of monosaccharide, carbon atoms involved in the glycosidic bond and configuration about the anomeric carbon. Each of these variables is specified in the nomenclature of oligosaccharides (see Table 3.4). An aldose or ketose in which the hemi-acetal group has been substituted is known as a glycosyl radical. When a glycosidic bond between two monosaccharides involves both hemi-acetal hydroxyl groups the disaccharide is called a glycosyl aldoside or glycosyl keto-side; when only one hemi-acetal hydroxyl group takes part the product is referred to as a glycosyl aldose or glycosyl ketose. Thus sucrose is glucosyl fructoside; and maltose is glucosyl glucose. The oligosaccharides are subdivided according to the number of monosaccharide units they contain, to give di-, tri-, tetra-, etc. saccharides. Most of the common oligosaccharides are formed from 2 to 4 hexose units. Those found in plants are given in Table 3.4, though some of them are found only as products of the hydrolysis of polysaccharides or heteroglycosides.

Metabolism

Oligosaccharides and polysaccharides are synthesized and degraded by a general reaction which may be represented:

$$G-OR + R_1O-H \rightleftharpoons G-OR_1 + H-OR$$

G—OR		R₁O—H		G—OR₁	H—OR
Glycosyl donor	$+$	Acceptor	$\rightleftharpoons$	Glycosyl-Acceptor	By-product

Sugar nucleotide   Sugar phosphate
Sugar phosphate   Alcohol
Oligo-and polysaccharides.   Mono-to polysaccharides
                           Phosphate.

The glycosyl group is transferred from a number of donors to a variety of acceptors. In all reactions examined the bonds broken are between C1 of the glycosyl unit and the glycosidic oxygen bridge. Thus the enzymes are transglycosylases and not transglycosidases. The hydrolytic enzymes (carbohydrases) may be regarded as a special case in which water is the glycosyl acceptor.

Table 3.4

DESIGNATION	FORMULA	OCCURRENCE

NON-REDUCING DISACCHARIDES

Sucrose

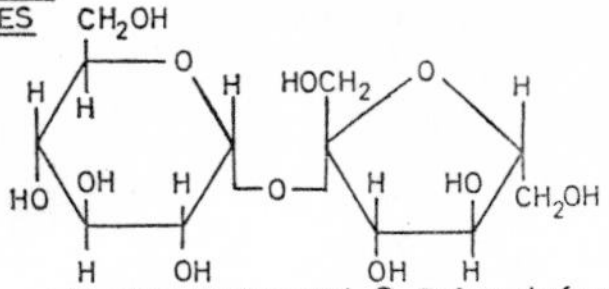

α-D-glucopyranosyl-β-D-fructofuranoside

Widely distributed in plants. Often present in vacuole in large quantities.

Trehalose

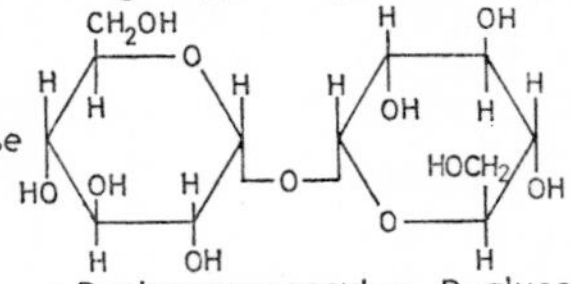

α-D-glucopyranosyl-α-D-glucopyranoside

Found in *Selaginella* sp., certain algae and possibly present in higher plants. The characteristic oligosaccharide of Fungi.

REDUCING DISACCHARIDES

Cellobiose

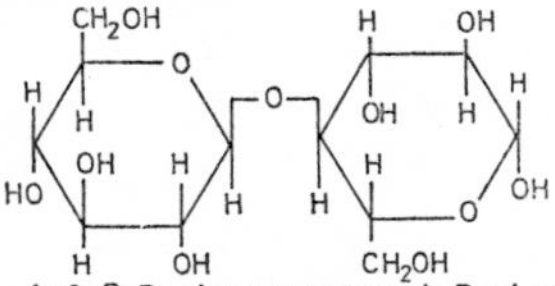

4-0-β-D-glucopyranosyl-D-glucose

Product of hydrolysis of cellulose.

Lactose

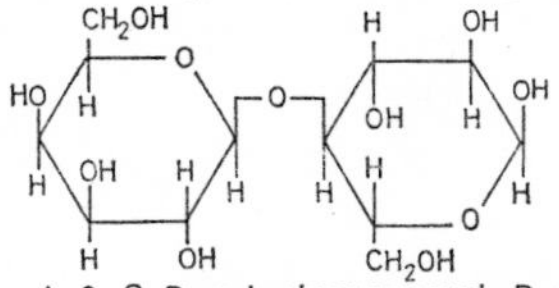

4-0-β-D-galactopyranosyl-D-glucose

Reported in *Forsythia* flowers. Found in milk of mammals.

Maltose

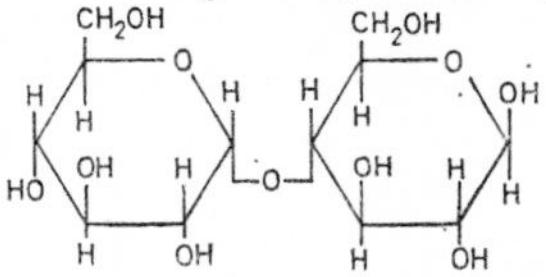

4-0-α-D-glucopyranosyl-D-glucose

Product of the hydrolysis of starch.

Primeverose

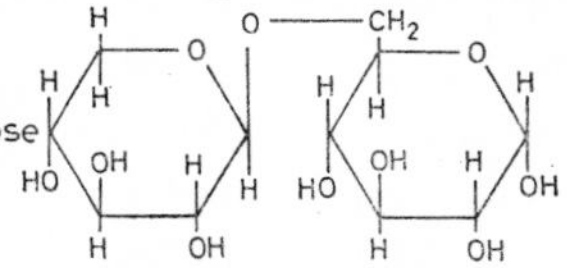

6-0-β-D-xylopyranosyl-α-D-glucopyranose

Found in a number of plant glycosides.

HIGHER OLIGOSACCHARIDES

Raffinose

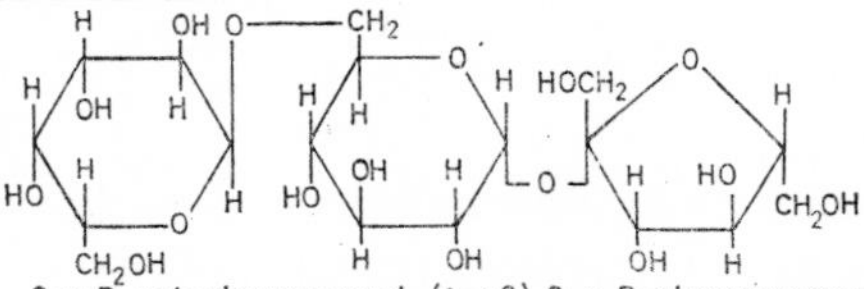

0-α-D-galactopyranosyl-(1$\rightarrow$6)-0-α-D-glucopyranosyl-(1$\rightarrow$2)-β-D-fructofuranoside

Widely distributed in small quantities as the free sugar.

Stachyose

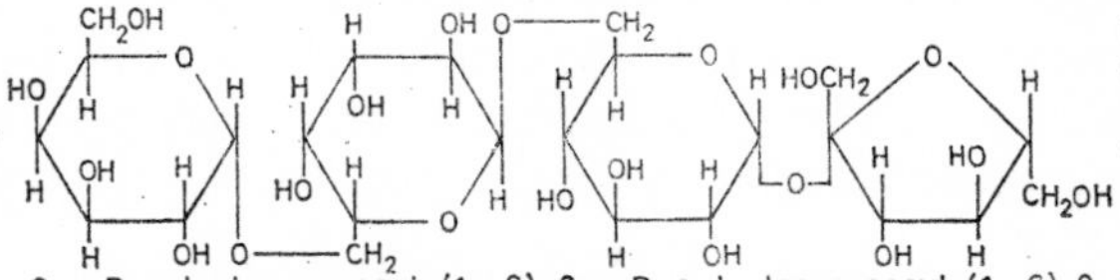

0-α-D-galactopyranosyl-(1$\rightarrow$6)-0-α-D-galactopyranosyl-(1$\rightarrow$6)-0-α-D-glucopyranosyl-(1$\rightarrow$2)-β-D-fructofuranoside

Free sugar frequently found, often with raffinose and sucrose.

Sucrose

Sucrose accumulates as a product of photosynthesis and appears to be the major soluble reserve carbohydrate in higher plants. There is evidence that carbohydrates are translocated as sucrose.

The enzyme classically associated with sucrose is invertase.

$$\text{sucrose} + H_2O \rightarrow \text{glucose} + \text{fructose}$$

Invertase has been isolated from a range of plant tissues. In corn coleoptiles a major portion of the activity is associated with the cell wall fraction. Sucrose may be regarded either as a β-fructofuranoside or an α-glucopyranoside. All the plant invertases which have been examined are β-fructofuranosidases which transfer the fructosyl residue to water or to other carbohydrates. Thus during the hydrolysis of sucrose two trisaccharides are formed by the transfer of the fructosyl group to either residue of sucrose. Although a fructosyl enzyme complex has not been demonstrated, the following mechanism is proposed:

$$\text{fructosyl-glucosyl} + \text{Enz. OH} \leftrightarrow \text{fructosyl-Enz.} + \text{glucose}$$

Hydrolysis

$$\text{fructosyl-Enz.} + H_2O \rightarrow \text{fructose} + \text{Enz. OH}$$

Transfer

$$\text{fructosyl-Enz.} + \text{fructosyl-glucosyl} \leftrightarrow \text{fructosyl-fructosyl-glucosyl}$$
$$+ \text{Enz. OH}$$

Yeast invertase is also a fructofuranosidase, and is specific for a substrate with a terminal β-D-fructofuranosyl residue, but will tolerate relatively large changes in the other part of the substrate molecule. For example, both raffinose and stachyose are hydrolysed. The plant enzyme may be expected to behave in the same way. Invertases which attack the sucrose molecule from the glucose end, α-glucosidases, have been reported from animals and micro-organisms.

The hydrolysis of sucrose by invertase may be regarded as irreversible since ΔG° is -6.6kcal. The physiological significance of the enzyme is uncertain. Experiments with *Canna* leaves indicate that endogeneous sucrose was not appreciably hydrolysed over a period of 6 hours. When sucrose was supplied to the leaf discs it was rapidly hydrolysed. These observations suggest that the hydrolysis took place at the surface of the cells.

Sucrose may be synthesized by the following enzymes:

Sucrose phosphorylase

This was the first enzyme shown to be capable of sucrose synthesis *in vivo*. It was isolated from *Pseudomonas* and shown to catalyse the reaction:

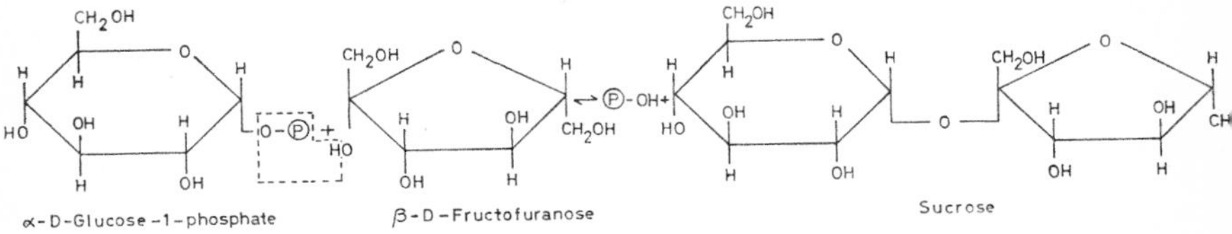

α-D-Glucose-1-phosphate   β-D-Fructofuranose   Sucrose

$$K = \frac{\text{(sucrose) (phosphate)}}{\text{(fructose) (glucose-1-phosphate)}} = 0.05, \ 30°C, \ pH \ 6.6$$

The equilibrium, though favouring phosphorolysis, would permit sucrose synthesis. The enzyme acts as a glucosyl transferase and the mechanism may be represented:

glucose-1-phosphate + Enz. ⇌ glucosyl-Enz. + phosphate

glucosyl-Enz. + fructose ⇌ sucrose + Enz.

The phosphate may be replaced by several monosaccharides. For example, glucosyl transfer to L-sorbose proceeds as follows:

sucrose + L-sorbose ⇌ D-glucosyl-1-sorboside

Attempts to demonstrate sucrose phosphorylase in plants have been unsuccessful.

Sucrose synthetase

UDPG + D-fructose ⇌ UDP + sucrose

$$K = \frac{\text{(sucrose) (UDP)}}{\text{(UDPG) (fructose)}} = 8, \ pH \ 7.4$$

This enzyme has been isolated from a wide range of plant tissues. The pea enzyme also transfers the glucosyl group from UDPG to D-xylulose and D-rhamnulose.

Sucrose phosphate synthetase

UDPG + D-fructose-6-phosphate ⇌ UDP + sucrose phosphate

$$K_{approx} = \frac{\text{(sucrose phosphate) (UDP)}}{\text{(UDPG) (fructose-6-phosphate)}} = 3250 \text{ at pH } 7.5 \text{ and } 53 \text{ at}$$

pH 5.5

This enzyme has been demonstrated in a number of plants. However, it is apparently absent from certain tissues which can nevertheless synthesize sucrose. In wheat germ the activity of sucrose phosphate synthetase is appreciably higher than that of sucrose synthetase. Wheat germ contains a phosphatase active with sucrose phosphate.

The results of feeding experiments are consistent with the view that plants synthesize sucrose via UDPG. Thus both UDPG and sucrose phosphate are rapidly labelled during photosynthesis. It is not possible to decide upon the relative roles of the two synthetases. The more favourable equilibrium and the higher activity of sucrose phosphate synthetase suggest this enzyme as the main route of glucose synthesis. Some support for this hypothesis is given by feeding experiments which provided no evidence for a direct role for free hexose in sucrose synthesis. Sucrose synthetase could also catalyse the breakdown of sucrose *in vivo* with greater conservation of energy than invertase.

TREHALOSE

Enzymes catalysing the following reactions have been isolated from yeast and preliminary experiments suggest their presence in peas.

$$\text{UDPG} + \text{glucose-6-phosphate} \rightleftharpoons \text{UDP} + \text{trehalose phosphate}$$
$$\text{trehalose phosphate} \rightleftharpoons \text{trehalose} + \text{phosphate}$$

OTHER OLIGOSACCHARIDES

Little is known of the ways in which plants metabolize the remaining oligosaccharides listed in Table 3.4. Carbohydrases, capable of the complete hydrolysis of these oligosaccharides, have been demonstrated in plants. α-Glucosidase, β-glucosidase, α-galactosidase, β-galactosidase and α-mannosidase may be added to the β-fructofuranosidase already mentioned. These enzymes appear to be similar to invertase in that they transfer a specific glycosyl group either to water or to another carbohydrate. When water is the acceptor the reaction is practically irreversible, but when the enzyme acts as a transferase there is only a small change in free energy. The function of these carbohydrases is unknown. They could be responsible for the degradation of oligosaccharides and the removal of glycosyl residues from plant hetero-glycosides. They could conceivably be responsible for the synthesis of oligosaccharides, though there is no evidence that this is so. It is probable that their synthesis is mediated by sugar nucleotides. Thus starch granules from a number of plants contain an enzyme catalysing

$$\text{UDPG} + \text{acceptor} \rightleftharpoons \text{UDP} + \alpha\text{-(1, 4)-glucosyl-acceptor}$$

where the acceptor may be an oligosaccharide of the maltose series or starch. The ability of sucrose phosphorylase to act as a glycosyl transferase raises the possibility that similar enzymes may be involved in the synthesis and degradation of the oligosaccharides.

POLYSACCHARIDES

The polysaccharides are a varied group of high polymers of monosaccharides in which the degree of polymerization (DP) may extend up to several thousand. The polymers may have a single repeating unit (homopolymers) or different units may be present (heteropolymers). The monosaccharide units may be linked in a linear fashion and branched structures may also be present. Since the degree of polymerization may be variable the identity of a polysaccharide is not restricted to a particular molecular species.

One of the consequences of this lack of definition is that polysaccharides are difficult to classify. Initially many polysaccharides were classified into storage and structural polysaccharides with the latter group being subdivided into cellulose, pectic substances and the hemicelluloses. The present tendency is to classify the polysaccharides on a chemical basis. With the exception of certain well-established trivial names the polysaccharides are denoted by the suffixes -*osan* or -*an*. The polysaccharides may be divided into homoglycans and heteroglycans, each category being subdivided according to the monomers, e.g. glucans, fructans, galactomannans, etc.

Glucans

STARCH

(a) STRUCTURE

Starch stains with iodine and occurs in characteristic granules which are insoluble in cold water. Most starch has two components, amylose and amylopectin, both of which are formed of α-D-glucopyranose units. Although there is some evidence that amylose is slightly branched it is generally regarded as a linear molecule composed entirely of α-1,4 linked glucose units. The number of units varies with the source of the amylose from 200 to over 1000. It is thought that glucopyranose units exist in either the B1 or B3 boat forms (p. 92). The α-1,4 linkages give the amylose chain a tendency to coil into a helix. In the characteristic reaction with iodine, the iodine is held by dipole forces in the core of the amylose helix.

Amylose from a single source is polydisperse and two main fractions are recognized, DP 50–200 and DP 200–1500.

Estimates of the DP of amylopectin molecules range from 2000 to 220 000. Amylopectin contains one non-reducing end group for every 20 units present. The molecule is branched; the main linkages are α-1,4 and the branch linkages are α-1,6. The probable structure of amylopectin is shown in Fig. 3.12 although an alternative laminated structure has been proposed.

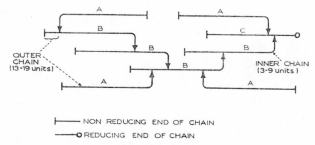

FIG. 3.12. Probable structure of amylopectin.

Three different unit chains may be recognized. *A* chains are attached only through their hemi-acetal group. *B* chains are attached through a hemi-acetal group and a free OH group at carbon 6 of at least one residue. *C* chains are attached only via OH groups at C6 and have a free reducing group. The relative extent of single and multiple branching and the exact length of the chains is not known. Amylopectin resembles glycogen except that glycogen is more branched and has shorter outer chains. The ratio of amylose to amylopectin is generally between 1:6 and 1:3 although ratios of 3:1 have been observed and in some starches amylose is absent. Waxy cereals have a very low amylose content whilst the highest amylose content is reported from varieties of maize. The proportion varies between varieties and there is evidence of variation between different organs of the same plant. A number of authorities hold that amylose and amylopectin form a single substance *in vivo*. At present the multiple concept of starch, which argues that the two components are separate substances commands more support but is not conclusively proven.

Starch differs from other polysaccharides in occurring in discrete granules. The size and shape of these granules varies widely but is specific for a particular plant. All the granules appear to be built upon a common pattern of a series of layers enveloping each other. These layers consist of radially arranged crystals of amylopectin and amylose. Evidence has been presented that the outer region of each layer consists mainly of high molecular weight amylose and amylopectin whilst the inner region consists mainly of low molecular weight amylose. Starch is widely distributed throughout the higher plants and is the main reserve poly-saccharide.

(b) METABOLISM

Plants contain a number of enzymes capable of forming the α-1,4 linkages of starch and one which can cause branching by forming α-1,6 links.

Starch phosphorylase

$$\text{glucose-1-phosphate} + \text{acceptor} \rightleftharpoons$$
$$\alpha\text{-1,4 glucosyl-acceptor} + \text{phosphate}$$

$$K = \frac{(\alpha\text{-1,4 glucosyl-acceptor}) (\text{phosphate})}{(\text{glucose-1-phosphate}) (\text{acceptor})} = 10 \cdot 8 \text{ at pH } 5 \cdot 0, 3 \cdot 1 \text{ at pH } 7 \cdot 0$$

Starch phosphorylase has been found in many plants and has been crystallized from potatoes. The enzyme catalyses the reversible transfer of glucosyl units between glucose-1-phosphate and the non-reducing end of α-1,4 linked glucose chains. Whilst a variety of compounds may act as acceptors the enzyme appears to require a non-reducing chain terminated by at least three α-1,4 linked glucosyl residues which are unsubstituted except at carbons 1 and 4. Maltotriose is the smallest molecule which will act as an acceptor; larger molecules are more effective and maximum effectiveness is found with a chain of about 20 α-1,4 linked glucosyl units. The activity of the enzyme is greater with a branched acceptor containing several such chains than with a linear acceptor. Maximum activity is measured with amylopectin. The number of non-reducing end groups is not altered by the enzyme and a small acceptor molecule can give rise to a large molecule. The acceptor (in this and similar reactions) has therefore been called a primer. However, it is merely the second reactant in a bimolecular reaction.

In the direction of phosphorolysis the enzyme degrades amylose to maltotriose or maltotetraose, but with amylopectin the action stops when the outer chains have been degraded to within two or three residues of the α-1,6 linkages. The partially degraded amylopectin molecule is called a limit dextrin.

Highly purified muscle phosphorylase has been shown to catalyse the slow synthesis of amylose from glucose-1-phosphate in the absence of primer. There is evidence that potato phosphorylase is also active without primer. The mechanism of this reaction appears to differ from that which occurs in the presence of primer.

The specificity towards glucose-1-phosphate appears to be absolute. Phosphate can be replaced by arsenate. The resulting arsenolysis leads to the formation of free glucose from starch, presumably because glucose-1-arsenate is unstable.

The phosphorylase reaction is readily reversible but pH has a marked effect upon the equilibrium. Polysaccharide synthesis is favoured at more acid pH. Within wide limits changes in the concentration of acceptor molecules do not alter the equilibrium.

It has been established that pyridoxal phosphate (see p. 362) is the prosthetic group for muscle phosphorylase. Potato phosphorylase has been shown to contain 2 moles of firmly bound pyridoxal phosphate per mole of enzyme. The mechanism of action of the enzyme is not known. The bonds broken are between the pyranose ring and the glycosidic oxygen bridge. There is evidence that a glucosyl enzyme complex is *not* formed during the reaction.

Potato phosphorylase differs from muscle phosphorylase in that it neither contains nor requires for activity either phosphoserine or 5'-adenylic acid.

UDPG transglycosylase

$$UDPG + acceptor \leftrightharpoons UDP + \alpha\text{-}1,4 \text{ glucosyl-acceptor}$$

Preparations of starch grains from *Phaseolus vulgaris* and several other plants have been shown to catalyse the above reaction. Starch, maltotetraose, maltotriose and maltose acted as acceptors but glucose and sucrose did not. When starch was used glucose was transferred to both amylose and amylopectin. It has recently been shown that this enzyme reacts about ten times faster with adenosine diphosphoglucose (ADPG) than with UDPG. The possibility that ADPG is the substrate *in vivo* is suggested by the demonstration in plants of an ADPG pyrophosphorylase which catalyses:

$$ATP + glucose\text{-}1\text{-}phosphate \leftrightharpoons ADPG + PP$$

'D' enzyme

The D enzyme, demonstrated in potatoes and *Vicia faba*, catalyses the reversible transfer of two or more glycosyl residues from malto-dextrins (α-1,4 linked glucose chains containing more than 2 units) to carbon 4 of a variety of acceptors. Glucose, xylose, mannose and any malto-dextrin act as acceptors, e.g.

maltotriose + maltotriose←→glucose + maltopentaose

'*Q*' *enzyme*

The Q enzyme is able to form amylopectin from amylose. It is a trans-glycosylase which transfers a portion of the amylose chain from an α-1,4 link to an α-1,6 link. The reducing group of the transferred chain forms a glycosidic bond with the primary OH group of the acceptor chain. The Q enzyme transfers a chain of 15–20 α-1,4 linked glucose units from a donor which must consist of at least 40 such units. There is evidence that the acceptor must contain three or four α-1,4 linked glucose residues and have a non-reducing end group. Both linear and branched molecules can act as donor or acceptor and the Q enzyme can catalyse the formation of multiply branched molecules. The equilibrium strongly favours the synthesis of the α-1,6 linkages and the enzyme is not thought to be responsible for their cleavage.

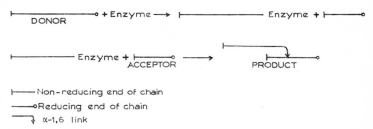

It is likely that Q enzyme and one or more of the enzymes known to form α-1,4 linkages are responsible for starch synthesis *in vivo*. However, it is not possible to decide upon the roles of UDPG transglycosylase, phosphorylase and D enzyme, all of which could synthesize amylose. In animals there is good evidence that glycogen is synthesized by a UDPG transglycosylase and that the role of the phosphorylase is degradative. A similar situation may exist with respect to starch. If the multiple concept of starch is accepted there is an additional problem in the mechanism of the concurrent synthesis of amylose and amylopectin. If starch phosphorylase and Q enzyme are incubated in the same reaction mixture the product is a mixture of branched polysaccharides and not a mixture of amylose and amylopectin. It is possible that the two components are formed in different regions of the starch grain.

There is similar uncertainty over the pathways of starch degradation *in vivo.* It is not known whether the UDPG transglycosylase is reversible but it is clear that the α-1,4 linkages can be broken by both phosphorylase and the D enzyme without appreciable loss of the energy. The equilibrium of the phosphorylase reaction permits the concentration of phosphate and glucose-1-phosphate to control the rate of starch degradation. Phosphorylase can degrade α-1,4 linked glucose chains to short chains of 3 or 4 units, which could be further degraded by the D enzyme until eventually only one molecule of maltotetraose remains. Similar degradation of the branched chains of starch occurs in the presence of the R enzyme which has been found in a number of plants and which hydrolyses α-1,6 linkages between glucose residues. The R enzyme appears to be solely hydrolytic and to require in its substrate a minimum number of α-1,4 linked glucose units in addition to the α-1,6 linkage.

The α-1,4 linkages of starch may also be broken by hydrolytic enzymes known as amylases. Amylases are widely distributed in plants and two general types are recognized, endoamylases which attack α-1,4 linkages in a polymer at random, and exoamylases which only attack α-1,4 linkages from the non-reducing end of the substrate. Only one type of endoamylase is known. This is α-amylase, so named because the reducing group which it liberates has the α configuration. The study of α-amylase action is complicated since the enzyme attacks α-1,4 linkages in a wide range of compounds and quickly converts starch into a variety of oligosaccharides for which the enzyme has varying affinities. Available evidence indicates that α-amylase hydrolyses all the α-1,4 links of starch except terminal linkages and those within 3 units of the α-1,6 links. The glucosyl residues appear to be transferred only to water and the bonds broken are between carbon 1 and the oxygen. α-Amylase contains at least 1 gram atom of calcium per mole. The calcium is necessary for enzymic activity and appears to hold the protein in the appropriate configuration.

Plants also contain an exoamylase called β-amylase which removes successive maltose units from the non-reducing end of an α-1,4 linked glucose chain. A change in configuration must occur during this hydrolysis since the product is β-maltose (p. 61). β-Amylase hydrolyses every other linkage in an α-1,4 linked glucose chain until it is degraded either to maltose in an even numbered chain or to maltotriose in an odd chain. There is evidence that the enzyme can reduce the *A* chains of amylopectin to 2 or 3 units and the *B* and *C* chains to within 2 units of an α-1,6 link. Activity is low with small substrates like maltotriose.

The role of the amylases is uncertain. The high activity of amylases in seeds has led to the suggestion that they mobilize starch reserves.

10

CELLULOSE

Cellulose is a large, apparently uniform, unbranched polymer of β-1,4 linked glucopyranose units which are present in the chair form.

Estimates of the number of glucose units in a cellulose molecule vary from 3000 to 10 000. The molecules are fairly rigid and are extended into ribbon-like structures. This rigidity is thought to result from the spatial arrangement of the glucose units produced by the β-1,4 linkage and possibly from hydrogen bonding between oxygen atoms attached to C6 and C2 of adjacent units.

Cellulose is universally distributed in plants where it forms the framework of cell walls. The cellulose molecules do not occur free but are arranged in parallel bundles of approximately 2000. These bundles are the microfibrils of the cell walls. Within the microfibrils the molecules are not regularly arranged; there are crystalline regions (micelles) and less ordered amorphous areas. The distinction between the two areas is not sharp and evidence has been presented that the microfibrils have a crystalline core which is surrounded and interrupted by amorphous cellulose. In the micelles the cellulose chains are held together by hydrogen bonding and van der Waal's forces. There is some evidence of an anti-parallel arrangement of the cellulose chains in the micelles. It has been suggested that the amorphous regions are caused by the presence of water which prevents crystallization of the cellulose. The microfibrils are themselves arranged in larger bundles of about 400 to form the macrofibrils.

Little is known of the biosynthesis of cellulose. Data from feeding experiments with plants indicate that glucose is the most suitable precursor and that it is incorporated intact into cellulose. Particulate preparations from *Acetobacter xylinum* transfer glucose from UDPG to cellulose. The transfer requires cellodextrins (a mixture of β-1,4 linked glucose chains containing up to 30 units.) The yield is very low.

Enzymes which degrade cellulose are termed cellulases and are widespread in micro-organisms but do not appear to be present in appreciable amounts in higher plants. Possible exceptions are a number of seeds where there is evidence that cellulase plays a role in germination. In general the ability of plants to degrade structural polysaccharides is quite limited. Cellulase preparations from micro-organisms show considerable variation but present evidence indicates that cellulose is hydrolysed by a random cleavage and that activity with the lower polymers is restricted.

OTHER GLUCANS

The cell sap of *Zea mays* contains compounds which are similar to animal glycogen. These have been regarded either as plant glycogens or highly branched amylopectins. Barley and oat seeds and a number of lichens contain a polymer formed of unbranched chains of D-glucopyranose in which half the linkages are $\beta1,4$ and half β-1,3. Callose of phloem sieve tubes has been isolated and shown to be a straight chain β-1,3 glucan which closely resembles laminarin, the reserve polysaccharide of the brown algae.

Apart from the demonstration of enzymes capable of forming and cleaving the β-1,3 linkages, little is known of the metabolism of these glucans. In the presence of a suitable acceptor particulate preparations from a number of plants catalyse the synthesis from UDPG of a β-1,3 linked polymer which appears to be very similar to callose. Glucose and a variety of glucosides, maltose, cellobiose, laminaribiose, act as acceptors. This synthesis involves an inversion of the configuration of the glucose and the acceptors are not incorporated into the polymer. A β-glucosidase which catalyses the degradation of the polymer formed in the above reaction has also been found in plants. This enzyme appears to be similar to the laminarase of algae.

Fructans

Fructans are widely distributed in plants and occur particularly in the Compositae and Gramineae. They are generally low molecular weight polymers of D- fructofuranose which act as food reserves. Most fructans also contain very small amounts of glucose. Detailed structures are unknown, but most fructans are branched. The group is divided according to the main linkages which are generally either β-2,1 or β-2,6. Inulin is the best known plant fructan. It is thought to consist of 35 D-fructofuranose units linked β-2,1 into a straight chain with one glucose molecule at the reducing end and another attached somewhere in the middle of the chain by a 1:3 link.

The way in which plants synthesise fructans is not clear. Most of the available data refer to inulin metabolism in tubers of *Helianthus tuberosus*. Data from feeding experiments, and the isolation of a series of fructosylated derivatives of sucrose are consistent with the view that inulin is formed from sucrose by transfructosylation. A number of transfructosylations are catalysed by extracts of tubers but none have yet been shown to result in the formation of inulin. The most rapid transfructosylation discovered is:

$$\overset{* \; * \; *}{G\text{-}F} + \overset{*}{G}\text{-}F\text{-}F \rightleftharpoons \overset{* \quad * \; *}{G\text{-}F\text{-}F} + G\text{-}F$$

Sucrose 1^f-Fructosyl

sucrose

The same preparation also catalysed the incorporation of the terminal fructose unit of fructosyl sucrose into an unidentified fructan. It is possible that this reaction represents the synthesis of inulin through the following reaction:

fructosyl-sucrose + acceptor $\rightarrow$ fructosyl-acceptor + sucrose

There is evidence that the tubers also contain an inulosucrase which catalyses the formation of the lower members of the inulin series of polymers from sucrose.

n sucrose $\rightarrow$ glucosidofructosan + $(n-1)$ glucose

This enzyme is analogous to the bacterial levansucrase which catalyses the formation of levan (a high molecular weight fructan) by the transfer of single D-fructosyl units to the fructose end of a sucrose terminated chain.

The hydrolysis of fructans is catalysed by extracts of artichokes. The preparations hydrolysed inulin, irisan B (a levan from rye grass), and appeared to contain fructofuranosidases which acted upon 2-1 linked terminal fructose residues. It is likely that similar enzymes are present in all tissues which contain fructan reserves.

Xylans

Xylan is the most abundant pentan and is universally distributed as a component of the matrix of cell walls. Straws and certain hard woods may contain up to 25 per cent xylan. Xylans are relatively small polysaccharides (DP 40–200) composed chiefly of β-1,4 linked D-xylopyranose units. Most xylans examined are either unbranched or possess branches of only one unit. Xylans may contain a number of other sugars which are generally located at the end of the chain or form the branches. L-Arabinose and D-glucuronic acid are the most frequently found additional components of xylans. The number of L-arabinose units present may justify the designation arabo-xylan.

Data from feeding experiments indicate that the xylose units of xylan are formed from hexose by the loss of carbon 6. The data are consistent with the pathway:

$$\text{Hexose} \longrightarrow \text{UDPG} \longrightarrow \text{UDP-glucuronic acid}$$
$$\text{Xylan} \longleftarrow \text{-----UDP-xylose} \qquad \searrow CO_2$$

Plants contain the enzymes necessary for the formation of UDP-xylose (p. 129). A preparation from asparagus shoots catalyses the transfer of D-xylose from UDP-xylose to β-1,4 linked xylo-oligosaccharides containing 2–5 units. The type of link formed by this transfer is not known. It appears that only one xylose unit can be transferred to any particular acceptor, thus the role of this enzyme is not clear. Xylanases have been reported from seeds and fungi. The plant enzymes have been little studied. The fungal preparations are thought to contain an enzyme which hydrolyses xylan randomly to a series of oligo-xylans and another enzyme which hydrolyses xylobiose.

Lesser known Polysaccharides

The available data are briefly summarized in Table 3.5.

Polyuronides

Plants contain a number of polysaccharides of which a uronic acid is the main component. The most important of these polyuronides are the pectic substances which may be defined as polymers consisting primarily of α-1,4 linked galacturonic acid units. The cell walls of brown algae contain a polymannuronide, alginic acid, which is formed of β-1,4 linked D-mannuronic acid residues.

PECTIC SUBSTANCES

(a) STRUCTURE

Three main classes of pectic substances are recognized: pectic acids, pectinic acids and protopectin. Pectic acid is the simplest pectic substance and is the basis of the others. Pure pectic acid appears to be an unbranched chain of α-1,4 linked D-galacturonic acid units which are present in the

TABLE 3.5

Lesser known plant polysaccharides

Type	Distribution	Structure	Notes
Galactans	Found in most primary cell walls.	There is evidence that galactans from *Lupinus albus* and *Strychnos nux-vomica* consist of chains of 120 β-1,4 linked D-galactopyranose units.	Galactans are invariably isolated with the pectic substances with which they are sometimes classified. Little data on their metabolism is available. It is likely that the galactosyl donor is UDP-galactose.
Mannans	(i) Ivory nut mannans from the thickened cell walls of seeds of some Palmae.	Probably composed of two fractions, both of which yield mainly D-mannopyranose on hydrolysis. There is evidence that the main linkage is β-1,4.	Function as insoluble food reserves.
	(ii) 'Salep' mannans—soluble mannans from tubers of some Orchidaceae.	Probably formed primarily of β-1,4 linked D-mannopyranose units.	Food reserves. These mannans are thought to owe their solubility to the presence of acetyl groups in the molecule.
	(iii) Structural components of some cell walls.	Not known.	Insoluble compounds found mainly in the gymnosperms where 10 per cent of the wood may be mannan.
			Mannase activity has been demonstrated in algae, malt extract and a number of fungi and is presumed to be present in plants which have mannan food reserves. GDP-mannose, present in plants, may be the mannosyl donor in mannan synthesis.
Arabans	Widely distributed as a component of cell walls. Isolated and often classified with pectic substances.	Those studied are relatively small polymers of L-arabofuranose. There is evidence that the units form an α-1,5 linked chain in which every other unit is linked α-1,3 to a branch of one residue.	Feeding experiments indicate that the units of arabans are formed from hexose by the loss of carbon 6. Since plant extracts catalyse the interconversion of UDP-D-xylose and UDP-L-arabinose, the units of arabans may be formed from hexose via UDP-xylose. However, it is unlikely that UDP-arabinose is the direct arabinosyl

Arabogalactans	Woods of certain coniferous trees, larch in particular.	Highly branched molecules in which galactose units predominate and the arabinose units tend to be found at the end of the branches. D-galactopyranose units linked either 1,6 or 1,3; arabinose as L-arabofuranose.	Also known as ε-galactan or larch galactan.
Galactomannans	Occur mainly in seeds of Leguminosae.	Large molecules in which proportion of galactose to mannose varies with the source. Most of those studied appear to consist of a chain of D-mannopyranose units chiefly linked β-1,4 with branches of a single galactopyranosyl unit attached through an α link.	Galactomannans appear to act as food reserves. Most of those studied have properties of gums. Guaran from *Cyamopsis tetragonolobus* and caroban from *Ceratonia siliqua* are of commercial importance.
Glucomannans	Reported from bulbs of some members of the Liliaceae and tubers of Araceae.	Proportion of glucose to mannose varies with source. There is evidence that β-1,4 links predominate in those examples studied. Glucomannan from *Amorphophallus oncophyllus* is held to be a straight chain of glucopyranose and mannopyranose units linked mainly β-1,4 with twice as many glucose units as mannose units.	Glucomannans probably act as food reserves. Many are gums. Glucomannans from some species of the Araceae are used as food, e.g. *Iles mannan* and *konjak mannan*.

C-1 chair form (p. 92) of the pyranose ring.

Any compound of this structure which is large enough to possess colloidal properties is classed as a pectic acid. Most pectic acids appear to contain about 100 units with a minimum of approximately 5 units. The molecule is an extended chain in which there is little free rotation about the glycosidic bonds. There is some evidence of a secondary structure of pectic acid molecules but the exact shape is not known.

Pectinic acids are pectic acids in which some of the free carboxyl groups are esterified with methanol. Pectinic acids which form gels with sugar and acid are called pectins. Pectinic acids are estimated to contain between 100 and 200 units, which are probably arranged as they are in pectic acids. The degree of methylation of pectinic acids is difficult to measure since the ester bonds are easily broken during extraction. The available evidence indicates that pectinic acids from different plants show different degrees of methylation and that no pectinic acid is completely methylated. Methylation affects the stability and solubility of the polymer. While pectic acid is relatively stable, pectinic acids readily depolymerize under alkaline, neutral and even slightly acid conditions. Both pectic and pectinic acids form colloidal solutions. Solubility increases with the degree of methylation and decreases with increasing size of the molecules. The presence of free carboxyl groups gives the colloidal particles a high negative charge and makes them susceptible to precipitation by metallic ions. This susceptibility is greatest where the degree of methylation is least.

Protopectin is a general term for all insoluble pectic substances. Protopectin is characterized by the ease with which it breaks down, and consequently its structure and composition are unknown. There are two main hypotheses as to the nature of protopectin. Protopectin preparations invariably contain cellulose and it has been suggested that protopectin consists of pectinic acids linked to cellulose by covalent bonds. It has also been suggested that protopectin consists of a number of chains of pectinic acid linked to each other. A variety of possible linkages has been proposed.

Linkage of adjacent chains through calcium has been suggested since there is evidence that removal of calcium leads to solubilization of protopectin.

Pectic substances are universally distributed as components of the cell wall matrix. The amounts present are usually small (less than 5 per cent). Fruits are a rich source of pectic substances. Available evidence indicates that most of the pectic substances present in plants are in an insoluble form. Extracts of pectic substances are extremely heterogeneous and ill-defined, and their relation to the compounds which exist *in vivo* is uncertain. It is said that no two pectic preparations are alike.

One of the most notable properties of pectic compounds is their ability to form gels at low concentrations. This property has led to their commercial use as jellying agents.

(b) METABOLISM

The lack of defined substrates has hampered the study of the metabolism of the pectic substances. Earlier suggestions that the pectic compounds were formed by direct conversion of galactans to galacturonides are incorrect. The galactans are β-linked and the pectic substances are α-linked. Glucose and galactose are both good precursors of pectic compounds and the results of feeding experiments are consistent with the following pathway:

$$\text{glucose} \rightleftharpoons \text{UDPG} \rightleftharpoons \text{UDP-glucuronic acid}$$
$$\text{galactose} \rightleftharpoons \text{UDP-galactose}$$
$$\text{pectinic} \leftarrow\text{---}\text{pectic} \leftarrow\text{----}\text{UDP-galacturonic acid}$$
$$\text{acid} \qquad \text{acid}$$

The formation of UDP-galacturonic acid is discussed on p. 129. The synthesis of pectic compounds from UDP-galacturonic acid has not yet been demonstrated. However, such a route is considered likely, particularly in view of the demonstration of a UDP-glucuronyl transferase in mammalian liver microsomes. The methyl groups of pectic substances are derived from the methyl group of methionine, probably via S-adenosylmethionine.

A number of enzymes which degrade pectic substances are known. Pectin esterases (pectin methylesterase, pectase, pectin methoxylase) catalyse hydrolysis of the methyl ester bonds of pectic substances. They are widely distributed in higher plants where they appear to be associated with the cell wall. The partially purified enzyme from oranges is specific for methyl esters of polygalacturonic acid and there is evidence that it preferentially attacks the ester linkage next to a free carboxyl group.

Compounds with less than ten galacturonic acid residues do not serve as substrates.

The α-1,4 glycosidic bonds of pectic substances are hydrolysed by poly-galacturonases (pectinase, pectolase, pectin depolymerase). The activity of polygalacturonases reported from plants is lower than that for pectin esterases. The data is difficult to interpret since polygalacturonase activity is frequently measured in fruits where there is a likelihood of microbial contamination.

Tomatoes have been reported to contain an endopolygalacturonase which attacks pectic acid chains at random and catalyses their complete hydrolysis. Smaller substrates were attacked much more slowly than the longer chains. An exopolygalacturonase, which catalyses a stepwise hydrolysis of pectic acid, has been reported in carrots. A polymethylgalacturonase occurs in micro-organisms but does not appear to have been demonstrated in higher plants. Polymethylgalacturonases attack pectinic acids and require a methyl ester group; they do not catalyse the complete hydrolysis of pectinic acid.

The enzymic degradation of protopectin has been reported in plants and ascribed to a protopectinase. This activity may be due to the action of polygalacturonase and pectin esterases.

(c) PLANT CELL WALLS

Much of the polysaccharide present in plants is found in the cell walls. The walls consist of a complex interwoven network of cellulose micro-fibrils set in an amorphous matrix. The main constituents of the matrix are pectic substances, lignin and hemicelluloses. The hemicelluloses are those cell wall polysaccharides which are not classified as pectic substances or cellulose. The hemicelluloses are such a heterogeneous and arbitrarily defined group that the usefulness of the term has been seriously questioned. The compounds most commonly found in hemicellulose preparations are xylans, mannans, glucomannans, galactans and arabans. L-Rhamnose and D-galacturonic acid are also frequently present. In most preparations the xylans predominate, though hemicellulose from some woods and seeds is particularly rich in mannans. Hemicellulose preparations from different tissues show marked differences in the number and type of compounds present, and in the relative proportions and detailed structure of these compounds.

The relative proportions of the main components of the cell wall differ widely according to the type and stage of differentiation of the cell. Primary cell walls contain relatively little cellulose and are characterized by large interfibrillar spaces filled by a matrix which is largely formed of hemicelluloses. In secondary cell walls the proportion of cellulose is very much higher and the interfibrillar spaces are mere micro-capillaries.

The way in which the components of the cell wall are held together is not known. The binding of lignin has been discussed on p. 392. It is generally assumed that hemicelluloses are bound to each other and to cellulose. Whether the binding is due to physical entanglement and secondary forces (e.g. hydrogen bonding and van der Waal's forces) or to chemical bonds is not known. The properties of the cell wall substances would permit both types of binding and both may be involved.

Little is known of the synthesis of cell walls. In addition to the metabolic pathways involved, there is the further problem of the relationship between the cytoplasm and the organization of cell wall components during synthesis. Many well-washed preparations of cell walls contain appreciable quantities of nitrogen which cannot be removed by rigorous extraction. There is evidence that a number of enzymes (e.g. invertase, ascorbic acid oxidase) are closely associated with plant cell walls, and a protein strikingly rich in hydroxyproline appears to be characteristic of cell wall preparations. The significance of these associations is not clear.

Gums

Gums may be broadly defined as substances which, when dispersed in water, swell to form gels, tacky dispersions or slimy solutions. Compounds which produce slimy solutions are sometimes called mucilages. Since a given preparation can exhibit slimy or tacky properties according to the degree of hydration or pH, it is thought inadvisable to distinguish between gums and mucilages.

The relationship between molecular structure and the properties of gums is not fully known. Gums tend to be large open flexible molecules where the secondary binding forces, such as hydrogen bonds and dipole forces, are satisfied by water molecules. Most plant gums are polysaccharides, the most important exceptions being the terpenoid resins discussed on p. 310. Many of the polysaccharide gums are highly branched heteroglycans which possess some of the most complex structures known. Complexity, though characteristic of many gums, does not appear to be an essential feature. The 'barley gums', for example, are unbranched β-1,4, β-1,3 glucans. The detailed structures of gums have not been elucidated. Available data indicate that there is considerable variation between different types of gums.

Three main classes of polysaccharide gums may be recognized:

(i) Acidic polysaccharides where the acidity is due to glucuronic or galacturonic acid. These gums are generally formed as a result of injury to the plant and appear as glassy hardened exudates, for example, gum arabic from *Acacia* species. Gum arabic may be used as an example of the structural complexity of gums. There is evidence for the following arrangement about a main chain of β-1,3 linked D-galactose units.

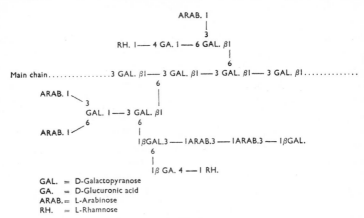

(ii) Acidic polysaccharides in which the acidity is due to sulphate groups. This type of gum has not been found in higher plants but occurs in large amounts in algae, e.g. agar from *Gelidium* and carrageenin from *Chondrus crispus* (Irish moss).

(iii) Neutral polysaccharides. These gums are generally either glucomannans or galactomannans. They are most frequently found in seeds (see p. 149).

Further details of the chemistry and distribution of gums are given by Hirst & Jones (1958) and Smith & Montgomery (1959).

There appears to be little data available on the metabolism of plant gums. It is probable that the synthesis of these and other complex heteroglycans involves the sugar nucleotide of the individual monomers. The recent demonstration of GDP-L-galactose in red algae almost completes the correspondence between the list of known monomers and that of their sugar nucleotides.

READING LIST

Wood H.G. (1955) Significance of Alternate Pathways in the Metabolism of Glucose. *Physiol. Revs.* **35**, 841

AXELROD B. & BEEVERS H. (1956) Mechanisms of Carbohydrate Breakdown in Plants. *Ann. Rev. Plant Physiol.* **7**, 267

PIGMAN W. (1957) *The Carbohydrates.* Acad. Press, New York

JAMES W.O. (1957) Reaction Paths in the Respiration of the Higher Plants. *Adv. Enz.* **18**, 281

HASSID W.Z., NEUFELD E.F. & FEINGOLD D.S. (1959) Sugar Nucleotides in the Interconversion of Carbohydrates in Higher Plants. *Proc. Natl. Acad. Sci. U.S.* **45**, 905

STROMINGER J.L. (1960) Mononucleotide Acid Anhydrides and Related Compounds as Intermediates in Metabolic Reactions. *Physiol. Revs.* **40**, 55

LELOIR L.F., CARDINI C.E. & CABIB E. (1960) Utilization of Free Energy for the Biosynthesis of Saccharides. In *Comparative Biochemistry*, Vol. 2, Chapter 2. Ed. Florkin M. & Mason H.S. Acad. Press, New York

HASSID W.Z. (1960) Biosynthesis of Complex Saccharides. In *Metabolic Pathways*, Vol. 1, Chapter 6. Ed. Greenberg D.M. Acad. Press, New York

BEEVERS H. (1961) *Respiratory Metabolism in Plants.* Row, Peterson & Co.

WOOD W.A. (1961) Fermentation of Carbohydrates and Related Compounds. In *The Bacteria*, Vol. 2, Chapter 2, Ed. Gunsalus I.C. & Stanier R.Y. Acad. Press, New York

SETTERFIELD G. & BAYLEY S.T. (1961) Structure and Physiology of Cell Walls. *Ann. Rev. Plant Physiol.* **12**, 35

LITERATURE CITED

HIRST E.L. & JONES J.K.N. (1958) *Encyclopedia of Plant Physiology*, **6**, 500

HOLZER H. (1959) *Ann. Rev. Biochem.* **28**, 171

KATZ J. & WOOD H.G. (1960) *J. Biol. Chem.* **235**, 2165

MAPSON L.W. (1960) *Proc. 4th Int. Cong. Biochem.* **11**, 1

SMITH F. & MONTGOMERY R. (1959) *The Chemistry of Plant Gums and Mucilages.* Reinhold Co.

CHAPTER 4

ORGANIC ACID METABOLISM

The presence of large amounts of organic acids in plants has long excited interest in their metabolism. In the 1920's Thunberg demonstrated the presence of a number of dehydrogenases active with certain organic acids and he proposed that these dehydrogenases form a respiratory cycle to oxidize acetate (Fig. 4.1).

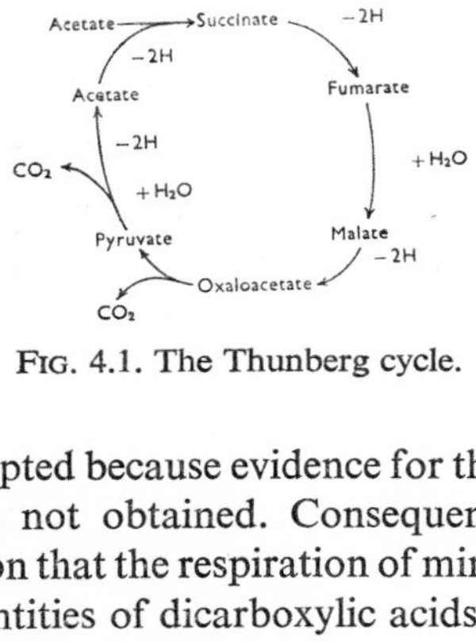

Fig. 4.1. The Thunberg cycle.

The cycle was not accepted because evidence for the formation of succinate from acetate was not obtained. Consequently, alternatives were sought. The observation that the respiration of minced muscle was stimulated by catalytic quantities of dicarboxylic acids, led Szent-Györgyi to formulate a dicarboxylic acid cycle (Fig. 4.2).

Fig. 4.2. The Szent-Györgyi dicarboxylic cycle.

The main weakness of the Szent-Györgyi cycle lay in the postulated oxidation of malate by yellow enzyme (a flavoprotein). The only well-defined system oxidizing malate to oxaloacetate is the NAD specific malic dehydrogenase. Malic dehydrogenase is implicated in the *reduction* of oxaloacetate, thus in the absence of an alternative system for oxidizing malate, the cycle leads into a 'blind alley' (Ball, 1939).

The dicarboxylic acid cycles did not explain the finding that catalytic amounts of citric acid stimulated respiration. Krebs observed the formation of citrate from oxaloacetate and pyruvate and proposed the existence of a citric acid cycle in muscle (Fig. 4.3).

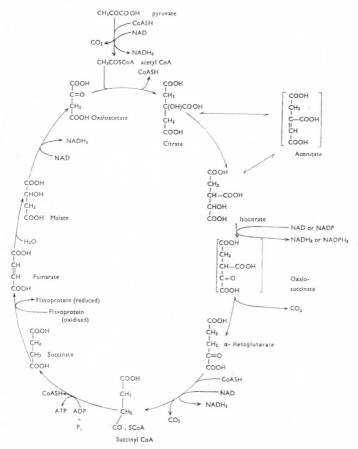

FIG. 4.3. The Krebs citric acid cycle, also known as the tricarboxylic acid cycle.

Chibnall (1939) first suggested that the Krebs cycle was functional in plants but the marshalling of evidence to support this view was delayed by the onset of war.

Evidence for the Existence of the Krebs Cycle in Plants

(a) All postulated intermediates have been demonstrated in plants.

(b) All the enzymes have been demonstrated.

(c) The respiration of slices of storage tissue can be increased by the addition of Krebs cycle intermediates.

(d) Malonic acid, which is said to more or less specifically inhibit the oxidation of succinate, inhibits the respiration of tissue slices and this inhibition is relieved by the addition of fumarate.

(e) When ^{14}C labelled acetate and pyruvate are supplied to tissues, the label appears in the cycle intermediates and the order of release of $^{14}CO_2$ from specifically labelled acetate and pyruvate is in accordance with the operation of the cycle (see p. 169).

(f) Careful analytical studies of potatoes at Cambridge (Barker & Mapson, 1955) and tobacco leaves at Connecticut (Vickery & Palmer, 1957) have produced results which are consistent with the operation of the Krebs cycle.

(g) The respiration of barley seedlings is inhibited by fluoroacetate and citric acid accumulates. Fluoroacetic acid is the active agent of the South African plant *Dichapetalum cymosum*. The investigations of Peters (1957) have shown that in animal tissues fluoroacetate is activated to form fluoracetyl CoA which condenses with oxaloacetate to form fluorocitrate. Fluorocitrate inhibits aconitase and leads to the accumulation of citric acid.

(h) In 1951 mitochondria were isolated from mung bean seedlings (Millerd, Bonner, Axelrod & Bandurski, 1951) which oxidized the acids of the Krebs cycle. Subsequent experiments have confirmed the intimate association between the Krebs cycle and mitochondria. Evidence for the operation of the cycle in preparations of mitochondria may be summarized as follows.

(i) All individual steps of the cycle have been demonstrated in mitochondria.

(ii) When radioactive acetate or pyruvate is supplied to mitochondria together with a C4 dicarboxylic acid the isotope can subsequently be detected in the intermediates of the cycle and the liberation of $^{14}CO_2$ from specifically labelled acetate and pyruvate is in accordance with the operation of the cycle.

(iii) In the absence of a Krebs cycle intermediate, washed mitochondria effect a limited oxidation of pyruvate. However on the addition of catalytic amounts of a Krebs cycle acid there is a marked stimulation of respiration.

(iv) Malonic acid inhibits the oxidation of pyruvate and leads to the accumulation of succinic acid.

The Single Step Reactions of the Krebs Cycle

CONDENSING ENZYME

The formation of citrate from oxaloacetate and pyruvate was demonstrated by Krebs but the details of the reactions were not established until the discovery of coenzyme A (CoA). Citrate can be regarded as a condensation product of acetate and oxaloacetate but activation of acetate is necessary for the aldol type condensation. The nature of acetate activation became susceptible to investigation when ATP was shown to be necessary for the acetylation of choline and sulphanilamide. Further investigation by Lipmann showed that a further cofactor was required. The structure of this cofactor, named coenzyme A (Fig. 4.4), was elucidated by work in

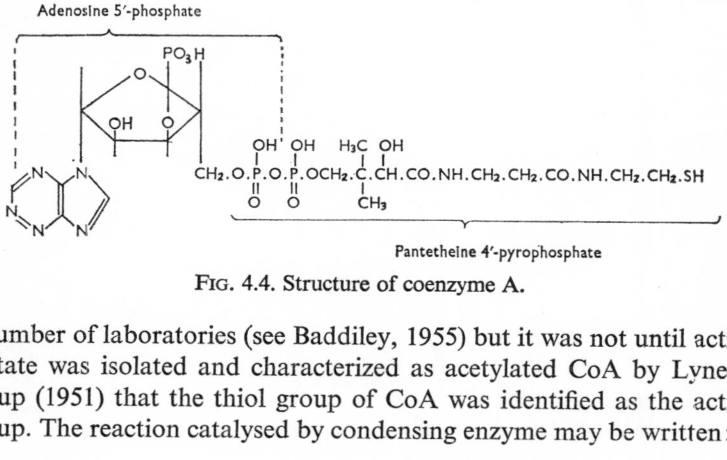

FIG. 4.4. Structure of coenzyme A.

a number of laboratories (see Baddiley, 1955) but it was not until active acetate was isolated and characterized as acetylated CoA by Lynen's group (1951) that the thiol group of CoA was identified as the active group. The reaction catalysed by condensing enzyme may be written:

$$
\begin{array}{c}
\text{COOH} \\
|\\
\text{COOH} \qquad\qquad\qquad\qquad \text{CH}_2 \\
|\qquad\qquad\qquad\qquad\qquad\quad | \\
\text{C=O} \;+\; \text{CH}_3\text{COSCoA} \;\rightarrow\; \text{C(OH)COOH} + \text{CoASH} \\
|\qquad\qquad\qquad\qquad\qquad\quad | \\
\text{CH}_2 \;+\; \qquad \text{H}_2\text{O} \qquad\qquad \text{CH}_2 \\
|\qquad\qquad\qquad\qquad\qquad\quad | \\
\text{COOH} \qquad\qquad\qquad\qquad \text{COOH} \\
\text{Oxalo-} \qquad\quad \text{Acetyl CoA} \qquad \text{Citrate} \\
\text{acetate}
\end{array}
$$

11

The keto form of oxaloacetate is the substrate for the aldol type condensation. The enzyme does not, as might have been expected, labilize the hydrogen atoms of the methyl group of acetyl CoA.

The enzyme has been crystallized from pig heart and partially purified from the leaves of *Xanthochymus guttiferae*.

ACONITASE

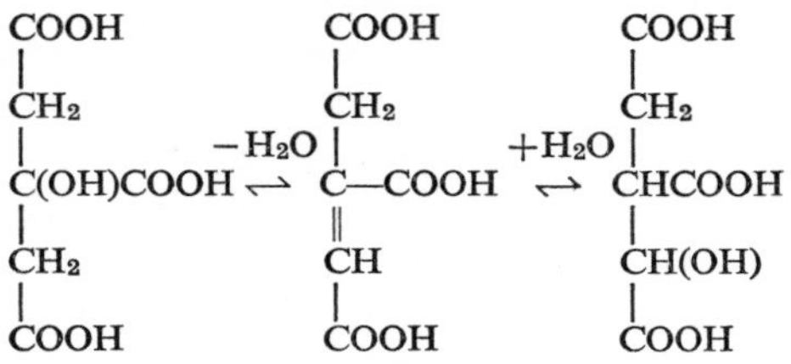

$$\begin{array}{ccc}
\text{COOH} & \text{COOH} & \text{COOH} \\
| & | & | \\
\text{CH}_2 & \text{CH}_2 & \text{CH}_2 \\
| \quad -\text{H}_2\text{O} & | \quad +\text{H}_2\text{O} & | \\
\text{C(OH)COOH} \rightleftharpoons & \text{C---COOH} \rightleftharpoons & \text{CHCOOH} \\
| & \| & | \\
\text{CH}_2 & \text{CH} & \text{CH(OH)} \\
| & | & | \\
\text{COOH} & \text{COOH} & \text{COOH} \\
\text{Citrate} & \text{Aconitate} & \text{Isocitrate}
\end{array}$$

Available evidence suggests that a single enzyme is involved, though *Aspergillus niger* contains in addition to aconitase, an enzyme which interconverts citrate and aconitate. Three mechanisms have been proposed.

(a)

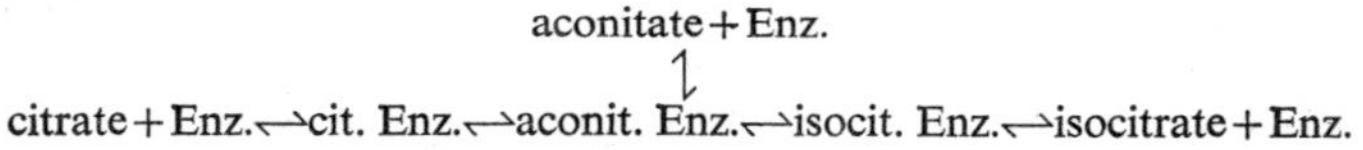

aconitate + Enz.

citrate + Enz.↽⇀cit. Enz.↽⇀aconit. Enz.↽⇀isocit. Enz.↽⇀isocitrate + Enz.

(b)

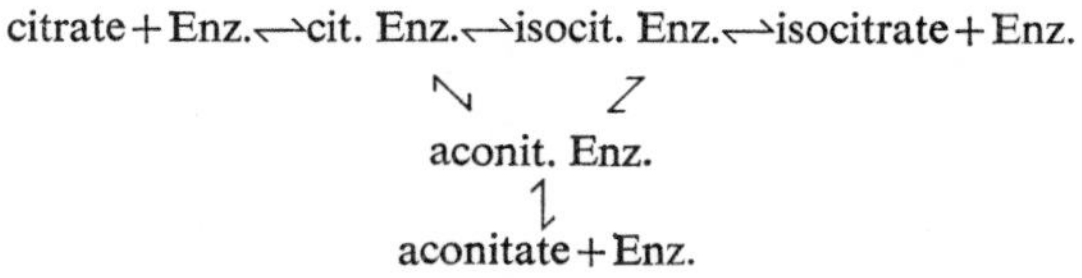

citrate + Enz.↽⇀cit. Enz.↽⇀isocit. Enz.↽⇀isocitrate + Enz.

aconit. Enz.

aconitate + Enz.

(c)

citrate + Enz.↽⇀cit. Enz.↽⇀'X'↽⇀isocit. Enz.↽⇀isocitrate + Enz.

aconit. Enz.

aconitate + Enz.

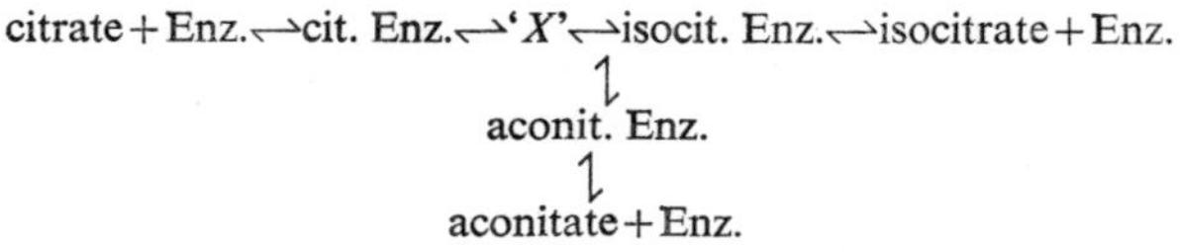

The three models have been analysed by Aronoff & Hearon (1960) who conclude that a choice cannot be made on the basis of kinetics. Experiments with deuterium, however, indicate that the formation of isocitrate from citrate does not necessitate the removal and addition of water, but rather an intramolecular rearrangement. Ferrous ions and cysteine activate the enzyme and it has been suggested by Speyer & Dickman (1956) that an enzyme-Fe^{++}-tricarboxylic acid carbonium ion-cysteine complex is the intermediate X shown in scheme c.

Mammalian aconitase attacks citrate between the central carbon atom and the methylene carbon derived from oxaloacetate. The enzyme thus differentiates between the two apparently symmetrical methylene groups. The explanation for this behaviour lies in the three point attachment theory of Ogston (1948), which can be illustrated by reference to Fig. 4.5.

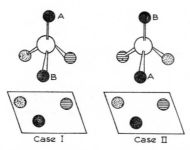

FIG. 4.5. Diagrammatic representation of optical specificity based on a three-point attachment between enzyme and substrate.

The 'identical' groups of citrate are for convenience labelled A and B. If citrate is attached to the enzyme surface by one or two points, discrimination between A and B is not possible. If citrate is attached to the enzyme by three points it can only fit in one way and as shown in Fig. 4.5., a three-point attachment can be made involving group B but not group A.

Prior to the Ogston hypothesis certain evidence indicated that citrate was not a direct intermediate in the Krebs cycle. The cycle will not oxidize pyruvate in the absence of a C4 dicarboxylic acid, but pigeon liver is able to rapidly form C4 acids from pyruvate and carbon dioxide, e.g. CO_2 + pyruvate + $NADPH_2 \rightleftharpoons$ malate + NADP. Consequently in the presence of carbon dioxide, pyruvate is rapidly oxidized and if the carbon dioxide is labelled with ^{14}C, the label appears in the acids of the Krebs cycle.

The expected pattern of labelling is shown in Fig. 4.6. Carbon dioxide enters the β-carboxyl group of malate but in the presence of fumarase, malate would be expected to equilibrate with fumarate which is a symmetrical molecule, so that label would be expected in both carboxyl groups of malate and oxaloacetate. Although only two of the three carboxyl groups entering citrate are labelled, the symmetry of citric acid equilibrates the carboxyl groups adjacent to the methylene carbons. Another way of looking at this is to consider that aconitase may attack citrate between the central carbon atom and *either* methylene carbons. The symmetrical labelling of citrate would be expected to be reflected in the carboxyl groups of α-ketoglutarate. However, isolation and degradation of α-ketoglutarate demonstrated the presence of label in the α-carboxyl group and its absence from the β-carboxyl group. The unsymmetrical labelling of α-ketoglutarate was argued to eliminate a symmetrical intermediate such as citrate and it was suggested that citrate should be regarded as a by-product of the cycle.

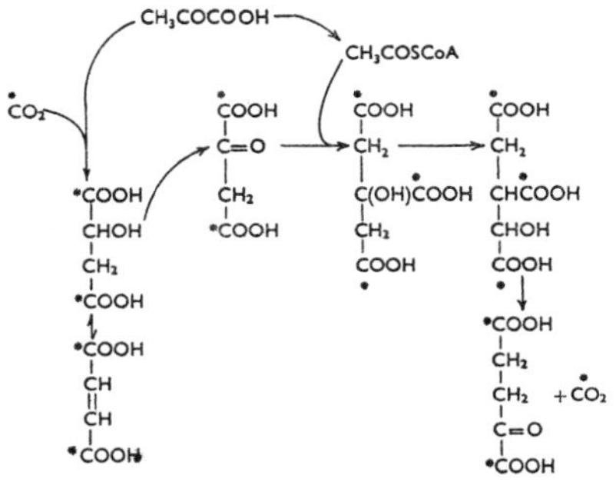

Fig. 4.6. Distribution of C^{14} (derived from $C^{14}O_2$) in the acids of the Krebs cycle, based on the assumption that citric acid behaves as a symmetrical molecule.

The Ogston hypothesis explains how citric acid may, when attached to aconitase, behave in an asymmetric fashion, and this suggests the possibility that citric acid is a cycle intermediate. Direct experimental evidence for the asymmetric behaviour of citric acid in the presence of enzymes has been obtained and citrate has been shown to be the product of crystalline condensing enzyme.

Isocitric Dehydrogenase (NADP specific)

This enzyme is present in preparations of mitochondria, but most activity is found in the supernatant after removing mitochondria. The enzyme catalyses three reactions in the presence of Mg^{++} or Mn^{++}.

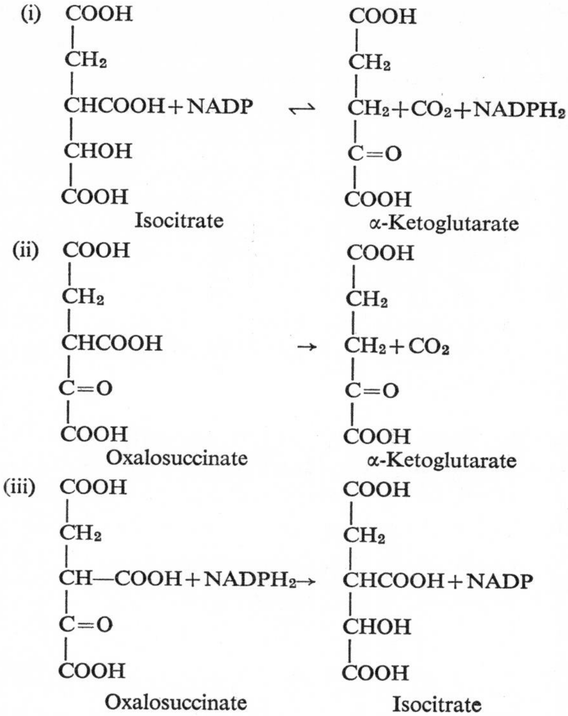

(i)

$$\begin{array}{ccc}
\text{COOH} & & \text{COOH} \\
| & & | \\
\text{CH}_2 & & \text{CH}_2 \\
| & & | \\
\text{CHCOOH} + \text{NADP} & \rightleftharpoons & \text{CH}_2 + \text{CO}_2 + \text{NADPH}_2 \\
| & & | \\
\text{CHOH} & & \text{C}=\text{O} \\
| & & | \\
\text{COOH} & & \text{COOH} \\
\text{Isocitrate} & & \alpha\text{-Ketoglutarate}
\end{array}$$

(ii)

$$\begin{array}{ccc}
\text{COOH} & & \text{COOH} \\
| & & | \\
\text{CH}_2 & & \text{CH}_2 \\
| & & | \\
\text{CHCOOH} & \rightarrow & \text{CH}_2 + \text{CO}_2 \\
| & & | \\
\text{C}=\text{O} & & \text{C}=\text{O} \\
| & & | \\
\text{COOH} & & \text{COOH} \\
\text{Oxalosuccinate} & & \alpha\text{-Ketoglutarate}
\end{array}$$

(iii)

$$\begin{array}{ccc}
\text{COOH} & & \text{COOH} \\
| & & | \\
\text{CH}_2 & & \text{CH}_2 \\
| & & | \\
\text{CH—COOH} + \text{NADPH}_2 \rightarrow & & \text{CHCOOH} + \text{NADP} \\
| & & | \\
\text{C}=\text{O} & & \text{CHOH} \\
| & & | \\
\text{COOH} & & \text{COOH} \\
\text{Oxalosuccinate} & & \text{Isocitrate}
\end{array}$$

Reactions (ii) and (iii) are irreversible suggesting that the complex between oxalosuccinate and the enzyme, which is a postulated intermediate in reaction (i), does not readily dissociate. The transfer of hydrogen between isocitrate and NADP is direct and stereospecific for the A side of the nicotinamide ring of NADP (see p. 202). The A side of the nicotinamide ring is defined as that stereoisomer of NADPD which after hydrolytic removal of phosphate yields NADD with deuterium on the A side of the ring.

ISOCITRIC DEHYDROGENASE (NAD specific)

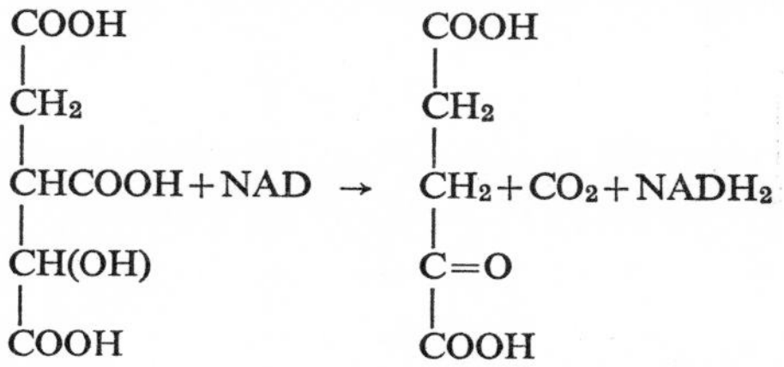

$$\begin{array}{ccc}
\text{COOH} & & \text{COOH} \\
| & & | \\
\text{CH}_2 & & \text{CH}_2 \\
| & & | \\
\text{CHCOOH} + \text{NAD} & \rightarrow & \text{CH}_2 + \text{CO}_2 + \text{NADH}_2 \\
| & & | \\
\text{CH(OH)} & & \text{C}=\text{O} \\
| & & | \\
\text{COOH} & & \text{COOH}
\end{array}$$

This enzyme appears to be localized in mitochondria. Although the reaction catalysed by the NADP-linked enzyme is readily reversible, attempts to demonstrate the reversibility of the NAD-linked enzyme have failed. An explanation for this apparent anomaly has not been advanced.

α-KETOGLUTARIC DEHYDROGENASE

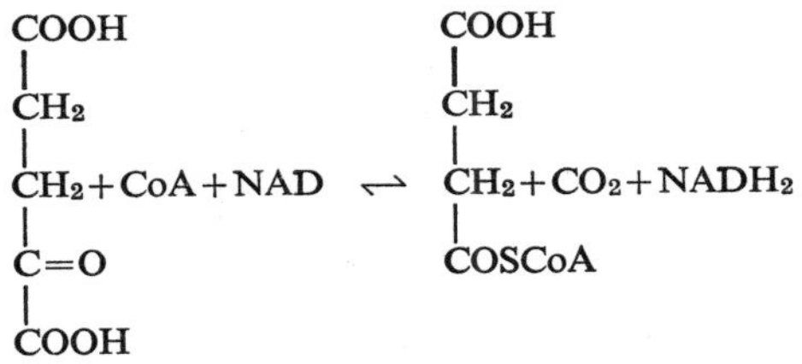

$$
\begin{array}{ll}
\text{COOH} & \text{COOH} \\
| & | \\
\text{CH}_2 & \text{CH}_2 \\
| & | \\
\text{CH}_2 + \text{CoA} + \text{NAD} \rightleftharpoons & \text{CH}_2 + \text{CO}_2 + \text{NADH}_2 \\
| & | \\
\text{C}=\text{O} & \text{COSCoA} \\
| & \\
\text{COOH} &
\end{array}
$$

This enzyme has been demonstrated in preparations of plant mito-chondria but has not been isolated in a soluble form. Soluble preparations have been obtained from bacteria and animals, suggesting that the dehydrogenase is a multi-enzyme unit catalysing the reactions shown in Fig. 4.7.

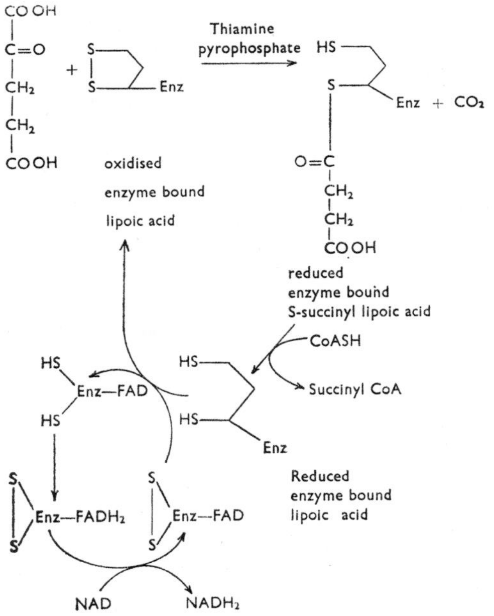

FIG. 4.7. Reactions involved in the oxidation of α-ketoglutarate.

Lipoic acid was first isolated by Reed (1951) and later shown to be 6,8-dithio-*n*-octanoic acid.

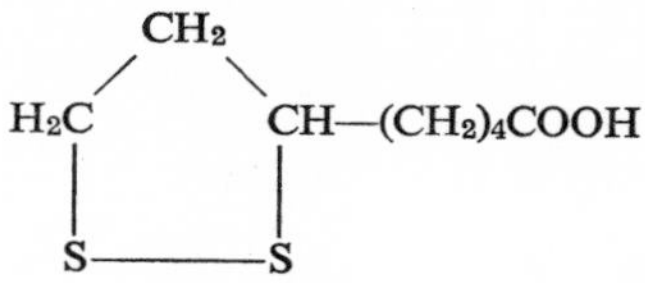

$$CH_2$$
$$H_2C \qquad CH-(CH_2)_4COOH$$
$$S-\!\!-\!\!-\!\!S$$

Reduction of the disulphide link gives dihydrolipoic acid. The reduced bound-S-succinyl lipoic acid mentioned above is:

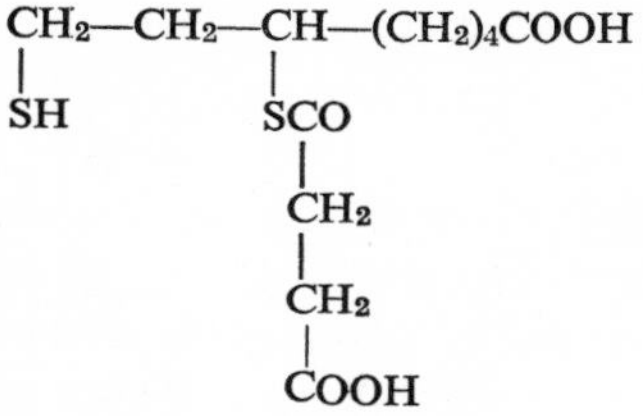

$$CH_2-CH_2-CH-(CH_2)_4COOH$$
$$SH \qquad SCO$$
$$CH_2 \qquad \text{6-S-succinyl-dihydrolipoic acid}$$
$$CH_2$$
$$COOH$$

It is important to distinguish between *bound* lipoic acid which is attached to the enzyme by a covalent linkage through its carboxyl group and *free* lipoic acid which does not activate the resolved complex but can be oxidized by it. An NAD specific dihydrolipoic dehydrogenase has been purified from spinach leaves, which is specific for (−)dihydrolipoic acid (Basu & Burma, 1960) in contrast to the corresponding enzymes from bacteria and animals which are not stereospecific. It should be noted that the naturally occurring form of lipoic acid is dextrorotatory and on reduction becomes laevorotatory. Dihydrolipoic dehydrogenase has strong diaphorase activity, that is, it catalyses the transfer of hydrogen from $NADH_2$ to various dyes such as methylene blue.

Succinyl CoA Synthetase

$$\text{succinyl CoA} + \text{ADP} + P_i \rightleftharpoons \text{succinate} + \text{ATP} + \text{CoA}$$

The enzyme has been purified from spinach leaves and the mechanism of action shown to be consistent with the following scheme:

$$\text{succinyl CoA} + P_i + \text{Enz.} \rightleftharpoons \text{succinate} + \text{Enz.} - \text{CoA} - P_i$$

$$\text{Enz.} - \text{CoA} - P_i \rightleftharpoons \text{Enz.} - P_i + \text{CoA}$$

$$\text{Enz.} - P_i + \text{ADP} \rightleftharpoons \text{Enz.} + \text{ATP}$$

The enzyme is specific for ATP and ADP in contrast to the animal enzyme which is specific for guanosine triphosphate (GTP).

Succinic Dehydrogenase

$$
\begin{array}{ccc}
\text{COOH} & & \text{COOH} \\
| & & | \\
\text{CH}_2 & +\text{dye} \ \rightleftharpoons & \text{CH} \quad +\text{reduced dye} \\
| & & \| \\
\text{CH}_2 & & \text{CH} \\
| & & | \\
\text{COOH} & & \text{COOH}
\end{array}
$$

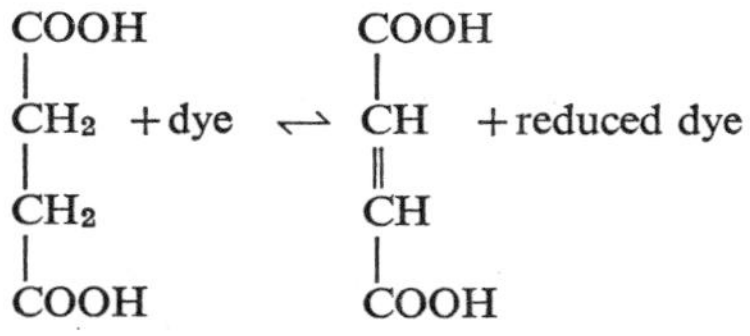

The synthetic dye phenazine methosulphate is the most efficient hydrogen acceptor for the soluble enzyme and the recent purification of the enzyme is in large measure due to the choice of this dye in the assay system. This dye has frequently been found to be an efficient hydrogen acceptor for flavoprotein dehydrogenases. The enzyme is intimately associated with mitochondrial membranes but has been solubilized and purified from beef heart mitochondria. Purified preparations contain ferrous iron and 1 mole of flavin per mole of protein which appears to be covalently linked to the protein. Recently (Hiatt, 1960) soluble preparations have been made from plant mitochondria.

The term succinic dehydrogenase is used to denote the soluble enzyme which reacts with dyes. The oxidation of succinate by oxygen is due to a complex of enzymes — the succinoxidase system (see p. 196). Succinoxidase activity of castor bean mitochondria is inhibited by carbon dioxide concentrations above 10 per cent, and the inhibition appears to be competitive with succinate (Bendall, Ranson & Walker, 1960). This observation may account for the accumulation of succinate in fruits stored in 10–20 per cent carbon dioxide. The best known inhibitor of succinic dehydrogenase is malonic acid. However, when using malonic acid as an inhibitor, it should be borne in mind that this acid is not metabolically inert. Particulate preparations of germinating peanut cotyledons and bush bean leaves metabolize malonate by the following scheme:

$$\text{malonate} \ \rightarrow \ \text{malonyl CoA} \ \rightarrow \ \text{acetyl CoA} + CO_2$$

Malonyl CoA has also been implicated in fatty acid synthesis (p. 295) and propionate oxidation (p. 284) in plants.

FUMARASE

$$
\begin{array}{ccc}
\begin{array}{l}
\text{COOH} \\
|\\
\text{CH} \\
||\\
\text{CH} \\
|\\
\text{COOH} \\
\text{Fumarate}
\end{array}
& +H_2O \ \rightleftharpoons &
\begin{array}{l}
\text{COOH} \\
|\\
\text{CHOH} \\
|\\
\text{CH}_2 \\
|\\
\text{COOH} \\
\text{Malate}
\end{array}
\end{array}
$$

The enzyme is present in mitochondria. Using tobacco leaves, Pierpoint (1960) found that 90 per cent of the total activity was located in the mitochondria and suggested that the presence of fumarase in the super-natant could be used as an index of mitochondrial damage.

In many mitochondrial preparations the rate of fumarate oxidation is considerably less than the rate of malate oxidation (see Table 4.1), indicating that the rate limiting step is the formation of malate. Oddly enough the fumarase activity is greatly in excess of that required for its expected role in the oxidation of fumarate.

MALIC DEHYDROGENASE

$$
\begin{array}{ccc}
\begin{array}{l}
\text{COOH} \\
|\\
\text{CHOH} \\
|\\
\text{CH}_2 \\
|\\
\text{COOH}
\end{array}
& +NAD \ \rightleftharpoons &
\begin{array}{l}
\text{COOH} \\
|\\
\text{CO} \\
|\\
\text{CH}_2 \\
|\\
\text{COOH}
\end{array}
\ + \ NADH_2
\end{array}
$$

The enzyme is usually regarded as specific for NAD, but the enzyme from spinach leaves reduces NADP at 1·5 per cent of the rate with NAD. Price & Thimann (1954) have shown that 75 per cent of the total malic dehydrogenase activity of pea epicotyls occurs in the supernatant after removing mitochondria. Electrophoretic and kinetic differences between malic dehydrogenase preparations obtained from mitochondria and supernatant have been recorded. However, animal mitochondrial preparations have generally been prepared by treating the mitochondria with acetone and it appears possible that the differences recorded are due to this treatment. A comparison of the enzyme from pea seedling mitochondria and supernatant did not reveal significant differences (Davies, 1961). The enzyme also oxidizes a number of other α-hydroxydicarboxylic acids including D(−)tartaric acid. The naturally occurring L(+)tartaric acid is not a substrate for malic dehydrogenase.

Pyruvic Dehydrogenase

The Krebs cycle was originally conceived as a terminal respiratory mechanism for the oxidation of pyruvate. Following the demonstration that acetyl CoA is the immediate condensing partner in the formation of citrate, the Krebs cycle has come to be considered as a system for oxidising acetyl CoA, and pyruvate as only one of a number of precursors of acetyl CoA.

$$\underset{\text{Pyruvate}}{\overset{\text{CH}_3}{\underset{\text{COOH}}{\overset{|}{\underset{|}{C=O}}}}} + \text{CoA} + \text{NAD} \;\rightleftharpoons\; \underset{\text{Acetyl CoA}}{\overset{\text{CH}_3}{\overset{|}{COSCoA}}} + CO_2 + NADH_2$$

The oxidation of pyruvate by plant mitochondria is well documented, but attempts to obtain soluble preparations have been unsuccessful.

Evidence from bacteria and animals indicates that the dehydrogenase is a multi-enzyme unit in which the individual steps correspond to the oxidation of α-ketoglutarate: the intermediates being an acetaldehyde thiamine pyrophosphate complex, S-acetyl lipoic acid and acetyl CoA.

In the absence of oxaloacetate to condense with acetyl CoA, the mitochondrial oxidation of pyruvate is very limited. The requirement for a cycle intermediate can, however, be replaced by a preparation of phosphotransacetylase (Walker & Beevers, 1956),

$$\text{acetyl S CoA} + P_i \rightleftharpoons \text{acetylphosphate} + \text{CoASH}$$

which transfers the acetyl group to phosphate and releases CoA for further production of acetyl CoA.

The Krebs Cycle as a Respiratory Mechanism

With each turn of the cycle 1 molecule of acetyl CoA enters and 2 molecules of carbon dioxide leave. The cycle can thus be regarded as a mechanism for oxidizing acetate to carbon dioxide. It should be noted that the oxidation of acetate is indirect, that is, the carbon atoms of acetate are not immediately released as carbon dioxide but only after a number of passages through the cycle. The carboxyl carbon of acetate appears as carbon dioxide on the second turn of the cycle and the methyl carbon appears as carbon dioxide on the third turn (Fig. 4.8).

The overall reaction may be written:

$$CH_3COOH + 2O_2 \rightarrow 2CO_2 + 2H_2O$$

The oxidation proceeds via four dehydrogenations, three of which are NAD-linked and succinic dehydrogenase is flavin linked. The reduced

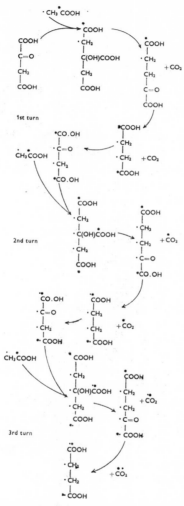

FIG. 4.8. Oxidation of specifically labelled acetate by the Krebs cycle.

coenzymes and flavin are then oxidized by the hydrogen or electron transporting system which, when coupled to a phosphorylating system (see p. 219), produces ATP. The overall reaction of the cycle as a respiratory pathway may thus be written:

$$CH_3COSCoA + 2O_2 + 12ADP + 12P_i \rightarrow$$
$$2CO_2 + CoASH + H_2O + 12ATP$$

Acetyl CoA is a product of the metabolism of carbohydrate, fatty acids, glycerol and several amino acids. The Krebs cycle is thus the terminal respiratory mechanism for all these compounds. In addition oxaloacetate and α-ketoglutarate are products of catabolism of several amino acids so that a wide variety of substrates can be oxidized by one cycle.

The Quantitative Role of the Krebs Cycle in Plant Respiration

There is abundant evidence that the Krebs cycle occurs in plants but few attempts have been made to determine its quantitative significance. A number of workers have observed that when ^{14}C-labelled organic acids are fed to leaves the rate of ^{14}C incorporation into other Krebs cycle acids is relatively slow. The conclusion that the Krebs cycle is slow should be avoided since a labelled acid may equilibrate with a large pool of unlabelled acid present in the vacuole. A different approach to the problem is to see if the various enzymes of the cycle are sufficiently active to account for observed rates of respiration. It has been claimed that the succinoxidase activity of mitochondria is sufficient to account for the total respiration of mung bean tissue but there is reason to doubt some of the approximations in the calculation. Price & Thimann (1954) have pointed out that since there are six dehydrogenases involved in the oxidation of carbohydrate, each dehydrogenase needs to operate at one-sixth of the total rate of oxygen consumption. Succinic and malic dehydrogenases were present in pea epicotyls in more than adequate amounts, whilst α-ketoglutarate oxidation was rather slower than the theoretical requirements. Whilst accepting the argument of Price and Thimann, it is also true that the rate at which mitochondria oxidize pyruvate in the presence of a Krebs cycle acid should be five-sixths of the rate of respiration of intact tissue. However, the results of many investigators show the rate of pyruvate oxidation is close to the rate observed with succinate or α-ketoglutarate (Table 4.1). The explanation appears to be that the rate of oxidation in mitochondrial preparations is limited by the turnover of ATP. This point is fully discussed in Chapter 5. Here we note that the oxidation is coupled to the phosphorylation of ADP to give ATP. In the presence of excess oxidizable substrate, the rate of

TABLE 4.1

Oxidation of Krebs cycle acids by plant mitochondria

(The rate of oxidation of succinate is set at 100 and all values are calculated from this)

Substrate	Avocado fruits		Spinach leaves	Seedlings Pinus lamber- tiana	Tomato stems	Castor bean seed- lings	Pea seed- lings
	A	B					
Succinate	100	100	100	100	100	100	100
α-Ketoglutarate	49	51	—	32	38	56	106
Citrate	38	31	—	45	31	63	—
Fumarate	30	27	47	29	11	88	—
Malate	41	54	100	29	73	77	79
Catalytic malate	—	—	—	8	—	—	44
Pyruvate	—	—	—	5	—	—	53
Catalytic malate + pyruvate	—	—	49	40	—	—	87

oxidation may be limited by the rate at which ADP is regenerated. In preparations of mitochondria the regeneration of ADP is usually achieved by adding glucose and the enzyme hexokinase. Consequently the ATP produced by oxidative phosphorylation reacts with glucose and ADP is regenerated.

$$glucose + ATP \rightarrow glucose\text{-}6\text{-}phosphate + ADP$$

The experimental results indicate that mitochondria may account for less than half the total respiration of many plant tissues.

The Role of the Krebs Cycle in Biosynthesis

A number of the intermediates of the Krebs cycle are utilized in various synthetic reactions. Thus α-ketoglutarate is the precursor of glutamate and so provides the carbon skeleton for the glutamate family of amino acids (p. 360); oxaloacetate provides the carbon skeleton for the aspartate family of amino acids (p. 379) and succinate is a precursor of δ-amino-levulinate and thus of porphyrins (p. 188). Available evidence indicates that the reactions of the Krebs cycle are the main reactions involved in the synthesis of α-ketoglutarate and succinate. However, as noted previously, the Krebs cycle oxidizes each mole of acetyl CoA to 2 moles of carbon dioxide so that the operation of the cycle cannot produce a net gain of carbon. Consequently, if intermediates are withdrawn from the cycle the amount of oxaloacetate available for condensation with acetyl CoA will decrease and eventually the cycle will stop. It follows that if the Krebs cycle is to provide intermediates for biosynthesis some mechanism for generating cycle intermediates must exist.

MALATE SYNTHETASE

Malate is formed by the reaction:

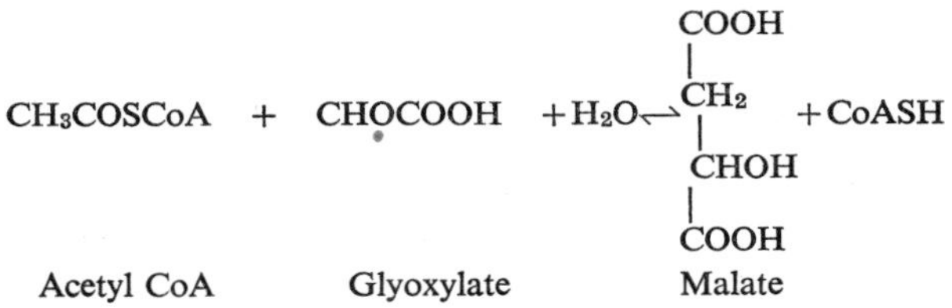

$$CH_3COSCoA \quad + \quad CH_2OCOOH \quad +H_2O \rightleftharpoons \begin{array}{c} COOH \\ | \\ CH_2 \\ | \\ CHOH \\ | \\ COOH \end{array} +CoASH$$

Acetyl CoA   Glyoxylate   Malate

The reaction is similar to the aldol condensation catalysed by condensing enzyme. The enzyme has been detected in a variety of plant tissues and there is evidence that a considerable portion of the malate present in tomato fruits is formed by malate synthetase (Doyle, Huff & Wang, 1960). In general, however, the physiological significance of this enzyme is uncertain, except in the case of germinating fatty seeds which produce glyoxalate by the reaction

$$isocitrate \rightleftharpoons glyoxylate + succinate$$

The distribution of the enzyme isocitritase in plants seems to be restricted to fatty seeds (Carpenter & Beevers, 1959) and its participation in metabolism is discussed on p. 307.

CARBON DIOXIDE FIXATION

The first indication that living tissue could fix carbon dioxide in the dark was obtained by de Saussure in 1804 who observed that *Opuntia* leaves removed carbon dioxide from air enriched with this gas. More than a hundred years later Wood and Werkmann noted that when propionic acid bacteria fermented glycerol to succinic and propionic acids, the carbon present in these products exceeded that present in the substrate. They traced the extra carbon to the calcium carbonate added to the medium to maintain an approximately neutral pH and proposed that carbon dioxide was fixed by pyruvate to form oxaloacetate:

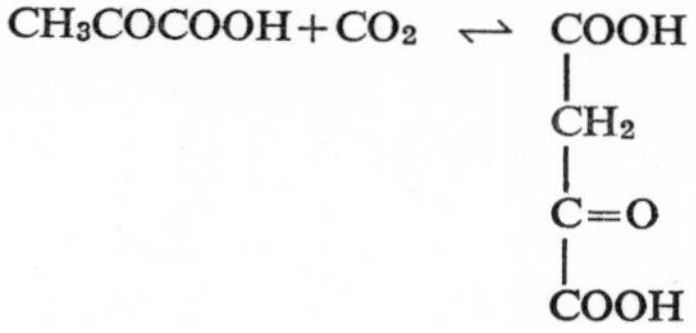

$$CH_3COCOOH + CO_2 \; \rightleftharpoons \; \begin{array}{l} COOH \\ | \\ CH_2 \\ | \\ C=O \\ | \\ COOH \end{array}$$

This reaction became known as the Wood-Werkmann reaction but numerous attempts to demonstrate the reaction in a defined system gave negative results leading to the quip — the 'would not work reaction'. The equilibrium of the Wood-Werkmann reaction strongly favours decarboxylation and subsequent investigations have demonstrated three reactions, related to the Wood-Werkmann reaction, which produce a net synthesis of organic acids by carbon dioxide fixation.

(1)

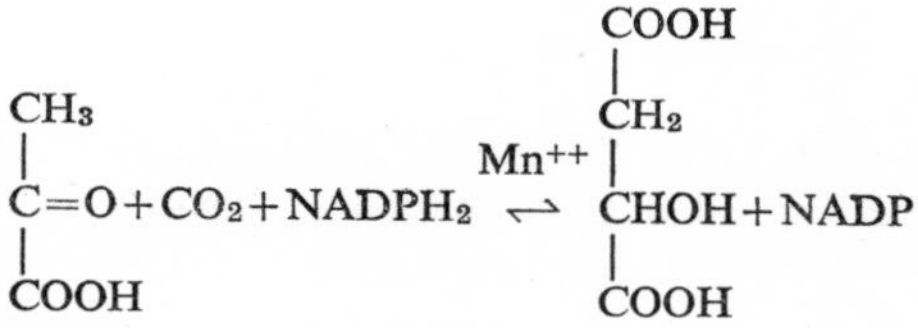

$$\begin{array}{l} CH_3 \\ | \\ C=O \\ | \\ COOH \end{array} + CO_2 + NADPH_2 \; \underset{Mn^{++}}{\rightleftharpoons} \; \begin{array}{l} COOH \\ | \\ CH_2 \\ | \\ CHOH \\ | \\ COOH \end{array} + NADP$$

$$\qquad\qquad Pyruvate \qquad\qquad\qquad\qquad Malate$$

The reaction catalysed by malic enzyme is freely reversible and the extent of carbon dioxide fixation is determined by the ratio $NADP/NADPH_2$. The enzyme is widely distributed in plants and at acid pH catalyses the decarboxylation of oxaloacetate.

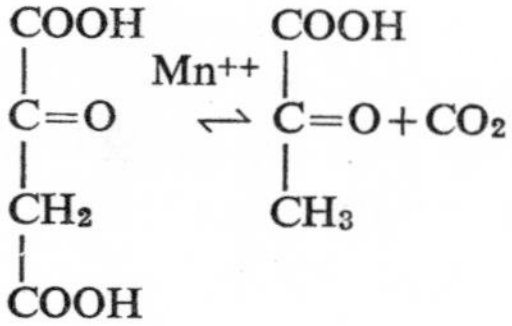

$$\begin{array}{l} COOH \\ | \\ C=O \\ | \\ CH_2 \\ | \\ COOH \end{array} \; \underset{Mn^{++}}{\rightleftharpoons} \; \begin{array}{l} COOH \\ | \\ C=O \\ | \\ CH_3 \end{array} + CO_2$$

$$\quad Oxaloacetate \qquad Pyruvate$$

Both reactions are catalysed by the same enzyme, but free oxaloacetate is not an intermediate in the reductive carboxylation of pyruvate.

(2)

$$
\begin{array}{cc}
\underset{\substack{\| \\ \text{C}-\text{O}-\text{PO}_3\text{H}_2 \\ | \\ \text{COOH}}}{\text{CH}_2} + \text{H}_2\text{O} + \text{CO}_2 \quad \underset{\text{Mg}^{++}}{\overset{}{\rightleftharpoons}} \quad \underset{\substack{| \\ \text{COOH}}}{\overset{\substack{\text{COOH} \\ | \\ \text{CH}_2 \\ |}}{\text{C}=\text{O}}} + \text{H}_3\text{PO}_4
\end{array}
$$

Phosphoenolpyruvate   Oxaloacetate

The enzyme phosphoenolpyruvic carboxylase is widely distributed in plants. The equilibrium is strongly in favour of carboxylation.

(3)

$$
\underset{\substack{\| \\ \text{C}-\text{O}-\text{PO}_3\text{H}_2 \\ | \\ \text{COOH}}}{\text{CH}_2} + \text{ADP} + \text{CO}_2 \quad \underset{\text{Mg}^{++}}{\overset{}{\rightleftharpoons}} \quad \underset{\substack{| \\ \text{COOH}}}{\overset{\substack{\text{COOH} \\ | \\ \text{CH}_2 \\ |}}{\text{C}=\text{O}}} + \text{ATP}
$$

Phosphoenolpyruvate   Oxaloacetate

Phosphoenolpyruvic carboxykinase is also widely distributed in plants. In contrast to the animal enzyme which is specific for guanosine triphosphate (GTP), the plant enzyme requires ATP.

All three reactions introduce labelled carbon dioxide into the β-position of either oxaloacetate or malate which are interconvertible in the presence of malic dehydrogenase. Consequently the relative amount of fixation into oxaloacetate or malate cannot be determined from the position of the isotope. Experiments to determine the primary product of carbon dioxide fixation have been interpreted to mean that oxaloacetate is the first formed product. For example, it has been found that when darkened succulent leaves were exposed to labelled carbon dioxide for 6 sec, 70 per cent of the radioactivity fixed was in malate and 30 per cent in aspartate. However with increasing time of exposure, the percentage fixed in aspartate decreased and this led Saltman, Kunitake, Spolter & Stitt (1956) to conclude that the primary product of CO_2 fixation was an intermediate common to aspartate and malate, namely oxaloacetate.

CARBON DIOXIDE FIXATION IN SUCCULENT PLANTS

Carbon dioxide is probably fixed by all plants, but is quantitatively most significant in certain succulent plants. Such plants show diurnal fluctuations of acidity and carbohydrate concentration (Fig. 4.9). The increase in acidity is almost entirely due to the accumulation of malic acid, and the reactions discussed in the previous section might be considered as responsible for the acidification. However, recent experiments have shown that the incorporation of radioactive carbon dioxide into malate yields a pattern of labelling which is specific to succulent plants. The carboxylation mechanisms discussed in the previous section introduce labelled carbon dioxide to the β-carboxyl group of malate. The presence

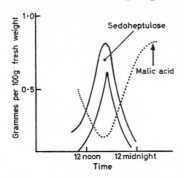

FIG. 4.9. The diurnal fluctuation in acid and sugar content of detached leaves of *Sedum praealtum* (after Bennet-Clark 1933). The heavy lines indicate maximal and minimal values for sedoheptulose.

of label in the α-carboxyl group of malate has generally been attributed to equilibration through the symmetrical acid fumaric acid. Bradbeer, Ranson & Stiller (1958) have found that in *Kalanchoe* and *Bryophyllum* the ratio of ^{14}C in the β-carboxyl group of malate to ^{14}C in the α-carboxyl group was 2:1 over fixation periods from 4 sec to 24 hr and at several temperatures. The constancy of this ratio led them to suggest that a double carboxylation was involved in dark fixation and they suggested the scheme shown below.

Ribulose-5-phosphate
    —ATP
    —ADP
Ribulose diphosphate $+C^{14}O_2$
   →phosphoglycerate-3-C^{14} → phosphoenolpyruvate-3-C^{14}
   →phosphoglycerate ——→ phosphoenolpyruvate ——$C^{14}O_2$
    $C^{14}O_2$
    oxaloacetate-4-C^{14} oxaloacetate-1,4-C^{14}
    NADH$_2$ NADH$_2$
    NAD ←   NAD ←
    malate-4-C^{14} malate-1,4-C^{14}

12

The enzyme carboxydismutase (see p. 246), which is involved in the dark fixation reactions of photosynthesis, catalyses the formation of 2 molecules of phosphoglycerate, only one of which is labelled. Subsequent reactions lead to this particular label appearing in the α-carboxyl group of malate whilst the β-carboxyl group is labelled in the second carboxylation. The asymmetry of labelling of malate is thus imposed during its synthesis.

Evidence to support the double carboxylation mechanism has come from Stiller who detected labelled phosphoglycerate after *Bryophyllum* leaves had been exposed to $^{14}CO_2$ for 15 sec. A number of labelled sugars were fed to discs of *Bryophyllum* and the observed distribution of label in malate was thought by her to be consistent with the participation of the pentose phosphate carboxylation pathway. Even if the double carboxylation mechanism occurs, the constancy of the ratio which gave rise to the hypothesis is surprising. To explain the constancy the following conditions must exist:

(1) Fumarase is absent from the site of malate synthesis.

(2) At the site of malate synthesis no phosphoglycerate is produced by reactions of the Embden-Meyerhof pathway. It should be noted that Stiller obtained evidence for the presence of enzymes of the pentose phosphate pathway and evaluation of the C6/C1 ratio was in accordance with the operation of the pentose phosphate pathway.

(3) Metabolic pools of phosphoglycerate and phosphoenolpyruvate must be small at the site of malate synthesis.

(4) Some mechanism is necessary to ensure that the rate of carboxylation of ribulose diphosphate is equal to the rate of carboxylation of phosphoenolpyruvate.

READING LIST

DAVIES, D.D. (1959) Organic Acid Metabolism in Plants. *Biol. Rev.* **34**, 407
RANSON S.L. & THOMAS M. (1960) Crassulacean Acid Metabolism. *Ann. Rev. Pl. Physiol.* **11**, 81.
KREBS H.A. & LOWENSTEIN J.M. (1960) The Tricarboxylic Acid Cycle. In *Metabolic Pathways*, Vol. 1, Ed. Greenberg D.M. Acad. Press, New York

LITERATURE CITED

ARONOFF S. & HEARON J.Z. (1960) *Arch. Biochem.* **88**, 302
BADDILEY J. (1955) *Adv. Enz.* **16**, 1
BALL E.G. (1939) *Cold Spring Harbour Symp.* **7**
BARKER J. & MAPSON L.W. (1955) *Proc. Roy. Soc.* B, **143**, 523

BASU D.K. & BURMA D.P. (1960) *J. Biol. Chem.* **235**, 509
BENDALL D.S., RANSON S.L. & WALKER D.A. (1960) *Biochem. J.* **76**, 221
BENNET-CLARK T.A. (1933) *New Phyt.* **32**, 128
BRADBEER J.W., RANSON S.L. & STILLER M. (1958) *Pl. Physiol.* **33**, 66
CARPENTER W.D. & BEEVERS H. (1959) *Pl. Physiol.* **34**, 403
CHIBNALL A.C. (1939) *Protein Metabolism in the Plant.* Yale Press, New Haven
DAVIES, D.D. (1961) *Biochem. J.* **80**, 93
DAVIES D.D. (1961) *Intermediary Metabolism in Plants.* Cambridge University Press
DOYLE W.P., HUFF R. & WANG C.H. (1960) *Pl. Physiol.* **35**, 745
HIATT A.J. (1960) *Pl. Physiol.* **35**, Supp. xi
MILLERD A., BONNER J., AXELROD B. & BANDURSKI R. S. (1951) *Proc. Nat. Acad. Sci. U.S.A.* **37**, 855
OGSTON A.G. (1948) *Nature* **162**, 963
PETERS R.A. (1957) *Adv. Enz.* **18**, 113.
PIERPOINT S. (1960) *Biochem. J.* **75**, 511
PRICE C.A. & THIMANN K.V. (1954) *Pl. Physiol.* **29**, 495
SALTMAN P., KUNITAKE G.M., SPOLTER H. & STITT C. (1956) *Pl. Physiol.* **31**, 464
SPEYER J.F. & DICKMAN S.R. (1956) *J. Biol. Chem.* **220**, 193
VICKERY H.B. & PALMER J.K. (1957) *J. Biol. Chem.* **225**, 629
WALKER D.A. & BEEVERS H. (1956) *Biochem. J.* **62**, 120

CHAPTER 5

OXIDATION AND PHOSPHORYLATION

BIOLOGICAL OXIDATION

Two main types of biological oxidation are known. The major pathway involves the passage of active hydrogen through the hydrogen carriers of the mitochondrial respiratory chain and its eventual combination with oxygen to form water. This pathway is important because the coupled process of respiratory chain phosphorylation provides most of the ATP derived from biological oxidation (p. 215). The other pathway involves a more direct combination of active hydrogen with oxygen in the presence of an oxidase. The 'direct oxidation pathway', however, does not appear to be coupled to the synthesis of ATP.

Oxidation Through the Respiratory Chain

In the oxidation of a number of substrates by tissue homogenates, Wieland and Thunberg observed that oxygen could be replaced by various hydrogen acceptors such as methylene blue. These workers therefore suggested that the essential part of biological oxidation was hydrogen activation — that is, activation of the hydrogen atoms of the substrate to a form which may react with either oxygen or methylene blue. Warburg, on the other hand, proposed that biological oxidation proceeds essentially through an activation of oxygen by a single iron-containing oxidase. These two apparently opposing theories were reconciled by Keilin in 1925, who pointed out that biological oxidation requires both hydrogen and oxygen activation, and that the cytochrome system links the two processes. Subsequently, it was shown that a number of other hydrogen carriers, in addition to the cytochromes, are involved in biological oxidation. These hydrogen carriers, together with the enzymes which catalyse their oxidation and reduction make up the mitochondrial respiratory chain.

The exact chemical nature of the 'activated hydrogen' involved in dehydrogenations and hydrogen transfer is not known. Three theoretical possibilities exist:

(a) Hydrogen atoms or free radicals: $\oplus\!\cdot$

(b) The hydrogen atom may dissociate into a proton (hydrogen ion) plus an electron: $\oplus$ + ·

(c) Two hydrogen atoms may produce a hydride ion plus a hydrogen ion: $\text{H}^{\cdot} + \text{H}^{\cdot} \rightarrow \text{H}\!:\! + \text{H}$

If highly reactive forms such as hydrogen atoms and hydride ions are involved, it is most unlikely that they would exist free in solution. They are probably firmly bound to the enzyme surface at all times.

Because the chemical nature of active hydrogen is uncertain, two terminologies are in use — 'hydrogen transport' and 'electron transport'. The authors prefer to use 'hydrogen transport' because it is more direct and possibly easier to understand. Many biochemists employ the terminology of 'electron transport', which probably arose from Michaelis' theory of oxidation by a compulsory withdrawal of electrons one at a time from the substrate. This hypothesis has not been proved. In fact, in the case of pyridine nucleotide reduction, it has been demonstrated that reduction does not proceed through electron transfer.

COMPONENTS OF THE RESPIRATORY CHAIN

(a) THE PYRIDINE NUCLEOTIDES, NAD AND NADP

The discovery of NAD is intimately connected with the study of the EMP pathway (p. 101). Warburg and Christian in 1934 isolated from mammalian erythrocytes a cofactor, similar to NAD, that stimulated the aerobic oxidation of glucose-6-phosphate. The structure of NAD (cozymase, coenzyme I, DPN) and NADP (coenzyme II, TPN), together with the main sites of enzymatic attack is shown below:

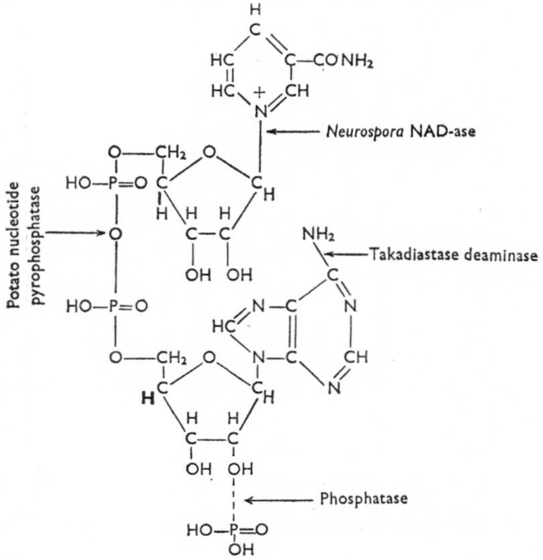

The additional phosphate group in NADP is indicated by a dotted line. Nucleotide pyrophosphatase and NAD-ase attack both NAD and NADP. Deaminase does not deaminate NADP.

All living cells which have been examined have been found to contain pyridine nucleotides. Their intracellular distribution has not been determined in plants but data from animals suggest that about 10 per cent of the total pyridine nucleotide content is present in the mitochondria. A number of enzymes bind NAD tightly. For example, triose phosphate dehydrogenase can be isolated in crystallized form and shown to contain bound NAD, and much of the mitochondrial pyridine nucleotide is tightly bound. There is some evidence that a transfer of hydrogen through pyridine nucleotide which is tightly bound to its apoenzyme may proceed without dissociation of the pyridine nucleotide from the enzyme surface (p. 203). Nevertheless, most pyridine nucleotide dehydrogenases form readily dissociable compounds with their coenzymes. The pyridine nucleotides may be considered as mobile carriers of hydrogen in contrast to the flavin nucleotides which are tightly bound to their enzymes.

The reduction of the pyridine nucleotides is readily followed by the increase in optical density at 340 mμ. Fig. 5.1 shows the absorption spectra of oxidized and reduced NAD. The absorption spectra of oxidized and reduced NADP are similar. The large absorption peak at 260 mμ in

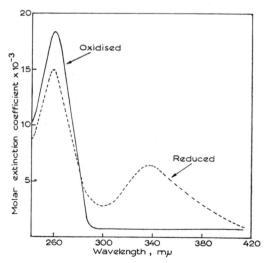

FIG. 5.1. Absorption spectra of oxidised and reduced NAD.

the oxidized forms is mainly due to the adenine moiety, though the oxidized nicotinamide ring makes a contribution. On reduction, a new resonating system is formed which absorbs light at 340 mμ and there is a decrease in light absorption at 260 mμ. The absorption spectra of the pyridine nucleotides are slightly modified when they are bound to an enzyme (p. 49).

The biosynthesis of the pyridine nucleotides from nicotinic acid has been elucidated in cell-free extracts of artichokes and germinating maize seedlings (Fig. 5.2).

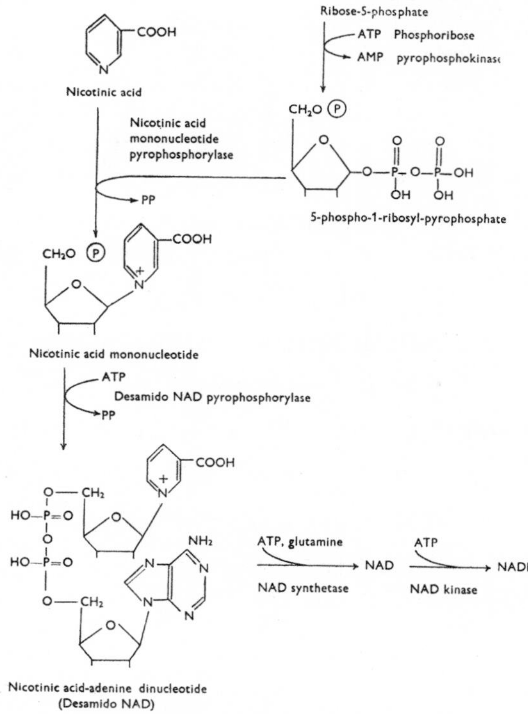

FIG. 5.2. Biosynthesis of pyridine nucleotides.

All the enzymes shown in Fig. 5.2 are specific for nicotinic acid and its derivatives and are inactive with nicotinamide and its derivatives. Phosphoribose pyrophosphokinase and nicotinic acid mononucleotide pyrophosphorylase are localized in the mitochondria, desamido NAD pyrophosphorylase in the nucleus, and NAD synthetase and NAD kinase in the supernatant fraction obtained after removal of mitochondria and nuclei. In animals nicotinic acid required for NAD synthesis arises from tryptophane. However, in plants this pathway does not appear to operate. Experiments with tobacco plants (Griffith, Hellman & Byerrum, 1960) indicate that glycerol and propionate are precursors of nicotinic acid.

(b) THE FLAVINS

Warburg and Christian first demonstrated the catalytic function of a flavoprotein. They observed that the transfer of hydrogen from glucose-6-phosphate to methylene blue or oxygen by extracts of red bood cells required the presence of a yellow-pigmented protein ('old yellow enzyme'). Work in the laboratories of Warburg, Kuhn, Karrer & Theorell characterized this pigment as flavin mononucleotide (FMN). Demonstration of the role of NADP in the reaction catalysed by glucose-6-phosphate dehydrogenase suggested the following catalytic role for FMN:

Glucose-6-phosphate dehydrogenase

glucose-6-phosphate + NADP→6-phosphogluconic acid + $NADPH_2$

'Old yellow enzyme'

$NADPH_2 + FMN \leftrightharpoons NADP + FMNH_2$

'Old yellow enzyme'

$FMNH_2 +$ methylene blue$\leftrightharpoons FMN +$ methylene blue $(H) + H^+$

'Old yellow enzyme'

$FMNH_2 + O_2 \rightarrow FMN + H_2O_2$

In 1939 Warburg isolated flavin adenine dinucleotide (FAD) from the flavoprotein D-amino acid oxidase:

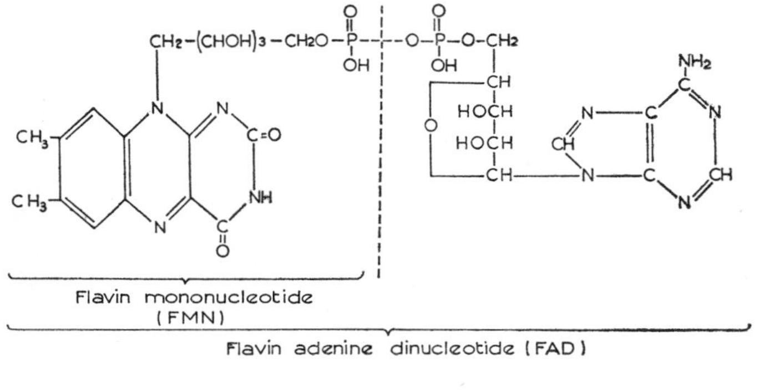

Flavin mononucleotide
(FMN)

Flavin adenine dinucleotide (FAD)

Strictly speaking, neither FMN nor FAD are nucleotides because the bond between the isoalloxazine nucleus and the sugar is not a glycosidic bond. The sugar is not ribose, but the corresponding alcohol of ribose, ribitol.

The flavins are widely distributed in the form of FMN and FAD, bound tightly to protein. Most flavoproteins can be resolved into their apoenzyme and flavin component by Warburg and Christian's method of

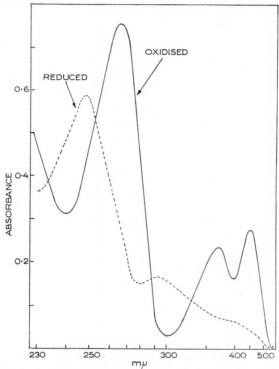

FIG. 5.3. Absorption spectra of oxidised and reduced FMN.

acidification in the presence of ammonium sulphate. The observation that FAD is more abundant than FMN may reflect the fact that the majority of flavoproteins contain FAD as a prosthetic group. Most of the FAD (over 60 per cent) of animal cells is present in the mitochondria. No data are available on the distribution of flavins in plant cells.

The absorption spectra of oxidized and reduced FMN are shown in Fig. 5.3. The spectra for both forms of FAD are similar. Upon reduction the yellow colour is bleached and the absorption peaks at 375 mμ and

450 mμ, present in the oxidized flavin, disappear. As in the case of the pyridine nucleotides, binding of flavins to protein causes slight modifications in the absorption spectra.

The biosynthesis of the flavins has been studied extensively in a number of micro-organisms such as *Eremothecium ashbyii* and *Ashbya gossypii* which produce large amounts of FMN and excrete it into the culture medium. Synthesis of the isoalloxazine nucleus by these micro-organisms is thought to proceed as follows:

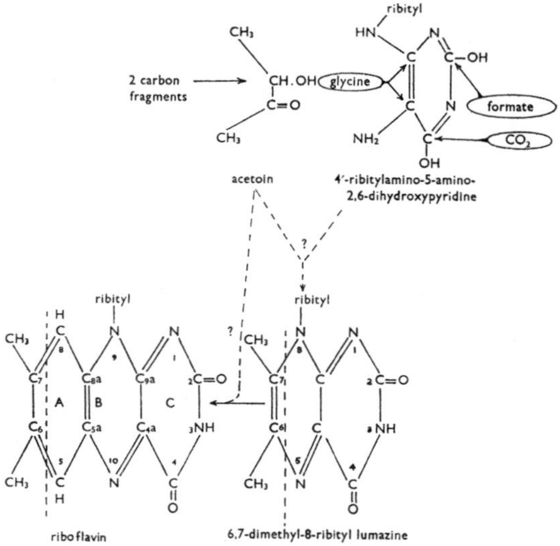

Glycine, formate and carbon dioxide supply the carbon atoms of both the carbon ring of flavin and of the purines. This observation suggests that either purines are intermediates in the biosynthesis of the carbon ring of flavin, or that an intermediate exists which is common to both flavin and purine biosynthesis. No information is available on the biosynthesis of the isoalloxazine nucleus in plants. The biosynthesis of FMN and FAD from riboflavin is shown below:

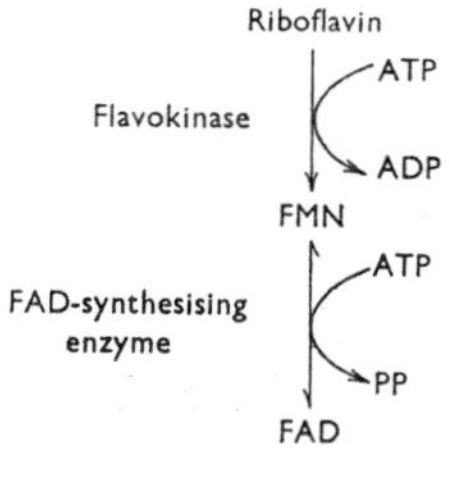

Both flavokinase and the FAD-synthesizing enzyme have been demonstrated in a number of plants and have been purified from germinating seedlings of *Phaseolus radiatus* (green gram).

Two flavoprotein enzymes of importance in the respiratory chain have been purified. These are succinic dehydrogenase and $NADH_2$-cytochrome c reductase. Succinic dehydrogenase has been obtained as an essentially homogeneous enzyme from beef heart mitochondria. It contains 1 molecule of FAD and 4 atoms of non-haem iron per molecule of enzyme. Succinic dehydrogenase catalyses the reduction by succinate of phenazine methosulphate and ferricyanide. Methylene blue, cytochrome c and oxygen are not reduced. $NADH_2$-cytochrome c reductase has been isolated from heart muscle and the 'electron transport particle' (p. 198). Like succinic dehydrogenase, it contains 1 molecule of flavin (precise chemical structure unknown) and 2-4 atoms of non-haem iron per molecule of enzyme. The non-haem iron in these two enzymes probably plays an important role in the reduction of cytochrome c. It has been shown (Beinert & Sands, 1959) that the non-haem iron in $NADH_2$-cytochrome c reductase undergoes reduction and oxidation during catalysis. Soluble preparations of succinic dehydrogenase have recently been obtained from plants and a soluble $NADH_2$-cytochrome c reductase has been partly purified from mitochondria prepared from pea seedlings and *Arum* spadix.

It is not certain what relation these soluble enzymes bear to the respiratory chain. In the sequence of hydrogen carriers described on p. 196 the reduction of cytochrome c proceeds through cytochromes b and c_1. Since neither of the soluble enzymes described above contain appreciable amounts of cytochrome, it must be assumed that these soluble enzymes somehow 'by-pass' the normal sequence in the respiratory chain. In addition to these soluble enzymes, a particulate $NADH_2$-cytochrome c reductase and a particulate succinate-cytochrome c reductase have been isolated. Both these particulate preparations appear to be fragments of the respiratory chain, containing all the hydrogen carriers required for cytochrome c reduction in the respiratory chain. Thus particulate $NADH_2$-cytochrome c reductase and succinate-cytochrome c reductase contain in addition to flavin and non-haem iron, cytochromes b and c_1.

(c) THE CYTOCHROMES

MacMunn in 1886 demonstrated the wide distribution of the cytochromes, and that they could be reversibly oxidized and reduced. MacMunn's work was severely criticized by Hoppe-Seyler who regarded

MacMunn's new pigment simply as haemoglobin or one of its derivatives. In 1925 the cytochromes were 'rediscovered' by Keilin, who showed that tissues of animals, plants and micro-organisms exhibit a characteristic multibanded spectrum. This spectrum could be attributed to the presence of three haem proteins, which Keilin named cytochrome a, b and c. In the same year Warburg provided strong evidence for the participation of cytochrome a_3 by demonstrating that the respiration of yeast was inhibited by carbon monoxide, and this inhibition was reversed by light. Since it was known that carbon monoxide combines with ferrohaems, and that the resulting complex is dissociated by light, the participation of ferrohaems in respiration was indicated. Final proof was provided by a comparison of the action spectrum for the reversal of inhibition with the absorption spectrum of the carbon monoxide-ferrohaem complex. It was found that the action spectra agreed closely with the absorption spectrum of a carbon monoxide-cytochrome a_3 complex.

All the cytochromes consist of an iron porphyrin bound to a protein. Cytochromes differ in their substituents on the porphyrin ring, in the protein moiety, and in the binding between the protein and the iron porphyrin. Cytochromes are associated with the particulate fraction (mitochondria, microsomes and chloroplasts) of the cell. Most information is available on the properties of cytochrome c, which is isolated relatively easily from animals and plants. Other cytochromes are more firmly bound to the particulate fraction and hence are difficult to obtain in pure form. In addition to the cytochromes mentioned here, there are a number of cytochromes which have so far been demonstrated only in bacteria.

The structure of the iron porphyrin of cytochrome c is shown in Fig. 5.4.

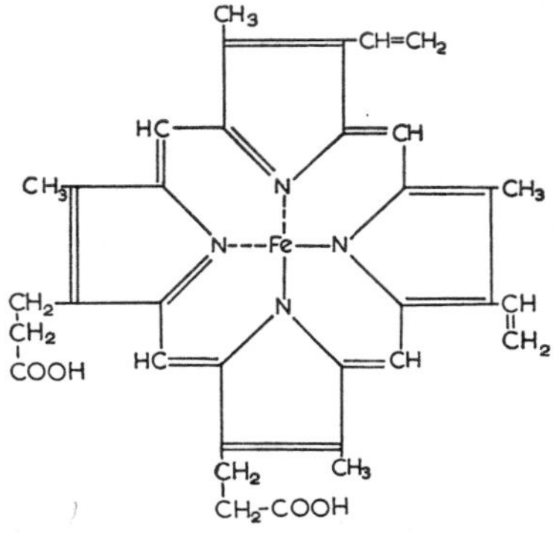

FIG. 5.4. Structure of ferrous protoporphyrin IX (haem).

The protein moiety of cytochrome *c* isolated from a number of different tissues has been found to be very similar in chemical and physical properties. For a number of tissues the amino acid sequence has also been determined on the part of the protein attached to the iron porphyrin. Although a number of minor differences were reported in each tissue, the basic sequence was the same. A probable structure of cytochrome *c* is shown below (Ehrenberg & Theorell, 1955):

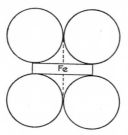

The haem group is tightly packed between four helical peptide chains, seen in end view. Iron is in the centre of the porphyrin disc, which is shown edgewise. The peptide chains are attached to the iron porphyrin

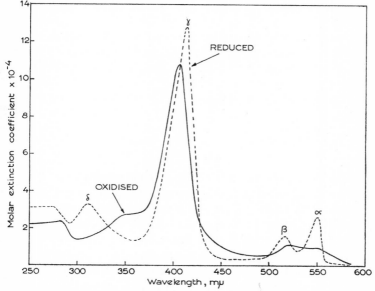

FIG. 5.5. Absorption spectra of oxidised and reduced cytochrome *c*.

by means of:

(i) Two thioether bonds. These bonds are between two cysteine molecules in the peptide chain and two vinyl substituents at the edge of the porphyrin disc.

(ii) Two co-ordinate bonds between iron and the imidazole nitrogen atom of two histidines in the peptide chain. These bonds project above and below, and at right angles to, the porphyrin ring.

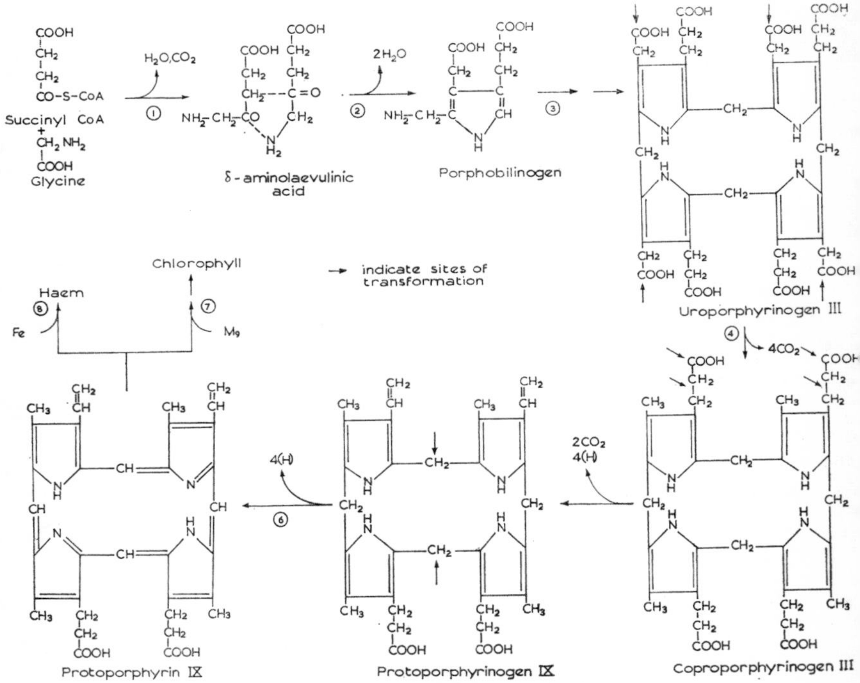

FIG. 5.6. Biosynthesis of porphyrins.

Characteristic absorption bands appear upon reduction of the cytochromes and the position of these bands is used for classification of the cytochromes. The absorption band at the longest wavelength is denoted the α-band and that at the lower wavelength the γ- or Soret band. In cytochromes b, c and f there is an intermediate β-band. The absorption spectrum of oxidized and reduced cytochrome c is shown in Fig. 5.5. A scheme for the biosynthesis of porphyrins is shown in Fig. 5.6.

This scheme was first outlined by Shemin's group (Shemin, 1956) in a study of the biosynthesis of the haem moiety of haemoglobin. Available evidence suggests that this pathway operates also for the biosynthesis of the porphyrin ring of the cytochromes, peroxidases, catalase and chlorophyll. Enzyme systems catalysing reactions 1, 2 and 3 have been demonstrated in extracts of green leaves and the conversion of uroporphyrinogen III to protoporphyrin is catalysed by frozen and thawed *Chlorella* cells. According to Granick (1961) the enzyme systems of chlorophyll biosynthesis (reactions 1–7) are localized in the plastids. Little information is available on the biosynthesis of haem in plants. However, in animals it appears that the enzymes catalysing reactions 1, 5 and 6 are mitochondrial. The details of the complex series of reactions shown in Fig. 5.6 have not been elucidated. The mechanism whereby 4 monopyrrole units (porphobilinogen) are arranged to produce the asymmetric arrangement of the side chains in uroporphyrinogen has been the subject of much speculation but is still poorly understood. The probable steps involved in the biosynthesis of chlorophyll from protoporphyrin IX will be discussed on p. 230.

The plant cytochromes

In higher plants the cytochromes are present in much smaller concentrations than in animals, yeast and bacteria. Nevertheless, all the cytochrome components of the respiratory chain shown in Table 5.1 with the possible exception of cytochrome c_1 have been detected in plants. Many of the components may be detected by examining a slice of plant tissue with a low dispersion spectroscope. Examination of mitochondrial preparations by the use of sensitive spectrophotometric techniques permits a more detailed study of the components (p. 195).

Only cytochrome c has been isolated in true solution, and has been crystallized from wheat germ. Cytochromes b, c, a and a_3 are all bound tightly to the respiratory chain, making extraction difficult. Cytochrome a is invariably associated with cytochrome a_3 in both animals and plants. This cytochrome a–a_3 complex is frequently referred to as the cytochrome oxidase complex. Neither cytochrome a nor cytochrome a_3 have been obtained in true solution and the two compounds have not been separated. In addition to the cytochromes listed above, four additional cytochromes appear to be unique to higher plants:

(i) Cytochrome b_7 is found in relatively large amounts in the mitochondria isolated from the spadices of *Arum* and *Symplocarpus foetidus* (skunk cabbage). Cytochrome b_7 has not been obtained in a soluble form. Since cytochrome b_7 is autoxidizable and does not react with carbon monoxide or cyanide, the operation of this cytochrome

TABLE 5.1

Some properties of the plant cytochromes

Cytochrome	Source	Absorption peaks of reduced form (mμ)			E'_0 (volts)	Reaction with		
		α	β	γ		CO	Cyanide	O_2
a	Mitochondria	604	None	450	(+0·29)	No	No	No
a_3	Mitochondria	604	None	445–450	—	Yes	Yes	Yes
b	Mitochondria	564	532	427	(−0·04)	No	No	Very slightly
b_3	Microsomes	559–560	525–528	425–428	+0·04	No	No	Yes
b_6	Chloroplasts	563	528	430	−0·06	No	No	Yes
b_7	Mitochondria of *Arum* and *Symplocarpus foetidus*	560	529	—	−0·03	No	No	Yes
c	Mitochondria	549–550	520–522	415–416	(+0·255)	No	No	No
c_1	Mitochondria	553–554	(522–524)	(416–419)	(+0·25)	No	No	No
f	Chloroplasts	555	526	422	+0·365	No	No	No

Figures included in brackets have been determined with animal cytochromes.

may explain the cyanide and carbon monoxide-resistant respiration of some plant tissues (p. 210).

(ii) Cytochrome b_3 is widely distributed in plants. It may be obtained in solution by autolysis of plant tissue but has not been purified. The function of this cytochrome, which is located in the microsomes, is not clear.

(iii) Cytochromes b_6 and f are localized in chloroplasts and may play a role in photosynthesis. Cytochrome b_6 has not been isolated or purified. Cytochrome f has been extracted from leaves of elder (*Sambucus niger*) and parsley. It has been highly purified and shown to possess properties similar to those of cytochrome c.

(d) OTHER COMPONENTS IMPLICATED IN THE RESPIRATORY CHAIN

In addition to the components listed above, coenzyme Q, α-tocopherol and vitamin K have also been implicated in hydrogen transport. However, the evidence is not at present sufficient to include these components in the respiratory chain.

Coenzyme Q (Ubiquinone)

Ubiquinone was first isolated from animal fat in 1955 by R. A. Morton and his colleagues, and is identical with coenzyme Q which was subsequently isolated by D. E. Green and co-workers.

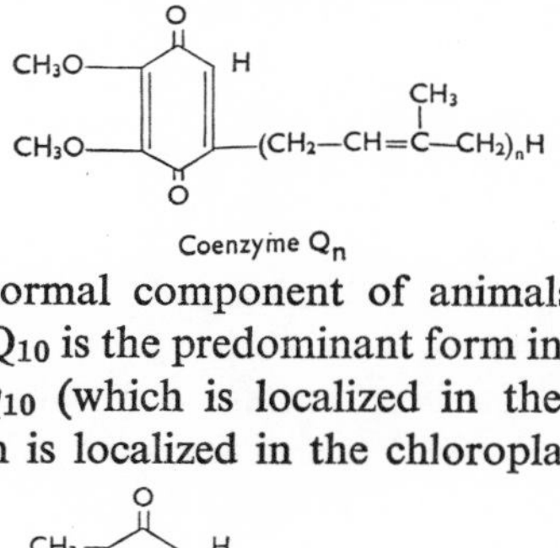

Coenzyme Q_n

Coenzyme Q is a normal component of animals, plants, yeast and bacteria. Coenzyme Q_{10} is the predominant form in animals. Plants also contain coenzyme Q_{10} (which is localized in the mitochondria) and plastoquinone (which is localized in the chloroplasts).

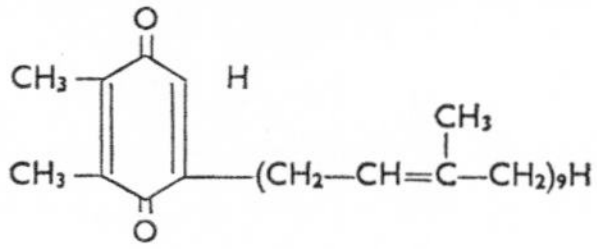

Plastoquinone

Other forms of coenzyme Q which have been isolated include coenzyme Q_7 and coenzyme Q_9 from *Torula*, coenzyme Q_8 from *Azotobacter vinelandii* and coenzyme Q_6 from *Saccharomyces cerevisiae*. The absorption spectrum of coenzyme Q_{10} is shown in Fig. 5.7.

13

The role of coenzyme Q in the respiratory chain in animals is not at present clear. Green's group (Green & Lester, 1959) claims that coenzyme Q is a component of the respiratory chain, functioning between cytochrome b and the antimycin-sensitive site (p. 200).

Pumphrey & Redfearn (1959) claim that coenzyme Q is not a component of the main respiratory chain but rather is on a branch pathway. Their evidence is based on the observation that the rate of reduction of endogenous coenzyme Q was not sufficiently high to account for its direct participation in succinate and $NADH_2$ oxidation.

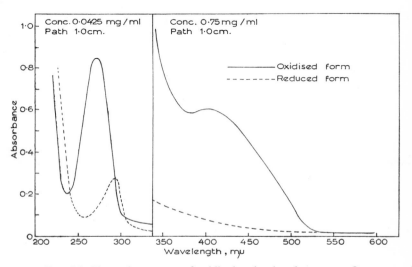

FIG. 5.7. Absorption spectra of oxidised and reduced coenzyme Q_{10}.

Tentative evidence has been presented for the participation of coenzyme Q in the respiratory chain of plants. When cauliflower mitochondria are supplied with succinate, a decrease in light absorption between 250 mμ and 300 mμ (peak at 275 mμ) is observed. This decrease in light absorption has been attributed to coenzyme Q reduction. Plastoquinone has been further implicated in hydrogen transport in photosynthesis (p. 237).

Vitamin E

Of the seven naturally occurring tocopherols, α-tocopherol has the greatest vitamin E (anti-sterility) activity.

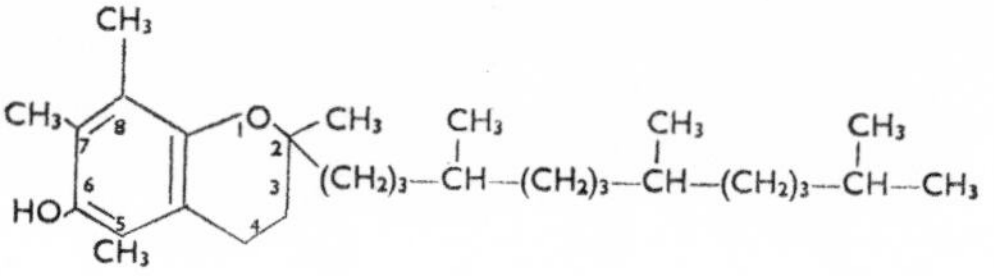

α-tocopherol

The structure of the other tocopherols differs only in the substituents on C5, 7 and 8.

The richest source of the tocopherols is oily seeds. Tocopherols also accumulate in animal fats. In non-storage tissues all the α-tocopherol appears to be concentrated in the mitochondria. The mechanism of biosynthesis of the tocopherols is unknown.

It has been suggested that α-tocopherol is a component of the respiratory chain acting between $NADH_2$ and cytochrome c, probably in the step between cytochrome b and cytochrome c. The evidence for this suggestion is based chiefly on the observation of loss in activity of preparations of $NADH_2$- cytochrome c reductase which have been aged, or extracted with isooctane (Donaldson, Nason & Garrett, 1958). The activity of the preparations treated in this way may be restored by the addition of α-tocopherol. However, the possibility that α-tocopherol restores activity by an indirect action not directly related to its role as a hydrogen carrier has not been positively eliminated.

Enzymatic reduction and oxidation of α-tocopherol has not been demonstrated. Chemical oxidation and reduction proceeds as follows:

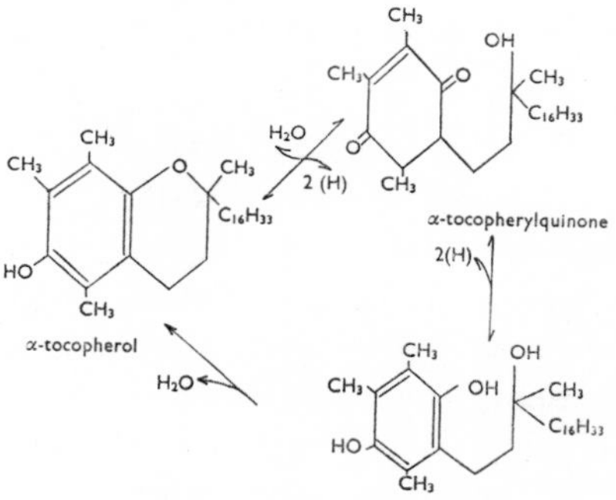

α-tocopherylquinone

α-tocopherol

α-tocopherylhydroquinone

The chemical reaction involved (reduction of a p-quinone derivative to a p-dihydroxy benzene derivative) is basically the same as in the oxidation and reduction of coenzyme Q and vitamin K.

The role of α-tocopherol in plant respiration is unknown.

Vitamin K

Vitamin K refers to a group of naphthoquinones with the general formula:

Vitamin K₁ R=Phytyl
Vitamin K₂ R=Difarnesyl

Only two K vitamins have been reported in nature. Vitamin K_2 is found in bacteria. Vitamin K_1 (phylloquinone) was first isolated from lucerne by Dam, Karrer and their associates and reported to be specifically associated with chloroplasts. Recently, however, a number of workers claim that chloroplasts contain no naphthoquinones of the vitamin K type but contain, instead, plastoquinone. The discrepancy between these reports is at present unresolved. Animal tissues contain relatively small amounts of vitamin K.

The precise role of vitamin K in the respiratory chain is in dispute. Bacterial extracts and liver mitochondria which have been irradiated with ultraviolet light lose the ability to catalyse respiratory chain phosphorylation. Phosphorylation can be restored specifically by the addition of vitamin K. The evidence available suggests that vitamin K restores phosphorylation between $NADH_2$ and cytochrome *b*. A possible function of vitamin K in respiratory chain phosphorylation is presented on p. 223. The role of vitamin K in the respiratory chain in plants is unknown.

SPECTROSCOPIC TECHNIQUES USED IN STUDYING THE
RESPIRATORY CHAIN

All the known hydrogen carriers of the respiratory chain exhibit characteristic spectral changes upon oxidation and reduction. This fact makes it possible to follow the flow of hydrogen through the respiratory chain by spectroscopic techniques. The measurement of specific compounds by spectroscopy in biological systems is complicated by the relatively large unspecific changes in background absorption. This problem has been overcome by the development of two types of spectrophotometers:

(a) The reduction of a particular component is best determined by a double beam spectrophotometer. In this method the change in optical density at a particular wavelength is referred to the change in optical density at a reference wavelength, suitably chosen to minimize interference from other components. For example, when measuring the reduction of pyridine nucleotides, light at 340 mμ, followed by light at 374 mμ (reference wavelength) is flashed through the sample. The concentration of reduced pyridine nucleotide is given by Δ optical density $_{340}$-Δ optical density $_{374}$.

(b) Changes in the state of reduction of all components of the respiratory chain are determined by using a split beam spectrophotometer. In this method two beams of light of the same wavelength are flashed through two samples. One sample, for example, may have its respiratory components in the oxidized state, due to lack of substrate. The other sample, under anaerobic conditions in the presence of substrate, has its respiratory components in the reduced state. The difference in optical density between the two samples determined at a variety of wavelengths permits the determination of a difference spectrum. Fig. 5.8 shows the reduction of flavoprotein and cytochromes b, c, a and a_3 upon reduction of potato tuber mitochondria with NADH$_2$ under anaerobic conditions (Hackett, Haas, Griffiths & Niederpruem, 1960).

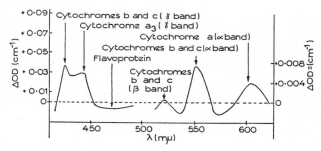

FIG. 5.8. Difference spectrum between a suspension of potato tuber mitochondria reduced with NADH2 and an aerobic suspension.

STRUCTURE OF THE RESPIRATORY CHAIN

The respiratory chain with its enzymes of hydrogen transfer and phosphorylation is located in the mitochondria. These enzymes appear to be firmly attached to the membranes and cristae of the mitochondria and appear to be structurally arranged in a unique pattern to facilitate their interaction. The high lipid content of mitochondria (over 30 per cent dry weight) and the observation that the respiratory chain may be fractionated by solvents which dissolve lipids, suggests that lipids may be important in the structural arrangement of the respiratory chain. One may envisage lipoproteins producing a non-aqueous phase in which high energy phosphate esters are formed.

A tentative scheme showing the relative molar ratio and sequence of the hydrogen carriers of the respiratory chain is shown in Fig. 5.9.

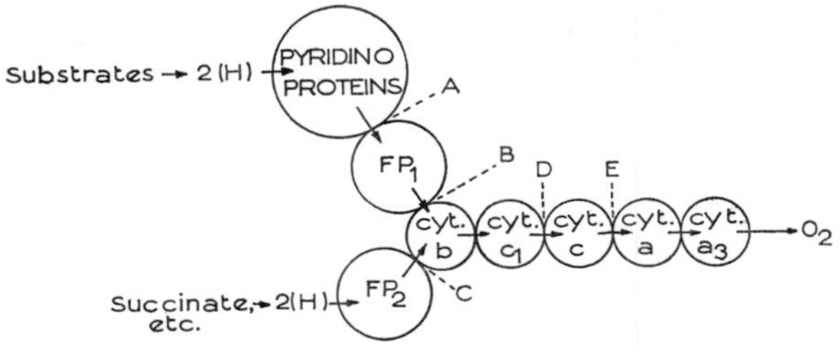

FIG. 5.9. Diagrammatic representation of the respiratory chain.

Studies with wheat roots (Lundergårdh, 1952) and plant mitochondria (Hackett et al., 1960) suggest that the cytochromes are present in approximately equimolar quantities, although there may frequently be less cytochrome a relative to cytochromes b and c. Flavoproteins are present at a concentration approximately two to three times that of each of the cytochromes. The concentration of pyridine nucleotides and coenzyme Q relative to the flavoproteins and cytochromes has not been determined for plants. In animal mitochondria the pyridine nucleotides are usually present in molar excess of the flavoproteins, and coenzyme Q has been reported in concentrations approximately equal to that of NAD.

No data is available on the relative proportion of NAD and NADP that constitutes the pyridine nucleotides of plant mitochondria. In animal mitochondria the relative proportion of NAD and NADP varies considerably and available evidence suggests that at least 50 per cent of the total pyridine nucleotide exists as NADP plus $NADPH_2$. The physiological function of NADP in the respiratory chain has yet to be explained. NADP, in contrast to NAD, does not appear to be involved directly in the transport of hydrogen from substrate to oxygen. Thus the rate of oxidation of $NADPH_2$ by mitochondria prepared from both plants and animals is very slow compared to that of $NADH_2$. There is increasing evidence to suggest that $NADPH_2$ is specifically associated with biosynthetic reactions (p. 80).

In the scheme shown in Fig. 5.9 activated hydrogen enters the respiratory chain at two points. Most substrates feed into the chain through pyridine nucleotide-dependent dehydrogenases. A few substrates such as succinate, α-glycerophosphate, and fatty acyl dehydrogenase feed into the cytochrome system via FP_2. Disagreement exists as to the exact nature of the components and sequence of the respiratory chain. For example, some investigators place the junction of the two pathways at cytochrome c_1. The sequence shown in Fig. 5.9 is based upon the following evidence:

(a) OXIDATION-REDUCTION POTENTIALS

The carriers of the respiratory chain must be so arranged that each component has an oxidation-reduction potential (E_h) more negative than that of the component which oxidizes it. Ball (1938) originally employed this approach to determine the sequence of cytochromes b, c and a. Values of E_h determined for these cytochromes as they existed in a crude heart muscle extract suggested that the cytochromes were linked on the chain as follows:

$$\text{cytochrome } b \rightarrow \text{cytochrome } c \rightarrow \text{cytochrome } a$$

Alternatively, E_h may be estimated using the following equation:

$$E_h = E_0' + \frac{RT}{nF} \ln \frac{\text{(oxidized component)}}{\text{(reduced component)}}$$

The *standard* oxidation-reduction potentials (E_0') of components associated with the respiratory chain are shown in Table 5.2.

TABLE 5.2

Standard oxidation-reduction potentials of components associated with the respiratory chain

Reaction	E_0' (volts)
$NAD \rightarrow NADH_2$	-0.32
Riboflavin $\rightarrow$ Leucoriboflavin	-0.22
Cytochrome b (Fe^{+++}) $\rightarrow$ Cytochrome b (Fe^{++})	-0.04
Cytochrome c_1 (Fe^{+++}) $\rightarrow$ Cytochrome c_1 (Fe^{++})	$+0.25$
Cytochrome c (Fe^{+++}) $\rightarrow$ Cytochrome c (Fe^{++})	$+0.26$
Cytochrome a (Fe^{+++}) $\rightarrow$ Cytochrome a (Fe^{++})	$+0.29$

Estimates of E_h calculated from the values of E_0' given in Table 5.2, and the ratios of (oxidized component)/(reduced component) in the respiratory chain determined by Chance & Williams (1955), confirm the sequence of components shown in Fig. 5.9.

(b) FRACTIONATION

The principle involved in this technique is basically the same as that used by Sanger to determine the sequence of amino acids in the insulin molecule. The respiratory chain is first fragmented by either mechanical means (sonic oscillation), or by breaking up the lipid cement of the respiratory chain with detergents, alcohols or desoxycholate. The fragments are then separated by ultracentrifugation. By determining the chemical and enzymatic properties of these fragments it is possible to reconstruct the sequence in the intact respiratory chain. This technique has been pioneered quite successfully by D. E. Green and his colleagues. As a matter of convenience, the work has been performed almost exclusively with animal mitochondria. The respiratory chain is particularly susceptible to fragmentation at certain points indicated by letters in Fig. 5.9. Fragmentation at A releases the pyridinoproteins from the respiratory chain and produces a fragment ('electron transport particle') which no longer oxidizes Krebs cycle intermediates but will (unlike the intact mitochondria) now oxidize $NADH_2$. Fragmentation at A thus removes the pyridino-proteins essential for the dehydrogenation of Krebs cycle acids, but at the same time makes sites available for the oxidation of $NADH_2$. Many of the fragmentation studies have been performed with this so-called electron transport particle. Fragmentation at points B and D produces a fragment with succinic-cytochrome c reductase activity but which is inactive with pyridine nucleotide-linked substrates. Usually there is a reasonably good agreement between the enzymatic activity and the chemical composition. For example, the succinate-cytochrome c reductase fragment contains FP_2 (succinic dehydrogenase), cytochrome b and cytochrome c_1.

Little success has been achieved in reconstituting the intact respiratory chain by recombination of the appropriate fragments. This lack of success probably reflects the high degree of structural integrity of the intact respiratory chain.

(c) SPECTROPHOTOMETRIC METHODS

Spectrophotometric methods have been used in two ways to determine the sequence of components in the respiratory chain.

(i) The first method is based on a determination of the time sequence in which the components react. One may determine the time sequence of reduction in a respiratory chain that is predominantly oxidized, or alternatively, determine the time sequence of oxidation in a chain that is predominantly reduced. In animal mitochondria, Chance & Williams

(1956) report the following order of reduction: the pyridine nucleotides are first reduced, followed by the flavoproteins, then cytochromes b, c_1, c, a and a_3. An opposite time sequence occurs during the oxidation of a predominantly reduced chain. Thus cytochrome a_3 is first oxidized, followed by cytochromes a, c, c_1, b, flavoproteins and finally the pyridine nucleotides.

Representing the respiratory chain as an 'equivalent homogeneous system' and using experimentally determined values for the velocity constants and effective concentration of the components of the respiratory chain, Chance & Williams (1956) have calculated that the time sequence in which spectroscopic changes occur will be the same as the sequence in which the chemical reactions occur.

With intact wheat roots, Lundergårdh (1959) has observed a time sequence of reactions opposite to that described by Chance and Williams. According to Lundergårdh the respiratory chain cannot be represented as a homogeneous system, but is an integrated system of multimolecular groups joined by 'factors' (Fig. 5.10).

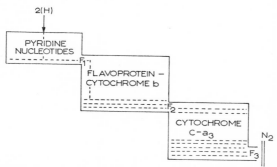

FIG. 5.10. Diagrammatic representation of the respiratory chain according to Lundergård (1959).

In Fig. 5.10 the pyridine nucleotides, flavoprotein and cytochrome b, and cytochromes c and a_3 are represented as three multimolecular groups. Each of these groups is linked by a factor F. If respiration is stopped by a shift from air to nitrogen, hydrogen entering the respiratory chain at the pyridine nucleotide level will fill up (reduce) the cytochrome c–a_3 multimolecular group before filling up the flavoprotein-cytochrome b multimolecular group. Finally the pyridine nucleotides will become reduced. Upon the addition of oxygen, the pyridine nucleotide multimolecular group will become oxidized first, then the cytochrome c–a_3 group.

(ii) The second method is based on a determination of cross-over points formed upon reduction of the respiratory chain in the presence of an inhibitor. A cross-over point may best be defined by means of an example. If the step in the chain between cytochrome b and c_1 is blocked (e.g. by antimycin) then all components on the substrate side of the inhibitor (pyridine nucleotides, flavoprotein and cytochrome b) will be predominantly reduced; all components on the oxygen side of the inhibitor (cytochrome c_1, c, a and a_3) will be predominantly oxidized. At the site of inhibition there is a cross-over from predominantly reduced components to predominantly oxidized components. The use of antimycin, for example, demonstrates that cytochrome b is on the substrate side of cytochrome c_1. A number of other inhibitors including urethane and British anti-Lewisite also block the respiratory chain at the 'Slater factor' site (between cytochrome b and c_1).

MECHANISM OF REDUCTION OF COMPONENTS
OF THE RESPIRATORY CHAIN

The mechanism whereby pyridine nucleotides, flavoproteins and cytochromes are reversibly oxidized and reduced in soluble systems is discussed below. It is reasonable to assume that these mechanisms apply when the components are bound to the respiratory chain. However, the mechanism whereby the integrated complex of enzymes and carriers of the respiratory chain permits a flow of hydrogen coupled to phosphorylation is far from understood.

(a) THE PYRIDINE NUCLEOTIDES

The properties of pyridine nucleotide reduction have been studied in a' most elegant manner by the use of 'heavy hydrogen' or deuterium (Vennesland, 1958). The principle involved in this technique is exactly the same as that employed in the use of the isotope ^{14}C to follow the path of carbon. Both deuterium and hydrogen react identically in chemical and enzymatic reactions.

Most experiments designed to study the mechanism of pyridine nucleotide reduction have been performed with yeast alcohol dehydrogenase since this enzyme is readily available in a high state of purity. Work with other pyridine nucleotide enzymes leaves little doubt that the basic properties determined with yeast alcohol dehydrogenase apply generally to all pyridine nucleotide enzymes involving NAD or NADP.

The enzymatic reduction of NAD involves the addition of hydrogen to the 4-position of the nicotinamide ring and the release of a hydrogen ion. For example, the reduction of NAD by alcohol may be represented as follows:

For many years it was widely believed that the mechanism of pyridine nucleotide reduction involved a transfer of electrons. In such a mechanism the extra hydrogen on the nicotinamide ring is derived from protons from the medium. The work of Vennesland's group, however, eliminated an electron transfer mechanism and demonstrated quite conclusively that the reduction of the pyridine nucleotides involves a direct hydrogen transfer. These two processes, represented diagrammatically below, may be distinguished by studying the transfer of hydrogen from substrate to NAD in the presence of D_2O.

Direct Hydrogen Transfer   *Electron Transfer*

Substrate $\;$ (H) $\;$ | Dehydrogenase | NAD (H)   Substrate $\;$ (H) | Dehydrogenase | NAD (D)
$\qquad\qquad\qquad\qquad\qquad\qquad\qquad\qquad\qquad\qquad\qquad\qquad\qquad\qquad\;\;\to D_2O$

It was shown experimentally that NAD reduced enzymatically by $CH_3.CH_2OH$ in a medium of D_2O contained no deuterium. On the other hand, NAD reduced by $CH_3.CD_2OH$ in a medium of H_2O yielded a molecule of reduced NAD containing 1 atom of deuterium. These observations are consistent with a direct transfer mechanism and eliminate an electron transfer mechanism. By similar techniques it has been shown that there is also a direct transfer of hydrogen from the 4-position of the nicotinamide ring of reduced NAD back to the carbonyl carbon of acetaldehyde to form ethanol. Whether or not there is also a direct transfer of the hydroxyl hydrogen of ethanol to the nitrogen atom of the nicotinamide ring cannot be determined with deuterium because both the hydroxyl hydrogen of ethanol and the hydrogen attached to the nitrogen atom exchange non-enzymatically with hydrogen ions of the medium:

The hydrogen atoms attached to the 4-position of the nicotinamide ring of $NADH_2$ are stereochemically different, one hydrogen projecting *above*, the other *below* the nicotinamide ring. Vennesland's group has established by the following series of experiments that the enzymatic transfer of hydrogen to and from C-4 is stereospecific. Reduced NAD, obtained in the following reaction:

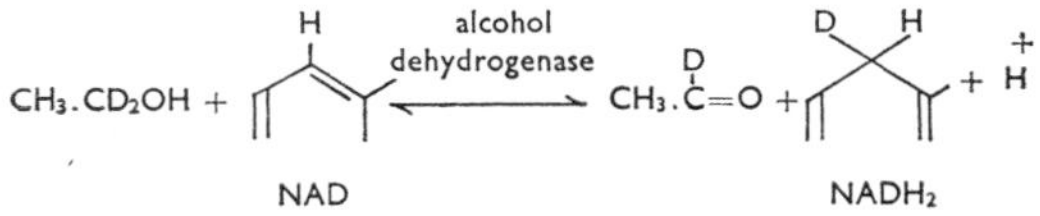

$$CH_3.CD_2OH + \underset{\text{NAD}}{[\text{ring structure}]} \xrightarrow[\text{dehydrogenase}]{\text{alcohol}} CH_3.\overset{D}{\underset{}{C}}=O + \underset{\text{NADH}_2}{[\text{ring structure, D H}]} + H^+$$

was oxidized enzymatically with acetaldehyde:

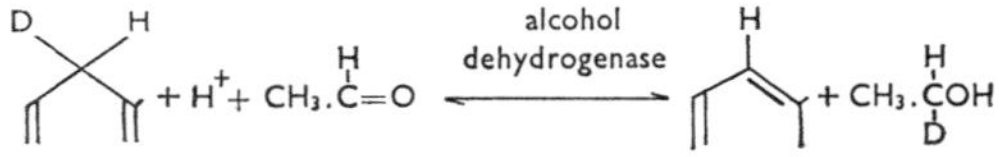

$$\underset{}{[\text{ring structure, D H}]} + H^+ + CH_3.\overset{H}{\underset{}{C}}=O \xrightarrow[\text{dehydrogenase}]{\text{alcohol}} \underset{}{[\text{ring structure, H}]} + CH_3.\overset{H}{\underset{D}{C}}OH$$

It was found experimentally that all the deuterium of reduced NAD was transferred to acetaldehyde to form $CH_3.CDHOH$. Thus the deuterium atom which is added to the nicotinamide ring is the same atom which is subsequently removed. This means that the reaction is stereospecific. All dehydrogenases do not attack the same side of the nicotinamide ring as alcohol dehydrogenase. Dehydrogenases possessing the same specificity as alcohol dehydrogenase (e.g. lactic dehydrogenase and malic dehydrogenase) are said to have *A* specificity. Dehydrogenases attacking the nicotinamide ring on the opposite side to alcohol dehydrogenase are said to have *B* specificity. Dehydrogenases with *B* specificity include α-glycerophosphate dehydrogenase, 3-phosphoglyceraldehyde dehydrogenase, glutamic dehydrogenase and $NADH_2$-cytochrome *c* reductase. By techniques similar to those described above it has been demonstrated that the removal of hydrogen from ethanol is also stereospecific. This asymmetric attack on a symmetrical molecule is readily explained by the three-point attachment theory of Ogston (p. 161).

It was stated on p. 201 that the reversible addition of hydrogen occurred at the 4-position of the nicotinamide ring of NAD. Now that the student is familiar with the main properties of pyridine nucleotide reduction, it is pertinent to present the proof for this statement. In the reaction sequence shown in Fig. 5.11, $NADH_2$ formed by chemical reduction contains both stereoisomers. Consequently when chemically reduced $NADH_2$ is oxidized enzymatically by acetaldehyde (step 1), the resulting NAD is labelled with deuterium. The addition of *Neurospora* NAD-ase (step 2) produces deuterium-labelled nicotinamide. Methylation of deuterium-labelled nicotinamide with methyl iodide (step 3), and oxidation of the product N^1-methylnicotinamide iodide with alkaline ferricyanide (step 4) yields a pyridone which contains deuterium. Since it is known that the chemical oxidation proceeds at the 2- and 6-positions, it follows that deuterium is not present at these positions. The possibility of reduction at the 2- and 6-positions is therefore eliminated. Reduction at positions 3 or 5 can be eliminated from considerations of electron structure. It may be concluded, therefore, that reduction must have occurred at the 4-position. The same conclusion is obtained using enzymatically reduced NAD followed by a chemical oxidation in step 1.

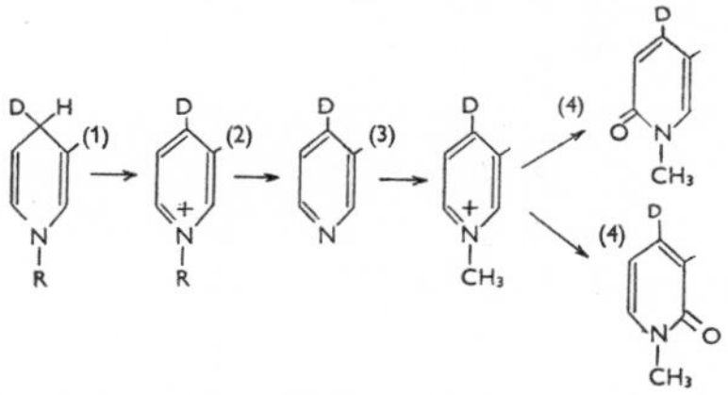

FIG. 5.11. Reactions demonstrating the site of reduction of NAD.

It is possible that, in spite of the ease of dissociation of pyridine nucleotides from the apoenzymes, there is not a well-mixed pool of pyridine nucleotides in the cell from which all the dehydrogenases draw a supply of oxidized and reduced pyridine nucleotides. For example, the transfer of hydrogen from triose phosphate to pyruvate, which occurs in the EMP pathway, is too rapid to be explained by the process of diffusion of NAD or $NADH_2$ from one dehydrogenase to the other. Kinetic measurements show that $NADH_2$ bound to triose phosphate dehydrogenase is oxidized at a faster rate than free $NADH_2$. It is suggested that hydrogen is transferred from one substrate to the other via NAD which is 'sandwiched' between the two dehydrogenases. The fact that triose phosphate dehydrogenase has B specificity and lactic dehydrogenase has A specificity makes it possible to add hydrogen to one side of the nicotinamide ring and remove it from the other. Hydrogen atoms would then be shuttled through the pyridine nucleotide which never leaves the enzyme surface:

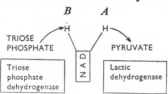

(b) The Flavins

The reduction of NAD involves an overall transfer of 2 hydrogen atoms. The generally accepted mechanism of cytochrome reduction, on the other hand, involves a single hydrogen transfer in the form of an electron and a H^+. The flavoproteins have therefore been described as 'transformers' which convert the flow of two hydrogens from NAD into a flow of single electrons in the cytochromes. The formation of a free radical during the reduction of flavins makes this transformation possible. A free radicle (or semiquinone) may be defined as a substance containing one unpaired electron.

A suggested mechanism of flavin reduction by a 2-step addition of hydrogen atoms is shown below. Although hydrogen atoms are shown in this mechanism, the actual atomic species is not known. Both extra hydrogens on reduced flavin exchange non-enzymatically with the medium, making it impossible to test experimentally whether direct transfer or electron transfer from NAD occurs. Flavin free radicals have been demonstrated in all flavoprotein enzyme systems studied.

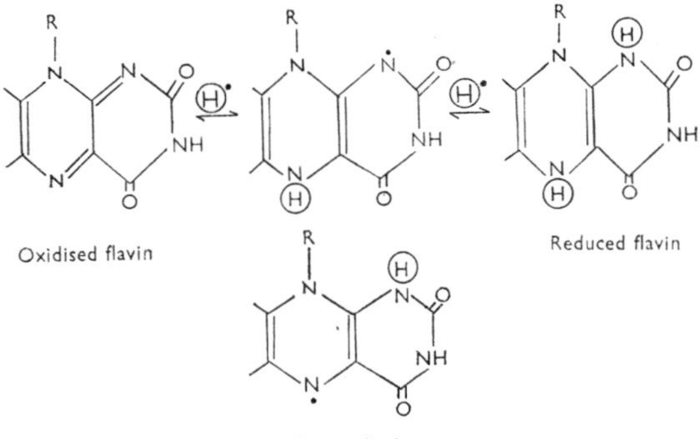

Oxidised flavin   Reduced flavin

Free radical
(2 resonance hybrids shown)

(c) The Cytochromes

The precise mechanism of cytochrome reduction is still under dispute. Many workers claim that the reduction involves a simple addition of an electron to the iron atom as follows:

$$Fe^{+++} + .\rightleftharpoons Fe^{++}$$

Other workers point out that the properties of iron in free solution and in cytochrome are quite different and that iron is too effectively shielded by cytochrome protein for a direct reduction as indicated by the equation above. An alternative theory was therefore suggested that the first step in cytochrome reduction is the addition of hydrogen to the free imidazole nitrogen of the histidine molecule attached to iron (see p. 187). A redistribution of charge occurs, resulting in the loss of a hydrogen ion and reduction of Fe^{+++} to Fe^{++}.

The mechanism of the final step in the respiratory chain, the reduction of oxygen to form water, is poorly understood.

The Direct Oxidases

PEROXIDASE

Peroxidase, which catalyses the general reaction

$$AH_2 + H_2O_2 \rightarrow A + 2H_2O$$

is widely distributed in plants and has been crystallized from horseradish and wheat germ. Peroxidases are conjugated proteins containing iron porphyrin. The ferric complex of protoporphyrin IX has been shown to be the prosthetic group of horse-radish peroxidase. Studies of the peroxidase reaction reveal that the enzyme forms complexes with H_2O_2. The following mechanism is proposed:

$$Enz.\text{-}H_2O + H_2O_2 \leftharpoondown Enz.\text{-}H_2O_2 + H_2O$$
$$\text{(complex 1)}$$

$$Complex\ 1 + AH_2 \rightarrow Complex\ 2 + AH. + H_2O$$

$$Complex\ 2 + AH. + AH_2 \rightarrow Enz.H_2O + A + AH_2$$
$$AH.\ \text{is half -oxidized electron donor}$$

A variety of compounds can act as electron donors, e.g. phenols, amines, flavones, tyrosine and cytochrome c.

Peroxidases also catalyse a number of direct oxidations:

$$AH_2 + O_2 \rightarrow A + H_2O_2$$

and possibly

$$AH_2 + \tfrac{1}{2}O_2 \rightarrow A + H_2O$$

In the presence of Mn^{++}, peroxidase catalyses the oxidation of dihydroxyfumaric acid to diketosuccinic acid. There is evidence that the catalyst in this reaction is a Mn^{++} activated peroxidase-peroxide compound.

$$\text{dihydroxyfumarate} + O_2 \rightarrow H_2O_2 + \text{diketosuccinate}$$
$$Mn^{++} \swarrow$$
$$\text{dihydroxyfumarate} + H_2O_2 \rightarrow 2H_2O + \text{diketosuccinate}$$
$$\text{Peroxidase-peroxide}$$
$$\text{compound}$$

If Mn^{++} and a suitable monophenol (e.g. resorcinol) are present, peroxidase will catalyse the oxidation of a wide range of metabolites, e.g. $NADH_2$, $NADPH_2$, tryptophan, oxaloacetic acid and indoleacetic acid. Exogenous H_2O_2 is not required for these reactions. That H_2O_2 is involved in these oxidations is indicated by the fact that catalase (which destroys H_2O_2) has been shown to be inhibitory in many cases.

The participation of peroxidase in oxidation *in vivo* has not been demonstrated and its physiological significance remains uncertain.

CATALASE

Catalase is similar to peroxidase and the two enzymes are often classified together as hydroperoxidases. Catalase has iron protoporphyrin IX as the prosthetic group and catalyses the reaction:

$$2H_2O_2 \rightarrow 2H_2O + O_2$$

At low concentrations of H_2O_2 catalase can also act as a peroxidase, e.g.

$$CH_3CH_2OH + H_2O_2 \rightarrow CH_3CHO + 2H_2O$$

Peroxidase does not catalyse the above reaction. Thus peroxidase and catalase, though able to catalyse similar types of reaction, differ in their specificity.

Catalase has been found in a number of plants but its function, other than to decompose excess H_2O_2, is not known.

ASCORBIC ACID OXIDASE

Ascorbic acid oxidase catalyses the reaction,

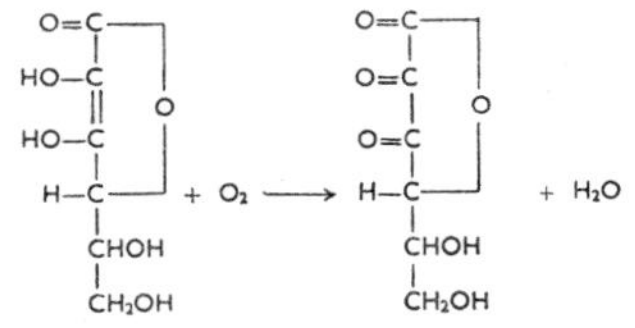

Ascorbic acid   Dehydroascorbic acid

It is widely, though apparently not universally, distributed in plants. Ascorbic acid oxidase is found in the soluble fraction of the cell and also firmly bound to the cell walls. It has been extensively purified from squash and shown to contain tightly bound copper which is essential for activity. The enzyme is specific for ascorbate or its close analogues. The reaction mechanism is not understood. There is some evidence that the semi-quinone monodehydroascorbic acid is an intermediate oxidation product. In general, the soluble enzyme is rapidly inactivated during ascorbate oxidation *in vitro*. The enzyme associated with the cell walls does not show this inactivation.

Ascorbate is widely distributed in plants and there is evidence that most of it is in the reduced form. A number of systems which couple the oxidation of reduced pyridine nucleotide to the reduction of ascorbate have been demonstrated, though none have been proven to operate *in vivo*. The most interesting is:

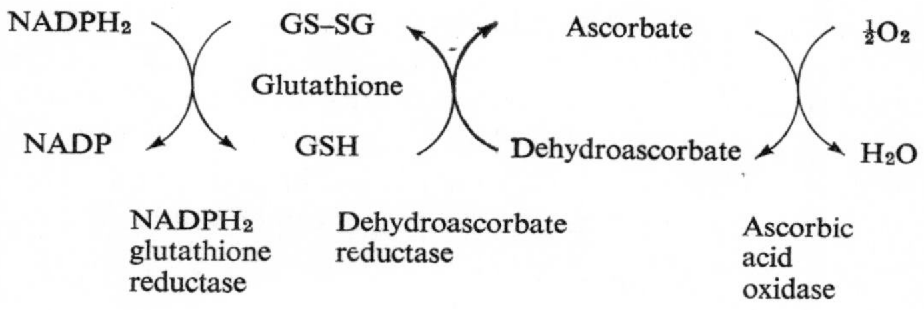

Both glutathione reductase and dehydroascorbate reductase are widely distributed.

PHENOL OXIDASES

Two types of phenol oxidases may be recognized, the polyphenolases or tyrosinases, and the laccases.

(a) POLYPHENOLASE

Polyphenolase or tyrosinase catalyses the aerobic oxidation of *o*-dihydric phenols (catecholase activity) and monophenols (cresolase activity). The ratio of catecholase to cresolase activity varies with source, method of preparation and degree of purification of the enzyme. Purification is often accompanied by a loss of monophenolase activity. The two activities may be due to separate but closely related enzymes. However, the available evidence favours the view that only one enzyme is involved and that it has separate sites for catecholase and cresolase activity. Polyphenolase

14

also catalyses the *o*-hydroxylation of monophenols (p. 399). The oxidative and hydroxylative activities have not been separated. Purified polyphenolase contains firmly bound copper which is essential for catecholase, cresolase and hydroxylase activites.

The oxidation of *o*-dihydric phenols may be represented as:

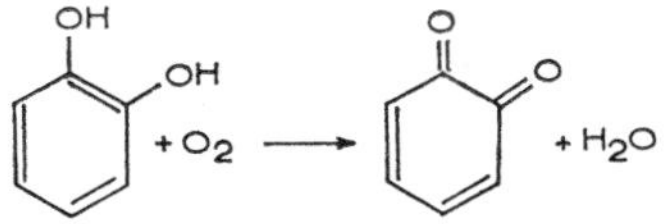

The amount of oxygen consumed exceeds the stoichiometric requirement of the above reaction. It has been suggested that during the reaction the copper changes from the cupric to the cuprous state and that the extra oxygen is required for the re-oxidation of the enzyme. The enzyme is often inactivated when *o*-dihydric phenols are provided as substrates. The hydroxylase activity of polyphenolase is discussed on p. 398.

Polyphenol oxidases are widely distributed in plants and sometimes present in large amounts. The enzyme appears to be soluble but activity has been reported in chloroplasts and mitochondria.

(b) LACCASE

Laccase is characteristic of the latex of the genus *Rhus*, and is responsible for the blackening of the latex of the 'lacquer' trees. Laccase differs from polyphenolase in being inactive with monophenols. Laccase appears to be insensitive to carbon monoxide whilst polyphenolase is reported to be inhibited. Laccase contains copper which is essential for activity.

Quinones formed in oxidase reactions are readily reduced. An NADP dependent quinone reductase is widely distributed in plants. The following system can be constructed *in vitro*, though its physiological significance is uncertain:

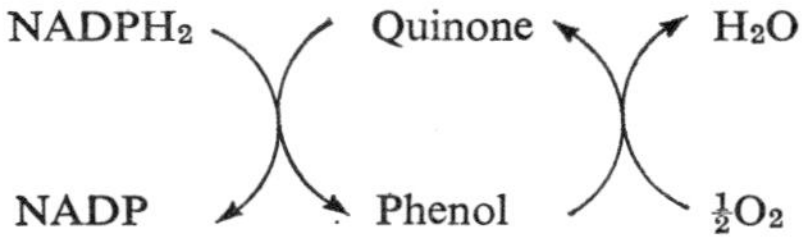

Phenol oxidases are probably responsible for the discoloration of damaged tissues. Suggestions that toxic products of phenol oxidase activity determine the resistance of plants to infection have been made but not proven.

GLYCOLIC ACID OXIDASE

Glycolic acid oxidase catalyses the reaction:

$$CH_2OH—COOH + O_2 \rightarrow CHO—COOH + H_2O_2$$

     Glycolic acid   Glyoxylic acid

The highest activities of glycolic acid oxidase are found in photosynthetic tissues, but activity is also found in non-green tissues. Its appearance in etiolated tissues exposed to light coincides with the onset of photosynthesis. At least some of the activity is associated with the chloroplasts. Glycolic acid oxidase has been crystallized from spinach and shown to contain flavin mononucleotide as the prosthetic group. The purified enzyme also catalyses the oxidation of L-lactic acid to pyruvic acid and glyoxylic acid to oxalic acid. The affinity for these substrates decreases in the order glycolate, lactate, glyoxylate. The enzyme is competitively inhibited by analogues of glycolic acid such as the α-hydroxysulphonates. Attempts to demonstrate a coupling between glycolic acid oxidase activity and ATP synthesis have been unsuccessful.

An NAD specific glyoxylic acid reductase has been crystallized from plants. In the presence of enzymes which remove H_2O_2 (catalase or peroxidase) the following system can be demonstrated:

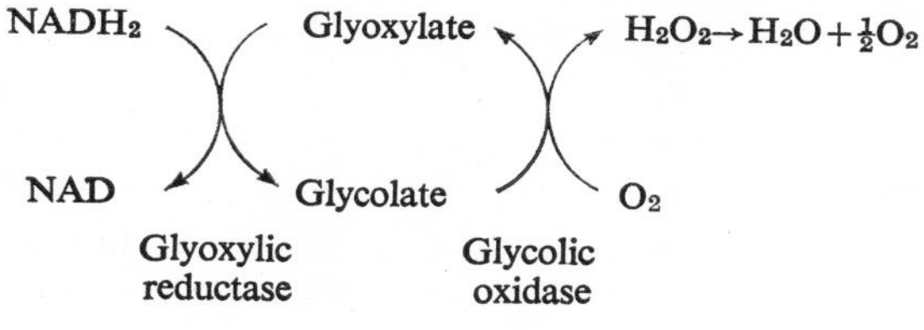

When leaves are treated with α-hydroxysulphonates a marked accumulation of glycolate occurs in the light but not in the dark. In the presence of α-hydroxysulphonates roughly half of the activity from photosynthetically fixed $^{14}CO_2$ appears in glycolate. These experiments suggest that glycolic acid oxidase catalyses some of the oxygen uptake of green tissues in the light.

AMINE OXIDASE

An enzyme which catalyses the oxidation of a number of mono- and diamines has been purified from peas (Mann, 1955).

Terminal Oxidation

A terminal oxidase is an enzyme which catalyses the final step in the transfer of hydrogen from substrate to oxygen. Plants possess a number of oxidases which could fulfil this role. Cytochrome oxidase, glycolic acid oxidase, ascorbic acid oxidase and phenol oxidase have all been proposed as *in vivo* terminal oxidases.

It is difficult to prove that a particular oxidase catalyses oxygen uptake *in vivo*. Of some possible relevance is the affinity of these enzymes for oxygen. Cytochrome oxidase has a high affinity for oxygen. Most of the other oxidases have a low affinity and at physiological partial pressures would be expected to have little activity. Most studies have depended upon the use of selective inhibitors (Table 5.3). With the exception of a light reversible inhibition of oxygen uptake by carbon monoxide, data from inhibitor experiments are rarely conclusive.

It appears almost certain that cytochrome oxidase catalyses at least part of the oxygen uptake of all plant tissues. *In vivo* studies of spectral changes of cytochromes similar to those described for mitochondria (p. 195) support this view. Further, the respiration of a variety of plant tissues is inhibited by carbon monoxide and this inhibition is reversed by light.

Whether all the oxygen uptake of plant tissues depends upon cytochrome oxidase has not been resolved. Respiration which is resistant to inhibitors of cytochrome oxidase has been frequently observed in plants, and also in animals. In animal biochemistry the climate of opinion strongly favours the dominant role of cytochrome oxidase. Animal biochemists do not readily accept the lack of carbon monoxide or cyanide inhibition as proof against the operation of cytochrome oxidase as a terminal oxidase (Ball, 1942; Chance & Hackett, 1959). In plant biochemistry the situation is less clear. For example, difference spectra strongly indicate that cytochrome oxidase catalyses oxygen uptake in the spadices of certain members of the Araceae. However, inhibitors of cytochrome oxidase not only do not inhibit oxygen uptake, but often cause a stimulation. In the presence of these inhibitors, cytochromes a and a_3 are largely reduced whilst cytochrome b_7 remains mainly oxidized. These, and other observations, suggest that hydrogen transfer by-passes the inhibited

TABLE 5.3

Effect of respiratory inhibitors upon plant oxidases

Inhibitor	Cytochrome oxidase	Peroxidase	Catalase	Polyphenol oxidase	Laccase	Ascorbic acid oxidase	Glycolic acid oxidase
Carbon monoxide	+ Reversed by light	−	−	+ Not reversed by light	−	Slight inhibition, not reversed by light	−
0·1–1·0 mM Cyanide	+	+	+	+	+	+	−
0·1–1·0 mM Azide	+	+	+	+	+	+	−
1 mM Sodium diethyl-dithiocarbamate	Slight inhibition	?	?	+	+	+	?

cytochrome a_3 via the autoxidizable cytochrome b_7. An alternative hypothesis is that the small fraction of cytochromes a and a_3, which remains uninhibited, is sufficient to account for the observed oxygen uptake.

OXIDATIVE PHOSPHORYLATION

Oxidative phosphorylation may be defined as the process of phosphorylation of ADP to ATP which accompanies biological oxidation. The process may be expressed as follows:

$$AH_2 + B \rightarrow A + BH_2 \tag{5.1}$$

$$ADP + P \rightarrow ATP + H_2O \tag{5.2}$$

Sum: $\qquad AH_2 + B + ADP + P \rightarrow A + BH_2 + ATP \tag{5.3}$

In the above equations, the exergonic reaction in which hydrogen is transferred from AH_2 to B is coupled to the endergonic phosphorylation of ADP to ATP. Although the possible transfer of excitation energy in biological systems has been emphasized by Szent-Györgyi (1957), at present the only well-known example of such a process is in photosynthesis. In all other examples of energy coupling, one reaction drives another through the participation of an intermediate common to both reactions. The nature of the common intermediate (not shown in eqns 5.1–5.3) is discussed below.

Two types of oxidative phosphorylation exist — substrate-linked phosphorylation and respiratory chain phosphorylation:

Substrate-Linked Phosphorylation

In substrate-linked phosphorylation AH_2 = 3-phosphoglyceraldehyde, α-ketoglutarate or pyruvate. In respiratory chain phosphorylation AH_2 and B are both oxidation-reduction intermediates of the respiratory chain. For example, AH_2 = reduced NAD and B = flavoprotein. Substrate-linked phosphorylation, in contrast to respiratory chain phosphorylation, is catalysed by soluble enzyme systems and it has therefore been possible to study its mechanism in some detail. With all three substrates a high energy intermediate is formed before reaction with inorganic phosphate or ADP.

A probable mechanism of reaction of glyceraldehyde phosphate dehydrogenase (p. 107) is shown below (Fig. 5.12). The enzyme first combines with NAD through two bonds, one of which appears to involve a link between the 4-position of the nicotinamide ring of NAD with a sulphydryl group (probably of glutathione) on the enzyme (reaction 5.4). Aldehydolysis of the enzyme-NAD complex (reaction 5.5) produces a high energy acyl-enzyme, together with reduced NAD. In reactions (5.6) a phosphorylysis of the acyl enzyme results in the formation of 1,3-diphosphoglyceric acid. The synthesis of ATP from 1,3-diphosphoglyceric acid (reaction 5.7) is catalysed by 3-phosphoglyceric acid kinase.

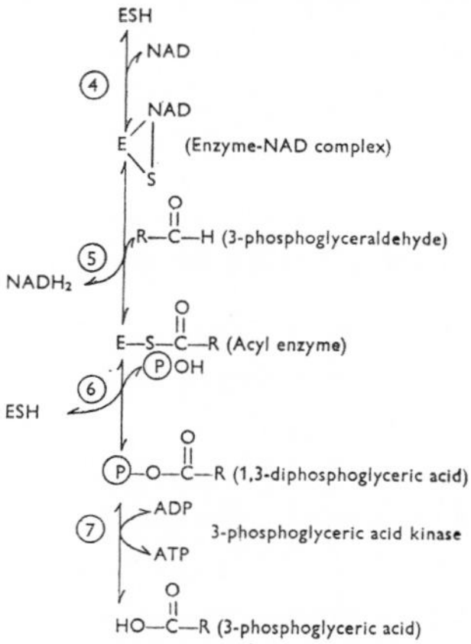

Fig. 5.12. Mechanism of phosphorylation coupled to the oxidation of 3-phosphoglyceraldehyde.

In the oxidation of α-ketoglutarate and pyruvate, the first high energy compound to be formed is a thioester of lipoic acid (p. 164) which subsequently reacts with CoA to form succinyl or acetyl CoA, respectively. In plants succinyl CoA phosphorylates ADP as follows:

$$\text{succinyl CoA} + \text{ADP} + \text{P} + \text{H}_2\text{O} \xrightarrow{\substack{\text{Succinic}\\ \text{thiokinase}}} \text{succinate} + \text{CoA} + \text{ATP}$$

Enzyme systems which catalyse the phosphorylation of ADP by acetyl CoA have been demonstrated only in bacteria:

$$\text{acetyl CoA} + \text{P} \xrightarrow{\text{Phosphotransacetylase}} \text{acetyl phosphate} + \text{CoA}$$

$$\text{acetyl phosphate} + \text{ADP} \xrightarrow{\text{Acetokinase}} \text{acetate} + \text{ATP}$$

Sum: $\quad$ acetyl CoA + ADP + P $\rightarrow$ acetate + ATP + CoA

Substrate-linked phosphorylation may be abolished by the addition of arsenate. This effect is thought to be due to the formation of a high energy arsenate compound which is much more unstable than the corresponding phosphate compound. For example, in the oxidation of 3-phosphoglyceraldehyde when phosphate is replaced by arsenate, 'arsenolysis' in reaction (5.6) produces a carbonyl arsenate group ($-CO-OAsO_3^=$) which is hydrolysed to produce 3-phosphoglyceric acid. The oxidation of 3-phosphoglyceraldehyde to 3-phosphoglyceric acid and reduction of NAD therefore proceeds in the presence of arsenate without concomitant synthesis of ATP. 2,4-Dinitrophenol (DNP), which uncouples respiratory chain phosphorylation, does not affect substrate linked phosphorylation.

Respiratory Chain Phosphorylation

Kalckar in 1937 first demonstrated that the conversion of inorganic phosphate into sugar phosphates in tissue extracts could be made dependent. upon respiration. Two years later Belitzer and Tsibakowa observed that minced muscle preparations oxidizing Krebs cycle acids esterified approximately 2 molecules of inorganic phosphate into phosphocreatine for each atom of oxygen consumed. The ratio of the number of molecules of inorganic phosphate esterified per atom of oxygen consumed is designated as the P/O ratio. If phosphorylation occurred only during dehydrogenation of the substrate, as in substrate linked phosphorylation, a P/O ratio of only 1 would be expected. A P/O ratio of 2 observed by Belitzer and Tsibakowa suggested a new type of phosphorylation associated with the oxidation of $NADH_2$ by oxygen. Belitzer and Tsibakowa suggested that this new type phosphorylation was coupled to the passage of hydrogen from $NADH_2$ to oxygen via the respiratory chain. Subsequent work has confirmed this suggestion and shown that a maximum of three phosphorylations can occur for each pair of hydrogen atoms or electrons passed through the respiratory chain. Direct proof that phosphorylation occurs beyond the substrate level was provided in 1951 when Lehninger showed that the oxidation of $NADH_2$ by oxygen in rat liver mitochondria was accompanied by a P/O ratio close to 3. Respiratory chain phosphorylation in plants was first demonstrated by Millerd, Bonner, Axelrod & Bandurski (1951) using mitochondria isolated from mung bean seedlings and Krebs cycle acids as substrates. The P/O ratios obtained in these studies were low compared to those reported for animal mitochondria and it was thought that plant mitochondria might be inefficient systems of phosphorylation. Later studies have shown that plant mitochondria oxidize Krebs cycle intermediates with P/O ratios comparable to those of animal mitochondria.

Most of the total free energy of oxidation is released during the passage of hydrogen through the respiratory chain to oxygen. For example, the complete oxidation of glucose to carbon dioxide and water proceeds with a standard free energy change of -688 kcal. The oxidation of 1 molecule of glucose through the combined action of the EMP pathway and the Krebs cycle produces a total of 10 molecules of reduced NAD and 2 molecules of reduced flavoprotein. Subsequent oxidation of these reduced carriers through the respiratory chain proceeds with a total standard free energy change of $-620 \cdot 1$ kcal ($NADH_2$ oxidation, $10 \times -53 \cdot 75$ kcal $+$ reduced flavoprotein oxidation, $2 \times -41 \cdot 3$ kcal). In the case of glucose oxidation, therefore, 90 per cent ($620 \cdot 1/688 \times 100$ per cent) of the total free energy change occurs in the respiratory chain. Assuming a P/O of 3 and 2 for the oxidation of reduced NAD and reduced flavoprotein respectively, it follows that the highly exergonic reactions of the respiratory chain are coupled to ATP synthesis with an efficiency of approximately 44 per cent $[(3 \times 8 \times 10 + 2 \times 8 \times 2)/(620 \cdot 1) \times 100$ per cent].

RESPIRATORY CONTROL

In 'tightly coupled' systems, respiration is dependent upon the presence of phosphate and ADP. This phenomenon of respiratory control was recognized almost as early as the phenomenon of respiratory chain phosphorylation. Thus Belitzer and Tsibakowa noted that the rate of respiration of minced muscle preparations was increased by the addition of creatine. This stimulation may be interpreted as resulting from the regeneration of ADP by creatine kinase:

$$ATP + creatine \rightleftharpoons phosphocreatine + ADP$$

Subsequent studies, notably those from the laboratories of H. A. Lardy and B. Chance have clearly demonstrated that the respiration of isolated mitochondria is greatly dependent upon the presence of ADP and phosphate.

The phenomenon of respiratory control is best illustrated with animal mitochondria (Fig. 5.13(A)). No oxygen uptake occurs when mitochondria are incubated in the presence of substrate (glutamate), phosphate and oxygen. Rapid oxygen uptake is initiated only upon the addition of ADP, and proceeds until the concentration of ADP is again reduced to a low level by the process of respiratory chain phosphorylation. This sequence of events can be repeated by further additions of ADP. In plant mitochondria (Fig. 5.13(B)) appreciable oxygen uptake proceeds in the absence of ADP. This indicates that the plant mitochondria used in this study were not as tightly coupled as the preparations of animal mitochondria. Addition of ADP to the plant mitochondria produces a significant increase in oxygen uptake. This initial increase in oxygen uptake declines as the added ADP is phosphorylated to ATP. Further additions of ADP produce a similar sequence of events. The type of respiratory control illustrated in Fig. 5.2(B) has been demonstrated in mitochondria derived from a variety of plant tissues.

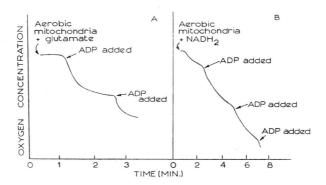

FIG. 5.13. Repiratory control in animal and plant mitochondria. A, guinea-pig liver mitochondria (Chance & Williams 1956); B, sweet potato mitochondria (Bonner & Voss 1961). The ordinates are not drawn to the same scale.

The precise nature of the coupling between respiration and phosphorylation is uncertain. The coupling appears to be very labile and disappears when mitochondria are disrupted by freezing and thawing, ageing and treatment with hypotonic solutions etc. The P/O ratio is a convenient measure of the degree of coupling and is frequently taken as an indication of structural integrity. A number of chemicals (e.g. DNP, calcium ions, thyroxin, dicoumarol etc.), when present in very low concentrations (approx. 10^{-5} M), are also able to uncouple respiration from phosphorylation. Uncoupled mitochondria can respire in the absence of ADP and phosphate but are no longer capable of phosphorylating ADP to ATP. A possible mechanism of action of the uncoupling agent DNP is presented on p. 221.

Respiratory control probably acts *in vivo* as a mechanism of gearing the rate of respiration to the energy demands of the cell. During periods of rapid ATP breakdown (e.g. during protein synthesis) the level of ADP and phosphate are high and respiration proceeds at near maximum rate. On the other hand, when requirements for ATP are low (e.g. in resting cells) ATP accumulates at the expense of ADP and phosphate. This deficiency of ADP and phosphate results in a low rate of respiration.

The rate limitation of coupled respiration imposed by the ratio (ATP)/(ADP)(P) may extend to more complex metabolic patterns. These effects may be illustrated by the 'Pasteur effect', which has been defined as 'Oxygen inhibits fermentation', or 'Oxygen inhibits the breakdown of carbohydrates'. It has been suggested that oxidative phosphorylation produces a high ratio of (ATP)/(ADP) which might slow down the reactions of glycolysis:

$$\text{glucose} + 2\text{ADP} + 2\text{P}_i \rightleftharpoons 2 \text{ lactate} + 2\text{ATP}$$

The Pasteur effect studied in apples by Blackman & Parija (1928) was widely believed by plant physiologists to involve an actual resynthesis of carbohydrates from organic acids. Calculations of the ratio (ATP)/(ADP) necessary to appreciably decrease the rate of glycolysis give values at least 1000 times as high as those observed. Consequently the ratio (ATP)/(ADP) cannot exert effective control. Oxidative phosphorylation could reduce the *concentration* of ADP to such a low level that it would limit the rate of glycolysis. This would mean that phosphorylation of glucose would proceed and sugar phosphates would accumulate. Since this effect has not been observed it is unlikely that the concentration of ADP controls the rate of glycolysis.

An alternative suggestion is that the Pasteur effect results from a competition between glycolysis and oxidative phosphorylation for P_i. Under aerobic conditions respiratory chain phosphorylation reduces the level of P_i to a point where the oxidation of triosephosphate is limited:

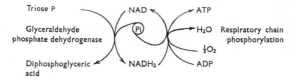

The phenomenon of respiratory control forms the basis of one of the theories of respiratory chain phosphorylation discussed on p. 220.

SITES OF PHOSPHORYLATION

A maximum P/O ratio approaching 3 indicates that three phosphorylations occur during the passage of each pair of hydrogen atoms or electrons through the respiratory chain to oxygen. The probable sites of these phosphorylations, shown in Fig. 5.14, are based upon the following evidence:

(a) Thermodynamic evidence: Consider the empirical equations for respiratory chain phosphorylation:

$$AH_2 + B \leftrightharpoons A + BH_2 \tag{5.1}$$

$$ADP + P \leftrightharpoons ATP + H_2O \tag{5.2}$$

$$\text{Sum: } AH_2 + B + ADP + P \leftrightharpoons A + BH_2 + H_2O + ATP \tag{5.3}$$

Phosphorylation can occur only at those sites where the coupled reaction (reaction 5.3) proceeds with a decrease of free energy. Values of $\Delta G_{\text{reaction (5.3)}}$, listed in Table 5.4, may be approximated as follows:

$$\Delta G_{\text{reaction (5.3)}} = \Delta G_{\text{reaction (5.1)}} + \Delta G_{\text{reaction (5.2)}}$$

$$= \Delta G_{\text{reaction (5.1)}} + \Delta G^\circ_{\text{reaction (5.2)}} + RT \ln \frac{(ATP)}{(ADP)(P)}$$

$$= \Delta G_{\text{reaction (5.1)}} + 8000 + RT \ln \frac{(ATP)}{(ADP)(P)}$$

$\Delta G_{\text{reaction (5.1)}}$ may be calculated from experimentally determined values of E_h (p. 197) by the equation:

$$\Delta G_{\text{reaction (5.1)}} = -nFE_h$$

A value of approximately 400 has been assumed for the ratio $(ATP)/(ADP)(P)$ (Slater, 1960).

TABLE 5.4

Calculation of the free energy changes of reactions of the respiratory chain

Reaction	$\Delta G_{\text{Rx. 5.1}}$ (Assuming no phosph.) (cal)	$\Delta G_{\text{Rx. 5.3}}$ (Assuming phosph.) (cal)
β-hydroxybutyrate + NAD → Acetoacetate + NADH$_2$	-80	11 470
NADH$_2$ + FP → NAD + FPH$_2$	$-13\,310$	-1760
FPH$_2$ + 2 Cyt. b^{+++} → FP + 2 Cyt. b^{++} + 2H$^+$	-3440	8110
2 Cyt. b^{++} + 2 Cyt. c^{+++} → 2 Cyt. b^{+++} + 2 Cyt. c^{++}	$-12\,800$	-1250
2 Cyt. c^{++} + 2 Cyt. a^{+++} → 2 Cyt. c^{+++} + 2 Cyt. a^{++}	-4180	7370
2 Cyt. a^{++} + $\frac{1}{2}$O$_2$ + 2H$^+$ → 2 Cyt. a^{+++} + H$_2$O	$-18\,775$	-7225

The free energy changes listed in Table 5.4 show that only three re-actions are sufficiently exergonic to permit a coupled synthesis of ATP. These phosphorylation sites are between NAD and flavoprotein, cyto-chromes b and c, and cytochrome a and oxygen.

(b) P/O ratios: By determining the P/O ratio obtained with substrates that reduce specific components of the respiratory chain, it is possible to define approximate sites of phosphorylation.

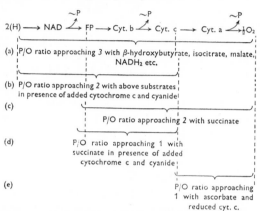

FIG. 5.14. Localisation of the sites of phosphorylation by the use of substrates that reduce specific components of the respiratory chain.

Determination of the amount of phosphorylation is frequently com-plicated by the presence of ATP-ases and phosphatases which result in apparently low P/O ratios. The effect of these enzymes may be minimized by the addition of fluoride or a glucose-hexokinase 'trap'. Fluoride in-hibits many, but not all, phosphatases and ATP-ases. In the presence of a glucose-hexokinase 'trap' ATP is converted into glucose-6-phosphate. During the formation of glucose-6-phosphate ADP is regenerated so that only catalytic quantities of ADP are required.

Phosphorylation is commonly determined by the decrease in inorganic phosphate, or by the increase in ATP (using ADP as acceptor) or glucose-6-phosphate (using a glucose-hexokinase 'trap'). Oxygen uptake may be determined either manometrically or by a vibrating platinum electrode. An alternative method of estimating oxygen uptake consists of determin-ing the amount of substrate oxidized, and is particularly convenient when oxidation of the substrate may be determined spectrophotometrically (e.g. oxidation of $NADH_2$ and ferrocytochrome c). When ferricyto-chrome c is the final oxidant (Fig. 5.14 (b) and (d)), the P/O ratio is equivalent to the number of moles of phosphate esterified for each 2 moles of ferricytochrome c reduced.

(c) Cross-over points: Since respiration is compulsorily linked with phosphorylation in a tightly coupled system, the respiratory chain will become inhibited in the absence of ADP or phosphate at the sites where phosphorylation normally occurs. These sites of inhibition may be determined by the cross-over technique described on p. 200. Three cross-over points caused by ADP depletion have been observed in animal mitochondria (Chance & Williams, 1956) between NAD and flavoprotein, cytochrome b and c, and cytochrome c and a. The phosphorylation sites between NAD and flavoprotein and between cytochromes b and c are in good agreement with the scheme shown in Fig. 5.14. However, the phosphorylation site suggested by this technique between cytochromes c and a is difficult to reconcile with thermodynamic data.

Plant mitochondria have not yet been examined for sites of phosphorylation by the cross-over technique.

MECHANISM

The two mechanisms described below are merely suggestions that are resonably consistent with the observed properties of respiratory chain phosphorylation. Almost all detailed studies on the mechanism of respiratory chain phosphorylation have been performed with animal systems. Until evidence to the contrary is obtained it is assumed that the same basic mechanism applies in plants.

(a) Type 1 mechanism: The essential feature of this mechanism is that a high energy intermediate compound is formed *before* the reaction with phosphate or ADP. The mechanism may be summarized as follows:

$$\text{Hydrogen transfer: } AH_2 + B + I \rightleftharpoons A \sim I + BH_2 \qquad (5.8)$$

$$A \sim I + X \rightleftharpoons X \sim I + A \qquad (5.9)$$

$$\text{Phosphorylation: } X \sim I + P \rightleftharpoons X \sim P + I \qquad (5.10)$$

$$X \sim P + ADP \rightleftharpoons ATP + X \qquad (5.11)$$

$$\overline{\text{Sum: } AH_2 + B + ADP + P \rightleftharpoons A + BH_2 + ATP} \quad (5.12)$$

$$\text{Uncoupling (DNP): } X \sim I + H_2O \rightarrow X + I \qquad (5.13)$$

This scheme was originally formulated on the basis of two observations:

(i) Tightly coupled mitochondria require ADP and phosphate for hydrogen transfer.

(ii) Hydrogen transfer and phosphorylation may be uncoupled by the addition of uncoupling agents such as DNP. In uncoupled mitochondria ADP and phosphate are no longer required for respiration.

These observations suggested that hydrogen transfer and phosphorylation are two separate reactions. During hydrogen transfer one of the reducible components of the respiratory chain (A) becomes 'bound' to form a high energy intermediate $A \sim I$ (I = an inhibitor, or intermediate). In order for hydrogen transfer to continue, free A and I must be regenerated from $A \sim I$. The conversion of $A \sim I$ to A and I may be accomplished either during phosphorylation (reactions 5.10 and 5.11) or by the addition of an uncoupling agent (reaction 5.13).

The participation of an additional intermediate, X, acting between the initial high energy compound $A \sim I$ and the phosphorylating reactions was suggested by the kinetic evidence of Chance & Williams (1956). Further evidence was provided by a study of the DNP-induced ATP-ase of the respiratory chain. DNP, in addition to uncoupling respiration from phosphorylation, also induces hydrolysis of ATP by the respiratory chain. It is generally considered that this ATP-ase represents a reversal of the phosphorylation reactions, which results from the DNP-induced hydrolysis of a high energy intermediate. If $A \sim I$ reacted directly in the phosphorylating reactions it would be expected that DNP-induced ATP-ase activity would be inhibited by the removal of A:

$$A \sim I + ADP + P \underset{\substack{\text{DNP-induced} \\ \text{ATP-ase}}}{\overset{\text{Phosphorylation}}{\rightleftarrows}} A + I + ATP$$

However, Myers & Slater (1957) observed that this ATP-ase activity was not inhibited when the reducible components of the respiratory chain were either removed or completely reduced. A non-reducible component of the respiratory chain, X, was therefore interposed between $A \sim I$ and the phosphorylation reactions.

The following evidence suggests that phosphate reacts before ADP:

(1) By the use of ^{18}O it has been demonstrated that phosphate transfer reactions proceed by a nucleophilic attack of an O (or N) atom in the acceptor molecule on the P atom of the donor (high energy) phosphate compound (Harrison, Boyer & Falcone, 1955; Cohn, 1956). If the donor compound is $X \sim P$, the 'bridge' oxygen in ATP will come from ADP:

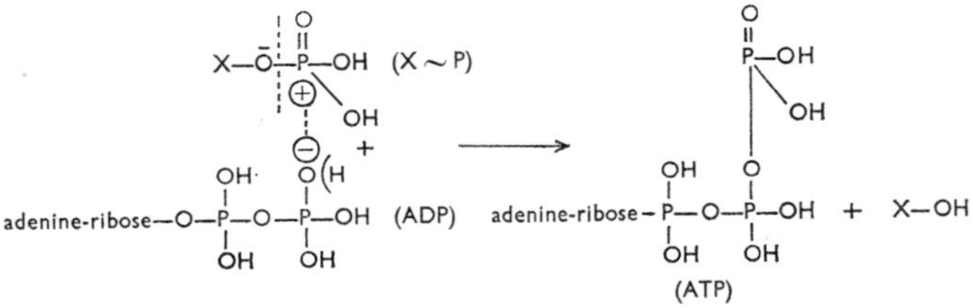

$$(5.14)$$

If, however, the donor compound is $X \sim ADP$, the 'bridge' oxygen in ATP will come from phosphate:

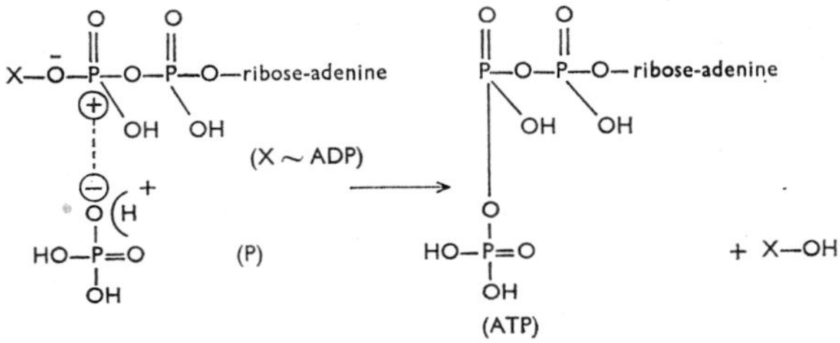

It was observed by Boyer (1957) that the 'bridge' oxygen in the terminal phosphate group of ATP was derived from ADP and not inorganic phosphate, suggesting that phosphorylation proceeds by reaction (5.14).

(2) In the absence of substrate and net hydrogen transfer, mitochondria catalyse an exchange reaction between ^{32}P and $AT^{32}P$, and between $AD^{32}P$ and $AT^{32}P$. The properties of these exchange reactions are consistent with the order of reactions shown in reactions (5.10) and (5.11). Thus the exchange between $AD^{32}P$ and $AT^{32}P$ is more rapid than that between ^{32}P and $AT^{32}P$. Furthermore, under certain experimental conditions the exchange between ^{32}P and $AT^{32}P$ requires ADP whereas that between $AD^{32}P$ and $AT^{32}P$ does not require P.

Many variations of the Type 1 mechanism have been proposed. Thus Chance claims that the primary high energy compound does not involve the oxidized carrier $A \sim I$, but the reduced carrier $AH_2 \sim I$. The nature of X and I are unknown. Purvis (1960) has presented evidence for a derivative of NAD in liver mitochondria which liberated free NAD upon incubation with ADP and P (but not ATP) or DNP, and suggests that this derivative may be $NAD \sim I$.

(b) Type 2 mechanism: In this mechanism, first proposed by Lipmann in 1946, the first high energy compound to be formed is a high energy phosphate compound. The mechanism may be illustrated by the following scheme proposed for the participation of vitamin K in the phosphorylation occurring between $NADH_2$ and cytochrome b (Wessels, 1954).

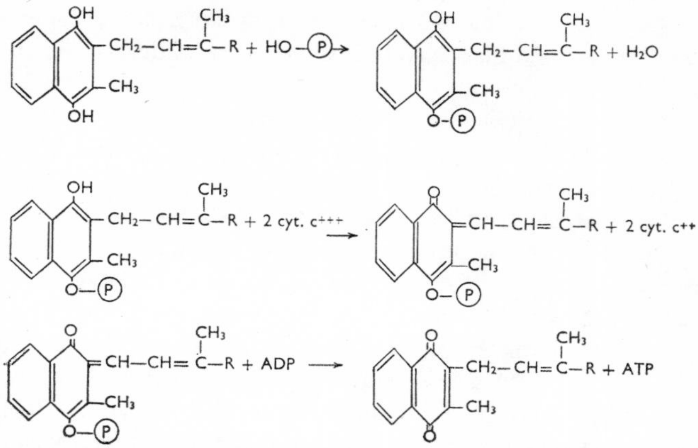

In this scheme the oxidation of reduced vitamin K phosphate results in the formation of a high energy phosphate intermediate which is capable of phosphorylating ADP to ATP.

Grabe (1958), on the other hand, proposes that the phosphorylation associated with $NADH_2$ oxidation involves the formation of a phosphatidyl$\sim FADH_2$ intermediate:

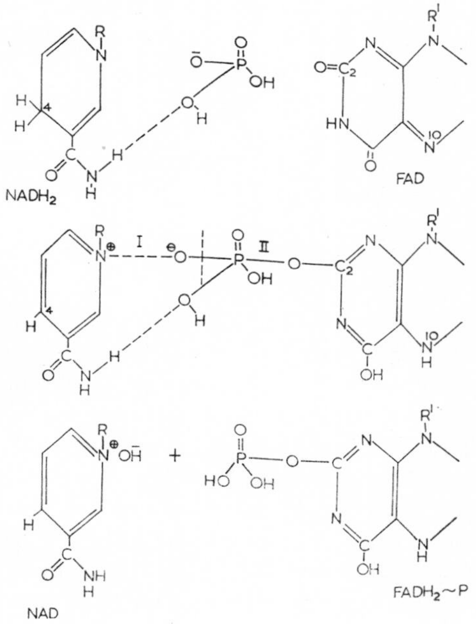

15

The nicotinamide ring of $NADH_2$ and the isoalloxazine ring of FAD are aligned in parallel planes so that the nicotinamide N-atom lies opposite the C-2 atom of riboflavin. Inorganic phosphate is bound between the two coenzymes by means of a hydrogen bond to the $-NH_2$ group of the nicotinamide ring. A hydrogen atom is transferred from the 4-position of the nicotinamide ring to the N-10 position of FAD. The simultaneous transfer of an electron from the nicotinamide N-atom to the $C=O$ group of FAD leaves the nicotinamide N-atom with a positive charge and gives the $C=O$ group of FAD an increased electron density. The positive charge of the nicotinamide N-atom attracts the negatively charged O-atom of the phosphate ion by an electrostatic bond (I). The electron transferred to the $C=O$ group tends to form bond (II). As a result of these two bonds, $FADH_2 \sim P$ is formed. Phosphoryl $FADH_2$ is a high energy compound which may phosphorylate ADP either directly or during subsequent oxidation. In this theory uncoupling and the induction of ATP-ase by DNP are suggested to be the result of a competition between DNP and O^- of inorganic phosphate for the quaternary nitrogen of the nicotinamide ring. This competition prevents the formation of $FADH_2 \sim P$ Grabe's theory provides a satisfactory explanation for the structural requirement of respiratory chain phosphorylation. However, in common with all Type 2 mechanisms, this theory is not consistent with the observation that reducible components of the respiratory chain do not appear to be intermediates in the phosphorylation reactions.

It is pertinent to note that the scheme described for vitamin K and for FAD both involve the formation of a phosphorylated hydroquinone. A similar role has been postulated for coenzyme Q in the phosphorylation occurring between cytochromes b and c_1.

Resolution of Respiratory Chain Phosphorylation

Four types of soluble factors are known to stimulate, or be required for the coupling of phosphorylation to hydrogen transfer. These factors are Mg^{++}, RNA, certain quinones and various protein factors. The addition of Mg^{++} is necessary to restore phosphorylation in animal and bacterial systems which have been resolved into a particulate oxidizing fraction and a soluble protein fraction. In the bacterial system derived from *Alcaligenes faecalis*, RNA is required in addition to Mg^{++} in order to couple the $NADH_2$-oxidizing particles with the soluble fraction. The possible participation of the quinones vitamin K and coenzyme Q in phosphorylation has been discussed above and on p. 194. A number of different soluble protein factors have been demonstrated to be required for respiratory chain phosphorylation in animal and bacterial systems. The precise relationship between these factors is unknown.

Pinchot (1960) has provided evidence for the formation of a high energy intermediate by a particulate phosphorylating complex isolated from *A. faecalis*. When the complex was incubated with $NADH_2$ (but not NAD), a soluble fraction was released which catalysed the net synthesis of ATP from phosphate and ADP. It was suggested that the oxidation of $NADH_2$ produced a high energy intermediate which dissociated from the particulate complex. Addition of ADP and phosphate to the soluble fraction containing the high energy intermediate resulted in the synthesis of ATP.

Fractionation of respiratory chain phosphorylation in plant mitochondria has not yet been performed.

READING LIST

BEEVERS H. (1960) *Respiratory Metabolism in Plants*. Ed. Brown A.H. Row, Peterson & Co., White Plains, New York

CONN E.E. (1960) Comparative Biochemistry of Electron Transport. In *Comparative Biochemistry* 1, 441. Ed. Florkin M. & Mason H.S. Acad. Press, New York

JAMES W.O. & LEECH R.M. (1960) The Plant Cytochromes. *Endeavour* 19, 74

HACKETT D. (1959) Respiratory Mechanisms in Higher Plants. *Ann. Rev. Pl. Physiol.* 10, 113

GREEN D.E. (1959) Electron Transport and Oxidative Phosphorylation. *Adv. Enz.* 21, 73

SLATER E.C. (1958) The Constitution of the Respiratory Chain in Animal Tissues. *Adv. Enz.* 20, 147

RACKER E. (1961) Mechanisms of Synthesis of Adenosine Triphosphate. *Adv. Enz.* 23, 323

LEHNINGER A.L. (1953–4) *Oxidative Phosphorylation*. Harvey Lectures Ser. 49, 176

SLATER E.C. (1958) Mechanism of Oxidative Phosphorylation. *Rev. Pure Appl. Chem.* 8, 221

LITERATURE CITED

BALL E.G. (1938) *Biochem. Z.* 295, 262

BALL E.G. (1942) *A Symposium on Respiratory Enzymes*. The University of Wisconsin Press, Madison

BEINERT H. & SANDS R.H. (1959) *Biochem. Biophys. Res. Commun.* 1, 171

BLACKMAN F.F. & PARIJA P. (1928) *Proc. Roy. Soc.* B 103, 412

BONNER W.D. & VOSS D.O. (1961) *Nature* 191, 682

BOYER P.D. (1957) *Proc. Int. Symp. on Enzyme Chem. Tokyo and Kyoto.* IUB Symp. Series 2, 301. Pergamon Press, London

CHANCE B. & HACKETT D.P. (1959) *Pl. Physiol.* 34, 33

CHANCE B. & WILLIAMS G.R. (1955) *J. Biol. Chem.* 217, 409

CHANCE B. & WILLIAMS G.R. (1956) *Adv. Enz.* 17, 65

COHN M. (1956) *Biochim. Biophys. Acta* 20, 92

DONALDSON K.O., NASON A. & GARRETT R.H. (1958) *J. Biol. Chem.* 233, 572

EHRENBERG A. & THEORELL H. (1955) *Acta Chem. Scand.* 9, 1193

GRABE B.G. (1958) *Biochim. Biophys. Acta* **30**, 560
GRANICK S. (1961) *Pl. Physiol. Suppl.* **36**, xlviii
GREEN D.E. & LESTER R.L. (1959) *Fed. Proc.* **18**, 987
GRIFFITH T., HELLMAN K.P. & BYERRUM R.U. (1960) *J. Biol. Chem.* **235**, 800
HACKETT D.P., HAAS D.W., GRIFFITHS D.K. & NIEDERPRUEM D.J. (1960) *Pl. Physiol.* **35**, 8
HARRISON W.H., BOYER P.D. & FALCONE A.D. (1955) *J. Biol. Chem.* **215**, 303
LUNDERGÅRDH H. (1952) *Arkiv. Kemi* **5**, 97
LUNDERGÅRDH H. (1959) *Biochim. Biophys. Acta* **35**, 340
MANN P.J.G. (1955) *Biochem. J.* **59**, 609
MILLERD A., BONNER J., AXELROD B. & BANDURSKI R.S. (1951) *Proc. Nat. Acad. Sci. U.S.A.* **37**, 855
MYERS D.K. & SLATER E.C. (1957) *Biochem. J.* **67**, 572
PINCHOT G.P. (1960) *Proc. Nat. Acad. Sci. U.S.A.* **46**, 929
PUMPHREY A.M. & REDFEARN E.R. (1959) *Biochem. J.* **72**, 2P
PURVIS J.L. (1960) *Biochim. Biophys. Acta*, **38**, 435
SHEMIN D. (1956) *Harvey Lectures* **50**, 258
SLATER E.C. (1960) In *Encyclopedia of Pl. Physiol.* **12**, 114. Ed. Ruhland W. Springer Verlag, Berlin
SZENT-GYÖRGYI A. (1957) *Bioenergetics*. Acad. Press, New York
VENNESLAND B. (1958) *Fed. Proc.* **17**, 1150
WESSELS J.S.C. (1954) *Rec. Trav. Chim.* **73**, 529

CHAPTER 6

PHOTOSYNTHESIS

The overall process of photosynthesis in plants is represented by the empirical equation:

$$\text{Light}$$
$$CO_2 + H_2O \rightarrow (CH_2O) + O_2 \quad \Delta G^\circ = 115 \text{ kcal} \quad (6.1)$$

Carbon dioxide is reduced to the level of carbohydrate with the concomitant evolution of oxygen. The reaction is strongly endergonic and is driven by the absorption of light energy. Energy stored in the form of carbohydrate and other reduced compounds may subsequently be 'recovered' in the form of ATP during respiration and respiratory chain phosphorylation. Recent developments have shown that light energy can be converted directly into ATP during photosynthetic phosphorylation. Although eqn (6.1) accurately represents the overall stoichiometry of photosynthesis in plants, it does not define the basic reaction of photosynthesis. In photosynthetic bacteria, for example, oxygen is never evolved and compounds such as acetate can replace carbon dioxide as a source of carbon. It appears that the basic reaction in photosynthesis is the phosphorylation of ADP to ATP by cyclic photosynthetic phosphorylation (see p. 244).

The study of the biochemistry of photosynthesis may be considered as dating from 1905 when Blackmann proposed that photosynthesis consisted of a light reaction and a dark reaction. This hypothesis has subsequently been confirmed in a number of ways. For example it has been shown that the photosynthetic yield from flashing light of high intensity is increased to a maximum by lengthening the dark period between flashes. Under these conditions of very high light intensity, the rate of photosynthesis is limited by the rate of the dark reaction. Including a dark period after the flash of light allows the dark reaction to 'catch up' with the light reaction. Recently the existence of a dark and light reaction has been demonstrated in isolated chloroplasts. The light reaction produces a 'chemical potential' which subsequently generates $NADPH_2$ and ATP.

These products constitute 'assimilatory power' which is used for the reduction of carbon dioxide in the dark reaction.

THE CHLOROPLAST

The photosynthetic apparatus is located in the chloroplast. The chloroplasts of higher plants are disc-shaped bodies ranging in length from 1–10μ. They are characterized by a system of lamellae which often become piled one upon the other to form grana. Optical studies originally suggested that the grana were suspended in a homogeneous matrix called the stroma. Studies with the electron microscope have revealed, however, that the grana are interconnected by lamellae. There is some disagreement on the fine structure of the lamellae. One view is that the grana lamellae and stroma lamellae are continuous and that the grana are regions where the stroma lamellae are thickened. In this book the term stroma will be used to describe the apparently homogeneous matrix lying between the lamellae.

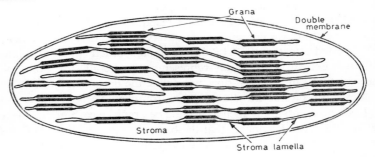

FIG. 6.1. Schematic representation of a chloroplast (von Wettstein 1959).

On a dry weight basis the chloroplasts are approximately 50 per cent protein, 35 per cent lipid and 7 per cent pigment.

Pigments of the chloroplast belong to two general classes — the chlorophylls and the carotenoids (carotenes and xanthophylls). In normal green leaves there is much more chlorophyll than carotenoids, the ratio sometimes approaching 5/1.

The chlorophylls are all magnesium porphyrin compounds. In higher plants the major chlorophylls are chlorophylls a and b. The structure of chlorophyll a is shown in Fig. 6.2. In chlorophyll b the methyl group attached to carbon atom 3 is replaced by a formyl ($-CHO$) group. The ester between phytol ($C_{20}H_{39}OH$) and the propionic acid side chain may be cleaved by the enzyme chlorophyll esterase (chlorophyllase).

The chlorophylls are localized in the lamellae where they appear to exist as a complex with lipid and protein. It has been suggested that chlorophyll is aligned between lipid and protein so that the hydrophilic porphyrin head is associated with protein, and the lipophilic phytol chain is associated with lipid layers. An enzymatically active chlorophyll-protein complex (chloroplastin) has been isolated from *Euglena* chloroplasts. This complex catalyses the Hill reaction (p. 232) and light catalysed incorporation of inorganic phosphate into labile phosphate.

The biosynthesis of chlorophyll up to the stage of protoporphyrin IX has been described on p. 188. A probable scheme for the further conversion of protoporphyrin IX to chlorophyll is shown in Fig. 6.2. All the intermediates in this scheme have been demonstrated in mutants of *Chlorella*. In addition, protoporphyrin monomethyl ester has been isolated from barley seedlings treated with δ-aminolaevulinic acid, and magnesium vinyl phaeoporphyrin a_5 is produced from δ-aminolaevulinic acid by etiolated barley and bean plastids. Two alternative pathways are shown for the conversion of protoporphyrin IX to magnesium protoporphyrin monomethyl ester. Chromatophores of *Rhodopseudomonas spheroides* have been shown to convert magnesium protoporphyrin IX to magnesium protoporphyrin monomethyl ester in the presence of S-adenosyl methionine. This observation is consistent with the participation of magnesium protoporphyrin IX as an intermediate in the formation of magnesium protoporphyrin monomethyl ester.

In leaves the main carotenoid constituent is β-carotene. The most common xanthophyll in green leaves is lutein, a dihydroxy derivative of α-carotene. Some properties and the possible biosynthetic route of the carotenoids are discussed in Chapter 8.

Photosynthesis proceeds most effectively in higher plants by light absorbed by chlorophyll *a*. The role of chlorophyll *b*, carotenoids and other accessory pigments is not fully understood. Chlorophyll *a* is the only pigment common to all photosynthetic organisms. It has therefore been suggested that chlorophyll *a* is the only pigment which donates energy directly to the photosynthetic reaction, and that all other pigments transfer their absorbed energy to chlorophyll *a*. This hypothesis is consistent with the action spectrum for photosynthesis, and with the observation that accessory pigments can sensitize the fluorescence of chlorophyll *a*. Other physiological functions have been postulated for the accessory pigments. For example it has been suggested that chlorophyll *b*, caroten-

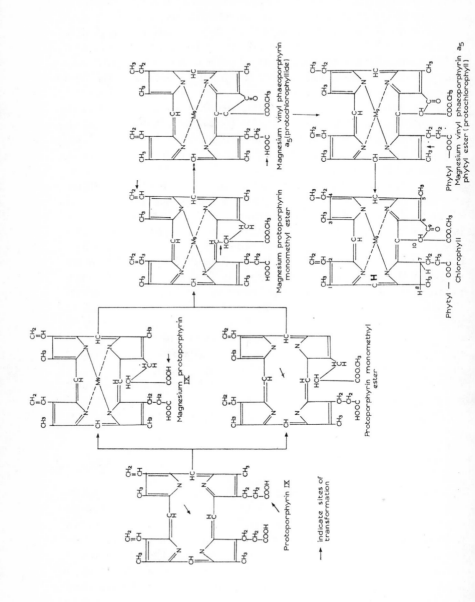

oids and phycocyanins (present in blue-green and red algae) play a role in protecting the cell from the photochemical reactions induced by illuminating chlorophyll. A possible role of accessory pigments in oxygen evolution is discussed on p. 243.

The galactolipids described on p. 262 comprise approximately two-thirds of the chloroplast lipids. The remaining lipid consists chiefly of phosphatidyl glycerol and the sulfolipid described on p. 262.

In addition to the major components mentioned above, chloroplasts contain a number of other compounds which are present in much lower concentrations. Among these minor constituents may be mentioned neutral triglycerides, cytochromes f and b_6 (p. 191), plastoquinone (p. 191) and pyridine nucleotides.

THE LIGHT REACTION

The light reaction is the special feature of photosynthetic cells. Most of the reactions involved in carbon dioxide fixation in the dark phase, on the other hand, are not unique to photosynthetic cells.

The essential function of the light reaction in plants is the production of 'assimilatory power' (ATP and $NADPH_2$) required for the assimilation of carbon dioxide in subsequent dark reactions. On the basis of the scheme proposed for the dark reaction (see p. 249), two equivalents of $NADPH_2$ and three equivalents of ATP are required for the assimilation of each equivalent of carbon dioxide to the oxidation level of carbohydrate:

$$3CO_2 + 6NADPH_2 + 9ATP + 5H_2O \rightarrow \text{glyceraldehyde-3-phosphate} +$$
$$6NADP + 9ADP + 8P_i \quad (6.2)$$

In higher plants, oxygen is evolved simultaneously with the generation of 'assimilatory power'.

In the light reaction, or photochemical reaction, light energy is converted into a 'chemical potential'. The student is referred to Calvin (1961) for a discussion of the first steps in which the energy of captured photons is stabilized as a chemical potential. To many biologists the light reaction is equivalent to the photolysis of water, although this concept has been recently challenged (see p. 241). At the present time the first stable, chemically-defined products of the light reaction demonstrated in plants are $NADPH_2$ and ATP.

Generation of NADPH$_2$

Thunberg in 1923 suggested that photosynthesis involved the production of 'active hydrogen' from water. Experimental evidence for this hypothesis was provided 14 years later by Hill who demonstrated that isolated chloroplasts, upon illumination, catalyse the reduction of an oxidant (A) and the evolution of oxygen as follows:

$$\underset{\text{Chloroplasts}}{\overset{\text{Light}}{H_2O + A \rightarrow AH_2 + \tfrac{1}{2}O_2}} \tag{6.3}$$

This reaction is called the Hill or chloroplast reaction. A number of oxidants have been employed, including ferric ions, benzoquinone and various dyes such as 2,6-dichlorophenol indophenol. Carbon dioxide is not assimilated, nor can it act as a hydrogen acceptor. However, catalytic quantities of carbon dioxide have been reported to stimulate the Hill reaction. The mechanism of this stimulation is not clear. The Hill reaction shares two characteristic features of plant photosynthesis: the conversion of light energy into chemical energy, and the production of molecular oxygen.

It was suggested that the primary light reaction in the Hill reaction and photosynthesis was the photolysis of water to form reducing potential (H) and oxidizing potential (OH). In photosynthesis (H) ultimately reduces carbon dioxide to form carbohydrates, but in the Hill reaction (H) reduces the added oxidant. In both the Hill reaction and photosynthesis (OH) is ultimately released as molecular oxygen. These reactions are presented in Table 6.1. Implicit in this scheme is that all the oxygen produced in photosynthesis comes from water. Using $H_2{}^{18}O$ it has been demonstrated that oxygen evolved during photosynthesis came from water and not from carbon dioxide.

This hypothesis of the photolysis of water applied equally well to photosynthetic bacteria. Photosynthetic bacteria, like plants, are able to convert carbon dioxide into carbohydrates. They differ from plants in that oxygen is *never* evolved, and photosynthesis is dependent upon the presence of a reducing substance (e.g. H_2S, H_2). van Niel (1950) proposed that in these organisms the primary light requiring reaction is also a photolysis of water. In common with plants, (H) is ultimately utilized for the reduction of carbon dioxide to carbohydrate. Bacteria differ from plants in that (OH) is not evolved as oxygen, but oxidizes the added reductant (Table 6.1).

The precise relationship of the Hill reaction to photosynthesis remained

TABLE 6.1

Relationship between the Hill reaction and plant and bacterial photosynthesis

	Hill reaction	Plant photosynthesis	Bacterial photosynthesis
Primary light reaction	$4H_2O \rightarrow 4(H) + 4(OH)$ Photolysis of water common to all photosynthetic reactions		
Utilization of reducing potential	$4(H) + 2A\dagger \rightarrow 2AH_2$	$4(H) + CO_2 \rightarrow (CH_2O) + H_2O$	
Utilization of oxidizing potential	$4(OH) \rightarrow 2H_2O + O_2$		$4(OH) + 2H_2B\ddagger \rightarrow 4H_2O + 2B$
Sum	$2H_2O^*\S + 2A \rightarrow 2AH_2 + O_2^*$	$2H_2O^* + CO_2 \rightarrow (CH_2O) + O_2^* + H_2O\Vert$	$4H_2O + CO_2 + 2H_2B \rightarrow (CH_2O) + 2B + 5H_2O\Vert$

Notes: † A = added oxidant such as ferric ions, benzoquinone etc.
‡ H_2B = external reductant such as H_2S or H_2.
§ The asterisk shows the origin of the oxygen atoms evolved in the Hill reaction and plant photosynthesis.
‖ These equations may be simplified by subtraction of H_2O molecules. However the simplified equation for plant photosynthesis would not be consistent with water being the source of evolved oxygen. The simplified equation for bacterial photosynthesis; $CO_2 + 2H_2B \rightarrow (CH_2O) + 2B + H_2O$ erroneously implies that H_2B is the source of reducing potential.

uncertain for many years. None of the artificial hydrogen acceptors, when reduced, would participate in the reduction of carbon dioxide. In 1956, NADP was implicated as a key cofactor in the utilization of light energy. In contrast to the reduction of artificial hydrogen acceptors, the reduction of NADP required the presence of the enzyme photosynthetic pyridine nucleotide reductase (PPNR):

$$\text{NADP} + H_2O \xrightarrow[\text{PPNR}]{\text{Light}} \text{Chloroplasts} \rightarrow \text{NADPH}_2 + \tfrac{1}{2}O_2 \qquad (6.4)$$

The stoichiometry of this reaction results in the production of 2 moles of NADPH_2 per mole of oxygen evolved, and is thus in accordance with the requirement of 2 moles of NADPH_2 per mole of CO_2 reduced. PPNR when originally isolated was shown to be active with both NADP and NAD. Further purification has revealed that the enzyme is specific for NADP and that the reduction of NAD probably proceeds via a trans-hydrogenase which has been isolated from spinach leaves:

$$\text{NADPH}_2 + \text{NAD} \rightarrow \text{NADP} + \text{NADH}_2 \qquad (6.5)$$

Cell-free preparations of photosynthetic bacteria also catalyse the reduction of pyridine nucleotides in the light. In contrast to chloroplasts, bacterial chromatophores contain a tightly bound NAD-specific pyridine nucleotide reductase. The reduction of each equivalent of NAD is coupled to the oxidation of one equivalent of a reductant such as succinate or FMNH_2.

Generation of ATP

In 1954 a completely new mechanism for generating ATP was reported. In the presence of catalytic quantities of a cofactor such as FMN or vitamin K_3 (menadione) chloroplasts were found to catalyse a light-dependent phosphorylation of ADP to ATP. This type of phosphorylation in which the only observable net change is a phosphorylation of ADP to ATP is termed cyclic photosynthetic phosphorylation. Cyclic photosynthetic phosphorylation has also been demonstrated in algae and in chromatophores of photosynthetic bacteria.

Subsequent research has shown that a second type of photosynthetic phosphorylation is associated with the reduction of NADP:

$$H_2O + \text{NADP} + \text{ADP} + P \xrightarrow[\text{PPNR}]{\text{Chloroplasts}} \text{Light} \rightarrow \text{NADPH}_2 + \text{ATP} + \tfrac{1}{2}O_2 \qquad (6.6)$$

A non-physiological variant of reaction (6.6) is the following in which NADP is replaced by ferricyanide:

$$H_2O + 2Fe^{+++} + ADP + P \xrightarrow[\text{Light}]{\text{Chloroplasts}} 2Fe^{++} + 2H^+ + ATP + \tfrac{1}{2}O_2 \quad (6.7)$$

No phosphorylation is associated with the reduction of dyes (see p. 242) or quinones. Non-cyclic photosynthetic phosphorylation has been demonstrated also during the reduction of NAD by bacterial chromatophores.

The processes of hydrogen transfer from water to the hydrogen acceptor (pyridine nucleotide or ferricyanide) and of phosphorylation are coupled in a manner similar to that of respiratory chain phosphorylation. Thus the reduction of ferricyanide or NADP is stimulated by the presence of ADP and phosphate. Uncoupling may be effected by ammonium ions, but not by the low concentrations of dinitrophenol which effectively uncouple respiratory chain phosphorylation. Uncoupling may also be achieved by the addition of arsenate in the presence of ADP. The significance of this ADP requirement is discussed on p. 240. It appears that the Hill reaction as normally measured in the absence of phosphorylation cofactors represents an uncoupled fragment of non-cyclic phosphorylation.

The two types of phosphorylation are indicated in Fig. 6.3. The reduction of NADP is accompanied by non-cyclic photosynthetic phosphorylation, 1 molecule of ATP being synthesized for each atom of oxygen involved, or molecule of NADP reduced (Fig. 6.3A). The precise stoichiometry of reactions (6.6) and (6.7) is uncertain. It is observed experimentally that 1 mole of ATP is formed for each 2 moles of electrons transferred in the reduction of ferricyanide or NADP. However, considerable reduction of ferricyanide or NADP proceeds in the absence of phosphorylating cofactors. When electrons carried by this 'non-phosphorylating' mechanism are subtracted from the total electron flux, P/2e ratios approaching 2 are obtained.

Addition of catalytic quantities (approximately 3×10^{-5} M) of FMN or vitamin K_3 to the system (Fig. 6.3B) completely abolishes oxygen evolution and net NADP reduction, and initiates the more rapid cyclic type of photosynthetic phosphorylation.

If 'microcatalytic' quantities (between 3×10^{-7} M and 3×10^{-6} M) of FMN or vitamin K_3 are added to the non-cyclic photosynthetic phosphorylation system, ATP formation is increased without appreciably decreasing oxygen evolution and concomitant NADP reduction. The ratio of ATP to NADPH$_2$ formed becomes greater than 1. It appears that cyclic photosynthetic phosphorylation is superimposed upon the non-cyclic process under these conditions.

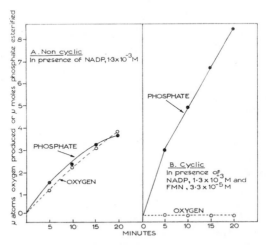

FIG. 6.3. Types of photosynthetic phosphorylation (Arnon, Whatley & Allen 1958).

The evolution of each molecule of oxygen in photosynthesis is associated with the assimilation of 1 molecule of carbon dioxide, which requires 2 molecules of NADPH$_2$, and 3 molecules of ATP. Non-cyclic photosynthetic phosphorylation therefore generates all of the NADPH$_2$ and two-thirds of the ATP required for the assimilation of carbon dioxide to triosephosphate. Cyclic photosynthetic phosphorylation, on the other hand, provides adequate ATP but no NADPH$_2$.

The requirement by isolated chloroplasts for both cyclic and non-cyclic photosynthetic phosphorylation in the assimilation of carbon dioxide to triose phosphate has been demonstrated. Under the conditions shown in Fig. 6.3, which permit either non-cyclic or cyclic photosynthetic phosphorylation, the main product of carbon dioxide assimilation is 3-phosphoglyceric acid. In the presence of 'microcatalytic' quantities of FMN, the combined processes of cyclic and non-cyclic photosynthetic phosphorylation permit the assimilation of carbon dioxide to triose and hexose phosphates.

A number of hydrogen carriers in addition to FMN and vitamin K$_3$ catalyse cyclic photosynthetic phosphorylation. The highest rates of phosphorylation have been obtained with the artificial hydrogen carrier phenazine methosulphate (PMS). The activity of PMS may be due to its photoconversion in the presence of oxygen to pyocyanin. The high rates of cyclic photosynthetic phosphorylation in the presence of PMS are probably due to a 'by pass' of one or more rate limiting steps. The cofactor(s) which catalyse photosynthetic phosphorylation *in vivo* is uncertain. FMN is a constituent of chloroplasts. The presence of vitamin K in chloroplasts is in dispute (p. 194). Recently it has been reported that plastoquinone, which is a normal constituent of chloroplasts, is essential for cyclic photosynthetic phosphorylation with PMS as a cofactor. Plastoquinone can also undergo oxidation-reduction reactions in the chloroplast.

Mechanism of Photosynthetic Phosphorylation

At present two types of mechanism have been postulated. The first is based on the hypothesis that the primary light reaction is the photolysis of water. The second, originally proposed by Arnon (1959), claims that the primary light reaction is the activation of an electron of chlorophyll to a higher energy level. Arnon *et al.* (1961) have further proposed that an additional light reaction associated with a pigment other than chlorophyll *a*, is required for the oxygen-evolving sequence in plants.

MECHANISM BASED ON THE PHOTOLYSIS OF WATER

The initial reaction is a photolysis of water to reducing potential (H) and oxidizing potential (OH).

Non-cyclic photosynthetic phosphorylation involves the reduction of NADP (in the presence of PPNR) or ferricyanide by (H) with the concomitant evolution of oxygen from (OH). The *reductive* phosphorylation observed in photosynthesis and the *oxidative* phosphorylation observed in respiration probably involve the same basic mechanism: coupling of phosphorylation to an exergonic reaction in which hydrogen is passed from one hydrogen carrier to another. In non-cyclic photosynthetic phosphorylation, the available evidence suggests that some acceptor, at present unidentified, accepts hydrogen before NADP. Oxidation of this unidentified hydrogen carrier and concomitant reduction of NADP is coupled to phosphorylation.

In the presence of a number of cofactors including FMN, vitamin K_3 and PMS, cyclic photosynthetic phosphorylation occurs. The normal mechanism of cyclic photosynthetic phosphorylation appears to involve a recombination of reducing potential (H) with oxidizing potential (OH) to reform water. The effect of oxygen is complicated and not well understood. Under certain experimental conditions (e.g. low concentrations of cofactor), the presence of oxygen greatly stimulates the rate of cyclic photosynthetic phosphorylation. Under these conditions it appears that free oxygen, and not an oxygen precursor (OH), is an intermediate. Oxygen-catalysed cyclic photosynthetic phosphorylation is illustrated

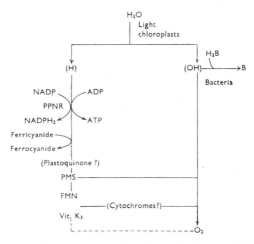

FIG. 6.4. Scheme for photosynthetic phosphorylation based on the photolysis of water.

by dashed lines in Fig. 6.4. Arnon has compared the efficiency of conversion of light energy into the chemical energy of ATP under anaerobic and aerobic conditions and has concluded that the participation of oxygen lowers the efficiency of phosphorylation.

The only site of phosphorylation which has been demonstrated directly is that associated with the reduction of NADP or ferricyanide. It is likely that additional sites of phosphorylation are present, probably associated with the oxygen-evolving sequence of reactions, or with the recombination of (H) with (OH).

It has been postulated that the cytochromes play a role in the recombination of (H) with (OH), and that phosphorylations occur along a cytochrome chain in photosynthetic phosphorylation in a manner similar to that postulated for respiratory chain phosphorylation. Characteristic spectral changes are observed when leaves or chloroplasts are illuminated.

These changes are consistent with a light-initiated oxidation of cytochrome f by (OH) and reduction of cytochrome b_6 by (H). Further evidence for the participation of cytochromes consists of the observation that cyclic photosynthetic phosphorylation catalysed by washed chromatophores of *Chromatium* and *R. rubrum* is inhibited by antimycin A and 2-heptyl-4-hydroxy-quinoline-N-oxide (HOQNO), which, in the respiratory chain, inhibits the reduction of cytochrome c by cytochrome b. Antimycin A has been reported not to cause a significant inhibition of cyclic photosynthetic phosphorylation by chloroplasts. However, these reports should be re-examined, since in bacterial chromatophores, resistance to antimycin A is afforded by factor(s) in the supernatant fluid. HOQNO is a potent inhibitor of non-cyclic photosynthetic phosphorylation in chloroplasts. It is a less effective inhibitor of cyclic photosynthetic phosphorylation with FMN and vitamin K_3, and does not inhibit cyclic photosynthetic phosphorylation with PMS (Avron, 1961).

The scheme of cyclic photosynthetic phosphorylation shown in Fig. 6.4 shows many of the basic features of respiratory chain phosphorylation. In the respiratory chain, phosphorylation is coupled to the passage of hydrogen from a reducing substrate, through a number of hydrogen carriers to the oxidant, oxygen. In cyclic photosynthetic phosphorylation, both the reductant (H) and the oxidant (OH) are generated by the photolysis of water. The reductant passes through the hydrogen carriers (possibly FMN and cytochromes) finally combining with the oxidant (OH) to reform water. However, in contrast to respiratory chain phosphorylation, the pyridine nucleotides do not appear to be directly involved in cyclic photosynthetic phosphorylation. Under certain conditions (low concentrations of FMN and chloroplasts) a requirement for NADP and PPNR can be demonstrated for cyclic photosynthetic phosphorylation with FMN. However under optimal FMN concentrations, no such requirement for NADP and PPNR can be demonstrated. Furthermore, during cyclic photosynthetic phosphorylation with optimal concentrations of FMN, there is no turnover of hydrogen in added NADP. The evidence available at present therefore does not justify placing NADP in the main chain of hydrogen flow, but suggests that NADP is on a branch pathway. Another difference between photosynthetic phosphorylation and respiratory chain phosphorylation is that the uncoupler DNP does not significantly inhibit cyclic photosynthetic phosphorylation.

At present little information is available on the mechanism of the reactions whereby hydrogen flow is coupled to the synthesis of ATP.

16

A coupling between hydrogen flow and phosphorylation has been demonstrated in non-cyclic photosynthetic phosphorylation. By analogy with respiratory chain phosphorylation it has been postulated that some high energy intermediate, similar to $A \sim I$ in the respiratory chain, is produced during photosynthetic phosphorylation. For continuous hydrogen flow to proceed, A and I must be regenerated, either by the addition of ADP and P to form ATP, or by uncoupling. The mechanism of non-cyclic photosynthetic phosphorylation may be represented as follows:

$$AH_2 + B + I \rightarrow A \sim I + BH_2$$
$$A \sim I + ADP + P \rightarrow A + I + ATP$$

In the above scheme AH_2 = an unknown reducing compound produced by the photolysis of water: $B =$ NADP or ferricyanide; $I =$ an intermediate or inhibitor. By analogy with the mechanism of action of DNP it might be expected that the addition of an uncoupler such as ammonium ions would induce the breakdown of ATP. In the presence of high concentrations of sulphydryl compounds such as glutathione or cysteine and catalytic quantities of PMS, chloroplasts catalyse a photohydrolysis of ATP to ADP and P. The relation of this ATP-ase to photosynthetic phosphorylation is suggested by its dependence on light and PMS and by its inhibition by diiodohydroxybenzene, a potent inhibitor of photosynthetic phosphorylation. It is not known what effect ammonium ions have on this photohydrolysis reaction.

Uncoupling by arsenate of photosynthetic phosphorylation associated with ferricyanide reduction requires the presence of ADP. It was therefore originally suggested that ADP reacted before phosphate to form a high energy compound of the type $A \sim ADP$.

Recent work has failed to corroborate this sequence, but rather indicates that in photosynthetic phosphorylation, as in respiratory chain phosphorylation, a high energy phosphate compound is formed first, which subsequently reacts with ADP to form ATP. These observations are as follows:

(a) During photosynthetic phosphorylation with PMS the bridge oxygen atom of ATP does not arise from phosphate and is in all probability furnished by ADP.

(b) A labile intermediate is formed by illuminating chloroplasts with ^{32}P in the absence of ADP. Subsequent addition of ADP results in the synthesis of $AT^{32}P$. This observation suggests that in the light a high energy phosphate intermediate was produced which could phosphorylate ADP in a dark reaction. Experiments in which ADP was incubated in the light failed to reveal any formation of a high energy ADP intermediate.

THE ELECTRON FLOW MECHANISM

In this mechanism, the basic reaction is the expulsion by absorbed light of an electron from chlorophyll to a higher energy level. This expulsion of an electron leaves chlorophyll in an oxidized state. The expelled electron may return to oxidized chlorophyll as follows:

(a) The expelled electron may return directly without going through the energy transforming steps of photosynthetic phosphorylation. This mechanism results in fluorescence, and the energy of the expelled electron appears as light.

(b) The expelled electron may be directed through the electron transport chain of cyclic photosynthetic phosphorylation resulting in the production of ATP.

(c) In non-cyclic photosynthetic phosphorylation the expelled electron may be transferred to an added oxidant such as NADP (in plants) or NAD (in bacteria) or ferricyanide. The electron returned to chlorophyll is derived from:

(1) hydroxyl ions produced by the *ionization* (not photolysis) of water. Utilization of hydroxyl ions as an electron donor with concomitant evolution of oxygen is unique to plants. Evidence will be presented that the transfer of an electron from the oxidation level of hydroxyl ions to the oxidation level of the cytochromes requires an additional light reaction.

(2) stronger reducing agents such as H_2S, succinate, thiosulphate etc. are required for bacterial photosynthesis, and for demonstrating non-cyclic photosynthetic phosphorylation coupled to NAD reduction by bacterial extracts. Under the appropriate conditions (see below) chloroplasts can also catalyse a bacterial-type non-cyclic photosynthetic phosphorylation using an external reducing agent.

The electron flow mechanism is illustrated in Fig. 6.5. For the sake of simplicity, the expulsion of only one electron is shown, whereas two electrons are actually required for the reduction of each molecule of pyridine nucleotide, and four electrons for the liberation of each molecule of oxygen. A requirement of two light reactions for the transfer of each electron to NADP would result in a minimum quantum requirement of eight for the liberation of each molecule of oxygen. This figure is consistent with a quantum requirement of seven to nine reported by Emerson's group.

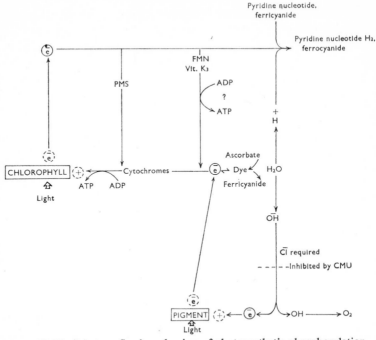

Fig. 6.5. The 'electron flow' mechanism of photosynthetic phosphorylation.

Losada, Whatley & Arnon (1961), have recently separated the two light reactions shown in Fig. 6.5. The light reaction associated with the evolution of oxygen is illustrated by the results of Table 6.2.

When ferricyanide is used as an electron acceptor, the evolution of each μatom of oxygen is associated with the phosphorylation of 1 μmole of ADP to ATP by the process of non-cyclic photosynthetic phosphorylation (Vessel 1). When a dye such as 2,6-dichlorophenol indophenol or 2,3,6-trichlorophenol indophenol was used as electron acceptor,

TABLE 6.2

Separation of photo-production of oxygen and photophosphorylation in chloroplasts

Vessel No.	Treatment	Effective electron acceptor	Oxygen produced μatoms	ATP formed μmoles
1	Ferricyanide	Ferricyanide	3·3	3·5
2	Ferricyanide + dye	Oxidized dye	3·5	0·8

oxygen evolution proceeded unaltered but phosphorylation was virtually abolished (Vessel 2). The catalytic quantities of dye added were kept in the oxidized state by non-enzymatic oxidation by ferricyanide. It was suggested that the oxidized dye withdraws electrons at the oxidation level of the cytochromes, and so by-passes the phosphorylation step between the cytochromes and chlorophyll. This non-phosphorylative process associated with reduction of dye and with oxygen evolution represents the photo-oxidation of hydroxyl ions. Although the nature of the 'pigment' that is involved in the photo-oxidation of hydroxyl ions is at present unknown, the action spectrum for the process suggests that it is not chlorophyll *a*. It has been suggested that the 'pigment' may be chlorophyll *b* or an accessory pigment that is found only in oxygen-evolving organisms (higher plants and algae).

Whereas the photo-oxidation of hydroxyl ions described above is unique to higher plants, the second photochemical reaction, associated with chlorophyll, is common to all photosynthetic systems. Losada *et al.* (1961) have, in fact, demonstrated that in isolated chloroplasts, non-cyclic photosynthetic phosphorylation coupled to ferricyanide or pyridine nucleotide reduction and oxygen evolution, may be converted into a bacterial-type non-cyclic photosynthetic phosphorylation in which an external electron donor is required and oxygen is not evolved (Table 6.3). In the presence of NADP as an electron acceptor, non-cyclic photosynthetic phosphorylation occurs coupled to the reduction of NADP and evolution of oxygen. The omission of chloride ions and addition of *p*-chlorophenyl dimethylurea (CMU), by blocking oxygen evolution,

TABLE 6.3

Non-cyclic photophosphorylation of the bacterial type by chloroplasts

Vessel No.	Conditions	Effective electron donor	Oxygen evolved μatoms	NADP reduced μmoles	ATP formed μmoles
1	—	Hydroxyl ions	3·0	3·4	2·4
2	Omission of chloride Addition of CMU	None	0	0·5	0·2
3	Omission of chloride Addition of CMU, dye, ascorbate	Reduced dye	0	3·2	3·4

inhibits NADP reduction and concomitant phosphorylation (Vessel 2). Further addition of reducing dye (catalytic quantities of dye maintained in the reduced state by ascorbate) restores NADP reduction and phosphorylation (Vessel 3). Oxygen evolution, however, is not restored. These observations suggest that in chloroplasts the normal source of electrons (hydroxyl ions) for non-cyclic photosynthetic phosphorylation may be replaced by electrons donated by reduced dye at the oxidation level of cytochrome. The action spectrum determined between 630 mμ and 699 mμ for the photoreduction of NADP by chloroplasts in the presence of a reduced dye agreed with the absorption spectrum of chlorophyll a.

The evidence presented above for two light reactions is consistent with the observations of Emerson and others that photosynthesis is enhanced by supplementary light of a different wavelength ('Emerson effect'). The participation of two light reactions has also been postulated by Hill & Bendall (1960).

Physiological Significance of the Light Reaction

In higher plants the light reaction provides the 2 molecules of NADPH$_2$ and 3 molecules of ATP required for the assimilation of each molecule of carbon dioxide in a subsequent dark reaction. According to Arnon's group, the production of ATP appears to be the basic function of the light reaction; only in plants and certain types of bacterial photosynthesis is the reduction of pyridine nucleotides in the light necessary. For example, no additional reductant is required for the photoassimilation of acetate into cell material. Studies with cell-free extracts of *Chromatium* have shown that the main requirement for light in the photoassimilation of acetate is for the production of ATP by cyclic photosynthetic phosphorylation. When an organic carbon source is replaced by carbon dioxide, an additional reductant is required. When hydrogen is used as a reductant, the main role of light is still the production of ATP, since pyridine nucleotide reduction by hydrogen has been shown to be catalysed in a dark reaction. Photoassimilation of carbon dioxide in the presence of hydrogen donors other than hydrogen requires the expenditure of light energy for the reduction of pyridine nucleotide. Under these conditions light is therefore required for photosynthetic phosphorylation *and* reduction of pyridine nucleotides. Finally, photoassimilation of carbon dioxide with water as a reductant (as in higher plants) again requires the participation of light for photosynthetic phosphorylation and pyridine nucleotide reduction.

The relative rates of non-cyclic photosynthetic phosphorylation associated with NADP reduction, and of cyclic photosynthetic phosphorylation in the intact plant are at present unknown. Rates of photosynthetic phosphorylation with PMS of over 2000 μmoles P/mg chlorophyll/hr have been obtained with isolated chloroplasts. Such rates should more than satisfy the requirement for photosynthesis, which is in the order of 200 μmoles of carbon dioxide absorbed/mg chlorophyll/hr in an intact leaf under saturating light. Although a direct comparison between intact tissues and cell-free systems is not always valid, it appears that cyclic photosynthetic phosphorylation can more than satisfy the needs of photosynthesis and that cyclic photosynthetic phosphorylation may also provide ATP required for other endergonic reactions in the plant. Rates of NADP reduction with isolated chloroplasts of approximately 200 μmoles of $NADPH_2$/mg chlorophyll/hr are commonly observed. These rates would appear to provide adequate amounts of $NADPH_2$ for photosynthesis.

THE DARK REACTION

The participation of a dark reaction in photosynthesis was proposed by Blackman in 1905. In 1937 McAlister and Myers observed that algae continued to take up carbon dioxide for a short time after illumination ceased. The use of $^{14}CO_2$ permitted confirmation of McAlister and Myers' observation that a 'pick up' of carbon dioxide occurred in the dark, following a period of illumination. Recently, fractionation of chloroplasts into grana and stroma has permitted a physical separation of the light and dark reactions. The light phase was completed first by illuminating chloroplasts (in the appropriate reaction mixture) in the absence of carbon dioxide. Oxygen is evolved and substrate amounts of ATP and $NADPH_2$ are produced. The grana are then centrifuged and discarded. The remaining stroma, containing ATP and $NADPH_2$ produced in the preceding light reaction, is able to assimilate carbon dioxide to triose phosphate and sugar phosphates in the dark.

The chloroplast is considered the site of photosynthesis, capable of catalysing separately the light and dark reactions thereby effecting the reduction of carbon dioxide to triose phosphate and sugar phosphates. Whereas the rate of the light reaction (synthesis of ATP and reduction of NADP) catalysed by isolated chloroplasts is more than adequate to account for the rate of photosynthesis *in vivo* (see above), the overall rate of carbon dioxide assimilation by isolated chloroplasts is low. For example isolated chloroplasts catalyse rates of approximately 4 μmoles carbon dioxide fixed/mg chlorophyll/hr, compared to rates of 200 μmoles carbon dioxide/mg chlorophyll/hr in whole tissue. The reason for this discrepancy is not clear.

The Carbon Reduction Cycle

The availability of ^{14}C and the development of paper chromatography provided the facilities necessary to study the chemical reactions of photosynthesis. $^{14}CO_2$ was supplied to *Chlorella* and after a fixed time the cells were transferred to boiling alcohol. The radioactive products of photosynthesis were separated and identified by paper chromatography. By reducing the time of exposure to $^{14}CO_2$, fewer products were radioactive. With the shortest exposures only 3-phosphoglyceric acid (PGA) was labelled. It can thus be concluded that PGA is the first *stable* product of carbon dioxide fixation. Subsequent investigations were concerned with the nature of the acceptor molecule. The simple expectation that a C-2 molecule accepted carbon dioxide to form PGA was not fulfilled. The demonstration that C-5 and C-7 sugar phosphates were among the early products of photosynthesis, and the discovery of new enzymic reactions involving these compounds (see 'The pentose phosphate pathway', p. 112) led to the formulation of the carbon reduction cycle.

Most of the reactions of the carbon reduction cycle (reductive pentose phosphate pathway) are also found in the oxidative pentose phosphate pathway (p. 112). Three additional enzymes are involved in the carbon reduction cycle:

D-RIBULOSE-1,5-DIPHOSPHATE CARBOXYLASE
(Carboxy dismutase, carboxylating enzyme)

The carboxylation of ribulose-1,5-diphosphate has been postulated to proceed as follows:

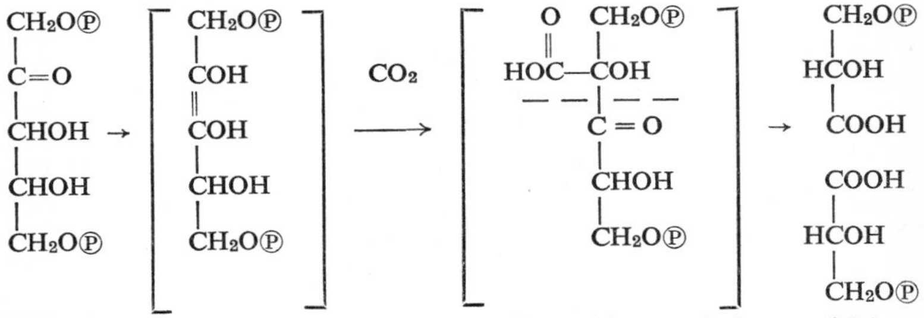

Ribulose-1,5-diphosphate　　　　　　2-Carboxy-3-ketopentitol-1,5-diphosphate　　　PGA

2-Carboxy-3-ketopentitol-1,5-diphosphate has been reported to be labelled after short periods of photosynthesis by *Chlorella* in $^{14}CO_2$. The reaction does not appear to be reversible at neutral pH. Ribulose-1,5-diphosphate carboxylase is found in high concentration in the chloroplast and at one time was thought to be identical to 'Fraction 1' (Wildman & Bonner, 1947). 'Fraction 1' is the major component, as determined by sedimentation in the ultracentrifuge, of the soluble protein of a variety of leaves. Ribulose-1,5-diphosphate carboxylase is also present in chemosynthetic organisms. There is only one report of the enzyme being present in a heterotroph. *E. coli* is able to elaborate ribulose-1,5-diphosphate carboxylase when grown on pentose in the presence of carbon dioxide. Ribulose-1,5-diphosphate carboxylase has been purified from spinach leaves and requires a divalent cation and sulphydryl compound for full activity.

It is clear that the product of carboxylation in isolated enzyme systems, and in the dark reaction *in vitro*, is 2 molecules of PGA. Some doubt exists, however, as to the exact products formed during photosynthesis *in vivo*. Kinetic data may be interpreted to mean that the 2 molecules of PGA behave differently. It is also possible that a reductive carboxylation occurs *in vivo* in the light, producing 1 molecule of PGA (containing the most recently fixed carbon), and 1 molecule of triose phosphate (Bassham & Calvin, 1961).

D-Ribulose-5-Phosphate Kinase

$$
\begin{array}{ccc}
\text{CH}_2\text{OH} & & \text{CH}_2\text{O}\textcircled{P} \\
| & & | \\
\text{C=O} & & \text{C=O} \\
| & +\text{ATP} \rightleftharpoons & | & +\text{ADP} \\
\text{CHOH} & & \text{CHOH} \\
| & & | \\
\text{CHOH} & & \text{CHOH} \\
| & & | \\
\text{CH}_2\text{O}\textcircled{P} & & \text{CH}_2\text{O}\textcircled{P}
\end{array}
$$

$$K = \frac{(\text{ribulose-1,5-diphosphate})(\text{ADP})}{(\text{ribulose-5-phosphate})(\text{ATP})}$$

$$= 214 \text{ (at pH 7)}$$

The enzyme has been crystallized from spinach leaves. It possesses an essential sulphydryl group and requires a divalent cation for maximal activity.

Glyceraldehyde Phosphate Dehydrogenase

NADP-dependent glyceraldehyde phosphate dehydrogenase appears to be closely associated with photosynthesis in higher plants. This belief is based on the following evidence:

(a) During the initial stages of germination of peas almost all the glyceraldehyde phosphate dehydrogenase present is NAD-dependent. During growth of the seedling in the light the concentration of NAD-dependent glyceraldehyde phosphate dehydrogenase falls whereas the concentration of NADP-dependent glyceraldehyde phosphate dehydrogenase increases. No significant increase in NADP-dependent glyceraldehyde phosphate dehydrogenase occurs in the dark. In fully expanded pea leaves the activities of the NAD- and NADP-dependent enzyme are approximately equal. Although these observations suggest a close association of the NADP-dependent enzyme with photosynthesis, it should not be concluded that NADP-dependent glyceraldehyde phosphate dehydrogenase is confined exclusively to photosynthetic cells. The NADP-dependent enzyme has been demonstrated also in castor beans, albino barley leaves and *Alcaligenes faecalis.*

(b) An NADP-dependent glyceraldehyde phosphate dehydrogenase of pea leaves has been reported to be localized exclusively in the plastids, whereas the NAD-dependent enzyme has been reported in both chloroplasts and cytoplasm (Smillie & Fuller, 1960).

The view that NADP-dependent glyceraldehyde phosphate dehydrogenase functions in photosynthesis is consistent with the specificity of PPNR for NADP, and with the wide use of $NADPH_2$, in preference to $NADH_2$, for biosynthetic reactions.

The photosynthetic and chemoautotrophic bacteria which have been examined, contain predominantly the NAD-dependent enzyme. This predominance of the NAD-specific enzyme in photosynthetic bacteria is consistent with the observation that PPNR of chromatophores is specific for NAD.

The net effect of the cycle (Fig. 6.6 A and B) is the conversion of 3 molecules of carbon dioxide to triose phosphate by 6 molecules of $NADPH_2$ and 9 molecules of ATP:

$$3CO_2 + 9ATP + 6NADPH_2 + 5H_2O \rightarrow$$
$$\text{triose-P} + 9ADP + 8P + 6NADP$$

The numbers in brackets in Fig. 6.6 show the stoichiometry involved in this conversion. Triose phosphate can serve as a precursor for sugar, glycerol, etc. Other intermediates of the cycle may also be drained off for

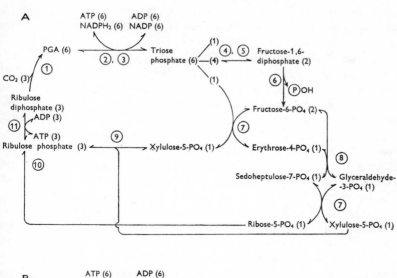

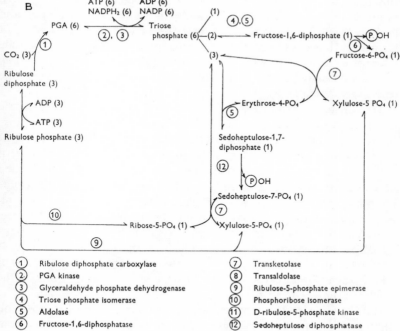

①	Ribulose diphosphate carboxylase	⑦	Transketolase
②	PGA kinase	⑧	Transaldolase
③	Glyceraldehyde phosphate dehydrogenase	⑨	Ribulose-5-phosphate epimerase
④	Triose phosphate isomerase	⑩	Phosphoribose isomerase
⑤	Aldolase	⑪	D-ribulose-5-phosphate kinase
⑥	Fructose-1,6-diphosphatase	⑫	Sedoheptulose diphosphatase

FIG. 6.6. Carbon reduction cycle.

synthetic reactions. For example, PGA can be converted to pyruvate for fatty acid or amino acid synthesis; erythrose phosphate can be used for the synthesis of shikimic acid.

Schemes A and B in Fig. 6.6 differ in the mechanism of resynthesis of ribulose-1,5-diphosphate from triose phosphate. Scheme A involves both transketolase and transaldolase, but does not account for the formation of sedoheptulose-1,7-diphosphate. Scheme B accounts for the formation of sedoheptulose-1,7-diphosphate and requires the presence of sedoheptulose diphosphatase, which is known to be present in chloroplasts. Scheme B does not assign a role to transaldolase. It is not possible at present to decide which cycle represents the reactions in the chloroplast, and both may operate. Evidence for the operation of the carbon reduction cycle is listed below:

(a) Variation of carbon labelling pattern with time. During photosynthesis in the presence of $^{14}CO_2$, the first compound to be labelled is PGA. Subsequently, label appears in triose phosphate and hexose phosphates, and in the sugar phosphates involved in the regeneration of ribulose-1,5-diphosphate. Short periods of illumination in $^{14}CO_2$, produce PGA labelled predominantly in the carboxyl group, and hexoses labelled predominantly in carbons 3 and 4. The distribution of label in the halves of hexose was reported to be symmetrical after a wide range of exposures to $^{14}CO_2$. These labelling patterns, observed in algae, leaves and isolated chloroplasts, are consistent with the operation of the carbon reduction cycle.

The scheme shown in Fig. 6.6 has been criticized on the basis of the observation of Gibbs & Kandler (1957) that the halves of the hexose molecule can have unequal distribution of ^{14}C following short periods of photosynthesis in $^{14}CO_2$. This observation is not, however, inconsistent with the operation of the carbon reduction cycle. Asymmetric labelling may result from a lag in isotopic equilibration between glyceraldehyde phosphate and dihydroxyacetone phosphate. Hexose which is asymmetrically labelled may also result from a back reaction of transketolase, in which the top two carbon atoms of xylulose-5-phosphate are transferred back to erythrose-4-phosphate (Fig. 6.7). This reaction produces hexose labelled in the top four carbon atoms. The relative proportion of label in each of these carbon atoms will depend on the relative rates of the reactions shown in Fig. 6.7.

(b) Changes in steady state transients. In this type of experiment, photosynthesis is allowed to proceed in the presence of a constant concentration of $^{14}CO_2$ until all the carbon atoms of the intermediates are at

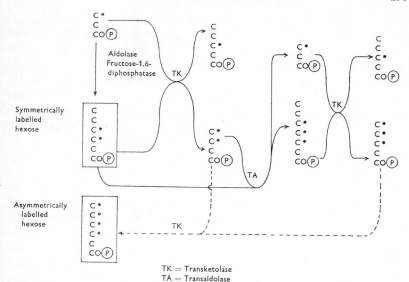

TK = Transketolase
TA = Transaldolase

Fig. 6.7. Suggested scheme for formation of asymmetrically labelled hexose by exchange reactions of carbon reduction cycle.

isotopic equilibrium. Any change in concentration of intermediates produced by disturbing this steady state can be measured simply by counting the radioactivity of any particular intermediate. The effect of light and dark on the level of PGA and ribulose-1,5-diphosphate is shown in Fig. 6.8.

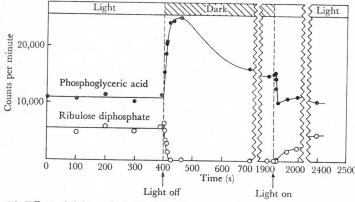

Fig. 6.8. Effect of light and dark on the concentration of phosphoglycerate and ribulose dephosphate.

Going from light to dark produces an initial increase in PGA and decrease in ribulose-1,5-diphosphate. These changes are consistent with the operation of the carbon reduction cycle in which PGA continues to be formed from ribulose-1,5-diphosphate in the dark. The utilization of PGA to form triose phospate and regeneration of the ribulose-1,5-diphosphate, on the other hand, require ATP and $NADPH_2$ derived from light energy. When the light is again turned on, the production of ATP and $NADPH_2$ is resumed, and the concentration of PGA and ribulose-1,5-diphosphate return to their original steady state level.

(c) Isolation of the enzymes of the carbon reduction cycle. All the enzymes of the carbon reduction cycle have been demonstrated in photosynthetic tissue and appear to be localized in the stroma of the chloroplasts. The activity of a number of the enzymes may be too low to satisfy the rate of carbon dioxide fixation in vivo. Peterkofsky & Racker (1961) for example have reported that the activity of transaldolase and sedoheptulose diphosphatase in homogenates of spinach leaves was too low to account for the rate of carbon dioxide fixation by the whole leaf. While these experiments establish that the in vitro activity was low, 'physiological conditions' within the chloroplast are unknown and could lead to greater activities than the in vitro experiments indicate.

The gross analytical products of photosynthesis depend on the physiological state and environment of the plant. In most cases the major proportion of carbon dioxide fixed appears as carbohydrate (sucrose and starch). Diversion of carbon into amino acids and proteins is, to some extent, a reflection of the nitrogen status of the plant. Under low partial pressures of carbon dioxide glycolate appears as the major product of photosynthesis.

Kearney & Tolbert (1961) claim that glycolic acid constitutes the major proportion of photosynthetic product excreted by isolated chloroplasts; the phosphate esters and sucrose are retained within the chloroplast. Although the mechanism of synthesis of glycolic acid is unknown, one suggestion is that it is produced from an 'active glycolaldehyde' unit associated with the activity of transketolase. This suggestion is supported by the report (Zelitch, 1960) that isolated chloroplasts convert ribose-5-phosphate to glycolic acid in the dark in the absence of carbon dioxide. When the partial pressure of carbon dioxide is low, pentose phosphates such as ribulose diphosphate would tend to accumulate and so provide a source of glycolate. Analogues of glycolic acid such as α-hydroxy-2-pyridine-methanesulphonic acid also cause the accumulation of glycolic acid. In the presence of these inhibitors leaves and isolated chloroplasts illuminated in $^{14}CO_2$ rapidly accumulate glycolate-^{14}C. Under these conditions glycolate probably accumulates because the further conversion of glycolate to glyoxylate, glycine, serine etc. is inhibited. These observations suggest that glycolate plays a significant role in the path of carbon in photosynthesis. The possible participation of glycolate in respiration is discussed on p. 209.

An alternative scheme of photosynthesis has been proposed by Warburg (1958). This scheme may be summarized as follows:

Light reaction: $3(\text{Chl. } C\overset{*}{O}_2) + \text{light (3 quanta)} + 3CO_2 \rightarrow$
$$3(\text{Chl. } CO_2) + 3C + 3O_2 \qquad (6.8)$$

Dark reaction: $2C + 2O_2 \rightarrow 2CO_2$ \qquad\qquad\qquad\qquad\qquad (6.9)

Dark reaction: $3(\text{Chl.}CO_2) \rightarrow 3(\text{Chl. } C\overset{*}{O}_2)$ \qquad\qquad\qquad (6.10)

Sum. $CO_2 + \text{light (3 quanta)} \rightarrow C + O_2$ \qquad\qquad (6.11)

The overall assimilation of 1 molecule of carbon dioxide with the concomitant liberation of 1 molecule of oxygen (reaction 6.11) consists of one light reaction and two dark reactions (reactions 6.9 and 6.10). In the light reaction, 1 molecule of oxygen is produced from an 'activated CO_2'-chlorophyll complex (termed the 'photolyte of photosynthesis' by Warburg).

The nature of the 'activated CO_2'-chlorophyll complex, shown as (Chl. $C\overset{*}{O}_2$) in reaction (6.8), is not clearly defined. Activation of carbon dioxide appears to be closely associated with the carboxylation of γ-aminobutyrate to form glutamate. In the dark reaction (6.9) two-thirds of the oxygen evolved and carbon assimilated in the light reaction (6.8) are respired to carbon dioxide. This strongly exergonic reaction is coupled to the regeneration of the 'activated CO_2'-chlorophyll complex (in reaction 6.10). The overall equation of photosynthesis contains three novel features:

(a) It is proposed that oxygen is derived from CO_2 and not from H_2O.

(b) The requirement of 3 quanta means that photosynthesis in red light proceeds at approximately 90 per cent efficiency.

(c) The requirement for oxygen in reaction 6.9 has led Warburg to expound the dogma: 'Without respiration, no photosynthesis'.

Evidence for the scheme may be summarized briefly as follows:

(a) Warburg's group has consistently observed a quantum requirement between 3 and 4. Under conditions of alternating light and dark, a quantum requirement approaching 1 is observed. It appears that under these conditions the quantum requirement for reaction (6.8) is determined.

(b) 'Activated CO_2' is postulated to be bound to chlorophyll, since the quantity of oxygen produced in the isolated light reaction (6.8) is equivalent at the chlorophyll content.

(c) The curves relating oxygen tension to respiration and photosynthesis were identical.

(d) If the 'activated CO_2'-chlorophyll complex is decarboxylated by the addition of fluoride, photosynthesis will proceed only after the addition of oxygen. Oxygen is required for the reactivation of carbon dioxide by reactions (6.9) and (6.10). This activation appears to involve the reaction:

$$\text{glutamate} \underset{\text{Respiration}}{\overset{\text{Fluoride}}{\longleftrightarrow}} CO_2 + \gamma\text{-aminobutyrate}$$

The equilibrium of this reaction strongly favours decarboxylation. Other amino acids such as aspartate and alanine have also been postulated to participate in the 'activation' of CO_2.

Many of the views expressed by Warburg are contrary to the schemes discussed in detail in this chapter. At the present time it is difficult to reconcile these apparent inconsistencies.

READING LIST

HILL R. & WHITTINGHAM C.P. (1956) *Photosynthesis*. Methuen & Co., London
RABINOWITCH E.I. (1945) *Photosynthesis*. Interscience, New York
The Photochemical Apparatus. Brookhaven National Lab., Upton, New York, 1959
McELROY W.D. & GLASS B. (Ed.) (1961) *Light and Life*. Johns Hopkins Press, Baltimore
BASSHAM J.A. & CALVIN M. (1957) *The Path of Carbon in Photosynthesis*. Prentice-Hall Inc., Englewood Cliffs, New Jersey

LITERATURE CITED

ARNON D.I. (1959) *Nature*, **184**, 10
ARNON D.I., LOSADA M., WHATLEY F.R., TSUJIMOTO H.Y., HALL D.O. & HORTON A.A. (1961) *Proc. Nat. Acad. Sci. U.S.A.* **47**, 1314
ARNON D.I., WHATLEY F.R. & ALLEN M.B. (1958) *Science* **127**, 1026
AVRON M. (1961) *Biochem. J.* **78**, 735
BASSHAM J.A. & CALVIN M. (1961) *Fifth Int. Cong. of Biochem., Moscow*, Preprint No. 48
CALVIN M. (1961) *J. Theoret. Biol.* **1**, 258
GIBBS M. & KANDLER O. (1957) *Pl. Physiol.* **31**, 411

GIBBS M. & KANDLER O. (1957) *Proc. Nat. Acad. Sci. U.S.A.* **43**, 446
GRANICK S. (1961) *Pl. Physiol.* **36**, xlviii
HILL R. & BENDALL F. (1960) *Nature* **186**, 136
KEARNEY P.C. & TOLBERT N.E. (1961) *Pl. Physiol.* **36**, xxvi
LOSADA M., WHATLEY F.R. & ARNON D.I. (1961) *Nature* **190**, 606
PETERKOFSKY A. & RACKER E. (1961) *Pl. Physiol.* **36**, 409
SMILLIE R.M. & FULLER R.C. (1960) *Biochem. Biophys. Res. Commun.* **3**, 368
VAN NIEL C.B. (1950) In *Photosynthesis in Plants*, p. 437. Ed. Franck J. & Loomis W.E. Iowa State College Press, Ames, Iowa
VON WETTSTEIN D. (1959) In *The Photochemical Apparatus*, p. 138. Brookhaven Nat. Lab., Upton, New York
WARBURG O. (1958) *Science* **128**, 68
WILDMAN S.G. & BONNER J. (1947) *Arch. Biochem.* **14**, 38
ZELITCH I. (1960) *Biochem. J.* **77**, 11P

17

CHAPTER 7

LIPID METABOLISM

The term 'lipid' refers to a heterogeneous collection of substances which have in common the property of being readily soluble in organic solvents, but sparingly soluble in water, and of yielding fatty acids on hydrolysis. The group includes:

(a) Fats and oils.
(b) Waxes.
(c) Phospholipids.
(d) Glycolipids.

CHEMISTRY AND DISTRIBUTION

Fats and Oils

The general formula for a fat or oil is as follows:

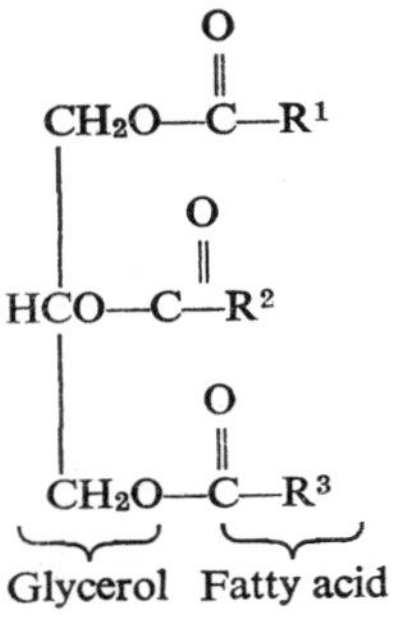

$$
\begin{array}{l}
\qquad\qquad\quad \overset{\displaystyle O}{\underset{\displaystyle \|}{}} \\
CH_2O-C-R^1 \\
\qquad\qquad\quad \overset{\displaystyle O}{\underset{\displaystyle \|}{}} \\
HCO-C-R^2 \\
\qquad\qquad\quad \overset{\displaystyle O}{\underset{\displaystyle \|}{}} \\
CH_2O-C-R^3 \\
\underbrace{\qquad\quad}_{Glycerol}\underbrace{\qquad\quad}_{Fatty\ acid}
\end{array}
$$

The chemical and physical properties of fats are determined by the constitution of the fatty acids esterified with glycerol. Fats containing a high proportion of double bonds are liquid at room temperature, and are termed oils. The fatty acid residues of both fats and oils are almost all straight chain fatty acids containing an even number of carbon atoms, ranging from C_2 to C_{22}.

Branched chain fatty acids, short chain fatty acids (less than 6 carbon atoms) and fatty acids containing an odd number of carbon atoms are extremely rare. None of the short chain fatty acids have been reported as a component of a triglyceride. However, formic acid is known to occur as the free acid in stinging nettle and other plants, and small amounts of acetic acid have been demonstrated in plants. Many of the rare fatty acids mentioned above have been detected in a number of fruits (apples, citrus, grapes etc.) and contribute to the aroma and flavour of the fruit. Formic, acetic, propionic, butyric, isobutyric, valeric, isovaleric and caproic are found either as their free acids or esterified with short chain saturated alcohols.

The unsaturated fatty acids (oleic, linoleic and linolenic) are the most widely distributed and most abundant. It has been estimated that oleic acid, together with linoleic acid, make up over 60 per cent of the world's supply of vegetable fats. Of the saturated fatty acids, palmitic, lauric and stearic are the most widely distributed and most abundant.

Acid	Number of carbon atoms	Formula
Oleic	18	$CH_3—(CH_2)_7—CH=CH—(CH_2)_7—COOH$
Linoleic	18	$CH_3—(CH_2)_4—CH=CH—CH_2—CH=CH—(CH_2)_7—COOH$
Linolenic	18	$CH_3—CH_2—CH=CH—CH_2—CH=CH—CH_2—CH=CH—(CH_2)_7—COOH$
Lauric	12	$CH_3—(CH_2)_{10}—COOH$
Palmitic	16	$CH_3—(CH_2)_{14}—COOH$
Stearic	18	$CH_3—(CH_2)_{16}—COOH$

In the unsaturated fatty acids, two stereoisomeric forms are possible about each of the double bonds. The *cis* form is most commonly encountered in the natural fatty acids, and all the double bonds in oleic, linoleic and linolenic contain the *cis* configuration.

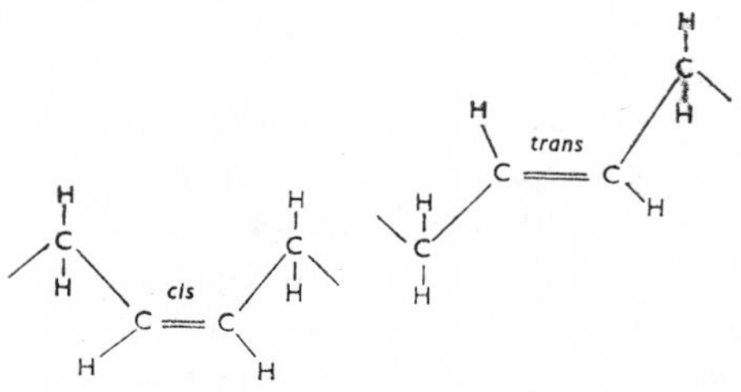

LAW OF MAXIMUM HETEROGENEITY

The fatty acids are esterified with glycerol in such a way that the formation of mixed glycerides is favoured. Thus in a fat containing glycerol, G, and fatty acids, F_1, F_2 and F_3, the mixed glyceride $GF_1F_2F_3$ will predominate. Molecules of the type $GF_1F_1F_2$ will be present in lower amounts, and those of the type $GF_1F_1F_1$ hardly at all.

Fats and oils occur in all portions of the plant. Usually the vegetative organs contain low concentrations of fat compared to the fruit and seed. Thus, in leaf, shoot and root tissue, the per cent fat on a dry weight basis rarely exceeds 5 per cent. Certain fruits and seeds, on the other hand, may contain over 50 per cent fat on a dry weight basis. The fresh fruit of the olive, for example, contains 50 per cent fat, and the seed of the coconut, 65 per cent fat.

It will be shown on p. 274 that, on a unit weight basis, the oxidation of fat yields approximately twice as much energy in the form of ATP as the oxidation of carbohydrate. Thus fat is ideally suited for the storage of food stuffs in both animals and plants. It has been estimated that the seeds of over 88 per cent of the families of higher plants contain fat, and of these, three-quarters contain fat to the exclusion of starch as a reserve food.

In addition to the fatty acids noted above, there are a large number of relatively rare fatty acids present in plants. These include various derivatives of unsaturated fatty acids containing 1, 2, 3 or 4 double bonds, those containing triple bonds, and cyclic fatty acids. Some plant species may contain high concentrations of these rare fatty acids. For example, the castor bean (*Ricinus communis*) is rich in ricinoleic acid (12-hydroxy oleic acid) and the seeds of the tree *Hydnocarpus* are rich in the cyclic acids chaulmoogric (13-$\Delta^{2,3}$-cyclopentenyl-*n*-tridecanoic acid) and hydnocarpic (11-$\Delta^{2,3}$-cyclopentenyl-*n*-undecanoic acid). Chaulmoogric oil, obtained from the seeds of *Hydnocarpus*, contains chaulmoogric and hydnocarpic acids and is used in the treatment of leprosy.

Waxes

In the waxes, fatty acids are esterified with long chain alcohols. The fatty acids have even number carbon atoms ranging from C_{24} to C_{36}. Waxes frequently contain free fatty acids, free alcohols, hydrocarbons with an odd number of carbon atoms ranging in chain length from C_{25} to C_{27}, and high molecular weight ketones.

Plant waxes occur predominantly as a protective coating on leaves, fruits and seed coats, and dispersed throughout the cell in the same manner as fats and oils. The seeds of *Simmondsia california* contain wax as a food reserve. With this one exception, waxes do not appear to play any part in plant metabolism. The mechanism of the biosynthesis of waxes has not been investigated.

The Phospholipids

The phospholipids may be defined as those lipids containing phosphoric acid in an ester linkage. They may be further subdivided into phosphatides, plasmalogens and sphingolipids.

1. *The phosphatides* all contain L-α-phosphatidic acid linked by a phosphate ester bond to the hydroxyl group of another compound:

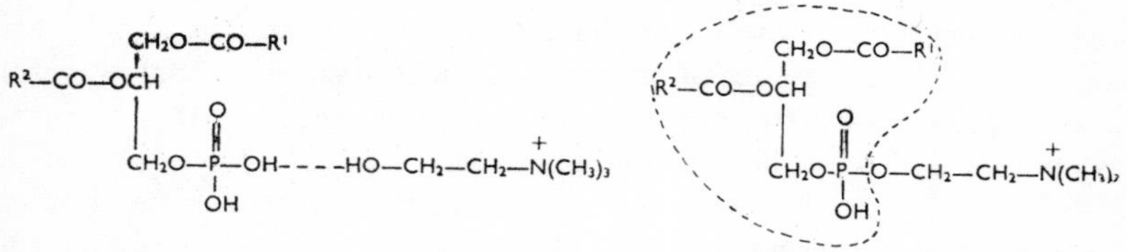

L-α-phosphatidic acid   Choline   Phosphatidylcholine

The long chain fatty acyl moieties denoted by R¹—CO— and R²—CO— are predominately those found in natural fats (oleic, linoleic, palmitic, stearic etc.). Denoting the phosphatidyl moiety (shown in circle) by 'Ph', the structures of the more common phosphatides are as follows:

$$Ph\text{—}O\text{—}CH_2\text{—}CH_2\text{—}N(CH_3)_3^+$$
L-α-Phosphatidylcholine (Lecithin)

$$Ph\text{—}O\text{—}CH_2\text{—}CH_2\text{—}NH_2$$
L-α-Phosphatidylethanolamine (Cephalin)

$$Ph\text{—}O\text{—}CH_2\text{—}\overset{\overset{NH_2}{|}}{\underset{\underset{H}{|}}{C}}\text{—}COOH$$
L-α-Phosphatidylserine

$$\overset{\overset{CH_2OH}{|}}{\underset{\underset{Ph\text{—}O\text{—}CH_2}{|}}{HOCH}}$$
L-α-Phosphatidylglycerol

$$\begin{array}{l} CH_2\text{—}O\text{—}Ph \\ | \\ HOCH \\ | \\ Ph\text{—}O\text{—}CH_2 \end{array}$$

L-α-Diphosphatidylglycerol

L-α-Phosphatidylinositol

All of the above phosphatides have been demonstrated in both plants and animals. The presence of phosphatidic acid in nature is controversial since its presence in extracts may result from a degradation of phosphatidylcholine and phosphatidylethanolamine by phospholipase D (see p. 289). The phosphatides are important constituents of cell membranes and are in general associated with chloroplasts, mitochondria and microsomes. Chloroplasts are particularly rich in phosphatidylglycerol. The rapid turnover of the glycerol moiety of phosphatidylglycerol during photosynthesis suggests that this phosphatide may participate in metabolism as well as being a structural element of the chloroplast. Benson, Wintermans & Wiser (1959) consider that phosphatidyl glycerol may act as a carbohydrate reservoir within the chloroplast.

2. *The plasmalogens or phosphoglyceracetals* derive their name from the 'plasmal' reaction, which is a histochemical test for aldehydes. The structure of the plasmalogens is similar to the phosphatides. However, whereas hydrolysis of phosphatides liberates fatty acids, hydrolysis of the plasmalogens yields long chain fatty aldehydes. The precise chemical link between the aldehyde and glycerol is not known. Originally it was thought that the aldehyde was bonded to glycerol by an acetal link:

$$\begin{array}{l} CH_2OH \\ | \\ HC\text{—}OH \\ | \\ CH_2O\text{—}P\text{—}choline \end{array} \quad + H\text{—}\overset{\overset{\displaystyle O}{\|}}{C}\text{—}R \quad \rightarrow \quad \begin{array}{l} CH_2O \\ | \quad\diagdown \;\; H \\ \quad\quad\;\; C\text{—}R \\ HCO \diagup \\ | \\ CH_2O\text{—}P\text{—}choline \end{array}$$

However, more recent work indicates that there are two long chain alkyl groups, one of which is present in a fatty acyl group linked as an ester, the other alkyl group being in the form of an α,β-unsaturated ether:

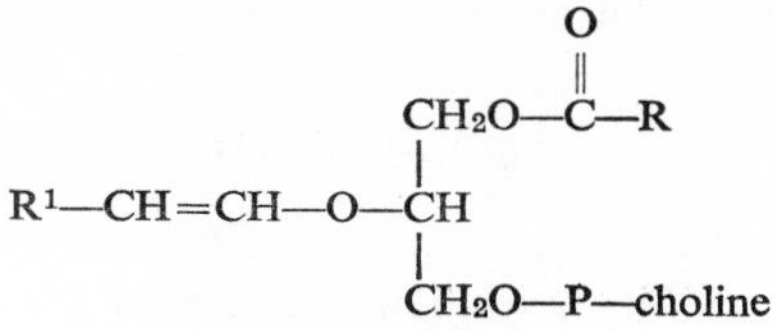

$$
\begin{array}{c}
CH_2O-\overset{\displaystyle O}{\overset{\|}{C}}-R \\
R^1-CH=CH-O-CH \\
CH_2O-P-\text{choline}
\end{array}
$$

Phosphatidalcholine

The base may be choline, ethanolamine or serine. The plasmalogens constitute an appreciable proportion of brain and muscle phospholipids. Although the presence of aldehydes has been reported in the crude phosphatides of soy bean and peanut, and in olive oil, the isolation and identification of a plasmalogen has not been accomplished in plant tissue.

3. *The sphingolipids* are defined as all lipids that contain derivatives of sphingosine:

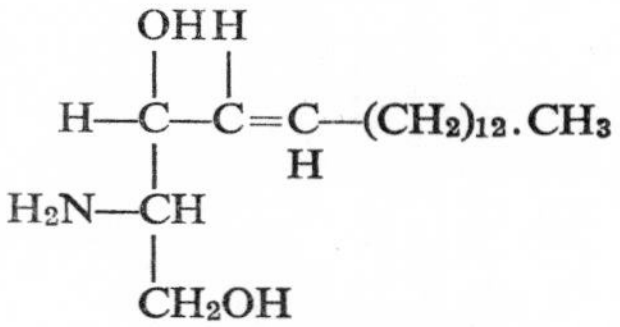

$$
\begin{array}{c}
\overset{\displaystyle OHH}{} \\
H-\overset{|}{C}-\overset{|}{C}=C-(CH_2)_{12}.CH_3 \\
\overset{|}{}H \\
H_2N-CH \\
\overset{|}{CH_2OH}
\end{array}
$$

Sphingosine

The terminology of the sphingolipids in plants is confused by the use of terms such as cerebrosides, gangliosides and sphingolipids, which describe sphingolipids originally found in nervous tissue.

The distribution of sphingolipids in plants appears to parallel that of the phosphatides. A lipid containing the base phytosphingosine (the 1, 3, 4-trihydroxy derivative of sphingosine) was isolated from the crude phosphatide mixture of a number of seeds (Carter *et al.*, 1958). The complexity of this lipid is shown below:

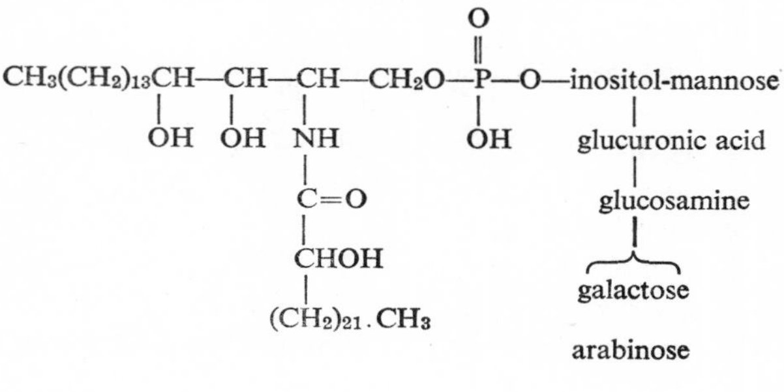

$$
\begin{array}{c}
\phantom{CH_3(CH_2)_{13}CH-CH-CH-CH_2O-P}\overset{\displaystyle O}{\overset{\|}{}} \\
CH_3(CH_2)_{13}CH-CH-CH-CH_2O-P-O-\text{inositol-mannose} \\
\phantom{CH_3(CH_2)_{13}}\overset{|}{OH}\overset{|}{OH}\overset{|}{NH}\overset{|}{OH}\overset{|}{}\text{glucuronic acid} \\
\phantom{CH_3(CH_2)_{13}CH-CH-}\overset{|}{C=O}\text{glucosamine} \\
\phantom{CH_3(CH_2)_{13}CH-CH-}\overset{|}{CHOH} \\
\phantom{CH_3(CH_2)_{13}CH-CH-CH-}\text{galactose} \\
\phantom{CH_3(CH_2)_{13}CH-}(CH_2)_{21}.CH_3 \\
\phantom{CH_3(CH_2)_{13}CH-CH-CH-}\text{arabinose}
\end{array}
$$

The native lipid may be even more complex, since the proposed structure may represent a degradation product formed by the extraction procedure.

The Glycolipids

The glycolipids may be defined as those lipids in which glycerol is linked to a sugar by a glycosidic bond. The glycolipids shown below comprise the major lipid of green leaves, where their concentration exceeds that of the phosphatides by approximately 5-fold (Benson, *et al.*, 1959). The non-sulphur-containing galactolipids appear to be specifically associated with the chloroplasts.

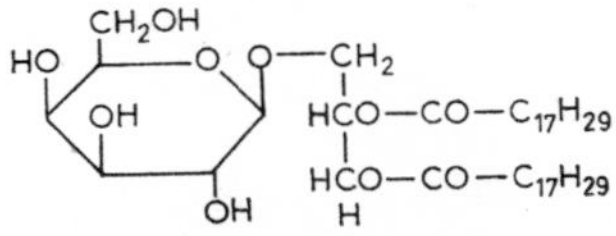

Monogalactosyldiglyceride

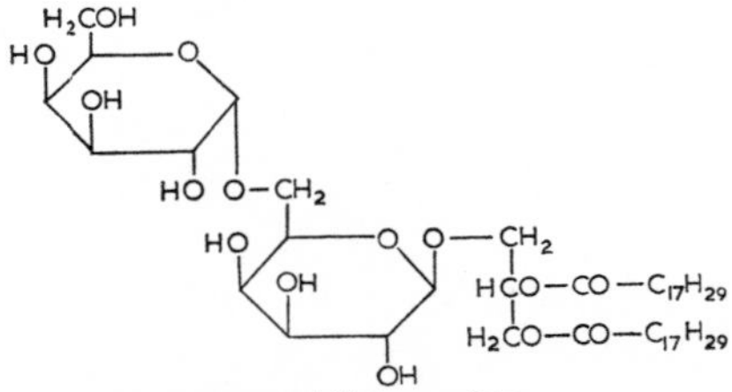

Digalactosyldiglyceride

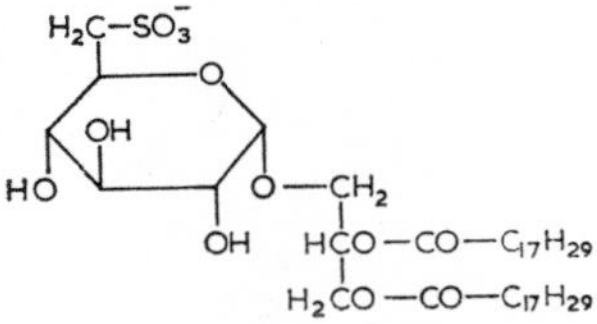

The plant sulpholipid

It seems likely that glycolipids containing sugars other than galactose and glucose also exist in leaves. None of the above galactolipids have been demonstrated in animals.

The galactose moiety of the galactolipids is rapidly labelled with ^{14}C during photosynthesis in $^{14}CO_2$. This observation has led to the suggestion that galactolipids may function as carbohydrate reservoirs.

CATABOLISM

The purpose of this section is to discuss the principal biochemical reactions involved in the catabolism of fats. In plant tissues, the germinating fatty seed represents the most active site of fat catabolism. Fig. 7.1 summarizes the general path of carbon during the catabolism of fats.

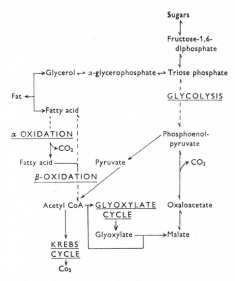

FIG. 7.1. Major metabolic pathways of fat catabolism in plants.

Initial Hydrolysis

The first step in the degradation of fats is their hydrolysis to fatty acids and glycerol by the action of lipases. Lipases are widely distributed in seeds and vegetative organs. Castor beans are particularly rich in lipase and the enzyme from this source has been highly purified.

The action of lipase may be represented as follows:

$$\text{triglyceride} \xrightarrow{\text{H}_2\text{O}} \text{diglyceride} \xrightarrow{\text{H}_2\text{O}} \text{monoglyceride} \xrightarrow{\text{H}_2\text{O}} \text{glycerol}$$
$$\text{fatty acid} \qquad \text{fatty acid} \qquad \text{fatty acid}$$

The rate at which glycerides are hydrolysed, in general, increases with the number of fatty acid residues on the glyceride and with the chain length and degree of unsaturation of the fatty acid.

The significance of lipase in the metabolism of fats in seeds is suggested by the increased lipase activity as germination proceeds. Although the reaction catalysed by lipase is reversible, under physiological conditions it is not likely that fats are synthesized by reversal of the hydrolytic reaction.

Glycerol

The pathway for glycerol metabolism in plants, shown in Fig. 7.2, has been presented on the basis of experiments performed with excised castor bean cotyledons and cell free extracts of peanut cotyledons. The scheme is essentially the same as that described for animal tissues.

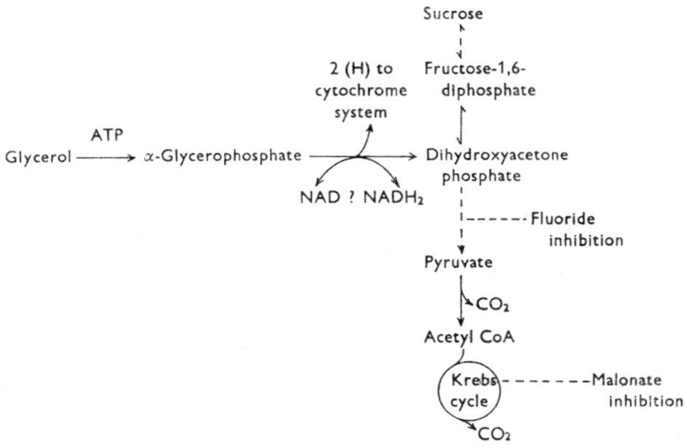

FIG. 7.2. Glycerol metabolism.

Beevers (1956) demonstrated the conversion of glycerol-1,3-^{14}C to sucrose-^{14}C and [14]CO_2 by slices of a number of plant tissues. The pathway of glycerol metabolism was studied in detail using non-green cotyledons excised from young germinating seedlings of castor beans. Over a 6-hour incubation period sucrose-^{14}C contained three to four times as much label as did [14]CO_2. The utilization of glycerol was strongly inhibited by anaerobiosis, malonate and fluoride. The sucrose-^{14}C formed was found to be equally labelled in the glucose and fructose moieties. Degradation of the glucose moiety showed that 97 per cent of the radio-activity was evenly distributed in carbons 1, 3, 4 and 6. This labelling pattern strongly suggests that the glycerol moiety is incorporated intact into glucose.

The degradation of glycerol to CO_2 was examined by Stumpf (1955) in cell-free extracts obtained from cotyledons of germinating peanuts. Glycerol-1, 3-^{14}C was oxidized to $^{14}CO_2$ in the presence of mitochondria, a soluble cytoplasmic fraction, and a number of cofactors. The cofactors required were ATP, α-ketoglutarate, thiamine pyrophosphate, Mg and NAD. The participation of the EMP sequence (glycolysis) in the soluble cytoplasmic fraction and the Krebs cycle in the mitochondria was consistent with the observed inhibition by fluoride and malonate respectively. Further evidence for the participation of the Krebs cycle was furnished by the isolation and characterization of a number of radioactive Krebs cycle acids during the oxidation of glycerol-1,3-^{14}C.

The mitochondria catalysed an oxidation of α-glycerophosphate to triosephosphate, 1 molecule of α-glycerophosphate requiring 1 atom of O_2. No cofactors were required for the oxidation. An α-glycerophosphate-dependent reduction of cytochrome c, however, could be demonstrated, suggesting that the mitochondria contain sufficient amounts of endogenous cytochrome c to catalyse the oxidation of α-glycerophosphate by O_2. The plant enzyme oxidizing α-glycerophosphate therefore appears similar to the particulate L-α-glycerophosphate dehydrogenase from animal tissues:

L-α-glycerophosphate $\rightarrow$ dihydroxyacetone + 2(H)

                     phosphate   to cytochromes

2(H) + $\frac{1}{2}O_2 \rightarrow H_2O$

L-α-glycerophosphate + $\frac{1}{2}O_2 \rightarrow$ dihydroxyacetone + H_2O

                     phosphate

The equilibrium for the overall oxidation of L-α-glycerophosphate greatly favours the formation of dihydroxyacetone phosphate. The soluble cytoplasmic fraction of peanut cotyledons was not examined for the presence of the soluble NAD-dependent α-glycerophosphate dehydrogenase reported by Baranofski (1949) in animal tissues:

L-α-glycerophosphate + NAD $\rightarrow$

                  dihydroxyacetone phosphate + NADH$_2$

A glycerol-1-phosphate cycle, which effects the transfer of H from extra-mitochondrial NADH$_2$ to the respiratory chain, has been postulated in insect flight muscle. This cycle involves the combined action of soluble NAD-dependent α-glycerophosphate dehydrogenase and particulate cytochrome-linked α-glycerophosphate dehydrogenase as follows:

Soluble α-glycerophosphate dehydrogenase

$$NADH_2 + \text{dihydroxyacetone} \longrightarrow NAD + L\text{-}\alpha\text{-glycerophosphate}$$
phosphate

Particulate α-glycerophosphate dehydrogenase

$$L\text{-}\alpha\text{-glycerophosphate} + \tfrac{1}{2}O_2 \longrightarrow \text{dihydroxyacetone phosphate}$$
$$+ H_2O$$

$$NADH_2 + \tfrac{1}{2}O_2 \longrightarrow NAD + H_2O$$

The significance of this cycle in tissues other than insect muscle is uncertain.

Even-Numbered Saturated Fatty Acids

β-OXIDATION

The theory of β-oxidation of fatty acids was first proposed by Knoop (1904). Knoop observed that ω-substituted straight chain fatty acids when fed to dogs were not oxidized completely to carbon dioxide. The nature of the products excreted in the urine yielded valuable information on the possible mechanism of oxidation. Phenyl derivatives of even-numbered fatty acids were excreted as phenyl-acetic acid whereas the phenyl derivatives of odd-numbered fatty acids were excreted as benzoic acid. Phenyl-acetic and benzoic acids were present in the urine as the glycine conjugates, phenyl-aceturic acid and hippuric acid, respectively. Knoop interpreted these results as being the result of successive removal of 2 carbon units following the oxidation of the β-methylene group to a β-keto group:

Even-numbered fatty acids

$$
\begin{array}{c}
\overset{\beta}{}\quad \overset{\alpha}{} \\
C_6H_5\text{—}CH_2\text{—}CH_2\text{—}CH_2\text{—}CH_2\text{—}CH_2\text{—}COOH \\
\downarrow \\
C_6H_5\text{—}CH_2\text{—}CH_2\text{—}CH_2\text{—}\overset{O}{\overset{\|}{C}}\text{—}CH_2\text{—}COOH \\
\downarrow \\
C_6H_5\text{—}CH_2\text{—}CH_2\text{—}CH_2\text{—}COOH + CH_3\text{—}COOH \\
\downarrow \\
C_6H_5\text{—}CH_2\text{—}\overset{O}{\overset{\|}{C}}\text{—}CH_2\text{—}COOH \\
\downarrow \\
\boxed{C_6H_5\text{—}CH_2\text{—}COOH} + CH_3\text{—}COOH
\end{array}
$$

Odd-numbered fatty acids

$$C_6H_5-CH_2-CH_2-\overset{\beta}{CH_2}-\overset{a}{CH_2}-COOH$$

$$\downarrow$$

$$C_6H_5-CH_2-CH_2-\overset{O}{\overset{\|}{C}}-CH_2-COOH$$

$$\downarrow$$

$$C_6H_5-CH_2-CH_2-COOH + CH_3-COOH$$

$$\downarrow$$

$$C_6H_5-\overset{O}{\overset{\|}{C}}-CH_2-COOH$$

$$\downarrow$$

$$\boxed{C_6H_5-COOH} + CH_3-COOH$$

Evidence for α,β-unsaturated, β-hydroxy and β-keto derivatives as inter-mediates was provided by Knoop, and extended by Dakin (1911).

Little progress was made in elucidating the mechanism of β-oxidation until Munoz and Leloir in 1943 demonstrated the oxidation of butyrate by homogenates of guinea-pig liver in the presence of AMP, inorganic phosphate, Mg^{++}, cytochrome c and one of the substrates of the Krebs cycle ('sparker'). This sparker was later shown to serve two functions. Firstly it provided a substrate for the operation of the Krebs cycle and concomitant production of ATP required for the activation of the fatty acid. Secondly, it provided a condensing partner for acetate units to be oxidized via the Krebs cycle. Kennedy and Lehninger localized the site of fatty acid oxidation in the mitochondria. In the presence of Mg, ATP, oxaloacetic acid and malonate (to block the Krebs cycle), citrate and succinate accumulated. In the absence of a 'sparker', acetoacetate accumulated.

The realization that CoA derivatives were the intermediates involved in fatty acid oxidation greatly facilitated the study of fatty acid oxidation in enzyme preparations. Barker and his colleagues in 1951 substantially elucidated the pathway of β-oxidation using soluble extracts of *Clostridium kluyveri*. Drysdale and Lardy later achieved an oxidative degra-dation of fatty acids by a soluble system of animal origin. They demon-strated the dehydrogenation of fats from C_4 to C_{18} by clear extracts of rat liver mitochondria in the presence of ATP. After treatment of the extract with Dowex 1, the system required CoA. The enzymes responsible for the fatty acid oxidation spiral (Fig. 7.3) were finally isolated and purified from animal mitochondria by Green's group in Madison and from animal tissues by Lynen's group in Munich.

All the intermediates in β-oxidation involve derivatives of CoA. The role of CoA in fatty acid metabolism may therefore be compared to the role of phosphate in carbohydrate metabolism. Just as the sugar molecule is introduced into the chain of degradations and transformations by conversion into a phosphorylated derivative, so must the fatty acid be converted into a derivative of CoA before enzymatic attack can occur.

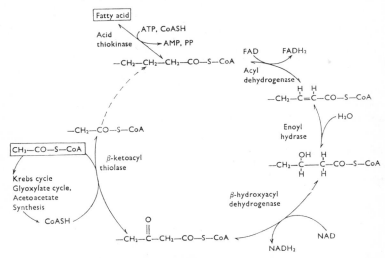

FIG. 7.3. β-oxidation of fatty acids.

The scheme of β-oxidation involves the initial activation of a fatty acid to its CoA derivative which is converted by the enzymes of β-oxidation to β-ketoacyl CoA. By a thiolytic cleavage involving CoA, β-ketoacyl CoA is converted to a fatty acyl CoA containing two less carbon atoms than the original fatty acid and acetyl CoA. The complete degradation of a long chain fatty acid regardless of its chain length requires only one activation together with catalytic amounts of CoA. Free CoA is constantly regenerated when acetyl CoA is utilized in the Krebs cycle and other reactions.

None of the CoA derivatives of β-oxidation accumulate in significant amounts. Once a fatty acid is converted to its acyl derivative and acted upon by a mitochondrial system, the next intermediate which can be detected is one of the intermediates of the Krebs cycle or acetoacetate. It is possible that in the mitochondria the intermediates are present in only trace amounts and are bound so tightly to the enzymes of β-oxidation that the intermediates do not 'leak out'. By the use of a reconstituted system of soluble enzymes, on the other hand, it is possible to isolate any desired intermediate. The enzymatic steps of β-oxidation listed below have been studied in purified enzyme systems obtained predominantly from animal tissues. While activities characteristic of the enzymes of β-oxidation have been described in plant systems, none of the enzymes has been isolated in pure form.

The enzymes listed below have been studied in a number of laboratories and different names have frequently been given to one and the same enzyme. The nomenclature used here is based on the systematic one proprosed by an international committee (Beinert *et al.*, 1956). Since it is well known that all the substrates of β-oxidation are derivatives of CoA, it was considered unnecessary to include CoA in the terminology. However, the participation of CoA is implied by employing the acid radical of the substrate in the name of the enzyme, e.g. β-hydroxyacyl dehydrogenase and not β-hydroxyacid dehydrogenase.

Acid thiokinase

$$R\text{—}CO\text{—}OH + CoASH + ATP \xrightleftharpoons{Mg^{++}} R\text{—}CO\text{—}S\text{—}CoA + AMP + PP$$

$$K_{(heptanoate)} = \frac{(RCO\text{—}S\text{—}CoA)\,(AMP)\,(PP)}{(R\text{—}CO\text{—}OH)(\,CoASH)\,(ATP)}$$

$$= 1\cdot11 \text{ at pH } 8\cdot0$$

In animal tissues, three separate kinases have been reported. Acetic thiokinase activates acetic and propionic acids. A general fatty acid thiokinase activates fatty acids from C_4 to C_{12}, and a long chain fatty acid thiokinase activates fatty acids from C_8 to C_{18} (Fig. 7.4).

Acetic thiokinase has been demonstrated in a number of plants and has been partly purified from spinach leaves. The enzyme from spinach resembles that from animals in that both require Mg^{++} and K^+ and are inhibited by Li^+ and Na^+. Although indirect evidence exists for the presence of kinases activating long chain fatty acids in plants, these kinases have not so far been isolated.

In addition to being activated directly in the presence of a kinase, ATP and CoA, fatty acids may also be activated by means of CoA-transfer reactions. Bacterial enzymes are able to catalyse the transfer of CoA between a number of short chain fatty acids and either acetate or succinate.

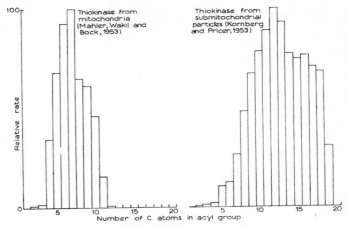

FIG. 7.4. Substrate specificity of animal thiokinases.

Acyl dehydrogenase

$$R—CH_2—CH_2—CO—S—CoA + FAD \rightarrow$$

Acyl CoA $R—CH=CH—CO—S—CoA + FADH_2$

$\qquad\qquad\qquad\qquad\qquad\alpha,\beta\text{-Enoyl CoA}$

$$K = \frac{(\text{butenoyl CoA}) (\text{indophenol } H_2)}{(\text{butyryl CoA}) (\text{indophenol})}$$

$$= 10$$

Three different acyl dehydrogenases have been demonstrated in animal tissues. Their substrate specificity is shown in Fig. 7.5.

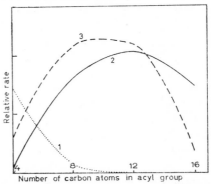

FIG. 7.5. Substrate specificity of animal acyl dehydrogenases.
1: butyryl dehydrogenase; 2: acyl dehydrogenase (caprylyl dehydrogenase);
3: lauryl dehydrogenase (palmityl dehydrogenase).

Except for traces of iron, the acyl dehydrogenases appear to be metal-free. The significance of the small amounts of iron is at present not clear. The exact number of moles of FAD/mole of enzyme is still uncertain. Sulphydryl groups seem to be essential for activity.

Addition of fatty acyl CoA to fatty acyl dehydrogenase results in a reversible reduction of the FAD groups of the enzyme. The reduced flavoprotein enzyme is incapable of being reoxidized unless another specific flavoprotein, called the electron transferring flavoprotein (ETF) is added. In the presence of ETF, reduced fatty acyl dehydrogenase is reoxidized by cytochrome c. ETF contains 1 mole of FAD/mole of enzyme and appears to be metal-free. The dehydrogenation of fatty acyl CoA may be represented as follows:

acyl CoA + acyl dehydrogenase (FAD)$\leftrightharpoons$

α,β-enoyl CoA + acyl dehydrogenase (FADH$_2$)

ETF

acyl dehydrogenase (FADH$_2$) + cytochrome $c\leftrightharpoons$

acyl dehydrogenase (FAD) + reduced cytochrome c

Acyl dehydrogenase

acyl CoA + cytochrome $c\leftrightharpoons\alpha,\beta$-enoyl CoA + reduced cytochrome c

ETF

All flavoprotein enzymes have been shown by Beinert to form free radical intermediates (p. 50). These free radical flavin intermediates are extremely reactive and usually have a lifetime of milliseconds. The acyl dehydrogenases form particularly stable free radical flavin intermediates when reduced by their substrates. Apparently the same phenomenon which prevents reduced acyl dehydrogenase from reacting further in the absence of ETF also prevents the free radical from reacting further.

Enoyl hydrase

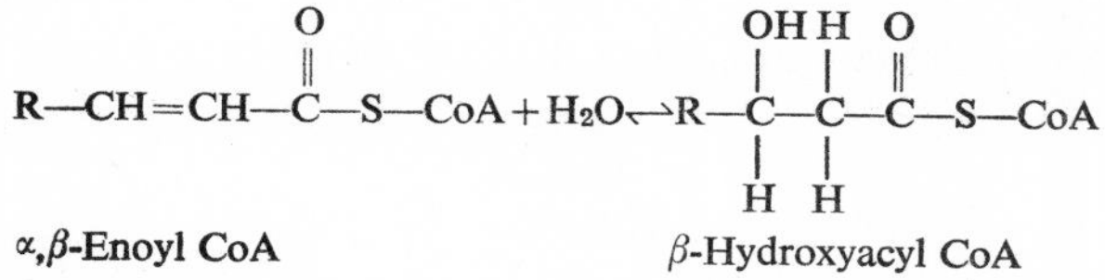

α,β-Enoyl CoA β-Hydroxyacyl CoA

$$K_{\text{(crotonyl CoA)}} = \frac{(\beta\text{-hydroxybutyryl CoA})}{(\text{crotonyl CoA})(H_2O)}$$

$$= 3\cdot6 \times 10^{-2}$$

18

Enoyl hydrase has been crystallized from ox liver and appears to act on all substrates from C_4 to C_{12}. The enzyme is widely distributed in animals. The only plant assayed, spinach, had a very low activity.

β-Hydroxyacyl dehydrogenase

$$R\overset{\overset{\text{OH}}{|}}{\underset{\underset{\text{H}}{|}}{C}}\text{—}CH_2\text{—}\overset{\overset{O}{||}}{C}\text{—}S\text{—}CoA + NAD \rightleftharpoons R\text{—}\overset{\overset{O}{||}}{C}\text{—}CH_2\text{—}\overset{\overset{O}{||}}{C}\text{—}S\text{—}CoA + NADH_2$$

β-Hydroxyacyl CoA   β-Ketoacyl CoA

$$K = \frac{(\text{acetoacetyl CoA}) (\text{NADH}_2) (\text{H}^+)}{(\beta\text{-hydroxyacyl CoA}) (\text{NAD})}$$
$$= 6\cdot3 \times 10^{-11} \text{ at pH } 7\cdot0$$

The enzyme has been crystallized from pig heart. The one enzyme acts on all substrates from C_4 to C_{12}, and is specific for the $L(+)$ isomer of β-hydroxyacyl CoA.

The unfavourable equilibrium is driven in the direction of β-hydroxyacyl CoA dehydrogenation by the general mechanisms discussed on p. 80.

β-Ketoacyl thiolase

$$R\text{—}\overset{\overset{O}{||}}{C}\text{—}CH_2\text{—}\overset{\overset{O}{||}}{C}\text{—}S\text{—}CoA + CoASH \rightleftharpoons R\text{—}\overset{\overset{O}{||}}{C}\text{—}S\text{—}CoA + CH_3\text{—}\overset{\overset{O}{||}}{C}\text{—}S\text{—}CoA$$

$$K = \frac{(\text{acetyl CoA})^2}{(\text{acetoacetyl CoA}) (\text{CoA})}$$
$$= 1\cdot7 \times 10^4 \text{ at pH } 8\cdot5$$

Two β-keto thiolases have been isolated. One is specific for acetoacetyl CoA. The other has a broad specificity and acts on substrates between C_4 and C_{16}. Sulphydryl groups appear to be involved in the activity of these enzymes.

Stereoisomers involved in β-oxidation

The problem of the stereoisomers involved in β-oxidation has been delayed up to this point, so as not to obscure the basic principles of β-oxidation. The α,β-unsaturated fatty acyl CoA produced in the reaction catalysed by acyl dehydrogenase has a *trans* configuration. The exact isomers involved in the subsequent reactions are not known. A scheme incorporating the data obtained with crotonyl CoA is shown below:

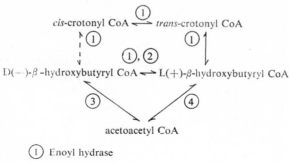

① Enoyl hydrase

② Racemase

③ D(−)-β-hydroxybutyryl CoA dehydrogenase

④ L(+)-β-hydroxybutyryl CoA dehydrogenase

Wakil claims that both the *cis* and *trans* isomers are hydrated, the *cis* yielding the D-isomer and the *trans* yielding the L-isomer. Studies with crystallized enoyl hydrase on the other hand, suggest that this enzyme converts the *cis* to the *trans* isomer, which is hydrated exclusively to L(+)-β-hydroxybutyryl CoA. The D(−) isomer arises by the action of enoyl hydrase and of racemase on the L-isomer. It is interesting to observe the multiple functions of enoyl hydrase. The enzyme not only hydrates double bonds, but also acts as a *cis-trans* isomerase, and a racemase. It has also been reported to act as a positional isomerase, converting β,γ-unsaturated CoA derivatives to α,β-unsaturated derivatives.

In addition to the widely distributed β-hydroxyacyl CoA dehydrogenase which is specific for the L-isomer, a dehydrogenase which is specific for D(−)-β-hydroxybutyryl CoA has been reported.

The Krebs cycle and β-oxidation of fats

The enzymes responsible for the oxidation of fatty acid, and the enzymes of the Krebs cycle, are both localized in the mitochondria. The close association of these two systems makes it possible for acetyl CoA units formed during β-oxidation to be oxidized via the Krebs cycle, with the concomitant production of ATP. It is possible to calculate the theoretical amount of ATP which can be generated during the complete oxidation of 1 mole of a common fat such as palmitate to CO_2 and H_2O through the combined action of β-oxidation and the Krebs cycle. The overall re-action may be represented as follows:

$$C_{16}H_{32}O_2 + 23O_2 + 30H_2O \rightarrow 16CO_2 + 46H_2O$$
$$\Delta G^\circ = -2330 \cdot 5 \text{ kcal}$$

Cleavage of each acetate fragment via β-oxidation produces 1 molecule of reduced NAD and 1 molecule of reduced FAD. Oxidation of each mole of reduced NAD through the respiratory chain yields 3 moles of ATP (p. 219). Oxidation of each mole of reduced FAD yields 2 moles of ATP (p. 219). A total of 5 moles of ATP is therefore formed during the forma-tion of each mole of acetyl CoA through β-oxidation. The β-oxidation process is carried out seven times during the oxidation of palmitate, so a total of $7 \times 5 = 35$ moles of ATP is produced. Since 1 mole of ATP is required for the initial activation of the fatty acid, a net gain of 34 ATP is obtained during the conversion of palmitate to 8 acetyl CoA units. Oxidation of 8 moles of acetyl CoA through the Krebs cycle yields $8 \times 12 = 96$ ATP.

Total net production of ATP from palmitate oxidation =
$$96 + 34 = 130 \text{ ATP.}$$

Assuming ΔG° for hydrolysis of ATP = 8000 cal

$$\text{Efficiency of palmitate oxidation} \quad = \frac{130 \times 8000}{2\ 330\ 000}$$
$$= 45 \text{ per cent}$$

A comparison of these figures with those obtained for the oxidation of glucose (p. 215) shows that the efficiency of ATP production from the oxidation of glucose or palmitate is about the same. On a unit weight basis, the oxidation of palmitate ($0 \cdot 51$ moles ATP/g) yields over twice as much ATP as does glucose ($0 \cdot 21$ moles ATP/g).

The importance of fats as a food store in seeds has already been pointed out. A germinating seed has two critical requirements: (a) a source of the precursors of carbohydrate, protein, etc. required for the synthesis of new cell material and (b) a source of energy (ATP) required to assemble the precursors ('building blocks') into cell material. Both these require-ments are effectively supplied by fats. The biochemical versatility of acetyl CoA, produced by β-oxidation, makes possible the synthesis of many compounds.

β-Oxidation in plants

Evidence for β-oxidation of fatty acids in higher plants was first obtained by Grace (1939). The technique and principles used in this study were essentially the same as those used by Knoop in his experiments on the β-oxidation of fatty acid in animals. Grace observed that the growth-promoting activity of ω-substituted aryl or aryl-oxyalkyl carboxylic acids was correlated with the length of the side chain. For example, when the first five members of the ω-(1-naphthyl) alkylcarboxylic acid series were examined for their capacity to promote the rooting of cuttings, only those compounds containing a side chain with an even number of carbon atoms possessed activity similar to that of 1-naphthyl-acetic acid. Those compounds with side chains containing an odd number of carbon atoms had very low activity.

Synerholm & Zimmerman (1947) prepared a series of 2,4-dichloro-phenoxyalkyl carboxylic acids and found that only those acids containing side chains with an even number of carbon atoms were active in producing epinastic responses in tomato plants. It was suggested that β-oxidation of the side chains would explain the results. By this means, acids containing side chains with an even number of carbon atoms become degraded to an active acetic acid derivative, whereas derivatives with side chains containing an odd number of carbon atoms yield phenol derivatives, with no growth-promoting activity:

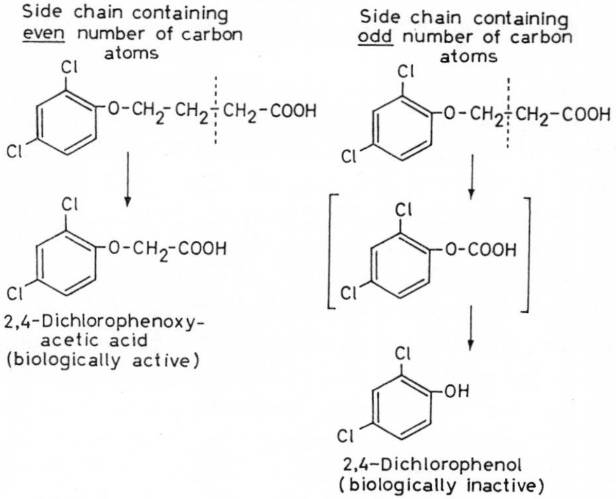

Similar results consistent with β-oxidation have been obtained by other workers, using a variety of chemical derivatives and plant tissues. The products of catabolism have been confirmed by a variety of techniques. Thus Fawcett et al. (1954) used colorimetric methods to demonstrate the production of phenol from those derivatives of ω-phenoxyalkyl carboxylic acid which contained an odd number of carbon atoms. Fawcett *et al.* (1958) used paper chromatographic, colorimetric and bioassay methods to examine the products of catabolism of ω-(2,4-dichlorophenoxy) alkyl carboxylic acids by wheat coleoptiles and pea-stem tissues.

The observation that a number of fatty acid derivatives can be degraded by a variety of plant tissues suggests that the enzymes participating in β-oxidation have a relatively broad specificity. However, certain observations suggest that the enzymes of β-oxidation from different tissues do show a difference in specificity towards the various ω-substituted fatty acids. Thus the 2,4,5-trichlorophenoxyalkylcarboxylic acids with side chains containing an even number of carbon atoms were active in the *wheat* cylinder test. With *pea* and *tomato* tissue, on the other hand, only 2,4,5-trichlorophenoxyacetic acid was active, and higher homologues exhibited no biological activity.

This observation has been applied in the development of methods for selective weed control. Thus one species of plant when treated with a derivative of butyric, caproic or octanoic acid might be expected to degrade the compound to a biologically active acetate derivative, and thus succumb to its herbicidal action. Another plant species, however, which is not capable of degrading the particular derivative would remain unharmed.

A number of workers subsequently showed that slices of plant tissue metabolized fatty acids labelled with ^{14}C to $^{14}CO_2$. It was not until 1956 that an unequivocal demonstration of β-oxidation of fatty acids by a cell-free system was accomplished (Stumpf & Barber, 1956). They showed that mitochondrial particles prepared from germinating peanut cotyledons, when supplemented with a number of cofactors, readily oxidized a series of aliphatic acids to CO_2.

The following carboxyl-labelled acids were oxidized to $^{14}CO_2$: C_2, C_3, C_4, C_5, C_8, C_{12}, C_{14}, C_{16} and C_{18}. In addition, palmitate labelled in C_2, C_3, C_{11} and C_{15} was readily oxidized to $^{14}CO_2$, thereby indicating an extensive degradation of the long chain fatty acid. The cofactors were determined for the oxidation of butyrate-1-^{14}C and for palmitate-11-^{14}C. The oxidation required ATP, CoA, a Krebs cycle acid, NAD, NADP, glutathione and Mn^{++}. The requirement for CoA and the pyridine nucleotides is interesting, since animal mitochondria fail to show a requirement for these cofactors. Only in soluble enzyme systems from animals can a requirement for CoA and NAD be demonstrated. It appears that CoA and the pyridine nucleotides are more easily removed from plant mitochondria, or that they are present in suboptimal amounts in the mitochondria prior to isolation. Since NADP is not required in the series of reactions of β-oxidation, NADP presumably stimulates the rate of oxidation of acetyl CoA units via the Krebs cycle. This stimulation could be accounted for by a stimulation in the rate of NADP-specific isocitric dehydrogenase.

On the basis of the following evidence it was concluded that the peanut mitochondrial system catalysed the β-oxidation of fatty acids to acetyl CoA units, which are oxidized through the Krebs cycle:

(a) The cofactors required in the peanut particulate system are, in general, those required for the β-oxidation of fatty acids by animal mitochondria and by the soluble enzyme systems described by Green and Lynen.

(b) Malonate, a competitive inhibitor of succinate oxidation and thus of the Krebs cycle, strongly inhibits the oxidation of butyrate to CO_2 and stimulates the production of acetoacetate. The increased production of acetoacetate is presumably due to the blocking of oxaloacetate production, so that acetyl CoA condenses with itself.

(c) The oxidation of butyrate-1-^{14}C gave rise to extensive labelling in the Krebs cycle acids, indicating that acetyl CoA units produced during the oxidation of fatty acids are oxidized to CO_2 by way of the Krebs cycle.

(d) As discussed on p. 169, the methyl carbon of acetyl CoA is not released as CO_2 until the third turn of the Krebs cycle. On the other hand the carboxyl carbon of acetate appears as CO_2 upon completion of the second turn of the cycle. Therefore, if the peanut particulate system carried out the β-oxidation of long chain fatty acids to acetyl CoA units which were then oxidized via the Krebs cycle, odd-numbered carbon atoms of long fatty acids should appear as CO_2 sooner than even-numbered carbon atoms. These expectations were confirmed using acetate labelled in the carboxyl and methyl carbons, and palmitate labelled in C_2 and C_3.

The evidence obtained from plant tissues and from plant mitochondria strongly suggests that the scheme of β-oxidation in plants is the same as in animals. However, the task of isolating and purifying the plant enzymes involved, and of reconstructing a system of β-oxidation using these purified enzymes still remains.

α-OXIDATION

Whereas animals use the β-oxidation pathway exclusively for the degradation of saturated fatty acids with chain lengths greater than C_3, plants may be able to utilize an additional pathway. This pathway of α-oxidation involves only two basic enzymatic reactions in each turn of the cycle, compared to a total of five involved in the β-oxidation pathway. The first of these reactions, catalysed by long chain fatty acid peroxidase (FAP), involves an α-peroxidation of a long chain fatty acid to CO_2 and an aldehyde containing one less carbon atom than the original fatty acid.

$$R\!-\!CH_2\overset{\cdot}{C}H_2\!-\!\overset{o}{C}\overset{*}{O}OH + H_2O_2 \rightarrow R\!-\!\overset{\cdot}{C}H_2\!-\!\overset{o}{C}HO + \overset{*}{C}O_2 + 2H_2O$$

The second reaction, catalysed by long chain fatty aldehyde dehydrogenase, involves an NAD-dehydrogenation of the aldehyde to an acid:

$$R\!-\!\overset{\cdot}{C}H_2\!-\!\overset{o}{C}HO + NAD + H_2O \rightarrow R\!-\!\overset{\cdot}{C}H_2\!-\!\overset{o}{C}OOH + NADH_2$$

The acid so formed may then proceed through the same series of reactions. The combined action of the two enzymes results in a stepwise decarboxylation of acids with chain length between C_{15} and C_{18} to acids of chain length of C_{14}.

The scheme postulated in Fig. 7.6 has been elucidated by Stumpf and his colleagues, using cell-free extracts of germinated peanut cotyledons:

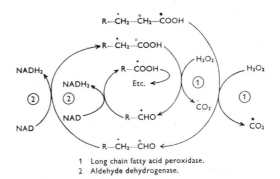

1 Long chain fatty acid peroxidase.
2 Aldehyde dehydrogenase.

FIG. 7.6. α-Oxidation of long chain fatty acids.

Fatty acid peroxidase

This enzyme has been demonstrated in cell-free extracts of cotyledons obtained from seedlings of peanuts, and safflower. Extracts of acetone powders of germinated peas were also active. No activity could be detected in lupine, soy bean, sunflower, castor beans or in animal tissues. When a cell-free extract of peanut cotyledons was subject to differential centrifugation, the enzyme was found in mitochondrial, microsomal and supernatant fractions. The enzyme was partially purified by treatment of an extract of acetone powder of peanut cotyledons with ammonium sulphate (AS enzyme).

Saturated fatty acids from C_{14} to C_{18} serve as substrates for this enzyme. Odd-numbered fatty acids are quite active, and the C_{15} acid appears to be the preferred substrate. Evidence is presented that oleic acid also undergoes α-peroxidation. Using palmitate as substrate, equimolar amounts of CO_2 and long chain fatty aldehyde were formed. The C_{15} aldehyde was isolated and characterized as the 2,4-dinitrophenyl hydrazone. No cofactors are required for the activity of long chain fatty acid peroxidase. Imidazole, azide and cyanide are potent inhibitors of the reaction.

The requirement for H_2O_2 in the above reaction is satisfied by a peroxide generating system. Free H_2O_2 is not active. In crude cell fractions it is sufficient to add glycolic acid or any of a number of L-α-hydroxy acids, since glycolic acid oxidase is present in the crude preparations.

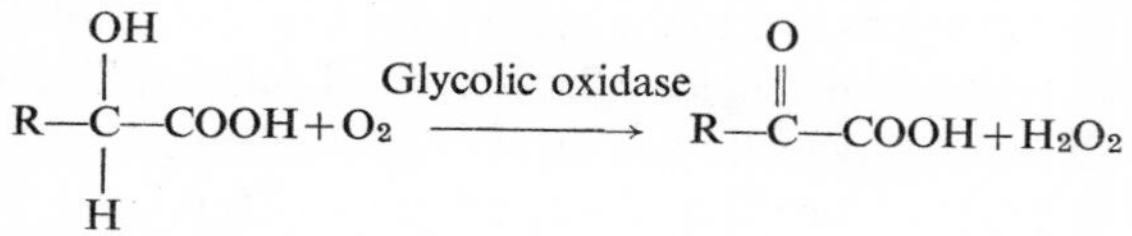

$$\underset{\text{L—}\alpha\text{—OH acid}}{R—\overset{\displaystyle OH}{\underset{\displaystyle H}{\overset{|}{\underset{|}{C}}}}—COOH} + O_2 \xrightarrow{\text{Glycolic oxidase}} R—\overset{\displaystyle O}{\overset{\|}{C}}—COOH + H_2O_2$$

Other H_2O_2-generating systems may be used in place of the endogenous system, and those from animals, bacteria and plants were active.

Fatty aldehyde dehydrogenase

$$R—CHO + NAD + H_2O \rightarrow R—COOH + NADH_2$$

Long chain fatty aldehyde dehydrogenase is present in the mitochondrial and microsomal fraction of germinated peanut cotyledons, but is absent from the supernatant fraction. The following evidence suggests the presence of the enzyme in the AS enzyme described above:

(a) Whereas the oxidation of palmitate-1-^{14}C to $^{14}CO_2$ requires only AS enzyme and a H_2O_2-generating system, oxidation of palmitate-2-^{14}C requires the addition of NAD. If palmitate-2-^{14}C is preincubated with AS enzyme and a H_2O_2-generating system, a product accumulates which releases $^{14}CO_2$ upon subsequent addition of NAD. These observations are consistent with the series of reactions shown in Fig. 7.6.

(b) When palmitate was incubated with the AS enzyme and a peroxide source (in the absence of NAD) it could be shown that a long chain fatty aldehyde accumulated. The addition of NAD resulted in a decrease of long chain fatty aldehyde. Incubation of AS enzyme with n-tetradecanal caused an NAD-dependent decrease of the aldehyde. The expected concomitant reduction of NAD was not reported.

(c) When palmitate-11-^{14}C was incubated in a reaction mixture containing AS enzyme and a H_2O_2 source, radioactive $C_{14}CHO$, but no radioactive acid other than palmitate was detected. When NAD was included in the reaction mixture the following radioactive compounds were identified: $C_{14}CHO$, $C_{14}COOH$, $C_{13}CHO$ and $C_{13}COOH$.

α-Oxidation in whole plants

Fawcett et al. (1958) have presented evidence for the operation of another α-oxidation pathway which, in contrast to the system oxidizing long chain fatty acids, metabolizes short chain substituted nitriles. The wheat cylinder test was used as a measure of the production of 2,4-dichlorophenoxyacetic acid from 2,4-dichlorophenoxyalkyl nitriles. The production of 2,4-dichlorophenoxyacetic acid was also confirmed by paper chromatography. 2,4-Dichlorophenol was estimated chemically.

Wheat tissue converted the nitriles predominantly to the products shown under 'pathway 1' in Table 7.1.

TABLE 7.1

Products of oxidation of 2,4-dichlorophenoxyalkyl nitriles by wheat tissue

Nature of side chain	Products	
	Pathway 1	Pathway 2
Even number of carbon atoms	2,4-Dichlorophenoxy-acetic acid	2,4-Dichlorophenol
Odd number of carbon atoms	2,4-Dichlorophenol	2,4-Dichlorophenoxy-acetic acid

The formation of these products is consistent with hydrolysis of the nitrile to the corresponding acid, which is degraded by β-oxidation. For example, γ-(2,4-dichlorophenoxy) butyronitrile is degraded to 2,4-dichlorophenoxyacetic acid as follows:

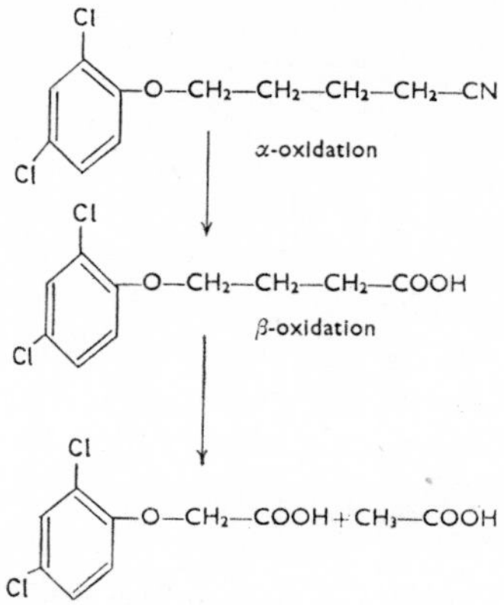

In addition to the products shown under 'pathway 1', small amounts of the products shown under 'pathway 2' were formed. The products obtained in 'pathway 2' are best explained as being formed from an α-oxidation of the nitrile to an acid with one less carbon atom. This acid is then degraded by β-oxidation. Thus 2,4-dichlorophenoxyvaleronitrile yields 2,4-dichlorophenoxyacetic acid as follows:

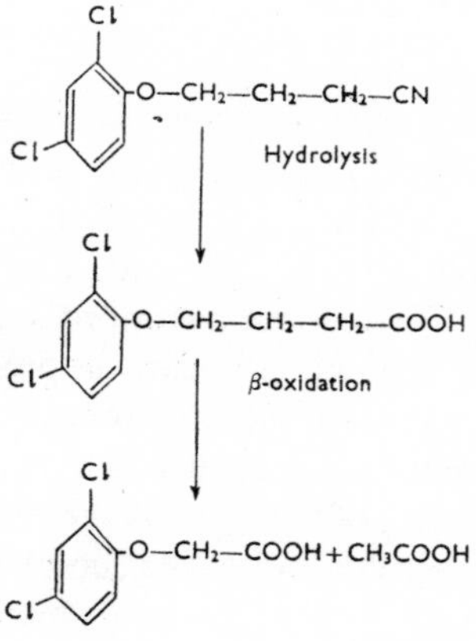

The mechanism of α-oxidation was investigated in detail by using 3-indolylacetonitrile as a substrate. This nitrile was chosen because of the convenience in detecting its possible intermediates of α-oxidation. Wheat tissue was observed to carry out the following reactions:

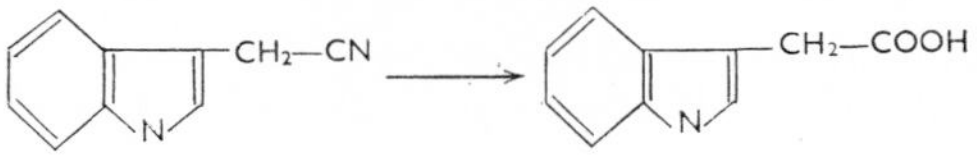

$$\text{Indolyl—CH}_2\text{—CN} \longrightarrow \text{Indolyl—CH}_2\text{—COOH} \quad (1)$$

Indolylacetonitrile   Indolylacetic acid

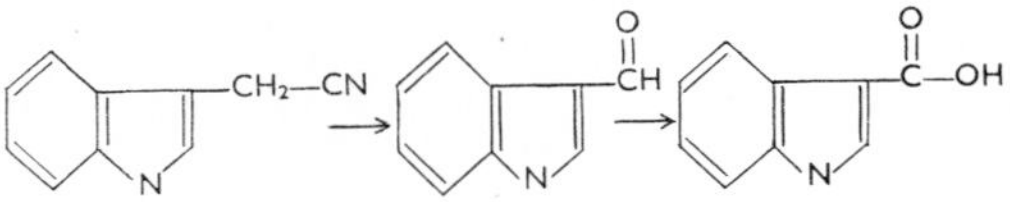

$$\text{Indolyl—CH}_2\text{—CN} \rightarrow \text{Indolyl—}\overset{\overset{\displaystyle O}{\|}}{C}\text{H} \rightarrow \text{Indolyl—}\overset{\overset{\displaystyle O}{\|}}{C}\text{—OH} \quad (2)$$

Indolylaceto-   Indole-   Indolecarboxylic
nitrile   aldehyde   acid

The exact mechanism of the conversion of indolylacetonitrile to indole-aldehyde is uncertain. Indolylacetic acid does not appear to be an intermediate.

On the basis of this evidence, the degradation of nitrile derivatives by the combined action of α-oxidation and β-oxidation may be represented as follows:

$$
\begin{array}{c}
\hspace{3cm} \beta\text{-oxidation} \\
R\text{—CH}_2\text{—CH}_2\text{—CH}_2\text{—COOH} \longrightarrow R\text{—CH}_2\text{—COOH} \\
\nearrow \text{Hydrolysis} \\
R\text{—CH}_2\text{—CH}_2\text{—CH}_2\text{—CN} \\
\searrow \\
\alpha\text{-oxidation} \hspace{2cm} \beta\text{-oxidation} \\
R\text{—CH}_2\text{—CH}_2\text{—CHO} \rightarrow R\text{—CH}_2\text{—CH}_2\text{COOH} \longrightarrow R\text{—COOH}
\end{array}
$$

The significance of α-oxidation in plants is uncertain. Studies with peanut mitochondria indicate that the rate of oxidation of palmitate-1-^{14}C by β-oxidation and by α-oxidation is approximately equal. Energetically, the scheme of α-oxidation is not nearly as productive as β-oxidation. Thus each turn of the α-oxidation cycle produces 1 molecule of reduced NAD. Oxidation of a molecule of reduced NAD through the respiratory chain produces 3 molecules of ATP. Thus the removal of each 2 carbon unit through α-oxidation yields only 6 ATP, compared to a net production of 16 ATP by removal of each 2 carbon unit through the combined activity of β-oxidation and the Krebs cycle. A further disadvantage of α-oxidation is that only a limited range of long chain fatty acids can be metabolized. One possible advantage of α-oxidation is that the scheme requires no initial activation of the fatty acid to an acyl CoA derivative.

Odd-Numbered Fatty Acids

The oxidation of odd-numbered fatty acids has not received as much attention by biochemists as the even-numbered fatty acids, since the odd-numbered fatty acids are extremely rare in both animals and higher plants. The following evidence obtained from animal systems indicates that odd-numbered fatty acids, like even-numbered fatty acids, are degraded by β-oxidation.

(a) The classical experiments of Knoop and Dakin (p. 266) are consistent with β-oxidation of odd-numbered fatty acids.

(b) Liver slices convert both even- and odd-numbered fatty acids to acetoacetate.

(c) Under the appropriate conditions animal mitochondria can oxidize a number of odd-numbered fatty acids to CO_2.

(d) All the odd-numbered fatty acids tested serve as substrates for the enzymes of β-oxidation that act on even-numbered compounds of approximately the same chain length.

In plant systems, the Knoop-type experiments described on p. 275 strongly suggest β-oxidation of the odd-numbered fatty acids. Although oxidation of odd-numbered fatty acids to CO_2 has been demonstrated with mitochondria prepared from cotyledons of germinated peanuts, no evidence for a β-oxidative pathway was presented.

Propionic Acid

Except in the ruminants, where propionic acid is one of the principal products of carbohydrate fermentation by the micro-organisms of the rumen, propionate does not occur free in animals or higher plants. Its metabolism is important, however, because it is produced in a number of degradative reactions. β-Oxidation of odd-numbered fatty acids ultimately produces propionic acid, and the degradation of the branched chain amino acids isoleucine and valine by enzyme systems obtained from animals also yields propionate (p. 384).

Propionic acid is readily oxidized by mitochondria obtained from the cotyledons of germinating peanuts (Giovanelli & Stumpf, 1958). The cofactors required for the oxidation of propionate-1-^{14}C to $^{14}CO_2$ by this system include ATP, CoA, NAD, glutathione and α-ketoglutarate. NADP and Mn^{++} stimulate the oxidation. β-hydroxypropionate-^{14}C was isolated as an intermediate in the oxidation of propionate-1, -2 and -3-^{14}C. β-Hydroxypropionate-^{14}C and propionate-^{14}C were used as substrates to determine the following labelling pattern:

(a) Propionate-1-^{14}C (or β-hydroxypropionate-1-^{14}C) rapidly released all of its label as $^{14}CO_2$, and other reaction products were completely devoid of ^{14}C.

(b) Propionate-2-^{14}C (or β-hydroxypropionate-2-^{14}C) and propionate-3-^{14}C released $^{14}CO_2$ only after a lag period during which time the Krebs cycle acids became labelled. $^{14}CO_2$ was released more rapidly from propionate-3-^{14}C than from propionate-2-^{14}C.

(c) Succinate-^{14}C produced during the oxidation of propionate-2-^{14}C and propionate-3-^{14}C was labelled predominantly in the methylene and carboxyl groups, respectively.

The combined evidence described above is consistent with the scheme shown in Fig. 7.7.

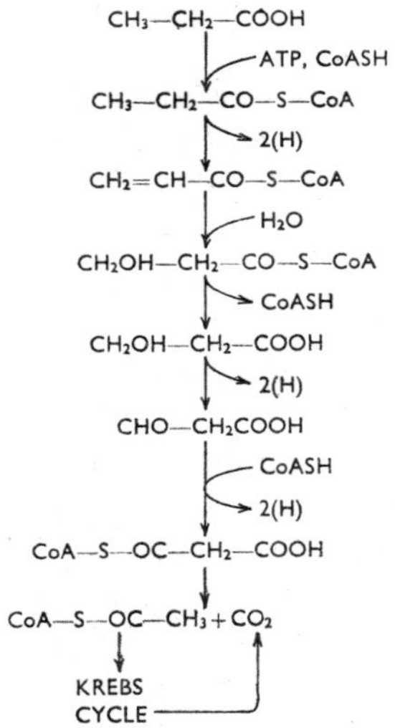

$$CH_3-CH_2-COOH$$
$$\downarrow \quad ATP, CoASH$$
$$CH_3-CH_2-CO-S-CoA$$
$$\downarrow \quad 2(H)$$
$$CH_2=CH-CO-S-CoA$$
$$\downarrow \quad H_2O$$
$$CH_2OH-CH_2-CO-S-CoA$$
$$\downarrow \quad CoASH$$
$$CH_2OH-CH_2-COOH$$
$$\downarrow \quad 2(H)$$
$$CHO-CH_2COOH$$
$$\downarrow \quad CoASH$$
$$\downarrow \quad 2(H)$$
$$CoA-S-OC-CH_2-COOH$$
$$\downarrow$$
$$CoA-S-OC-CH_3 + CO_2$$
$$\downarrow$$
$$KREBS$$
$$CYCLE$$

Fig. 7.7. Modified β-oxidation of propionate.

In this scheme the carboxyl group of propionate rapidly appears a CO_2. C3 of propionate is converted to the carboxyl group of acetate, which enters the Krebs cycle and becomes the carboxyl groups of succinate. These carboxyl groups are converted to CO_2 during the second turn of the Krebs cycle. This explains the lag in the production of $^{14}CO_2$ from propionate-3-^{14}C. C2 of propionate is converted to the methyl group of acetate, which enters the Krebs cycle and becomes the methylene groups of succinate. The methylene groups of succinate are converted to CO_2

during the third turn of the Krebs cycle. This explains the extremely long lag period obtained for the conversion of propionate-2-^{14}C to $^{14}CO_2$.

The preliminary steps in the oxidation of propionate (up to the formation of β-hydroxypropionyl CoA) are the same as those in conventional β-oxidation. However, the subsequent reactions of β-hydroxypropionyl CoA depart from those of conventional β-oxidation, and so the term 'modified β-oxidation' is used to describe the pathway in Fig. 7.7. In peanut mitochondria propionate appears to be oxidized exclusively by the modified β-oxidation pathway. Evidence was obtained for the operation of this pathway also in avocado mitochondria and lupine mitochondria. A similar mechanism of propionate oxidation has been reported in animal and bacterial enzyme systems.

Two additional mechanisms of propionate oxidation have been demonstrated in animals and bacteria. The carboxylation pathway (Flavin, Ortiz & Ochoa, 1955) shown below is the principal pathway of propionate oxidation in animals:

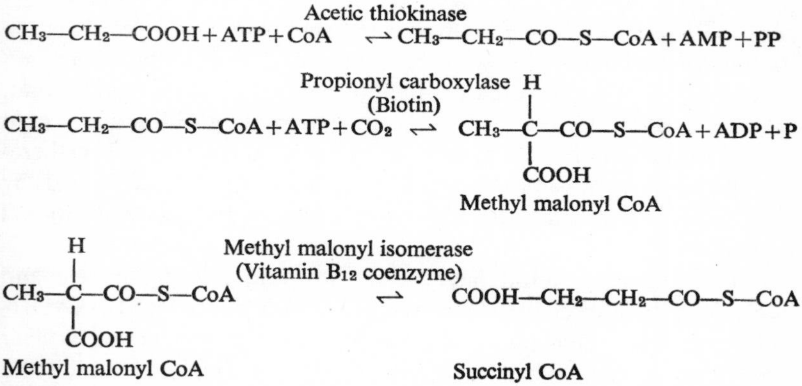

Acetic thiokinase

$$CH_3—CH_2—COOH + ATP + CoA \;\rightleftharpoons\; CH_3—CH_2—CO—S—CoA + AMP + PP$$

Propionyl carboxylase
(Biotin)

$$CH_3—CH_2—CO—S—CoA + ATP + CO_2 \rightleftharpoons CH_3—\overset{\displaystyle H}{\underset{\displaystyle COOH}{C}}—CO—S—CoA + ADP + P$$

Methyl malonyl CoA

Methyl malonyl isomerase
(Vitamin B$_{12}$ coenzyme)

$$CH_3—\overset{\displaystyle H}{\underset{\displaystyle COOH}{C}}—CO—S—CoA \rightleftharpoons COOH—CH_2—CH_2—CO—S—CoA$$

Methyl malonyl CoA   Succinyl CoA

Evidence for an α-oxidation pathway involving acrylyl CoA and lactyl CoA has been presented in animals and bacteria. No evidence has been obtained for the participation of either an α-oxidation or carboxylation pathway during the oxidation of propionate by the peanut mitochondrial system described above.

Unsaturated Fatty Acids

Despite the abundance and wide distribution of oleic, linoleic and linolenic acids, little is known of their metabolism. Some possible mechanisms for their oxidation are discussed below:

β-OXIDATION

Oleic, linoleic and linolenic acids all contain a double bond in the 9, 10 position:

$$\overset{10}{-}C = \overset{9}{C}-C-C-C-C-C-C-C-COOH$$

Obviously β-oxidation of oleic acid with the production of 3 acetate units could theoretically take place until the derivative:

$$\overset{10}{\underset{H}{C}} = \overset{9}{\underset{H}{C}} - \overset{8}{\underset{\underset{H}{|}}{C}} - \overset{7}{COOH}$$

is produced. Further oxidation of this derivative by β-oxidation is complicated by the position of the double bond. The derivative is unsaturated in the β,γ position instead of the α,β-unsaturation required for normal β-oxidation. The unfavourable position of the double bond could be overcome, however, by the action of enoyl hydrase, which converts β,γ-unsaturated acyl CoA to α,β-unsaturated acyl CoA. In linoleic acid, the second double bond, between carbons 12 and 13, falls in the normal α,β position required for β-oxidation. In linolenic acid the third double bond, between carbons 15 and 16 is in an unfavourable position and would require the action of enoyl hydrase as a positional isomerase. It is therefore theoretically possible to degrade oleic, linoleic and linolenic acids by β-oxidation by utilizing the activity of enoyl hydrase as a positional isomerase.

Rat liver mitochondria have been shown to oxidize linoleic and linolenic acids, labelled in the carboxyl group with ^{14}C, to $^{14}CO_2$. $NADH_2$ was required for the oxidation. Extracts of acetone powders of rat liver mitochondria also oxidized linolenic and linoleic acids and exhibited a requirement for ATP and CoA, in addition to $NADH_2$. The requirement for ATP and CoA is consistent with, but does not prove, β-oxidation. The requirement for $NADH_2$ is not understood.

Plant systems have not been examined for their possible β-oxidation of unsaturated fatty acids.

α-OXIDATION

α-Oxidation permits a convenient method of subtracting 1 carbon atom from a long chain fatty acid. Decarboxylation of oleic acid would produce a long chain fatty acid with one less carbon atom which could be degraded directly by β-oxidation. Oleic acid-1-^{14}C is converted to $^{14}CO_2$

by a peanut enzyme system by way of α-oxidation. The metabolic fate of the decarboxylation product, however, was not determined.

LIPOXIDASE

Unsaturated fatty acids containing a methylene-interrupted multiple-unsaturated system in which the double bonds are all *cis* are oxidized in the presence of lipoxidase. Substrates conforming to this requirement include linoleic, linolenic and arachidonic. Oleic acid is not attacked. Lipoxidase is widely distributed in plants and has been crystallized from

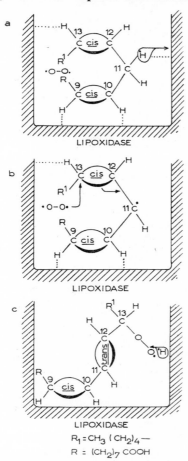

FIG. 7.8. Proposed mechanism of oxidation of linoleic acid by lipoxidase.

19

soy bean. Thiol groups appear to be required for activity. No prosthetic groups or cofactors have been detected.

A proposed mechanism (Siddiqi & Tappel, 1957) for the oxidation of linoleic acid by lipoxidase is shown in Fig. 7.8.

The overall reaction involves a peroxidation of the methylene-interrupted *cis-cis* acid to a conjugated *cis-trans* peroxide. The product of the reaction is optically active, which means that only one of the two possible isomers at the newly formed asymmetric C13 is produced. By the use of atomic models, it can be observed that the formation of the required *cis-trans* product can only be obtained when the hydrogen on C11, which is pointing upwards, is removed. The attack at C13 by oxygen must also be stereospecific if the final product is to be optically active.

The mechanism proposed in Fig. 7.8 may be summarized as follows:

(a) Linoleic acid and oxygen are bound to lipoxidase in a definite spatial arrangement to allow a stereospecific attack of oxygen at C13 and a stereospecific removal of a hydrogen atom from C11. The removal of a hydrogen atom (or a hydrogen ion plus an electron) produces a free radical at C11.

(b) Electron migration occurs to form the *cis-trans* conjugated system. At the same time the oxygen diradical attacks C13 in a stereospecific fashion to form the peroxyl radical.

(c) The formation of a hydroperoxide occurs by the addition of a hydrogen atom (or a hydrogen ion plus an electron) to the peroxyl radical. This hydrogen atom may be derived from the H atom (produced in step (*a*)) in the same molecule, or may arise from C11 of another molecule. The latter case would result in a lipoxidase-modulated and controlled chain reaction.

The physiological significance of lipoxidase is uncertain. In the presence of linoleate, lipoxidase can catalyse the oxidation of a number of unsaturated substances including carotenoids, chlorophyll, haemin, and ascorbic acid. Presumably the hydroperoxide, or some free radical intermediate produced from linoleate oxidizes these substances non-enzymatically.

Branched Chain Fatty Acids

β-Oxidation of branched long chain fatty acids with an even or odd number of carbon atoms ultimately produces isobutyryl CoA or isovaleryl CoA, respectively. Although animal mitochondria have been shown to convert isocaproate to isobutyrate via β-oxidation, the significance of this series of reactions is doubtful, since branched chain fatty acids do not occur naturally to any great extent. Probably the main source of branched chain fatty acids is from the degradation of the three branched chain amino acids, isoleucine, valine and leucine.

Almost nothing is known of the metabolism of branched amino acids and fatty acids in plants. Isobutyric acid-1-^{14}C, isovaleric acid-1-^{14}C and isocaproic-1-^{14}C are converted to $^{14}CO_2$ under the conditions described for β-oxidation of fatty acids by peanut mitochondria (p. 276). However, the activity with these acids was only 10 per cent of the activity observed with acetate-1-^{14}C.

Phospholipids

A scheme for the catabolism of lecithin is shown in Fig. 7.9. The sites of action of the phospholipases are indicated by arrows. It should be noted that phospholipase B requires L-α-lysolecithin as substrate, and is not active on L-α-lecithin. The terminology of phospholipases C and D is confused. Phospholipase C is frequently referred to as phospholipase D, and vice versa. The nomenclature used here is that suggested by Rossiter (1960).

All the reactions shown in Fig. 7.9, with the exception of that catalysed by glycerophosphocholine diesterase, have been demonstrated in plants. Only phospholipase D has been found extensively in plants, and appears to be present mainly in plastids. Phospholipase A is found in plants, animals and micro-organisms, and in the venom of snakes, bees and scorpions. The harmful effects of these venoms are thought to be due to phospholipase A catalysing the production of the haemolysing agent lysolecithin from lecithin.

The enzymes shown in Fig. 7.9 are, in general, also active on phosphatidyl ethanolamine and phosphatidyl serine and their products of catabolism. The mechanism of degradation of the other phosphatides is unknown. The mode of degradation of the plasmalogens and sphingolipids is also uncertain, but preliminary studies suggest that they may be catabolised by reactions similar to those shown for lecithin. Thus phospholipase A is able to remove a molecule of fatty acid from phosphatidal ethanolamine and phosphatidal choline. Phospholipase C removes phosphocholine from phosphatidal choline and from sphingomyelin.

ANABOLISM

Even-Numbered Fatty Acids

Since all the steps of β-oxidation are theoretically reversible, it seemed logical to postulate that the synthesis of fatty acids proceeded in the mito-

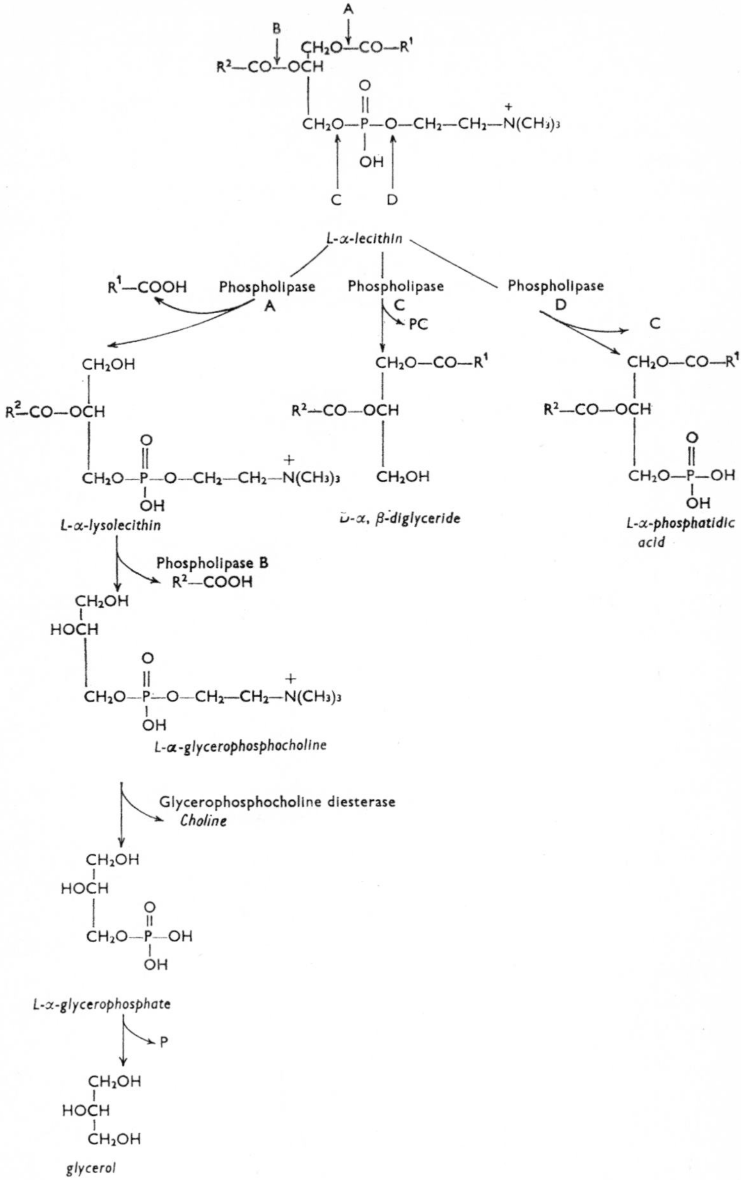

FIG. 7.9. Catabolism of lecithin.

chondria by the same repertoir of enzymes responsible for β-oxidation. Purified enzymes of β-oxidation were observed to synthesize butyrate from acetyl CoA. However, synthesis did not proceed beyond butyrate, and required the presence of dyes of low reducing potential to reverse the reaction catalysed by fatty acyl dehydrogenase.

The discovery of the enzyme enoyl reductase (NADPH$_2$-ethylene reductase, reducing enzyme of the fatty acid cycle) made it possible to replace reducing dyes by the more physiological reduced NADP:

Enoyl reductase

$$\alpha,\beta\text{-enoyl CoA} + \text{NADPH}_2 \rightleftharpoons \text{acyl CoA} + \text{NADP}$$

This enzyme has been reported bound to microsomes of liver and as a soluble enzyme in yeast and rat liver. In the presence of highly purified β-ketoacyl thiolase, β-hydroxyacyl dehydrogenase, enoyl hydrase and enoyl reductase, plus a source of reduced NAD and NADP, acetyl CoA was condensed with hexanoyl CoA to form octanoyl CoA together with progressively smaller amounts of the higher homologues. Although this system would not catalyse a *de novo* synthesis of long chain fatty acids from acetyl CoA, it would at least lengthen the fatty acid chain by the addition of acetate units.

Demonstration of the synthesis of long chain fatty acids from acetate awaited the discovery that the biosynthesis was catalysed, not by the enzymes of β-oxidation present in the mitochondria, but by another series of enzymes present in the soluble fraction of the cell. The soluble system from pigeon liver catalysed the *de novo* synthesis of long chain fatty acids from acetyl CoA in the presence of ATP, Mn^{++}, NADPH$_2$ and CO$_2$. Palmitate was the major product, together with small amounts of myristic and stearic acids. The system is located primarily in the supernatant fluid obtained after centrifuging at $100\,000 \times g$ for 2–4 hours.

The fact that ATP was still required, even though acetyl CoA is used as a substrate, suggested that an additional unknown activation was involved in the synthesis. The requirement for CO$_2$ was puzzling because CO$_2$ is not incorporated into the synthesized fatty acid. It must be assumed, therefore, that CO$_2$ plays a catalytic role. The role of ATP and CO$_2$ was clarified by the demonstration that the fatty acid synthesizing system could be resolved into two enzyme fractions. The first enzyme fraction (acetyl carboxylase) catalyses the following reaction:

$$
\underset{\text{Acetyl CoA}}{\overset{\overset{\displaystyle O}{\parallel}}{CH_3-C-S-CoA}} + CO_2 + ATP \quad \overset{\text{Enzyme 1 (Biotin)}}{\underset{Mn^+}{\rightleftharpoons}} \quad \underset{\text{Malonyl CoA}}{\overset{\overset{\displaystyle O}{\parallel}}{COOH-CH_2-C-S-CoA}} + ADP + P^i
$$

In the presence of the second enzyme fraction, malonyl CoA condenses
with acetyl CoA or higher fatty acyl CoA as follows:

$$
\underset{\substack{| \\ \text{S—CoA}}}{\overset{\overset{\text{O}}{\|}}{CH_3—C}}
\quad +
\underset{\substack{| \\ \text{CO—S—CoA}}}{\overset{\text{COOH}}{CH_2}}
\quad \overset{\text{Enzyme 2, 2NADPH}_2}{\longrightarrow}
\quad CH_3—CH_2—CH_2—\overset{\overset{\text{O}}{\|}}{C}—S—CoA + CO_2 + CoASH
$$

Fig. 7.10 illustrates the combined action of these two enzymes to bring
about the synthesis of long chain fatty acids from acetyl CoA, reduced

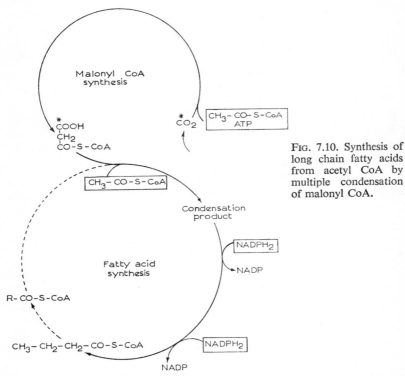

FIG. 7.10. Synthesis of
long chain fatty acids
from acetyl CoA by
multiple condensation
of malonyl CoA.

NADP, ATP and catalytic amounts of CO_2. Each condensation of the
α-carbon of malonyl CoA with the carboxyl carbon of acyl CoA results
in an extension of the carbon chain of the acyl CoA molecule by 2 carbon
units. Since the original carbon atom used to carboxylate acetyl CoA to
malonyl CoA is subsequently released as CO_2, no CO_2 is ever fixed into
the fatty acid. This system circumvents the unfavourable equilibrium of
direct condensation of acetyl CoA with acyl CoA. The participation of

$NADPH_2$ is another example of the direct use of the reducing potential of $NADPH_2$ in biosynthesis (p. 80).

In all the enzyme systems synthesizing fatty acids which have been studied so far, palmitate is the major product. In these systems the fatty acid synthesis cycle thus continues to revolve and condense 2 carbon units until palmityl CoA is produced. Elongation of the fatty acid chain presumably stops here because palmityl CoA shows a greater affinity to participate in deacylation reactions, or in the synthesis of phosphatidic acid (p. 298) than in condensing once more with malonyl CoA.

Although there is unanimous agreement that extension of the carbon chain occurs through successive condensation of malonyl CoA, some doubt exists on the precise mechanism of this reaction. At the present time, two possible mechanisms are postulated:

(a) Wakil & Ganguly (1959) observed that Enzyme 2 did not contain any β-ketothiolase, β-hydroxyacyl dehydrogenase, enoyl hydrase or enoyl reductase. Furthermore, none of the CoA derivates of β-oxidation could replace acetyl CoA. On the basis of these observations the following scheme of fatty acid synthesis was proposed:

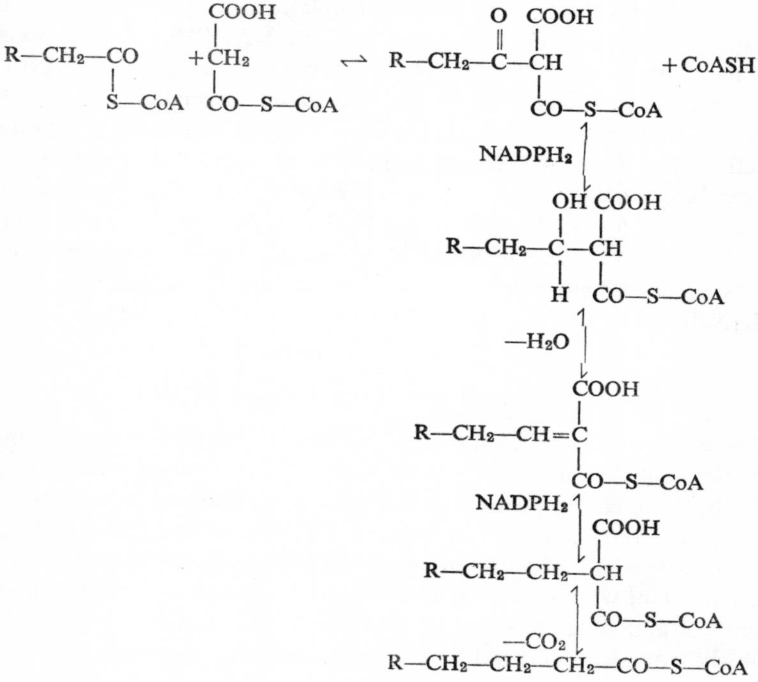

Enzyme 2 was shown to catalyse the condensation of acetyl CoA or butyryl CoA with malonyl CoA to form substituted malonyl derivatives. Carrot root plastids also catalysed this condensation. The condensation product could be reduced with one equivalent of $NADPH_2$ by another partially purified enzyme obtained from pigeon liver. The chromatographic properties of the reduction product suggested that the free carboxyl group of malonyl CoA was still retained.

(b) Lynen (1959) and Brady (1960) postulate that condensation and decarboxylation occur simultaneously to yield a β-ketoacyl derivative:

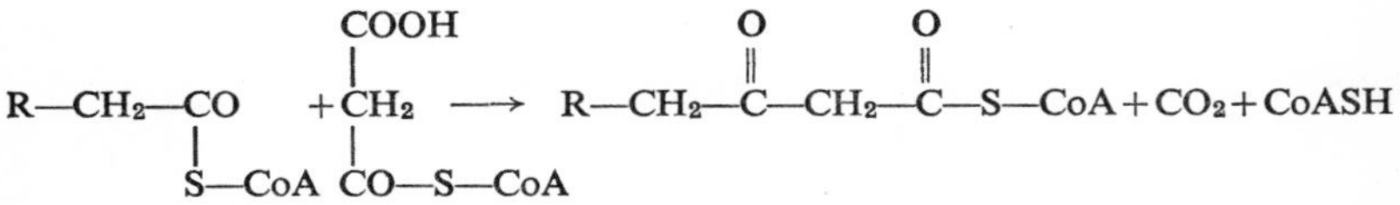

$$R—CH_2—CO \begin{matrix} COOH \\ | \\ +CH_2 \\ | \\ CO—S—CoA \end{matrix} \longrightarrow R—CH_2—\overset{O}{\overset{\|}{C}}—CH_2—\overset{O}{\overset{\|}{C}}—S—CoA + CO_2 + CoASH$$

(with $R—CH_2—CO$ bearing $S—CoA$ below)

Reduction of β-ketoacyl CoA by 2 molecules of $NADPH_2$ ultimately yields acyl CoA. Brady succeeded in purifying an enzyme system from brain capable of catalysing this overall reaction which was free of malonyl CoA decarboxylase. Thus it was possible to demonstrate an absolute requirement of acyl CoA, malonyl CoA and $NADPH_2$ for the synthesis of palmitate. In the presence of acyl CoA, but in the absence of $NADPH_2$, the enzyme system catalysed a decarboxylation of malonyl CoA. These observations provide evidence for the condensation-decarboxylation reaction shown above. Whether or not the product of the condensation-decarboxylation reaction is reduced to fatty acyl CoA by a reversal of the reactions of β-oxidation, but using $NADPH_2$ exclusively as a reductant, is still uncertain. Lynen (1961) has recently suggested that the intermediates in this scheme exist as acyl-S-enzyme complexes, and not as CoA derivatives.

EVEN-NUMBERED FATTY ACID SYTHESIS IN THE PLANT

The incorporation of acetate into long chain fatty acids has been amply demonstrated in a number of plant tissues including maturing peanut fruits, germinating peanut cotyledons and developing flax fruits. The long chain fatty acids synthesized from acetate-1-^{14}C by developing flax fruits were labelled in the odd-numbered carbon atoms. This observation is consistent with a synthesis by multiple condensation of either acetate units or malonate units derived by carboxylation of acetate.

Mitochondria prepared from avocado fruit mesocarp synthesize palmitate, stearate and oleate from acetate in the presence of ATP, CoA and Mn^{++}. CO_2 stimulated the rate of synthesis but was not incorporated into the long chain fatty acid. No clear-cut source of the reducing capacity could be demonstrated (Stumpf & Barber, 1957; Squires, Stumpf & Schmid, 1958). When an extract of an acetone powder of avocado mitochondria was used, however, an additional requirement for $NADPH_2$ could be demonstrated. $NADH_2$ was ineffective. When acetyl CoA was used as a substrate, ATP was still required. Inhibition by avidin suggests that biotin is involved in the synthesis.

This evidence suggests that the synthesis of long chain fatty acids by multiple condensation of malonyl CoA with fatty acyl CoA operates in plants. The site of synthesis in the avocado system appears to be in the mitochondria, in contrast to the soluble enzyme system in animals.

Odd-Numbered Fatty Acids

Evidence for the synthesis of odd-numbered long chain fatty acids by the multiple condensation of malonyl CoA units with propionyl CoA has been obtained in animal systems. A partly purified enzyme system from rat adipose tissue, in the presence of $NADPH_2$, was shown to catalyse the multiple condensation of malonyl CoA with propionyl CoA to yield pentadecanoic acid. This system has not yet been examined in plants. In plants, odd-numbered long chain fatty acids could be formed by the α-oxidation of even-numbered long chain fatty acids.

Unsaturated Fatty Acids

Our understanding of the biosynthesis of the most common unsaturated fatty acids, oleic acid, linoleic acid and linolenic acid is uncertain. In animals linoleic acid and linolenic acid are essential for normal growth, although their precise biological function is undefined. Since a source of dietary linoleic acid and linolenic acid is required, presumably the acids cannot be synthesized at rates sufficient to meet the needs of the animal body. Oleic acid is probably synthesized in animals by dehydrogenation of stearic acid.

Studies of the synthesis of unsaturated fatty acids from sucrose-^{14}C in soy bean pods suggest that sucrose is converted preferentially into oleic acid, and that linoleic acid and linolenic acid are formed by successive dehydrogenation of oleic acid. No evidence was obtained for a synthesis of oleic acid from stearic acid (Simmons & Quackenbush, 1954). Likewise, the synthesis of oleic acid from acetate by particulate preparations from avocado mesocarp does not appear to involve stearate as an intermediate.

Branched Chain Fatty Acids

Evidence has been presented for the synthesis in animals of branched chain fatty acids by the multiple condensation of malonyl CoA units with a branched chain acceptor. A partly purified enzyme from rat adipose tissue, in the presence of $NADPH_2$, was shown to catalyse the multiple condensation of malonyl CoA with a variety of branched chain acceptors. When acetyl CoA was used as an acceptor, palmitate was the major product. When acetyl CoA was replaced by a branched chain acceptor, the following products were tentatively identified:

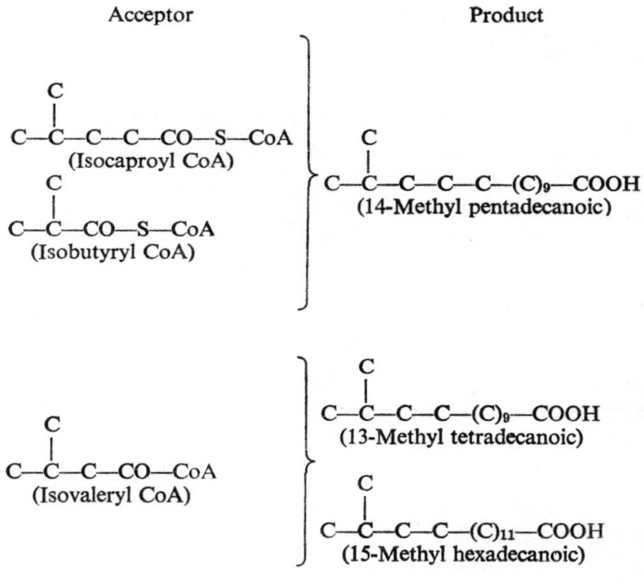

Acceptor   Product

$$C$$
$$|$$
$$C{-}C{-}C{-}C{-}CO{-}S{-}CoA$$
(Isocaproyl CoA)

$$C$$
$$|$$
$$C{-}C{-}CO{-}S{-}CoA$$
(Isobutyryl CoA)

$$C$$
$$|$$
$$C{-}C{-}C{-}C{-}C{-}(C)_9{-}COOH$$
(14-Methyl pentadecanoic)

$$C$$
$$|$$
$$C{-}C{-}C{-}CO{-}CoA$$
(Isovaleryl CoA)

$$C$$
$$|$$
$$C{-}C{-}C{-}C{-}(C)_9{-}COOH$$
(13-Methyl tetradecanoic)

$$C$$
$$|$$
$$C{-}C{-}C{-}C{-}(C)_{11}{-}COOH$$
(15-Methyl hexadecanoic)

No information is available on the synthesis of branched chain fatty acids in plants.

Branched chain fatty acids could also be synthesized by a multiple condensation of α-substituted derivatives of malonyl CoA. The enzymatic synthesis of two such derivatives, methyl malonyl CoA and ethyl malonyl CoA, has been demonstrated in enzyme systems derived from animals.

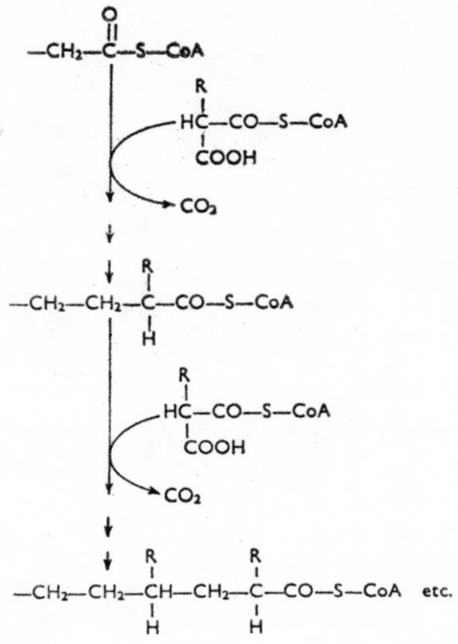

Streptomyces erythreus synthesizes erythronolide (the macrocyclic agly-cone of the antibiotic erythromycin) which has a similar basic structure to the product of the reaction mechanism described above. Although it is known that erythronolide is synthesized from propionate units:

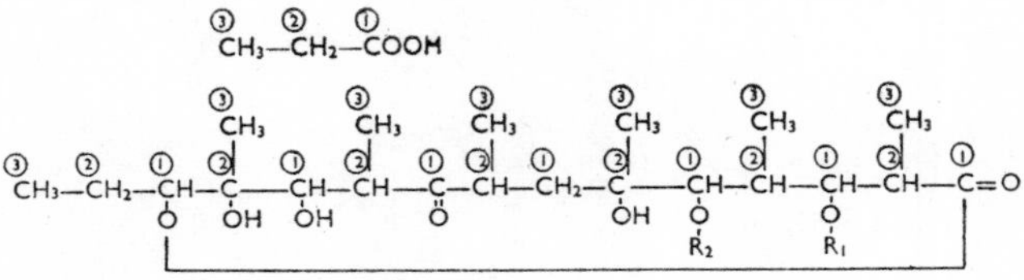

it is not known whether propionate is incorporated directly as propionyl CoA, or via methyl malonyl CoA.

Phospholipids and Triglycerides

It is convenient to discuss the synthesis of phospholipids and triglycerides together because, in animal tissues at least, their synthesis is closely linked through the common intermediate, D-α,β-diglyceride. Intensive investigations with animals (Kennedy, 1957) suggest that the biosynthesis of phospholipids and triglycerides proceeds as shown in Fig. 7.11.

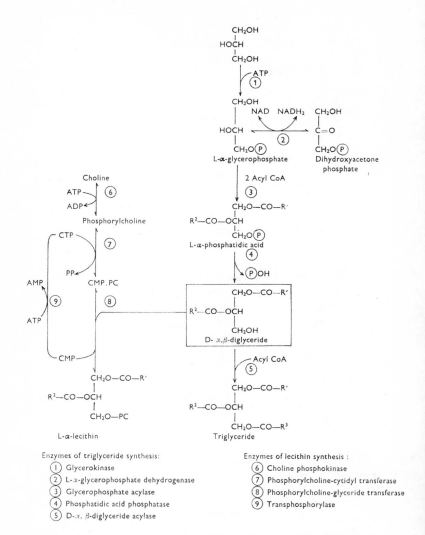

Enzymes of triglyceride synthesis:
① Glycerokinase
② L-α-glycerophosphate dehydrogenase
③ Glycerophosphate acylase
④ Phosphatidic acid phosphatase
⑤ D-α, β-diglyceride acylase

Enzymes of lecithin synthesis :
⑥ Choline phosphokinase
⑦ Phosphorylcholine-cytidyl transferase
⑧ Phosphorylcholine-glyceride transferase
⑨ Transphosphorylase

FIG. 7.11. Synthesis of triglyceride and lecithin in animals.

It is somewhat surprising that a total of at least five enzymatic steps is required for the acylation of glycerol to a triglyceride. The direct acylation of glycerol by acyl CoA has not so far been observed, and the pathway presented is the only known route for the synthesis of a triglyceride from glycerol.

Synthesis of lecithin involves the participation of cytidine diphosphate choline (CMP.PC). This compound is abbreviated as CMP.PC, and not as CDPC, in order to emphasize the fact that it is the phosphorylcholine group which is transferred.

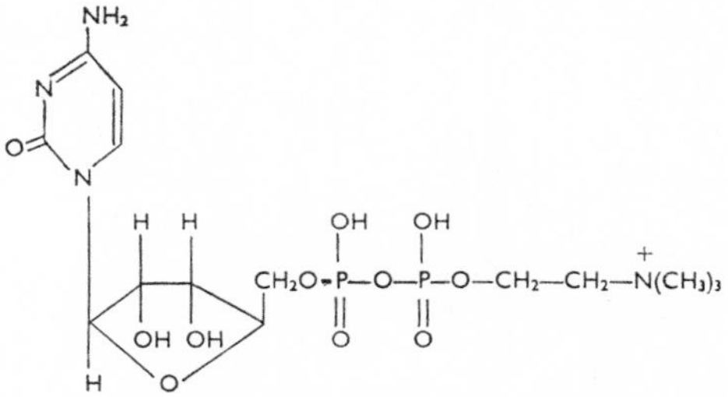

Cytidine diphosphate choline (CMP.PC)

A series of reactions, analagous to those shown in Fig. 7.11 accounts for the synthesis of phosphatidylethanolamine and possibly of phosphatidylglycerol.

An alternative mechanism has been suggested for the synthesis of lecithin and phosphatidylethanolamine:

phosphatidylserine→phosphatidylethanolamine→

phosphatidylcholine

This mechanism is based on the report that phosphatidylethanolamine can be formed directly from phosphatidylserine and that phosphatidylethanolamine can be methylated directly to phosphatidylcholine. The mechanism of phosphatidylserine synthesis is still in doubt.

The synthesis of phosphatidylinositol proceeds by way of a modification of the scheme shown for the biosynthesis of lecithin (Fig. 7.11). Cytidine is attached to the *glyceride* moiety to form CMP.P diglyceride. L-α-phosphatidic acid, instead of D-α,β-diglyceride, is the precursor of the glycerol moiety of the final phosphatide:

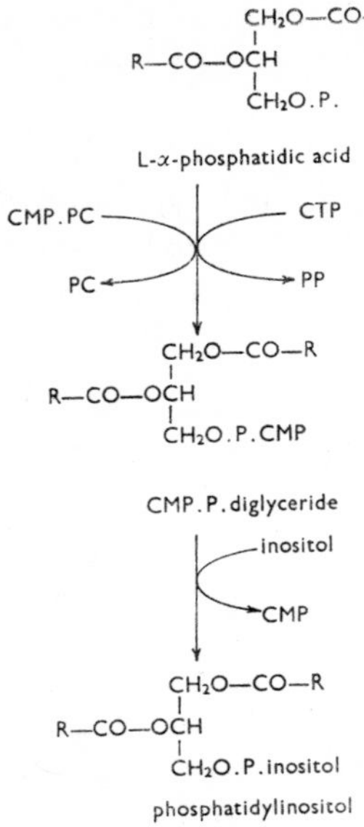

$$CH_2O-CO-R$$
$$R-CO-OCH$$
$$CH_2O.P.$$

L-α-phosphatidic acid

CMP.PC ———⟍ ⟋——— CTP

PC ◄——— ⟋⟍ ———► PP

$$CH_2O-CO-R$$
$$R-CO-OCH$$
$$CH_2O.P.CMP$$

CMP.P.diglyceride

⟍—inositol

◄—CMP

$$CH_2O-CO-R$$
$$R-CO-OCH$$
$$CH_2O.P.inositol$$

phosphatidylinositol

Evidence has been presented for the synthesis of CMP.P diglyceride from L-α-phosphatidic acid by two pathways — either through a reaction with CMP.PC or with CTP. CMP.P diglyceride then reacts with the hydroxyl group of inositol, in a phosphorylytic reaction analogous to the phosphorylcholine-glyceride transferase reaction between CMP.PC and the hydroxy group of D-α,β-diglyceride.

Little is known of the synthesis of plasmalogens except the final stage, which is similar to lecithin synthesis. A phosphorycholine-transferase catalysing the following reaction has been reported in rat liver:

$$
\begin{array}{cccc}
 & CH_2O-CO-R & & CH_2O-CO-R \\
H\ H & | & & H\ H & | \\
R^1-C=C-OCH & +CMP.PC\rightarrow R^1-C=C-OCH & & +CMP \\
 & | & & | \\
 & CH_2OH & & CH_2O-PC \\
\end{array}
$$

Sphingosine is synthesized in animals from palmityl CoA and serine.

Conversion of sphingosine to sphingomyelin may be represented as follows:

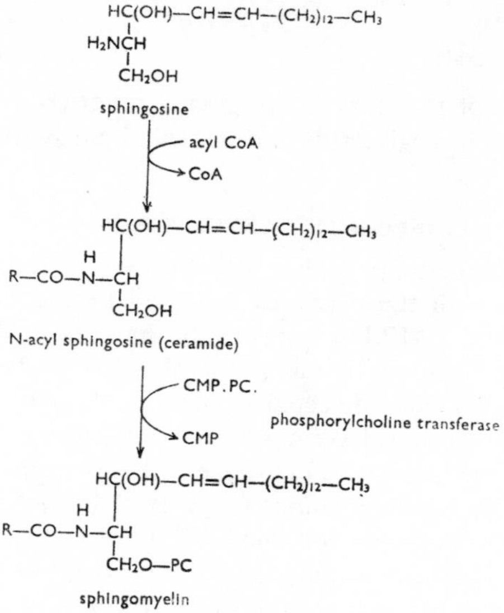

HC(OH)—CH=CH—(CH₂)₁₂—CH₃
|
H₂NCH
|
CH₂OH

sphingosine

    acyl CoA

    CoA

HC(OH)—CH=CH—(CH₂)₁₂—CH₃
   H |
R—CO—N—CH
      |
      CH₂OH

N-acyl sphingosine (ceramide)

    CMP.PC.

                 phosphorylcholine transferase

    CMP

HC(OH)—CH=CH—(CH₂)₁₂—CH₃
   H |
R—CO—N—CH
      |
      CH₂O—PC

sphingomyelin

One of the most striking features of phospholipid synthesis is the ubiquitous participation of cytidine as a transferring coenzyme.

TRIGLYCERIDE SYNTHESIS IN PLANTS

Microsomes isolated from Avocado mesocarp appear to synthesize glycerides via a pathway essentially similar to that demonstrated in animals. Indirect evidence is available for the activation of glycerol to L-α-glycerophosphate by peanut mitochondria (p. 265). L-α-Glycerophosphate dehydrogenase, which catalyses the NAD-dependent formation of L-α-glycerophosphate from dihydroxyacetone phosphate, has not been reported in plants.

Peanut mitochondria incorporate the label of AT^{32}P predominantly into phosphatidic acid together with a small incorporation into phosphatidylethanolamine (Bradbeer & Stumpf, 1960). This incorporation did not involve L-α-glycerophosphate as an intermediate, but resulted from the phosphorylation of α,β-diglyceride by ATP:

$$CH_2O—CO—R \qquad \text{Diglyceride} \qquad CH_2O—CO—R$$

$$R^1—CO—OCH \qquad \text{phosphokinase} \qquad R^1—CO—OCH$$
$$+ATP \quad \rightleftharpoons \qquad +ADP$$
$$CH_2OH \qquad\qquad\qquad\qquad CH_2O.P.$$

$$\alpha,\beta\text{-Diglyceride} \qquad\qquad\qquad \alpha\text{-Phosphatidic acid}$$

The significance of this enzyme, originally reported in microsomes of guinea-pig brain, in triglyceride and phospholipid synthesis in plants is uncertain.

PHOSPHOLIPID SYNTHESIS IN PLANTS

Choline phosphokinase, phosphorylcholine cytidyl transferase, together with the products of the reactions catalysed by these enzymes, phosphorylcholine and CMP.PC respectively, have been demonstrated in plants. Phosphorylcholine is the major phosphate ester in some plant saps. CMP.PE has been detected in plants although the reactions responsible for its synthesis have not been demonstrated.

The available evidence therefore suggests that phosphatidylcholine and perhaps phosphatidylethanolamine are synthesized in the plant by a pathway similar to that described for animals (Fig. 7.11). Insufficient information is available to determine the pathway of biosynthesis of phosphatidylserine, phosphatidylinositol and phosphatidylglycerol, or of plant plasmalogens or sphingolipids.

Glycolipids

Although no confirming evidence is available, it seems probable that the biosynthesis of the glycolipids proceeds through the UDP-sugars.

THE GLYOXYLATE CYCLE

This cycle was originally described by Kornberg & Krebs (1957) to account for the growth of a number of micro-organisms (yeasts, many molds, *E. coli* and pseudomonads) on 2 carbon units such as acetate as a sole carbon source. These organisms are able to produce from acetate their basic requirements for energy and simple carbon skeletons required for the elaboration of cell material. The energy requirements may be supplied by the oxidation of acetate through the Krebs cycle. The Krebs cycle also contains a number of intermediates required for biosynthesis (p. 171). However, the Krebs cycle cannot provide a net synthesis of these intermediates. Utilization of any intermediate of the Krebs cycle for a biosynthetic reaction would, by removing an intermediate essential for the regeneration of the two carbon acceptor, cause the cycle to stop. Some mechanism must therefore exist to regenerate the two carbon acceptor from acetate.

The glyoxylate cycle plays an integral role in the conversion of acetate to a 2-carbon acceptor. The glyoxylate cycle, as shown in Fig. 7.12, is a modified Krebs cycle in which isocitritase replaces isocitric dehydrogenase and the α-ketoglutarate dehydrogenase system of the Krebs cycle.

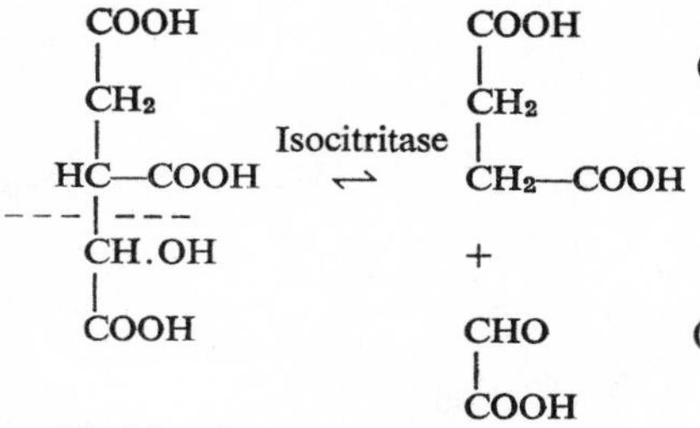

$$
\begin{array}{lll}
\text{COOH} & & \text{COOH} \\
| & & | \\
\text{CH}_2 & & \text{CH}_2 \qquad \text{(Succinate)} \\
| & \text{Isocitritase} & | \\
\text{HC—COOH} & \rightleftharpoons & \text{CH}_2\text{—COOH} \\
\text{---}|\text{---} & & \\
\text{CH.OH} & & + \\
| & & \\
\text{COOH} & & \text{CHO} \qquad \text{(Glyoxylate)} \\
& & | \\
& & \text{COOH}
\end{array}
$$

L(+)-Isocitrate

$$
K = \frac{(\text{glyoxylate})\,(\text{succinate})}{(\text{isocitrate})}
$$

$$
= 0.07 \text{ at pH 7}
$$

In the version shown in Fig. 7.12, the net effect of the glyoxylate cycle is the conversion of acetyl CoA to glyoxylate. In the presence of malate synthetase, glyoxylate condenses with acetyl CoA to form malate:

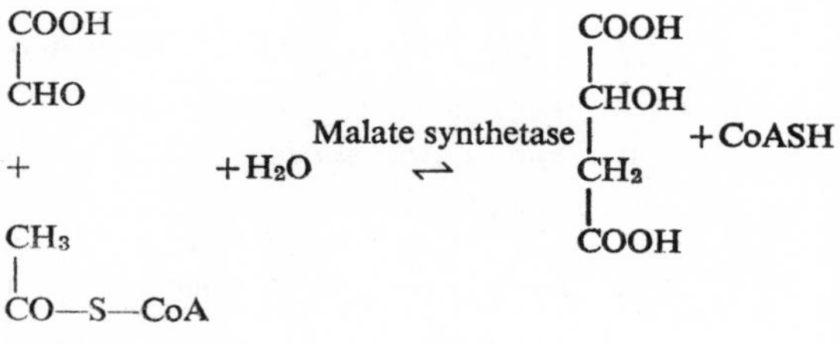

$$
\begin{array}{lll}
\text{COOH} & & \text{COOH} \\
| & & | \\
\text{CHO} & & \text{CHOH} \\
& \text{Malate synthetase} & | \qquad + \text{CoASH} \\
+ & + \text{H}_2\text{O} \quad \rightleftharpoons & \text{CH}_2 \\
& & | \\
\text{CH}_3 & & \text{COOH} \\
| & & \\
\text{CO—S—CoA} & &
\end{array}
$$

$$
K = \frac{(\text{malate})\,(\text{CoASH})}{(\text{glyoxylate})\,(\text{acetyl CoA})}
$$

$$
= 10^8 \text{ at pH 7}
$$

Malate is converted to oxaloacetate in the presence of malic dehydrogenase. The combined action of the glyoxylate cycle and malate synthetase

20

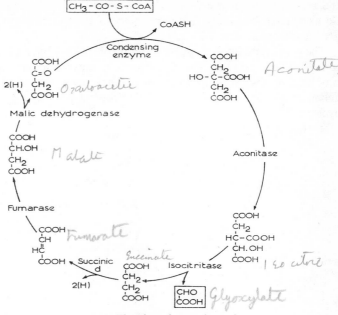

FIG. 7.12. The glyoxylate cycle.

therefore results in the conversion of 2 molecules of acetyl CoA to oxalo-acetate. The three dehydrogenation reactions involved in this conversion are presumably linked to oxygen through the respiratory chain.

$$2CH_3—CO—S—CoA + \tfrac{3}{2}O_2 \rightarrow$$
$$COOH—CH_2—CO—COOH + 2CoASH$$

The glyoxylate cycle has been shown to operate only in micro-organisms utilizing acetate as a sole carbon source, and in germinating fatty seeds. It has not been detected in animals.

The Glyoxylate Cycle in Plants

The metabolism of germinating fatty seeds is similar in many respects to that of micro-organisms which utilize acetate as a sole carbon source. The germinating seed utilizes acetyl CoA, produced by the degradation of fats, for the production of energy and carbon skeletons required for the elaboration of cell material.

It is characteristic of germinating fatty seeds that a considerable proportion of the fat is converted into sugar, predominantly sucrose. The water solubility and non-polar character of sucrose make it ideally suited to the task of transporting food reserves from the seed to the sites of synthesis of new cell material. The course of fat degradation and sugar synthesis in a germinating castor bean is shown in Fig. 7.13.

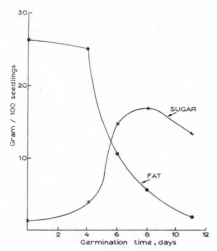

FIG. 7.13. Degradation of fat and synthesis of sugar in germinating castor bean (Desveaux & Kogane-Charles 1952).

The utilization of fat, which commences on the fourth day after germination, closely parallels the synthesis of sugars. At the end of 8 days germination almost all the fat, which originally represented approximately 70 per cent of the dry weight of the seed, has been utilized. Of the total fat utilized, 75 per cent can be accounted for as sugars. The conversion of fat to sugars is clearly a major metabolic process in germinating fatty seeds.

A mechanism for the conversion of fat to sugar in germinating fatty seeds is shown in Fig. 7.14.

This scheme is based on the following evidence:

(a) When acetate-1-^{14}C or acetate-2-^{14}C was incubated with castor bean endosperm slices, the organic acids (chiefly malate) contained most of the incorporated ^{14}C during the early periods of incubation. As the incubation progressed, the methyl carbon of acetate accumulated predominantly in sucrose. The carboxyl carbon of acetate, on the other hand, produced approximately equal labelling in CO_2 and sucrose. Similar results were obtained when malate-^{14}C and succinate-^{14}C were used. Thus succinate-2-^{14}C was converted predominantly to sucrose-^{14}C, whereas succinate-1-^{14}C and malate-1-^{14}C contributed equal label to sucrose and CO_2. These results are consistent with the scheme shown in Fig. 7.14 in which both carbon atoms of acetate are first converted to malate. The methyl carbon of acetate then appears quantitatively in triose phosphate and sucrose. The carboxyl carbon of acetate, on the other hand, is distributed equally between CO_2 (produced during the phosphoenol-pyruvate carboxykinase reaction) and triose phosphate.

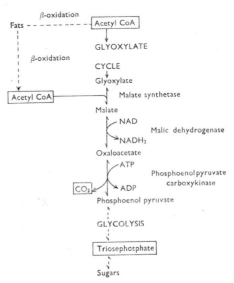

FIG. 7.14. Conversion of fat to sugar via the glyoxylate cycle.

The metabolism of acetate by the Krebs cycle was quantitatively insignificant even though all the enzymes of the Krebs cycle were present. The mechanism whereby isocitrate is metabolized via isocitritase to the almost complete exclusion of isocitric dehydrogenase of the Krebs cycle is still uncertain.

(b) Cotyledons from germinating peanut and sunflower seedlings (Bradbeer & Stumpf, 1959) and slices of castor bean endosperm (Canvin & Beevers, 1961) converted acetate-1-^{14}C into carboxyl-labelled malate and into sucrose in which the glucose moiety was labelled in C3 and 4. Acetate-2-^{14}C was converted into methylene-labelled malate, and into sucrose in which the glucose moiety was labelled in C1, 2, 5 and 6.

(c) All the enzymes of the glyoxylate cycle and malate synthetase have been demonstrated in germinating fatty seeds. The enzymes are present in mitochondrial preparations and also appear in the supernatant. The rates of the individual reactions are sufficiently high to account for the overall rate of carbohydrate synthesis from fats. The enzymes responsible for the synthesis of sugars from a C4-dicarboxylic acid are also known to occur in plants.

(d) The level of aconitase, isocitritase, malate synthetase and condensing enzyme in homogenates of germinating peanut cotyledons increases as germination proceeds. Isocitritase is restricted to those tissues in which active fat catabolism occurs. In a number of fatty seeds, isocitritase activity was initially negligible and increased rapidly during germination to a maxium value and then rapidly declined. The maximum isocitritase activity corresponded to the period of maximum fat degradation, and the decline to the decreased rate of fat degradation. These observations are similar to those reported with bacteria, where isocitritase is an adaptive enzyme and is not formed when glucose or succinate are present in the growth medium. Isocitritase, therefore, appears to be specifically associated with tissues using acetate as a main carbon source.

Although malate synthetase was present in high amounts only in seeds undergoing active fat breakdown, its distribution was not as specifically associated with fat degradation as was isocitritase. The change in malate synthetase activity upon germination was also not as closely geared to the metabolism of fat as in the case of isocitritase. Ungerminated seeds contain significant amounts of malate synthetase, which increased three-fold over the period of maximum fat breakdown. The activity did not decline with the decline in the rate of fat degradation. These observations are comparable to those made with bacteria where malate synthetase, unlike isocitritase, is a constitutive enzyme.

A possible alternative mechanism for the conversion of acetate to a C4-dicarboxylic acid is suggested by the report of Seaman (1957) of a *direct* condensation of 2 molecules of acetyl CoA to form succinate:

$$2 \text{ acetyl CoA} + 2\text{ADP} + 2\text{P}_i + \text{NAD} \rightharpoonup$$
$$\text{succinate} + 2\text{ATP} + 2\text{CoA} + \text{NADH}_2$$

The enzyme system has been purified approximately 150-fold from homogenates of the ciliated protozoan *Tetrahymena pyriformis*. The reaction as written greatly favours succinate cleavage ($K = 2 \cdot 83 \times 10^{-6}$ at pH 8·4). However, the equilibrium could be made to favour succinate synthesis by oxidizing reduced NAD through the respiratory chain.

READING LIST

STUMPF P.K. & BRADBEER C. (1959) Fat Metabolism in Higher Plants. *Ann. Rev. Pl. Physiol.* **10**, 197

STUMPF P.K. (1960) Lipid Metabolism. *Ann. Rev. Biochem.* **29**, 261

GREEN D.E. & GIBSON D.M. (1960) Fatty Acid Oxidation and Synthesis. In *Metabolic Pathways I*, 301, Ed. Greenberg D.M. Acad. Press, New York

ROSSITER R.J. (1960) Metabolism of Phosphatides. In *Metabolic Pathways* **1**, 357. Ed. Greenberg, D. M. Acad. Press, New York

JAENICKE J. & LYNEN F. (1960) Coenzyme A. In *The Enzymes*, second ed., Ed. Boyer, P.D., Lardy H. & Myrbäck K. **3** (B), 3. Acad. Press, New York

LANGDON R.G. & PHILLIPS A.H. (1961) Lipid Metabolism. *Ann. Rev. Biochem.* **30**, 189

BLOCH K. (Ed.) (1960) *Lipid Metabolism*, John Wiley & Sons, Inc., New York

Symposium on Lipid Metabolism (1961) *Fed. Proc.* **20**, 921

LITERATURE CITED

BARANOFSKI T. (1949) *J. Biol. Chem.* **180**, 535

BEINERT H., GREEN D.E., HELE P., HOFFMAN-OSTERHOF O., LYNEN F., OCHOA S. POPJAK G. & RUYSSEN R. (1956) *Science* **124**, 614

BENSON A.A., WINTERMANS J.F.G.M. & WISER R. (1959) *Pl. Physiol.* **34**, 315

BRADBEER C. & STUMPF P.K. (1959) *J. Biol. Chem.* **234**, 498

BRADBEER C. & STUMPF P.K. (1960) *J. Lipid Research* **1**, 214

BRADY R. (1960) *J. Biol. Chem.* **235**, 3093, 3099

CANVIN D. T. & BEEVERS H. (1961) *J. Biol. Chem.* **236**, 988

CARTER H.E., GIGG R.H., LAW J.H., NAKAYAMA T. & WEBER E. (1958) *J. Biol. Chem.* **233**, 1309

DAKIN H.D. (1911) *J. Biol. Chem.* **9**, 123

DESVEAUX R. & KOGANE-CHARLES M. (1952) *Ann. Inst. Nat. Rech. Agronom.* **3**, 385

FAWCETT C.H., INGRAM J.M.A. & WAIN R.L. (1954) *Proc. Roy. Soc.* B, **142**, 60.

FAWCETT C.H., TAYLOR H.F., WAIN R.L. & WIGHTMAN F. (1958) *Proc. Roy. Soc.* B, **148**, 543

FLAVIN M., ORTIZ P.J. & OCHOA S. (1955) *Nature*, **176**, 823

GIOVANELLI J. & STUMPF P.K. (1958) *J. Biol. Chem.* **231**, 411

GRACE N.H. (1939) *Can. J. Research* **17**, 247

KNOOP F. (1904) *Beitr. Chem. Physiol. Path.* **6**, 150

KORNBERG A. & PRICER W.E., Jr (1953) *J. Biol. Chem.* **204**, 329

LYNEN F. (1959) *J. Cell. Comp. Physiol.* **54**, Supp. 1, 33

LYNEN F. (1961) *Fed. Proc.* **20**, 941

MAHLER H., WAKIL S.J. & BOCK R.M. (1953) *J. Biol. Chem.* **204**, 453

ROSSITER R.J. (1960) In *Metabolic Pathways* **1**, 357, Ed. Greenberg D.M. Acad. Press, New York

SIMMONS, R.O. & QUACKENBUSH F.W. (1954) *J. Am. Oil Chem. Soc.* **31**, 441, 601

SQUIRES C.L., STUMPF P.K. & SCHMID C. (1958) *Pl. Physiol.* **33**, 365

STUMPF P.K. (1955) *Pl. Physiol.* **30**, 55

STUMPF P.K. & BARBER G.A. (1957) *J. Biol. Chem.* **227**, 407

SYNERHOLM M.E. & ZIMMERMAN P.W. (1947) *Contrib. Boyce Thompson Inst.* **14**, 369

WAKIL S.J. & GANGULY J. (1959) *J. Am. Chem. Soc.* **81**, 2598

CHAPTER 8

THE ISOPENTANE GROUP OF COMPOUNDS

CHEMICAL STRUCTURE

A large group of plant products including such apparently diverse compounds as camphor, rubber, carotene and the phytosterols can, as Ruzicka (1922, 1953) pointed out, be constructed from C5 units in which the carbon atoms are arranged as in isoprene.

$$\text{(head)} \quad CH_2{=}\overset{\overset{\displaystyle CH_3}{|}}{C}{-}CH{=}CH_2 \quad \text{(tail)}$$
Isoprene

The order of linking the isoprene units has led to the formulation of various 'isoprene rules'. The 'general isoprene rule' simply states that the terpenic compounds should be derivable from isoprene units. The 'special isoprene rule' states that the isoprene units should be joined head to tail as in the monoterpene geraniol.

$$CH_3{-}\overset{\overset{\displaystyle CH_3}{|}}{C}{=}CH{-}CH_2{-}CH_2{-}\overset{\overset{\displaystyle CH_3}{|}}{C}H{=}CH{-}CH_2OH$$
Geraniol

The special rule, however, has a number of exceptions and is only applicable to the simpler isoprenoid compounds. Thus the carotenoids, steroids and triterpenes have a tail-to-tail link usually in the middle of the molecule, though in the case of the steroids and the triterpenes the position of the link is not obvious due to cyclization. Finally the 'biogenetic isoprene rule' states that members of the isopentane group should be derivable from simple hypothetical precursors such as farnesol, geraniol and squalene.

The Terpenes

Steam distillation of plant material removes the so-called essential oils which contain substances possessing 5, 10, 15 or 20 carbon atoms. These compounds are the hemiterpenes, mono-, sesqui- and diterpenes respectively and collectively form the lower terpenes. The fragrance of many species is proof that some volatile compounds are released from the plant, and quantitatively the loss of volatile compounds may be quite significant. Thus Haagen-Smit (1958) cites the exceptional case of *Dictamnus albus* which releases sufficient volatile oil to cause the whole plant to burn when a lighted match is held some distance away. The volatile or essential oils contain a range of compounds such as aromatic compounds, straight chain hydrocarbons and their derivatives. Certain compounds are restricted to a few species, but most characteristic are those compounds whose carbon skeleton can be constructed out of branched C5 units — the terpenes. The name terpene is derived from turpentine which is the steam volatile fraction obtained from oleoresin which exudes from the cut surface of pine tree bark. Resins are produced by many shrubs and trees and are secreted by specialized cells into ducts or canals. Following wound injury or fungal infection an abnormal flow of resin may occur (resinosis). Resins of commercial importance include copal, extracted from tropical trees of the Leguminosae, dammar from trees of the Dipterocarpaceae, and Kauri gum from *Agathis australis*. The most important commercial resin is oleoresin from which rosin is obtained after removal of turpentine. Rosin is a complex mixture of resin acids which are diterpenes of the general formula $C_{19} H_{29} COOH$.

The Hemiterpenes

Isoprene has not been isolated from plants, but a number of branched chain 5-carbon compounds are known. Dimethylacrylic acid which is present in the rubber producing plant *Parthenium argentatum* was once thought to be the building unit for terpenoid biosynthesis.

$$CH_3$$
$$CH_3—C=CH—COOH \quad \text{Dimethylacrylic acid}$$

A number of branched C5 compounds present in plants are not biogenetically related to the terpenes. These include valine whose biosynthesis is discussed on p. 382. The biogenetic relationships of a number of other C5 compounds are unknown, though reasonable guesses may be made. Thus isovaleraldehyde and isovaleric acid may be formed from leucine by the following reactions catalysed by the widely distributed enyzmes, amino acid decarboxylase, monoamine oxidase and aldehyde dehydrogenase.

$$\underset{\text{Isoleucine}}{\overset{\text{CH}_3}{\underset{\text{CH}_3}{>}}\text{CH—CH}_2\text{—CH(NH}_2)\text{—COOH}} \longrightarrow \underset{\text{Methyl butylamine}}{\overset{\text{CH}_3}{\underset{\text{CH}_3}{>}}\text{CH—CH}_2\text{CH}_2(\text{NH}_2) + \text{CO}_2}$$

$$\underset{\text{Isovaleric acid}}{\overset{\text{CH}_3}{\underset{\text{CH}_3}{>}}\text{CH—CH}_2\text{—COOH}} \xleftarrow{\text{NADH}_2 \quad \text{NAD}} \underset{\text{Isovaleraldehyde}}{\overset{\text{CH}_3}{\underset{\text{CH}_3}{>}}\text{CH—CH}_2\text{—CHO} + \text{NH}_3}$$

$\downarrow \frac{1}{2}\text{O}_2$

2-Methyl butyric acid may be formed by analogous reactions from isoleucine:

$$\underset{\text{Isoleucine}}{\text{CH}_3\text{—CH}_2\text{—}\overset{\overset{\text{CH}_3}{|}}{\text{CH}}\text{—CH(NH}_2)\text{—COOH}} \xrightarrow{\text{O}_2} \underset{\text{2-Methyl butyric acid}}{\text{CH}_3\text{—CH}_2\text{—}\overset{\overset{\text{CH}_3}{|}}{\text{CH}}\text{—COOH} + \text{CO}_2 + \text{NH}_3}$$

The Monoterpenes

With few exceptions the monoterpenes can be derived from 2 isoprene units and thus follow what Ruzicka has called the geraniol rule. Some possible interrelationships are shown in Fig. 8.1. Geraniol may cyclize via the intermediate (a) which is drawn as a carbonium ion, though its identity is not meant to be specified. Fenchol and α-pinene may be formed via (c) and borneol via (b). Alternatively cyclization may occur via the biradicals (d) and (e) leading to α- and β-pinene and limonene. This mechanism assumes the reversibility of the experimentally demonstrated ring opening of (1) α-pinene to yield limonene and alloocimene (formed

TABLE 8.1

Analysis of turpentine from Pine species

Species	Component	Per cent
Pinus ponderosa	α-Pinene	1
(California)	β-Pinene	50
	Δ^3-Carene	30
	Limonene	3–4
	Sesquiterpenes	10
Pinus monticola	α-Pinene	45
(Idaho)	β-Pinene	32
	Limonene	7
	Bornyl acetate	2
	n-Undecane	2
	n-Heptane	1
	Sesquiterpenes	4–5
P. attenuata	α-Pinene	98
P. contorta	β-Phellandrene	98
P. pinea	Limonene	95

by isomerization from the primary product ocimene) and (2) β-pinene to yield limonene and myrcene.

Over 100 monoterpenes are known and few of the possible cyclizations have been demonstrated. It is generally assumed that enzymes bring

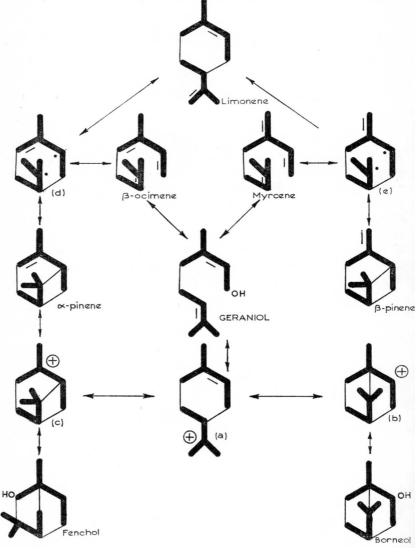

FIG. 8.1. Possible biogenetic relationships between monoterpenes (the heavy lines represent the parent isoprene units).

about the required positioning of the intermediates and cause cyclization to follow a specific course. A given species may form one major diterpene or a limited number as shown in the analysis of turpentines obtained from pines (Table 8.1).

The Sesquiterpenes

According to Ruzicka most sesquiterpenes follow the 'farnesol rule', that is, they can be derived from farnesol which consists of 3 isoprene units.

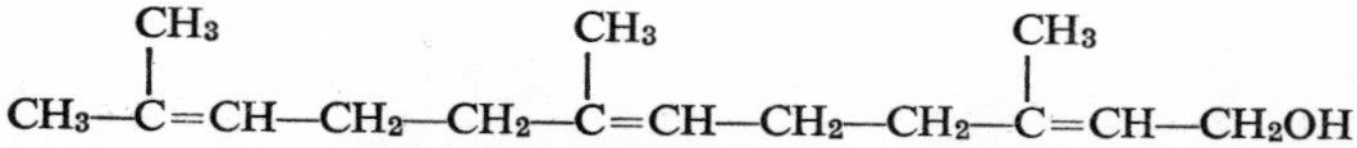

$$CH_3-\overset{\overset{\textstyle CH_3}{|}}{C}=CH-CH_2-CH_2-\overset{\overset{\textstyle CH_3}{|}}{C}=CH-CH_2-CH_2-\overset{\overset{\textstyle CH_3}{|}}{C}=CH-CH_2OH$$

Farnesol

The most frequent structural types correspond to the monocyclic bisabolene, bicyclic cadinene, guaiol with fused 5- and 7-membered rings and caryophyllene with a 9-membered ring.

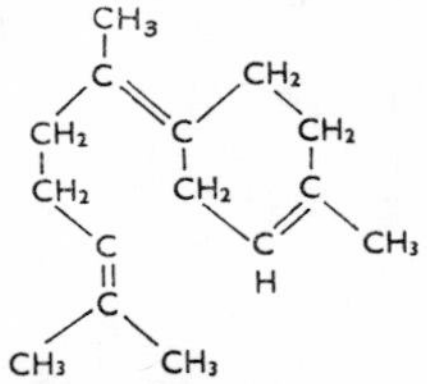

γ Bisabolene

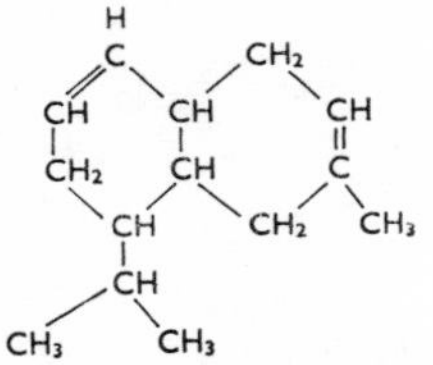

Cadinene

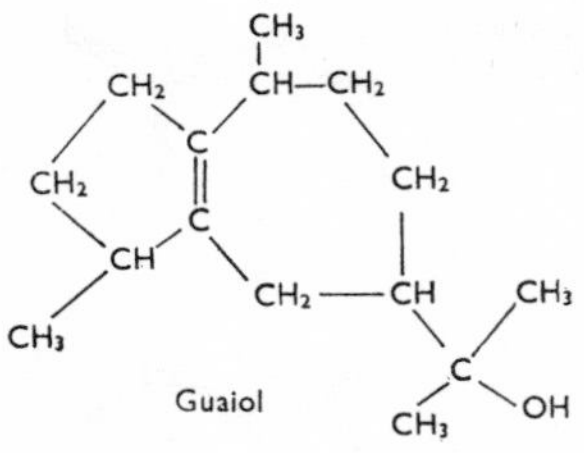

Guaiol

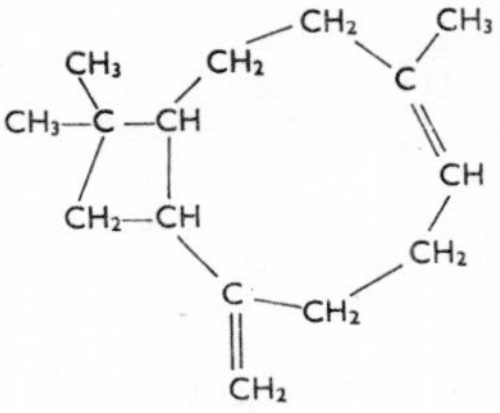

Caryophyllene

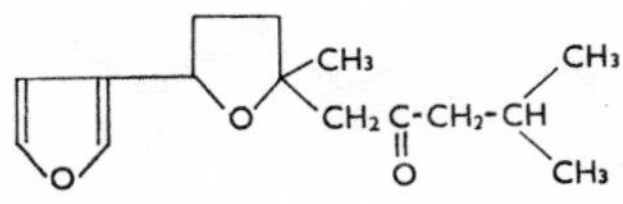

Ipomeamarone

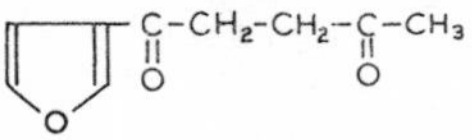

Ipomeanine

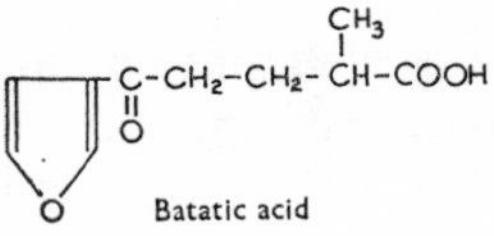

Batatic acid

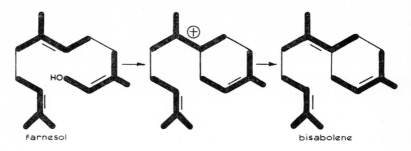

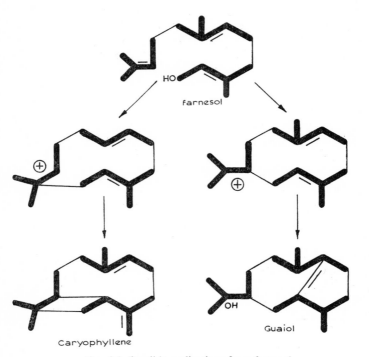

Fig. 8.2. Possible cyclizations from farnesol.

The sesquiterpenoid ïpomeamarone and the closely related ipomeanine and batatic acid have been shown to accumulate in sweet potato infected by *Cerastomella fimbriata*. Uritani's group have demonstrated that ipomeamarone is fungitoxic in the host tissue and that there is a close correlation between the amount of ipomeamarone produced and the degree of resistance to infection.

The transformations from farnesol have been discussed by Ruzicka. Under acid conditions farnesol undergoes ring closure to give bisabolene. Other possible ring closures are shown in Fig. 8.2.

The Diterpenes

Among the most widely distributed diterpenes are the resin acids. When oleoresin is steam distilled, the non-volatile fraction (rosin) contains the diterpene abietic acid as a major component. In the untreated oleoresin, abietic acid is a minor component, but during the removal of turpentine, the action of heat on labile precursors gives rise to much abietic acid. Freshly collected oleoresin crystallizes on cooling to give a mixture known as galipot from which a number of resin acids have been obtained. Other important diterpenes include marrubiin, the bitter principle of horehound (*Marrubium vulgare*), cafestol found in coffee beans and manool found in wood oil from yellow pines. The most important diterpene is phytol, which does not occur free but is the terpene moiety of such important compounds as chlorophyll and vitamins K and E. The diterpenes can be derived from geranyl geraniol which has not yet been found in nature. Phytol is a reduced derivative of geranyl geraniol.

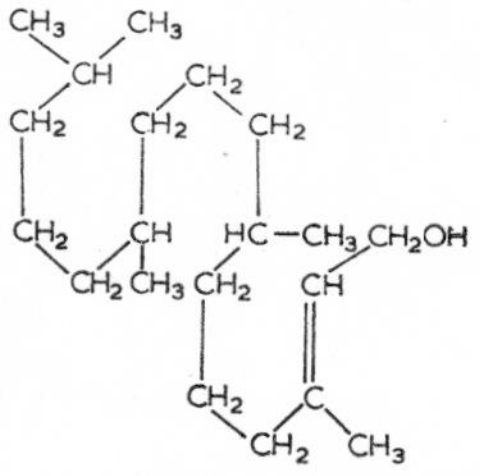

Phytol 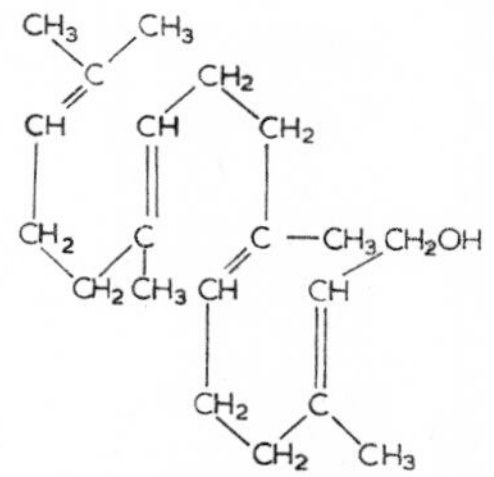   geranylgeraniol

Reactions taking place after cyclization may make it difficult to recognize the terpenoid nature of compounds, as for example in the gibberellins. The gibberellins were first recognized as products of the fungus *Gibberella fujikuroi* which infects rice seedlings, producing an elongation of the stem and leaves and subsequent death. Workers in the University of Tokyo isolated a crystalline compound–gibberellin A–which produced the usual pathological symptoms when applied to rice plants. Subsequent work has shown that *Gibberella fujikuroi* produces a number of closely related compounds to which the collective name gibberellins has been applied. Other fungi do not produce gibberellins but they have been isolated from a wide variety of higher plants, where they occur in small quantities and function as hormones.

The gibberellins promote elongation in shoots but have little or no action on root growth. When applied to genetically dwarf plants the treated plants develop a form similar to that of the tall variety. In certain species gibberellins have a marked effect on flowering.

When applied to plants, gibberellic acid is usually the most active, followed by gibberellin A. Members of the Cucurbitaceae respond most readily to gibberellins A_4 and A_7. The gibberellins are allotted numbers as they are isolated. The basic structure is gibbane, the numbering system is shown below together with the structure of some gibberellins.

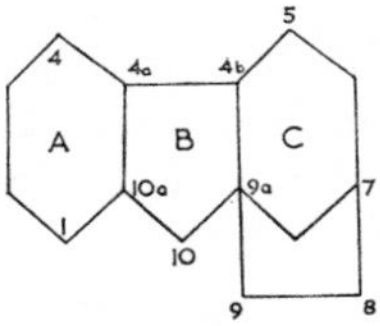

gibbane

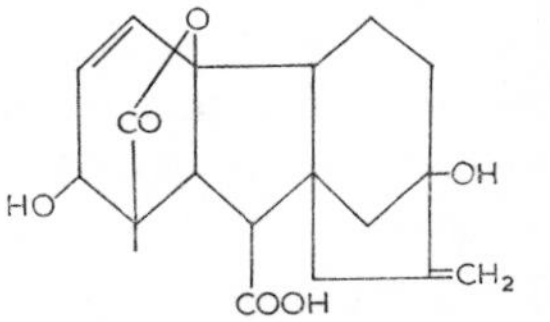

gibberellic acid

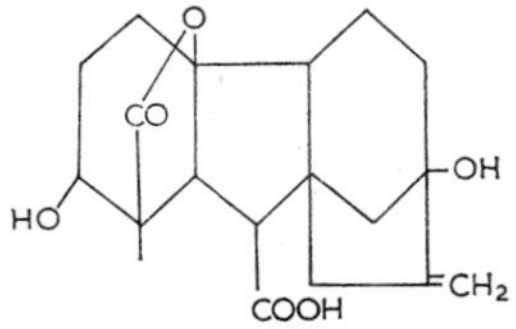

gibberellin A1

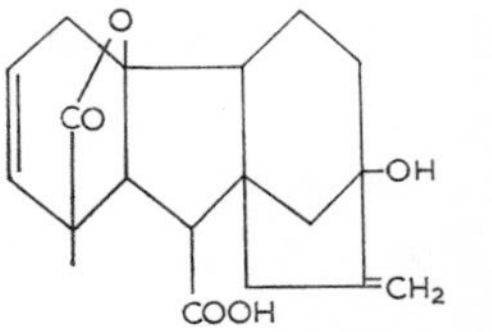

gibberellin A5

The Triterpenes

The triterpenes can be derived from squalene which consists of two farnesyl chains joined tail to tail. Squalene was first isolated from shark liver oil but is now known to be present in small amounts in a number of vegetable oils (Dickhart, 1955). Almost all the triterpenes have irregular pentacyclic carbon skeletons but some such as euphol possess a tetracyclic nucleus which is characteristic of the steroids. Examples of triterpene structure are given on p. 335 in relation to their biosynthesis.

The Steroids

The steroids are derivatives of a four-ringed system called cyclo-pentano-perhydro-phenanthrene.

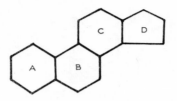

This ring structure is also found in some triterpenes, but the steroids have less than 30 carbon atoms. The group includes the sterols, which are monohydric containing 27-29 carbon atoms and related compounds in which the side chain forms one or two oxygen-containing rings.

Cholesterol, the most abundant steroid in animals is present in algae but not in higher plants. Higher plants contain a number of steroids structurally related to cholesterol. The carbon structure of cholesterol is given below (Fig. 8.3).

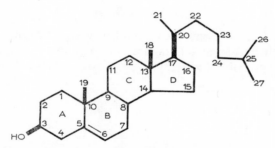

FIG. 8.3. Structure and numbering system of cholesterol.

At nuclear centres of asymmetry, such as C10 and C13, the angular carbon atoms C19 and C18 may lie above or below the general plane of the ring system. In cholesterol, these groups lie above the plane of the ring system, they are shown by a heavy full-line bond and are designated as the β-configuration. A group lying below the plane of the ring system is shown by a broken line and is designated as the α-configuration.

The designation "α" and "β" is also used to distinguish between similar structures without specifying a particular configuration. For example in "α-" and "β"-sitosterol, which are the most abundant phytosterols, the designation "α" or "β" is trivial and a specific configuration is denoted only in the expanded name for β-sitosterol, Δ^5-stigmastene-3β-ol.

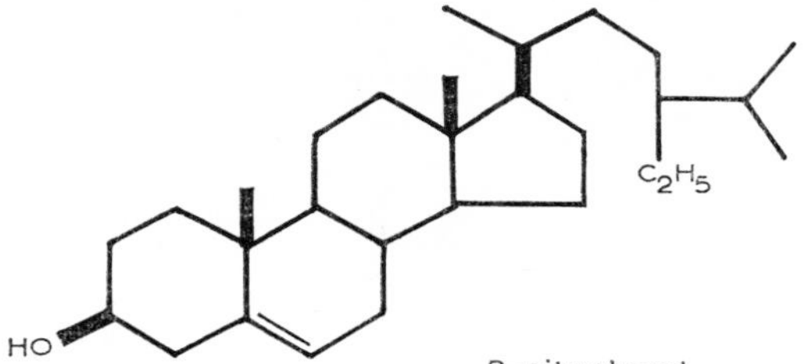

β-sitosterol

The side chain differs from that of cholesterol in possessing an ethyl group attached to C24. Variation in structure of the side chain is found in a number of phytosterols. Thus stigmasterol found in the calabar bean (*Physostigma venenosum*) has a 22, 23 double bond and an ethyl group at C24. Brassicasterol found in rapeseed oil (*Brassica rapa*) differs from stigmasterol in possessing a methyl group at C24.

4 α-METHYL STEROLS

α-Sitosterol is a representative of another group of phytosterols which have a methyl group at C4 and are known as the 4-methyl sterols. α-Sitosterol is probably 4 α-methyl-$\Delta^{7, 24(28)}$ stigmastadiene-3β-ol.

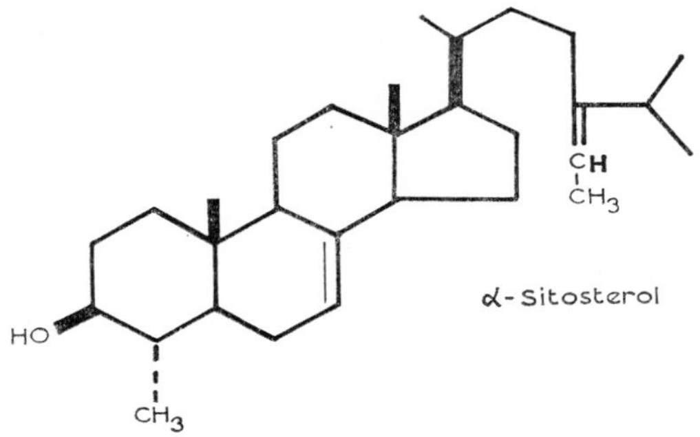

α-Sitosterol

This structure differs from citrostadienol (found in grapefruit peel oil) only in the configuration of the 24, 28 double bond. Lophenol found in the cactus *Lophocereus schottii* is 4 α-methyl-Δ^7-cholestene-3β-ol.

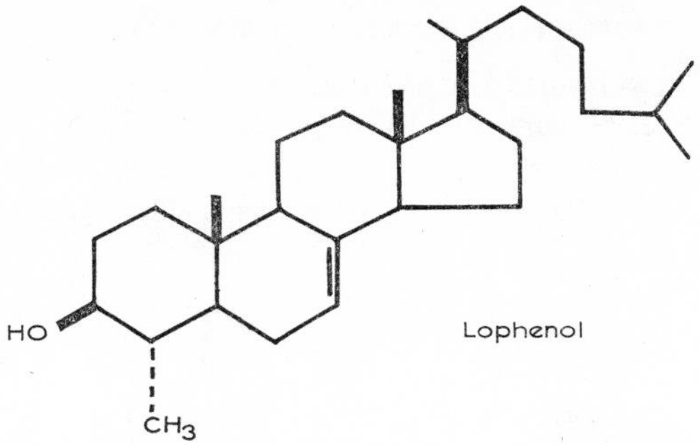

Lophenol

THE METHYL STEROLS

Most triterpenes are pentacyclic but a few, known as methyl sterols, are tetracyclic C_{30} secondary alcohols. These compounds are closely related to the sterols in both structure and stereochemistry. The most fully investigated methylsterol is lanosterol which is found in wool fat but has not been reported in plants.

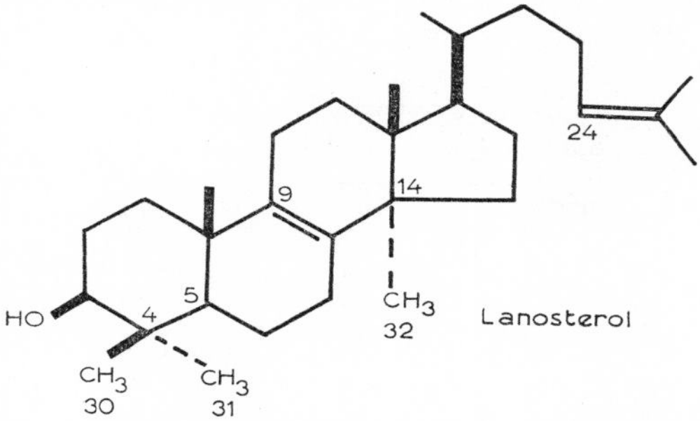

Lanosterol

Note. The numbers 30–32 are used to denote the methyl groups at 4 and 14 because the numbers 28 and 29 are used to designate methyl and ethyl groups at C24.

Cycloaudenol present in opium is structurally related to lanosterol.

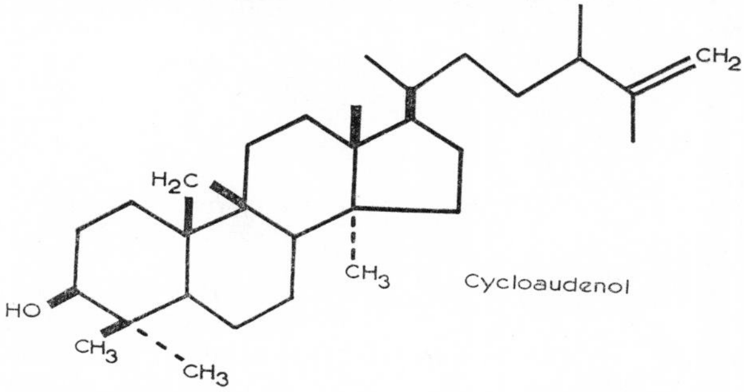

Cycloaudenol

21

THE CARDIAC GLYCOSIDES

In 1785 William Withering introduced digitalis (made from dried leaves and seeds of *Digitalis purpurea*) for heart therapy. Subsequently *Digitalis* has been shown to contain a number of glycosides of C23 steroids known as cardenolides, in which the side chain forms a 5-membered ring.

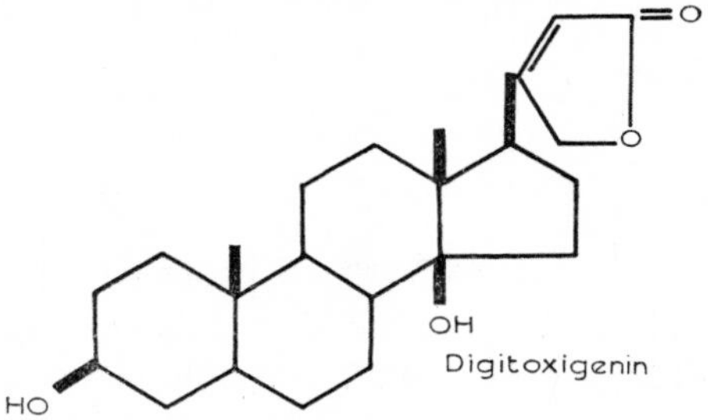

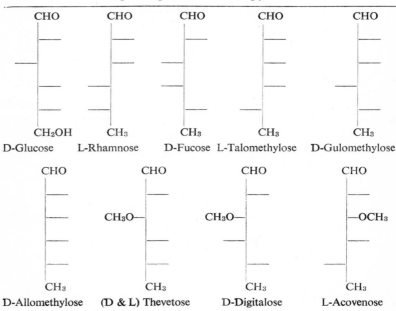

Digitoxigenin

Digitoxigenin is the aglycone of a number of arrow poisons and is present in digitalis. Some twenty sugar components are known to form cardiac glycosides (Table 8.2) but only glucose, rhamnose and fucose have been isolated from other plant sources.

TABLE 8.2

Sugar components of cardiac glycosides

CHO	CHO	CHO	CHO	CHO
CH₂OH	CH₃	CH₃	CH₃	CH₃
D-Glucose	L-Rhamnose	D-Fucose	L-Talomethylose	D-Gulomethylose

CHO	CHO	CHO	CHO
	CH₃O—	CH₃O—	—OCH₃
CH₃	CH₃	CH₃	CH₃
D-Allomethylose	(D & L) Thevetose	D-Digitalose	L-Acovenose

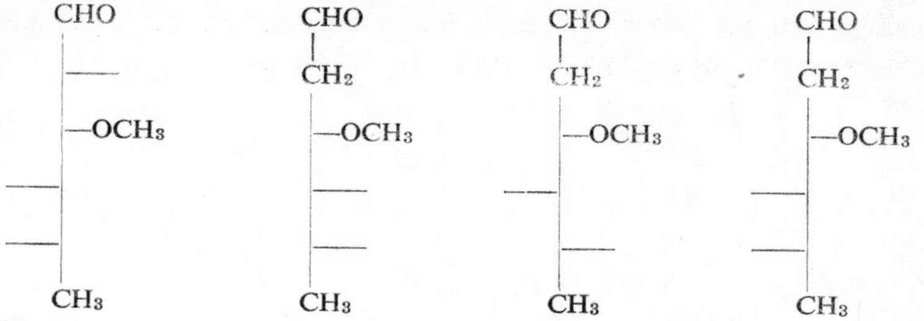

L-Acofriose   D-Cymarose   D-Sarmentose   (D & L) Oleandrose

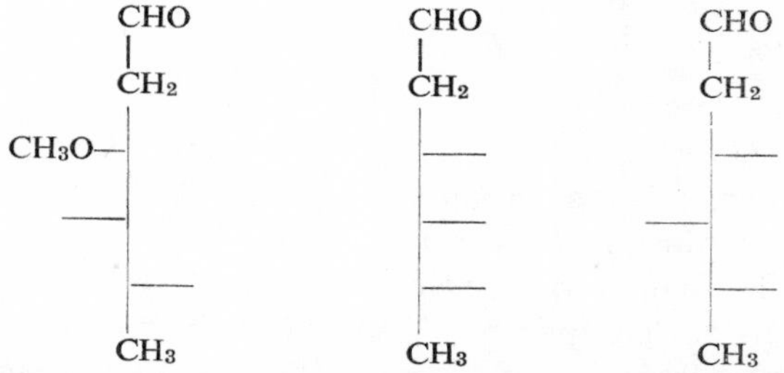

(D & L) Diginose   D-Digitoxose   D-Boivinose

A number of C24 steroids known as bufadienolides occur in plants, though they are best known as toad poisons. The side chain of the bufadienolides forms a doubly unsaturated 6-membered lactone ring.

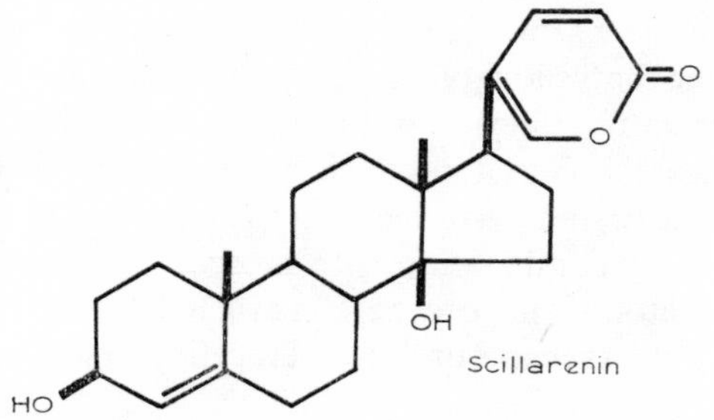

Scillarenin

Scillarenin is the aglycone of scillaren A, one of a number of bufadienolides (sometimes called scilladienolides) found in *Scilla maritima*.

THE SAPONINS

The cardiac glycosides have the property of forming a soapy lather in water, but the term saponin is reserved for non-cardiac steroid glycosides which produce a lather. The most important commercial sapogenin is hecogenin, present in the sisal plant (*Agave sisalana*).

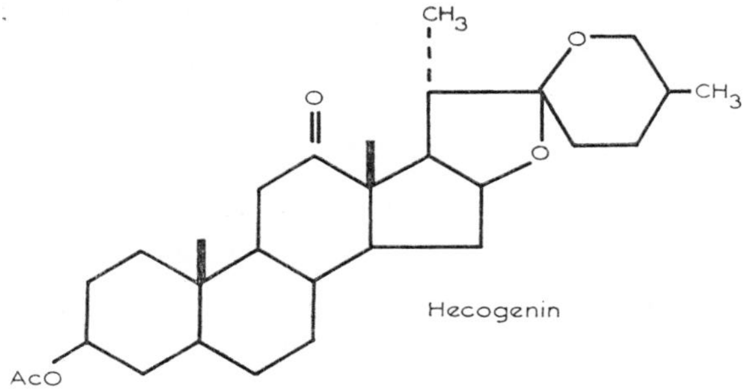

Hecogenin

This sapogenin has a ketone group at C12 which is also present in the 12-ketobile acids which had been used in the early synthesis of the adrenocorticol hormone cortisone (which has an 11-keto group). Trans-position of the ketone group from C12 to C11 can be carried out in three steps with an overall yield of 55 per cent. The 11-keto tigogenin can be converted into cortisone so that hecogenin is one of the main starting materials for the commercial production of cortisone.

The Carotenoid Pigments

The carotenoids are a group of yellow to red pigments found in all plants and named after the yellow pigment of carrot (β-carotene). Because of their non-polar nature, they do not normally occur dissolved in the cell fluid, but are usually present in the chromatophores. Water solubility is conferred in some cases by esterification as in crocetin (Fig. 8.4) and in a number of cases by combination with proteins. Most carotenoids contain 40 carbon atoms and can be constructed from 8 isoprene units, though a few have less than 8 units (e.g. crocetin), and others have carbon

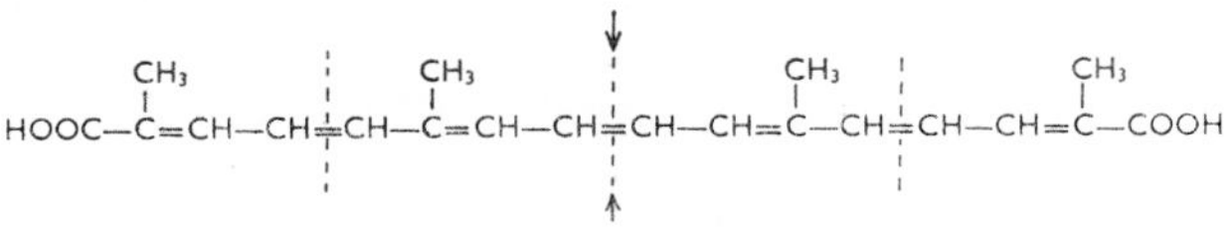

Fig. 8.4. Crocetin, $C_{20}H_{24}O_2$. The aglycone of the digentiobiose ester, crocin—the colouring principle of saffron obtained from *Crocus* species. The dotted lines show the dissection into isoprene units, the arrows the position of the tail-to-tail link.

atoms extra to the isoprene units (e.g. azafrin, Fig. 8.5). It is characteristic of all carotenoids that the arrangement of the isoprene units is reversed at one point. With few exceptions (e.g. azafrin), the tail-to-tail link occurs in the centre of the molecule suggesting that carotenoids are formed by the combination of two identical diterpenes.

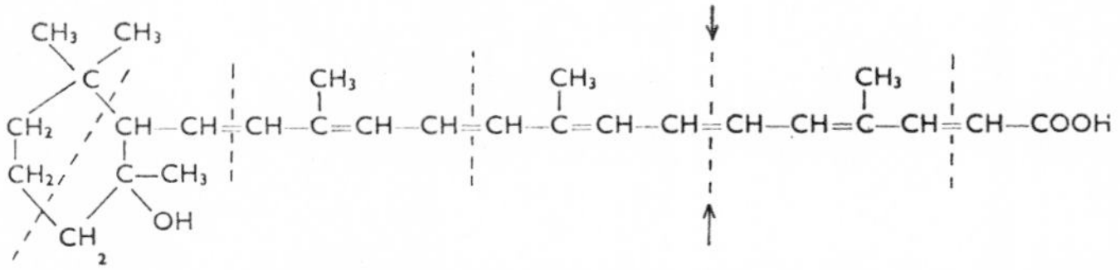

FIG. 8.5. Azafrin, $C_{27}H_{38}O_4$, found in two South American plants *Escobediasca brifolia* and *Escobedia linearis*. Under the name azafran *Escobedia linearis* is used to colour margarine in Paraguay.

Carotenoids can be divided into two groups — the carotenes which are unsaturated hydrocarbons and the xanthophylls which contain oxygen.

THE CAROTENES

Quantitatively the major carotene found in higher plants is β-carotene, the structure of which is shown in Fig. 8.6 together with a 'shorthand' formula.

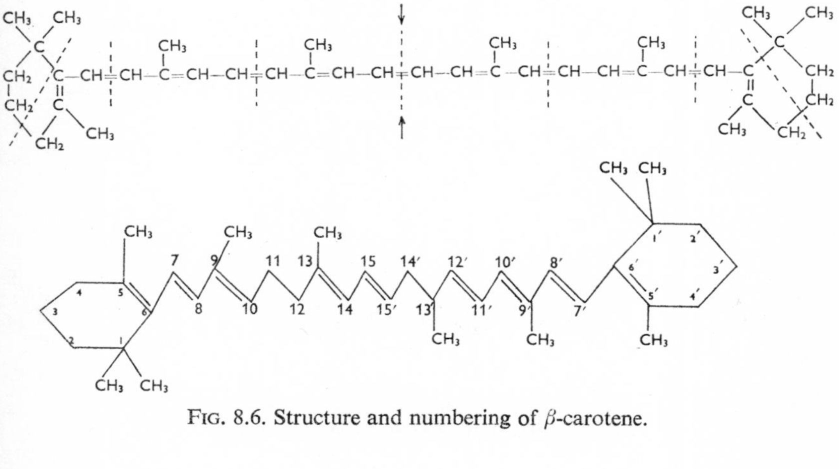

FIG. 8.6. Structure and numbering of β-carotene.

The convention for numbering carotenes is that plain numbers are given to that part of the molecule containing a β-ionone group.

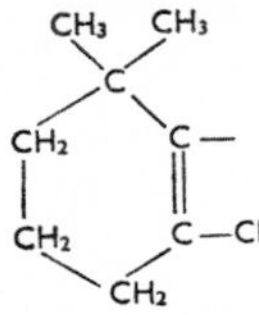

β-ionone group

α-Carotene has one β-ionone group and is numbered as in Fig. 8.7.

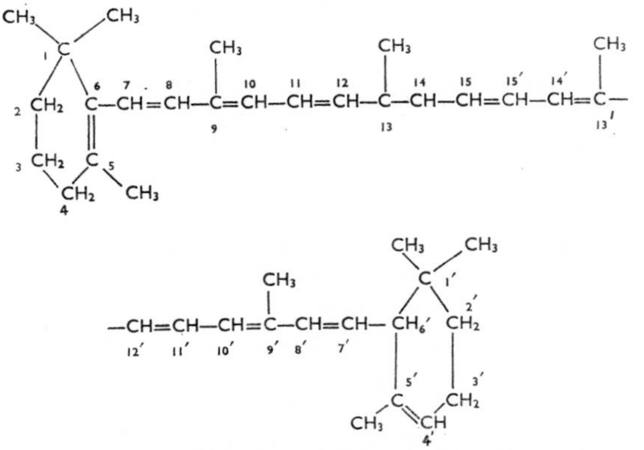

FIG. 8.7. Structure and numbering of α-carotene.

The two other isomeric hydrocarbons are shown by means of their shorthand formulae in Fig. 8.8.

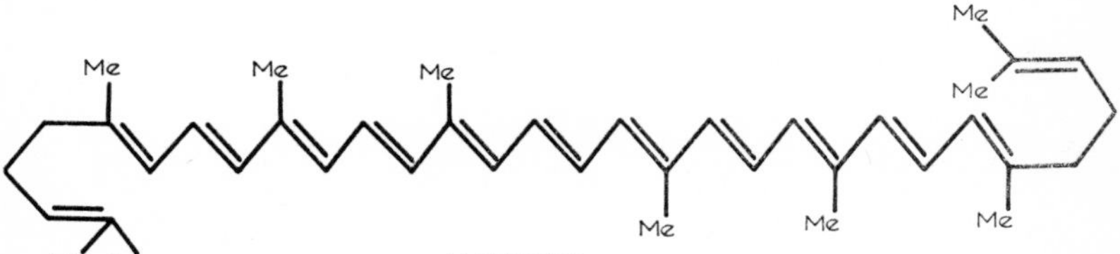

Lycopene

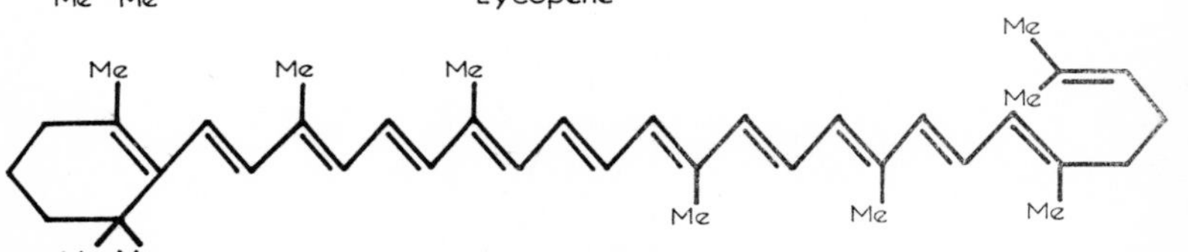

γ-Carotene

FIG. 8.8. Structure of lycopene and γ-carotene.

Lycopene is the main carotenoid of ripe tomato fruits. γ-Carotene is found in the green sulphur bacteria, in some algae, and a derivative (3-hydroxy-γ-carotene) is found in roses.

It is clear from these formulae that a very large number of geometrical isomers are possible. Most carotenoids appear to have an all-*trans* configuration, though a few *cis* isomers are known and isomerization may take place during isolation.

THE XANTHOPHYLLS

The oxygen-containing carotenoids are termed xanthophylls and are structually derived from the carotenes as shown in Table 8.3.

TABLE 8.3
Classification of xanthophylls

Parent Carotene	Xanthophyll	Synonyms	Distribution
α-Carotene	3,3'-Dihydroxy-α-carotene	Lutein, xanthophyll	In all green plants.
	5,8-Epoxy-xanthophyll	Flavoxanthin	Fairly wide distribution but only as a minor pigment.
β-Carotene	3,3'-Dihydroxy-β-carotene	Zeaxanthin	Wide distribution, high concentration in maize.
	5,8-5',8'-Diepoxyzeaxanthin	Violaxanthin	Wide distribution.
	3,3'-Diketo-β-carotene	Rhodoxanthin	Fairly wide distribution but usually low concentration, large quantities in *Taxus baccata*.
γ-Carotene	3-Hydroxy-γ-carotene	Rubixanthin	Mainly in roses.
Lycopene	3-Hydroxylycopene	Lycoxanthin	*Solanum* species.
	3,3'-Dihydroxylycopene	Lycophyll	*Solanum* species.

Rubber and Gutta-percha

Rubber and gutta are polyisoprene hydrocarbons but differ in the arrangement of atoms around the double bonds. Rubber is a *cis*-isomer,

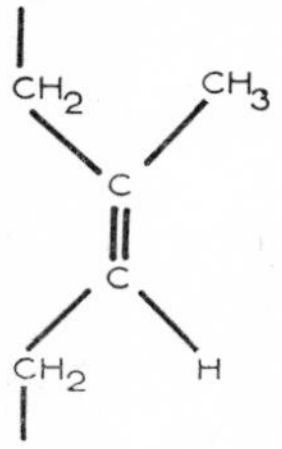

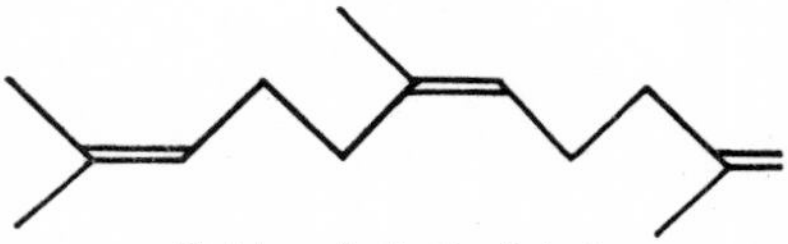

Rubber (all cis-links)

whilst gutta is a *trans*-isomer.

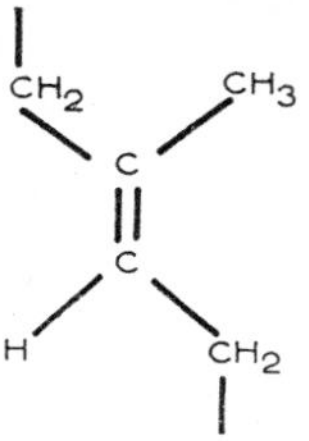

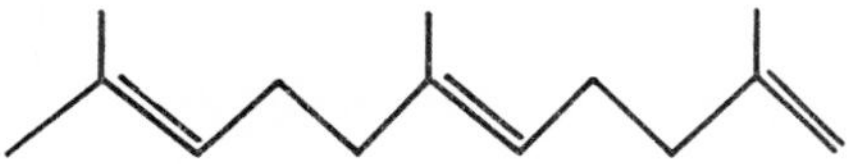

Gutta (all trans-links)

Gutta, which is obtained from the chicle tree, can exist in two crystal forms. In the tree, gutta is in the β-form, which X-ray analysis has shown to have a molecular repeat distance of 4·7 Å. Rubber has a molecular repeat distance of 8·1 Å.

BIOSYNTHESIS

The isoprene rule was proposed by Ruzicka in 1922 but it was not until 1958 that the C5 building unit was identified as

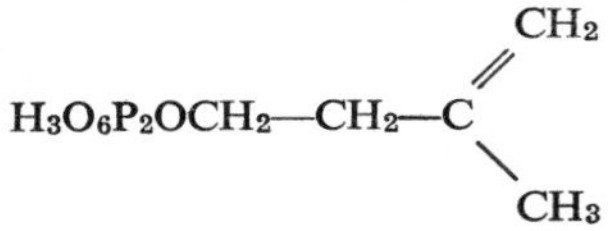

Isopentenyl pyrophosphate

and its isomer

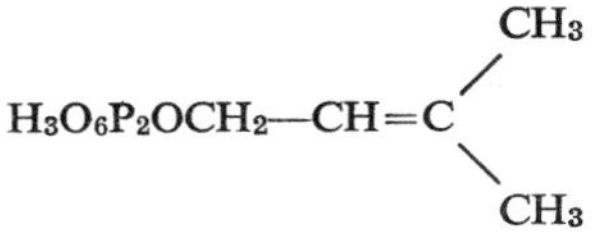

Dimethylallyl pyrophosphate

In 1942 Bloch and Rittenberg demonstrated in liver slices, that cholesterol can be formed from acetate. Subsequent work in Bloch's laboratory and in that of Popjak and Cornforth, led to a determination of the position of all the acetate carbon atoms in cholesterol. From this labelling pattern it became clear (Bloch, 1953) that the isoprene unit derived its carbon from the methyl group (M) and the carboxyl group (C) of acetate as shown below:

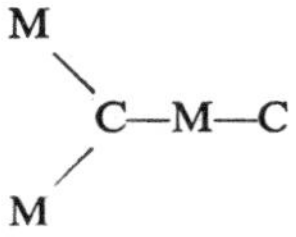

In 1949 Bonner and Arreguin demonstrated that small slices of the branches of guayule (*Parthenium argentatum*) can synthesize rubber from acetate, and they suggested that the isoprene unit might be synthesized from 3 molecules of acetate with the loss of one carboxyl. The finding that acetate-1-^{14}C was incorporated by flax seedlings into acetoacetate and the derivatives 3-methyl-3-hydroxyglutarate and dimethylacrylate led Johnston, Racusen & Bonner (1954) to postulate the following scheme:

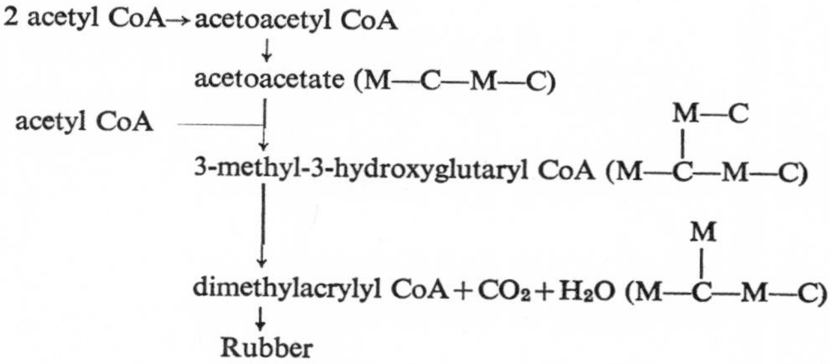

2 acetyl CoA→ acetoacetyl CoA
↓
acetoacetate (M—C—M—C)

acetyl CoA ————| M—C
↓ |
3-methyl-3-hydroxyglutaryl CoA (M—C—M—C)

| M
↓ |
dimethylacrylyl CoA + CO$_2$ + H$_2$O (M—C—M—C)
↓
Rubber

Though the labelling of dimethylacrylate was in agreement with the labelling of the isoprene unit of cholesterol, only a very limited incorporation into rubber could be demonstrated and more extensive investigations on the biosynthesis of cholesterol failed to establish dimethylacrylate as the precursor of the isoprene unit.

Mevalonic Acid

The next important advance came from research unconnected with the isoprenoids. A mutant of *Lactobacillus acidophilus* required acetate for growth, but this requirement could be replaced by a factor present in 'distillers solubles'. This factor was isolated and proved to be 3,5-dihydroxy-3-methylpentanoic acid and was named mevalonic acid.

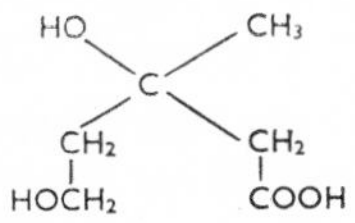

The resemblance of this structure to 3-methyl-3-hydroxyglutarate, suggested that mevalonic acid might be on the pathway of cholesterol biosynthesis. Tavormina, Gibbs & Huff (1956) were able to demonstrate an almost quantitative formation of cholesterol from mevalonate-2-^{14}C in liver homogenates and so initiated a series of experiments in which the feeding of mevalonate-2-^{14}C has led to incorporation into a variety of isoprenoid compounds.

FORMATION OF MEVALONATE FROM ACETATE

Mevalonic acid is a highly reactive metabolite and does not usually accumulate in plants. However, when acetate-2-^{14}C is fed to shoots of *Pinus attenuata*, radioactive mevalonate can be isolated (Stanley, 1958). The individual steps are shown in Fig. 8.9. The condensation of acetyl CoA to give acetoacetate has been demonstrated in cell-free systems, but the reported activities are low. The formation of a derivative of

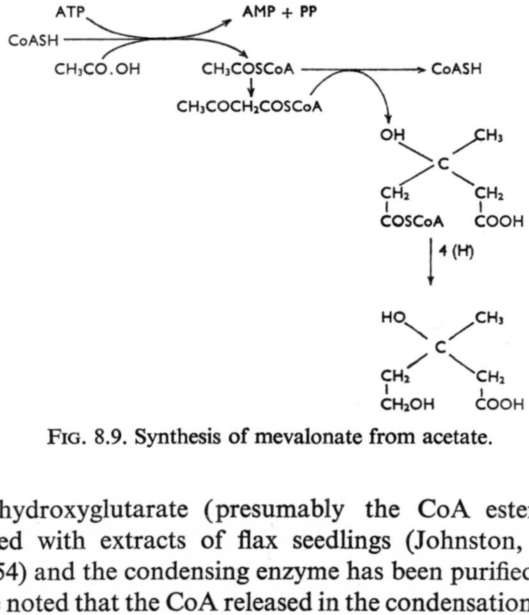

FIG. 8.9. Synthesis of mevalonate from acetate.

3-methyl-3-hydroxyglutarate (presumably the CoA ester) has been demonstrated with extracts of flax seedlings (Johnston, Racusen & Bonner, 1954) and the condensing enzyme has been purified from yeast. It should be noted that the CoA released in the condensation comes from acetyl CoA. The equilibrium of the reaction strongly favours condensation, but a cleavage enyzme catalyses the virtually irreversible cleavage of 3-methyl-3-hydroxyglutaryl CoA to acetyl CoA and acetoacetate.

The reduction of 3-methyl-3-hydroxyglutaryl CoA to mevalonic acid is essentially the reduction of an activated carboxyl group to an alcohol and would be expected to proceed via the aldehyde mevaldic acid. Attempts to demonstrate this have been unsuccessful.

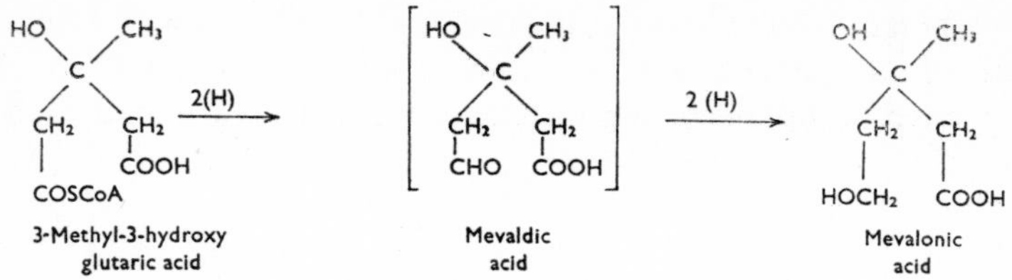

3-Methyl-3-hydroxy
glutaric acid

Mevaldic
acid

Mevalonic
acid

Formation of Isopentenyl Pyrophosphate from Mevalonate

Liver homogenates and yeast autolysates are able to form squalene from mevalonate and these two systems have been used to elucidate the intermediary stages of metabolism. The requirement for ATP suggested the existence of phosphorylated intermediates and the first intermediate to be demonstrated was 5-phosphomevalonic acid (Fig. 8.10).

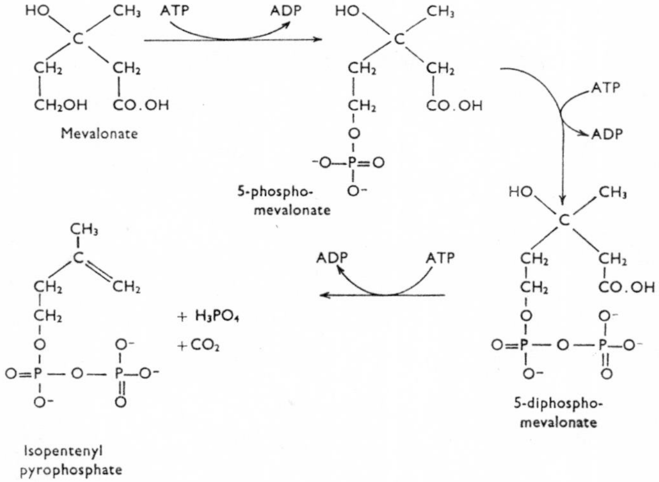

FIG. 8.10. Formation of isopentenyl pyrophosphate from mevalonic acid.

When 5-phosphomevalonate was used as a substrate for squalene synthesis, the requirement for ATP remained and this led to the demonstration of a second kinase and the isolation of 5-diphosphomevalonate.

The finding that the ATP requirement for squalene synthesis remained when 5-diphosphomevalonate was used as substrate, led to the isolation of isopentenyl pyrophosphate (3-methylbut-3-en-1-yl pyrophosphate).

The carbon dioxide released in the reaction is derived from C1 of mevalonate and available evidence suggests the formation of a labile phosphate ester (5-diphospho-3-phosphomevalonate) prior to decarboxylation.

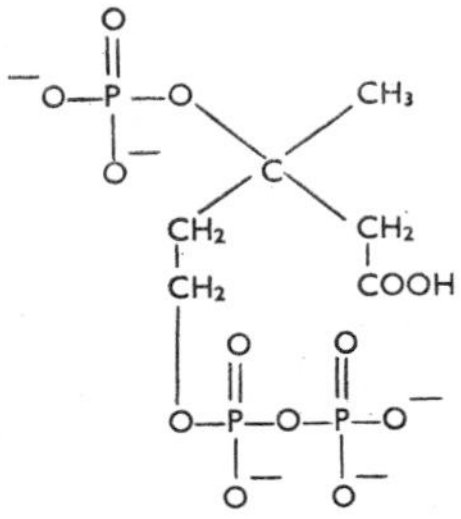

5-diphospho-3-phosphomevalonate

Isoprene Building Units

Isopentenyl pyrophosphate can be considered as a disguised isoprene unit.

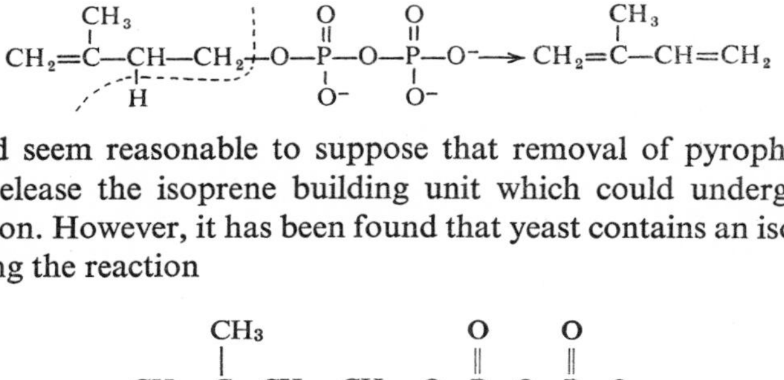

It would seem reasonable to suppose that removal of pyrophosphate
would release the isoprene building unit which could undergo polymerization. However, it has been found that yeast contains an isomerase
catalysing the reaction

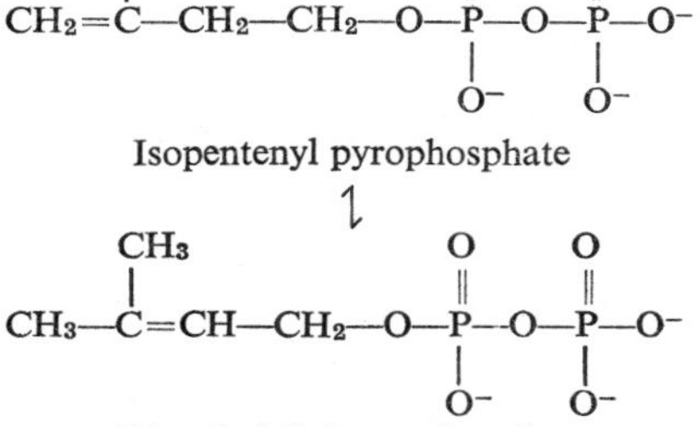

Isopentenyl pyrophosphate

Dimethylallyl pyrophosphate

The two isomers may then condense to form geranyl pyrophosphate. The condensation may be compared with the formation of fructose diphosphate from phosphoglyceraldehyde and its isomer dihydroxyacetone phosphate.

phosphoglyceraldehyde ⟶ dihydroxyacetonephosphate

fructose 1 : 6-diphosphate

isopentenylpyrophosphate ⟶ dimethylallylpyrophosphate

geranyl pyrophosphate

The reaction forming fructose diphosphate is an aldol condensation, but the reaction forming geranyl pyrophosphate is an alkylation. The esterified allylic structure is a strong electrophilic agent and readily forms a carbonium ion which can attack the reactive double bond of isopentenyl pyrophosphate (Fig. 8.11).

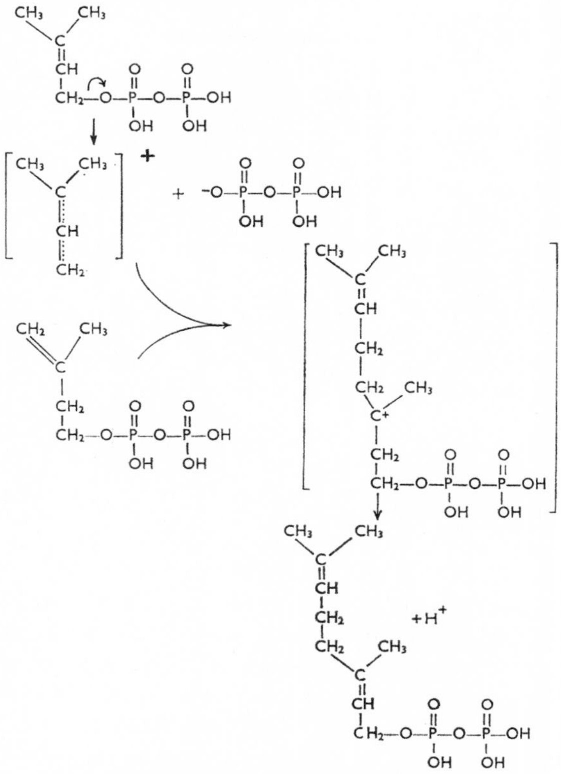

FIG. 8.11. Formation of geranyl pyrophosphate.

Geranyl pyrophosphate also has an allylic structure and by the same mechanism can alkylate another molecule of isopentenyl pyrophosphate to form farnesyl pyrophosphate.

$$CH_3$$
$$\diagdown$$
$$C=CH-CH_2-CH_2-\overset{\overset{\displaystyle CH_3}{|}}{C}=CH-CH_2-CH_2-\overset{\overset{\displaystyle CH_3}{|}}{C}=CH-CH_2-O-\overset{\overset{\displaystyle O}{\|}}{\underset{\underset{\displaystyle OH}{|}}{P}}-O-\overset{\overset{\displaystyle O}{\|}}{\underset{\underset{\displaystyle OH}{|}}{P}}-OH$$
$$\diagup$$
$$CH_3$$

Farnesyl pyrophosphate

Farnesyl pyrophosphate has an allylic structure and a further alkylation of isopentenyl pyrophosphate gives geranyl-geranyl pyrophosphate.

$$CH_3$$
$$\diagdown$$
$$C=CH-CH_2-CH_2-\overset{\overset{\displaystyle CH_3}{|}}{C}=CH-CH_2-CH_2-\overset{\overset{\displaystyle CH_3}{|}}{C}=CH-CH_2-CH_2-\overset{\overset{\displaystyle CH_3}{|}}{C}=CH-CH_2-O-\overset{\overset{\displaystyle O}{\|}}{\underset{\underset{\displaystyle OH}{|}}{P}}-O-\overset{\overset{\displaystyle O}{\|}}{\underset{\underset{\displaystyle OH}{|}}{P}}-OH$$
$$\diagup$$
$$CH_3$$

Geranyl-geranyl pyrophosphate

Condensation of 2 molecules of geranyl-geranyl pyrophosphate could lead to the symmetrical carotenoid structure. Similarly, condensation of 2 molecules of farnesyl pyrophosphate could lead to the formation of the symmetrical triterpene squalene. The mechanism of this condensation has not yet been established, but available evidence suggests that a C-alkylation is involved. Thus farnesyl pyrophosphate may give rise to its isomer nerolidyl pyrophosphate.

$$CH_3$$
$$\diagdown$$
$$C=CH-CH_2-CH_2-\overset{\overset{\displaystyle CH_3}{|}}{C}=CH-CH_2-CH_2-\overset{\overset{\displaystyle CH_3}{|}}{C}-CH=CH_2$$
$$\diagup$$
$$CH_3$$

$$O-\overset{\overset{\displaystyle O}{\|}}{\underset{\underset{\displaystyle OH}{|}}{P}}-O-\overset{\overset{\displaystyle O}{\|}}{\underset{\underset{\displaystyle OH}{|}}{P}}-OH$$

Nerolidyl pyrophosphate

The reactive methylene group of nerolidyl pyrophosphate may then be alkylated by farnesyl pyrophosphate, thereby forming the tail-to-tail link found in the triterpenes and steroids. A similar reaction starting with geranyl-geranyl pyrophosphate would give a carotenoid precursor.

The general reactions of isoprenoid biosynthesis are shown in Fig. 8.12, but the synthesis of the individual groups will be considered under separate headings.

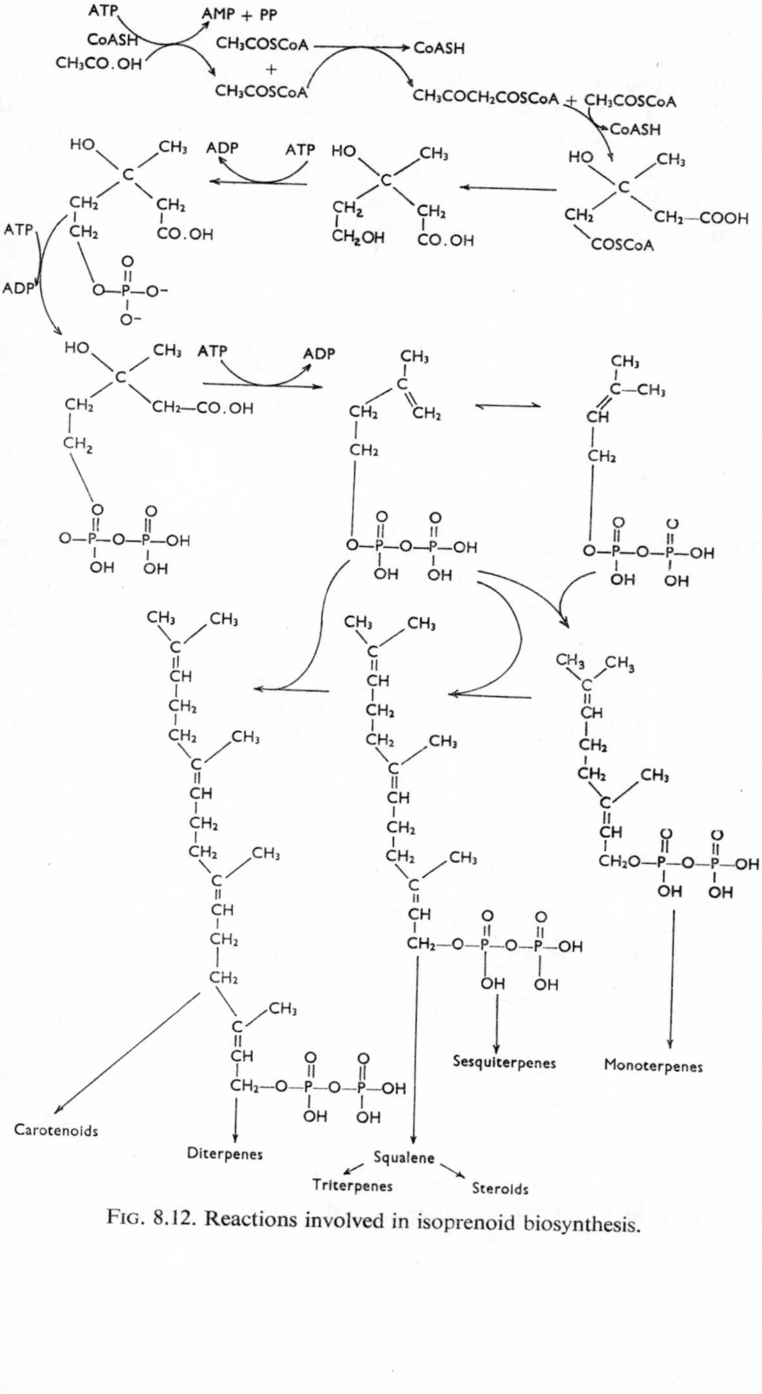

FIG. 8.12. Reactions involved in isoprenoid biosynthesis.

Terpenes

The most characteristic feature of the terpenes is the variety of cyclizations which occur during their biosynthesis. Two main factors are involved in cyclization — (1) the fixation of the polyene chain in a particular configuration; (2) activation of the molecule at specific atoms.

The configuration adopted for cyclization is not related to the conventional drawing of cyclohexane rings, but rather to the chair or boat forms (p. 91).

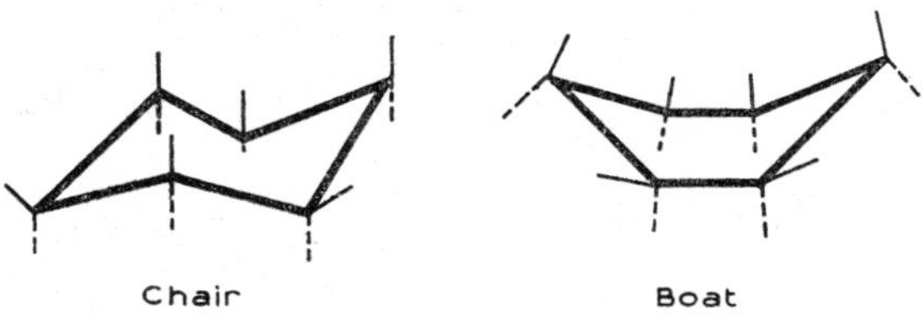

Chair   Boat

The chair conformation is the more stable but can undergo conversion into the boat form by passage over a small energy barrier.

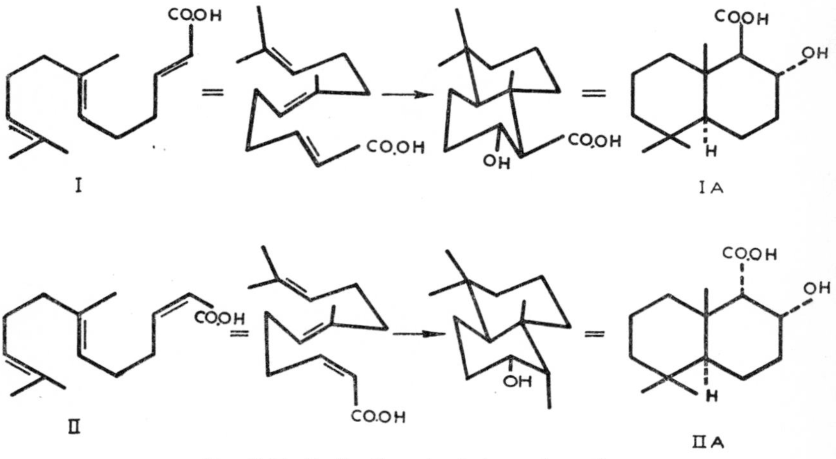

FIG. 8.13. Cyclization via chair configuration.

Consider the case of compounds I and II whose conventional formulae are shown in Fig. 8.13, together with the chair conformation, which is energetically most favourable. Compounds IA and IIA are formed by cyclization and it is probable that prior to cyclization the most favoured chair-type foldings are adopted. We see in this example that the spatial position of the carboxyl group is a consequence of the fact that ring closure proceeds by way of a chair-type conformation. It might appear at first sight that we should be able to predict the type of folding involved in cyclization by inspection. However, it happens that cyclization is usually accompanied by rearrangement of carbon atoms thereby masking the structural origin of the carbon framework. Thus the formation of cholesterol from squalene involves the migration of one methyl group and the elimination of three other methyl groups. In view of the difficulties, the determination of the conformation of squalene prior to cyclization has been a particularly happy union between organic chemistry and biochemistry. It is convenient to list some of the ways in which squalene may cyclize.

If squalene adopts a chair-chair-chair-boat-boat folding as in (a) cyclization may proceed via a, b, c and d. The step b to c is essentially the change from a boat to a chair conformation and it produces a rearrangement of the carbon atoms in the D ring which is characteristic of most of the pentacyclic terpenes, e.g. β-amyrin.

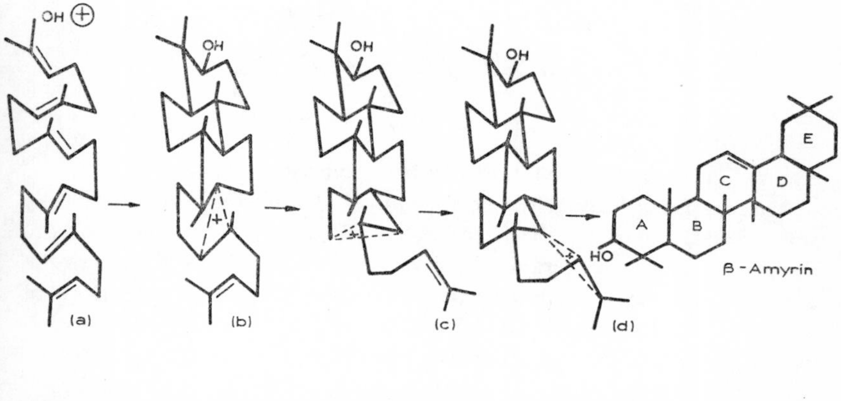

(a)   (b)   (c)   (d)   β-Amyrin

If squalene adopts a chair-chair-chair-chair-boat configuration cyclization may proceed via e, f and g without any change of the carbon sequence. There are few examples of such pentacyclic terpenes but an example is hydroxyhopanone.

22

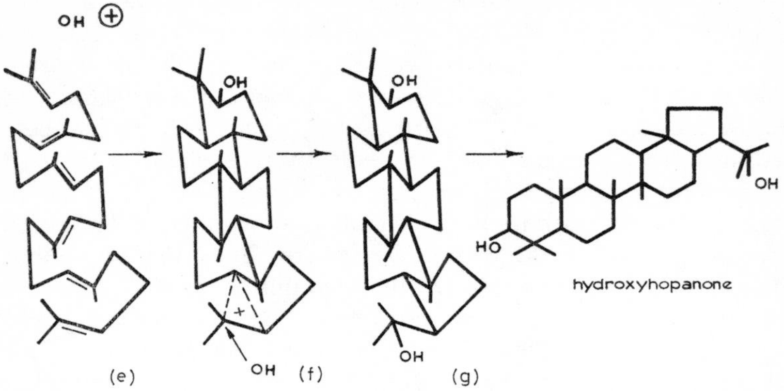

(e)   OH   (f)   (g)

hydroxyhopanone

If squalene adopts a chair-chair-chair-boat configuration

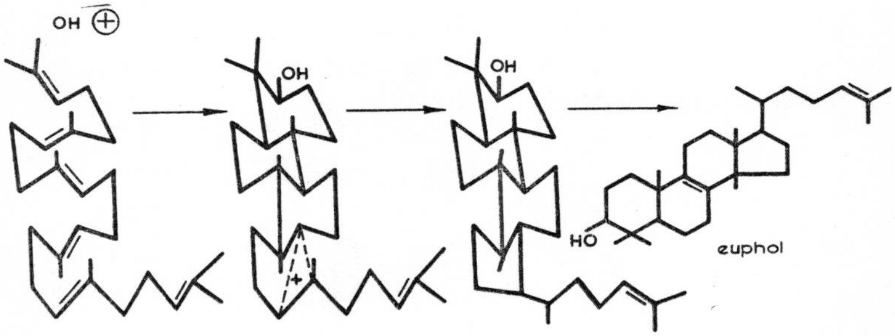

euphol

cyclization then leads to tetracyclic triterpenes such as euphol.

The reactions leading to the formation of gibberellins are not fully understood, but it has been suggested (Wenkert, 1955) that they are formed from geranyl geraniol by a variant of the process leading to the formation of the tricyclic diterpene skeleton. The labelling pattern of geranyl geraniol formed from acetate-1-^{14}C and mevalonate-2-^{14}C is shown below together with the labelling pattern of a tricyclic diterpene. If the formation of gibberellin involves (i) loss of C-17, (ii) contraction of ring B to a 5-membered ring with extrusion of C-9 as a carboxyl group and (iii) formation of the bridged ring structure from ring C and its side chain, then the expected labelling pattern is shown below. The degradation of gibberellic acid obtained from *Gibberella fujikuroi* grown on acetate-1-^{14}C and mevalonate-2-^{14}C, reveals a labelling pattern in agreement with that predicted by Wenkert's scheme.

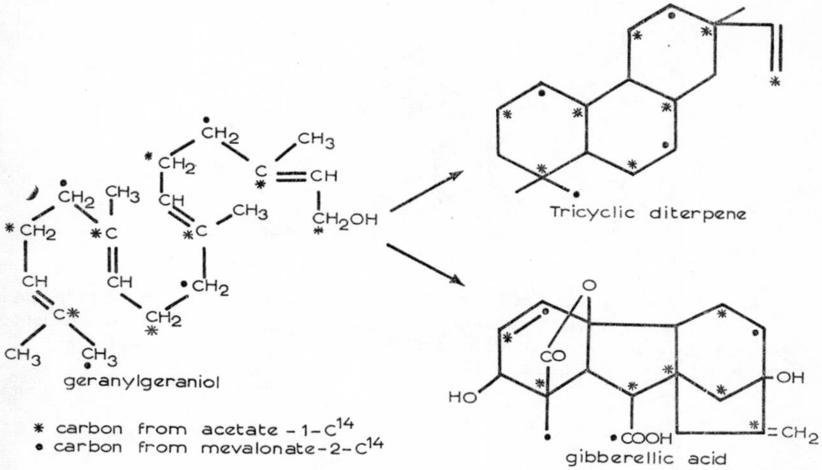

Tricyclic diterpene

geranylgeraniol

* carbon from acetate – 1–C^{14}
• carbon from mevalonate–2–C^{14}

gibberellic acid

The incorporation of mevalonic acid-2-^{14}C into terpenes has been demonstrated in a number of cases. For example, twigs of *Pinus attenuata* incorporate mevalonate into monoterpenes, flowering shoots of *Salvia sclarea* incorporate it into the bicyclic diterpene sclareol and soy bean seedlings incorporate it into triterpenes.

Sterols

In 1934 Sir Robert Robinson proposed that squalene may be cyclized to a tetracyclic derivative which could be converted into cholesterol. The suggested mechanism of cyclization is shown in Fig. 8.14, together with the distribution of carbon atoms derived from the methyl group of acetate, which was experimentally determined by Bloch. In squalene the distribution of carbons derived from the methyl group of acetate is determined prior to folding and the distribution of label in cholesterol is a function of the mechanism of folding. The discrepancies at carbon atoms 7, 12 and 13 eliminate the Robinson mechanism and support the Woodward-Bloch mechanism, which is also shown in Fig. 8.14. A possible folding of the squalene molecule to permit concerted electron shifts leading to ring closure and the formation of lanosterol is shown in Fig. 8.15. Lanosterol, the immediate product of cyclization, is thought to be the precursor of sterols. The final step shown in Fig. 8.15 involves the

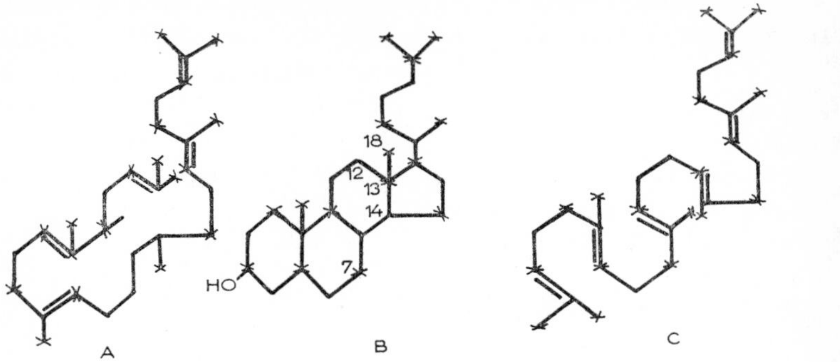

FIG. 8.14. Labelling pattern of the methyl carbon atoms of acetate in squalene (A and C), and cholesterol (B) in relation to the folding of squalene. Folding of squalene according to the Robinson, or Woodward-Bloch mechanism is shown in A and C, respectively.

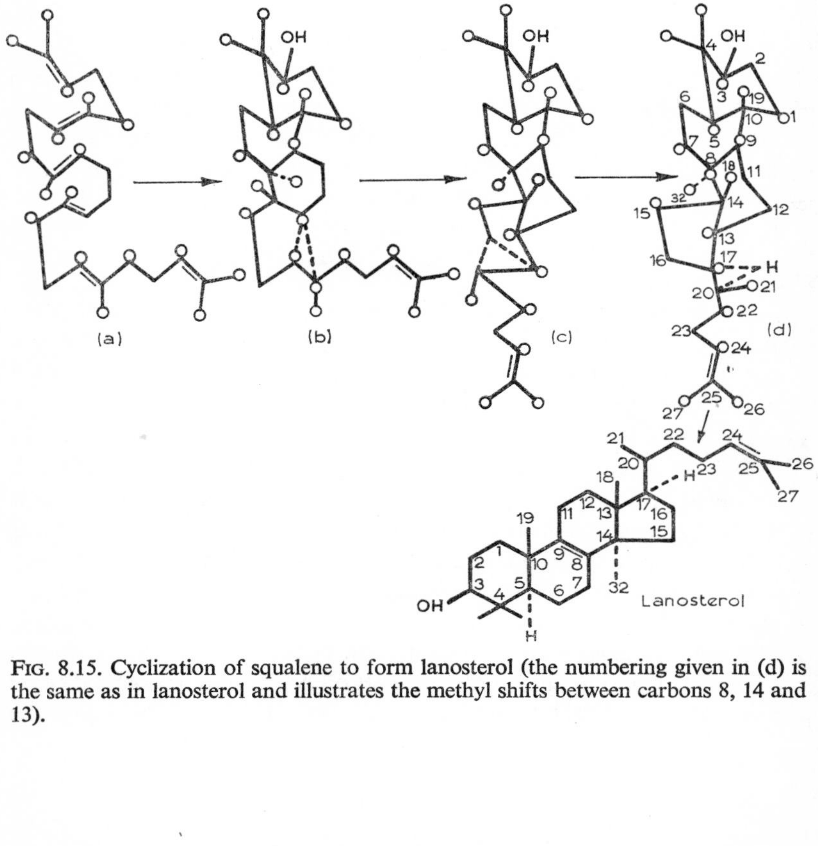

FIG. 8.15. Cyclization of squalene to form lanosterol (the numbering given in (d) is the same as in lanosterol and illustrates the methyl shifts between carbons 8, 14 and 13).

migration of two methyl groups to neighbouring carbon atoms and the removal of a proton from C9 to form the 8,9 double bond. The student should note that some confusion over the nomenclature for the migration of methyl groups exists in the literature. The confusion stems from the Swiss practice of relating the methyl shifts to the numbering of the squalene molecule from 1–22 (the eight methyl groups being unnumbered). British and American literature refer methyl shifts to the numbering of the ring system shown in Fig. 8.3. Thus, the 1,2 methyl group shifts are from C14 to C13 and from C8 to C14. In Swiss literature the shift would be given as C14 to C13 and C9 to C14.

Lanosterol is a triterpene but is sometimes classified as a methyl sterol; it is probably the precursor of other methyl sterols such as cycloartenol and cycloaudenol. The formation of sterols from lanosterol involves demethylation at C14 and C4. The presence of 4-α-methyl sterols in plants suggests that the removal of the β-methyl of lanosterol occurs before the α-methyl group. However, this conclusion should be avoided since a change in configuration could occur during the demethylation step. Other steps in the conversion of lanosterol to cholesterol involve the formation of a 5,6 double bond in place of the 8,9 double bond and the elimination of the side chain double bond.

The phytosterols differ from cholesterol in the structure of the side chain and in particular by the substitution of methyl, ethyl or ethylidene groups at C24. No studies on the origin of these groups have been reported; however, ergosterol produced by yeast has a methyl group attached at C24 and this group is derived from methionine by transmethylation (see p. 376). Similarly eburicoic acid produced by the mould *Polyporus sulphureus* has a methylene group attached at C24 for which formate is an efficient source.

Carotenoids

The incorporation of acetate-^{14}C and mevalonate-2-^{14}C into a number of carotenoids has been demonstrated with fruits and tissue slices and incorporation into β-carotene has been demonstrated with cell-free preparations of carrot. The distribution of label in carotenoids has, with one exception, been in accordance with expectation. The anomalous results reported for the incorporation of acetate into the lycopene of tomatoes by Zabin (1957) were probably due to the method of lycopene degradation (Goodwin, 1959).

Assuming that the C40 precursor of the carotenoids is derived from 2 molecules of geranyl-geranyl pyrophosphate, the precursor would be highly reduced. Two naturally occurring carotenoid hydrocarbons are phytoene and phytofluene:

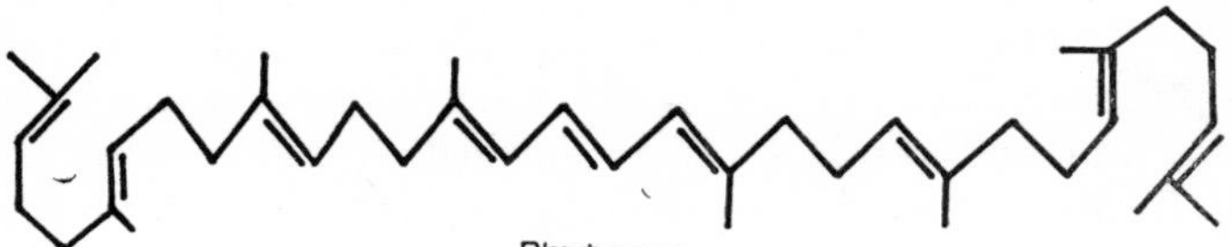

Phytoene

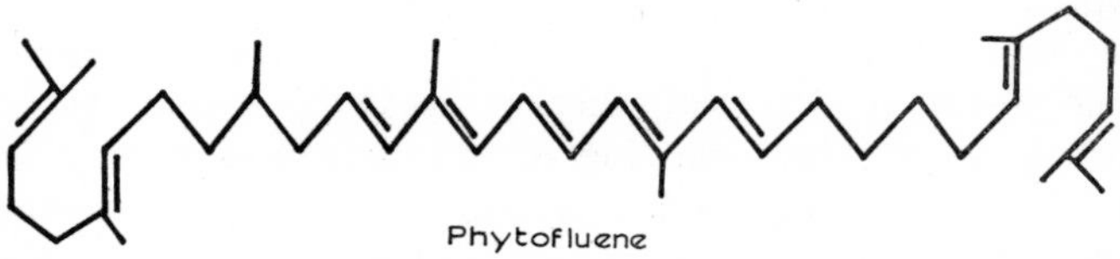

Phytofluene

Both show important differences from the expected precursor:

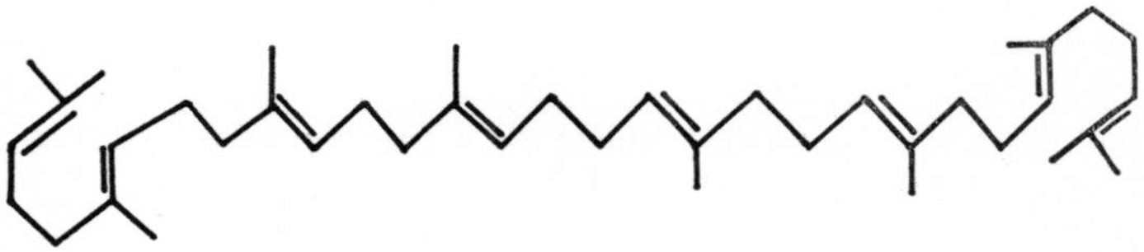

Nevertheless, it has been suggested that phytoene and phytofluene are precursors of carotene.

Diphenylamine, an anti-oxidant which may be used to prevent 'scald' in apples, is a potent inhibitor of carotenoid formation. When carotenoid synthesis is inhibited, certain organisms accumulate weakly conjugated carotenoids such as phytoene and phytofluene. If these compounds are precursors, removal of the inhibitor diphenylamine could be expected to allow the conversion of phytoene and phytofluene into more conjugated forms. Experiments to test this in *Phycomyces blakesleeanus* gave negative results (Goodwin, 1959) but positive results for phytofluene have been obtained with the purple bacterium *Rhodospirillum rubrum* (Stanier, 1960).

In the case of tomatoes, the experiments of Purcell, Thompson & Bonner (1959) would seem to eliminate phytoene as a general carotenoid precursor. Mevalonate-2-^{14}C and acetate-1-^{14}C were injected into tomatoes, and after 24 hr the carotenoids were isolated and their specific activities determined (Table 8.4).

TABLE 8.4

Incorporation of mevalonate-2-¹⁴C and acetate-2-¹⁴C into tomato carotenoids

Substance	Specific activity (counts per min per mg)	
	After feeding mevalonate-2-¹⁴C	After feeding acetate-1-¹⁴C
Phytoene	725	260
Crude phytofluene	74 400	1 740
Fraction II	72 800	212
α-Carotene	47 800	1 010
β-Carotene	32 480	182
γ-Carotene	13 060	183
Lycopene	1 480	158

Much of the radioactivity in the crude phytofluene is probably due to the presence of a xanthophyll. Recent work (Thompson, Purcell & Bonner, 1960) has provided indirect evidence for the participation of fraction II in carotene synthesis. Spectroscopic and degradative studies indicate a probable structure of 3, 7, 11, 15-tetramethylhexadeca-1, 3, 6, 10, 14-pentaene.

XANTHOPHYLLS

Xanthophylls are probably formed from their corresponding carotenes by an oxidase-peroxidase system. This mechanism is illustrated in Fig. 8.16.

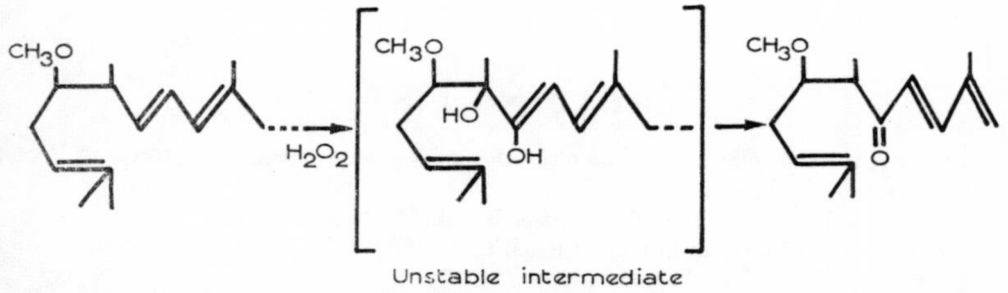

FIG. 8.16. Proposed mechanism for the insertion of oxygen to form spheroidenone.

Rubber

Latex of the rubber tree *Hevea brasiliensis* incorporates ¹⁴C-labelled acetate, mevalonate and isopentenyl pyrophosphate into rubber. The distribution of isotope expected in rubber formed from isopentenyl pyrophosphate-1 and -4-¹⁴C is shown below, together with the expected distribution in squalene.

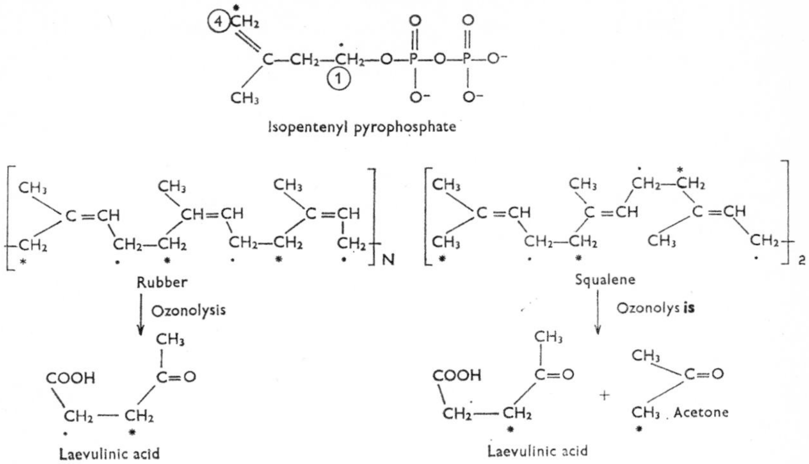

Isopentenyl pyrophosphate

Rubber

Ozonolysis

Squalene

Ozonolysis

Laevulinic acid

Laevulinic acid

CH₃ Acetone

Ozonolysis of rubber and squalene causes rupture at the double bonds, leading to the production of laevulinic acid and, in the case of squalene, to acetone as well. In experiments with *Hevea* latex, isopentenyl pyrophosphate-4-^{14}C labelled rubber and, following ozonolysis, label was present in laevulinic acid but not in acetone — indicating the formation of a linear polymer (i.e. a polymer with few end groups which could yield acetone).

READING LIST

ROBINSON R. (1955) *The Structural Relations of Natural Products.* Clarendon Press, Oxford

FIESER L. F. & FIESER M. (1959) *Steroids.* Reinhold Publishing Co., New York

WOLSTENHOLME G. E. W. & O'CONNOR M. (Ed.) (1959) *Biosynthesis of Terpenes and Sterols.* J. & A. Churchill Ltd., London

POPJAK G. & CORNFORTH J. W. (1960) The Biosynthesis of Cholesterol. *Adv. Enz.* **22**, 281

LYNEN F. & HENNING U. (1961) Uber den Biologischen Weg zum Naturkantschuk. *Angew. Chemie* **72**, 820

WAGNER A. F. & FOLKERS K. (1961) Discovery and Chemistry of Mevalonic Acid. *Adv. Enz.* **23**, 471

WAGNER A. F. & FOLKERS K. (1961) The Organic and Biological Chemistry of Mevalonic Acid. *Endeavour* **20**, 177

GOODWIN T. W. (1961) Biosynthesis and Function of Carotenoids. *Ann. Rev. Pl. Physiol.* **12**, 219

GROVE J. F. (1961) Gibberellins. *Quart. Rev.* **15**, 56

LITERATURE CITED

BLOCH K. (1953) *Helv. Chim. Acta* **36**, 1611

DICKHART W. (1955) *Am. J. Pharmacy* **127**, 359

GOODWIN T. W. (1959) *Adv. Enz.* **21**, 295

HAAGEN-SMIT A.J. (1958) *Encyclopedia of Pl. Physiol.* **10**, 52. Ed. Ruhland W. Springer, Verlag

JOHNSTON J.A., RACUSEN D.W. & BONNER J. (1954) *Proc. Nat. Acad. Sci. U.S.A.* **40**, 1031

PURCELL A.E., THOMPSON G.A. & BONNER J. (1959) *J. Biol. Chem.* **234**, 1081

RUZICKA L. (1953) *Experientia* **9**, 359

RUZICKA L. & STOLL M. (1922) *Helv. Chim. Acta* **5**, 929

STANIER R. Y. (1960) *Harvey Lectures* **54**, 219

STANLEY R. G. (1958) *Nature* **182**, 738

TAVORMINA P.A., GIBBS M.H. & HUFF J.W. (1956) *J. Am. Chem. Soc.* **78**, 4498

THOMPSON G.A., PURCELL A.E. & BONNER J. (1960) *Pl. Physiol.* **35**, 678

WENKERT E. (1955) *Chem. and Industry*, 282

ZABIN I. (1952) *J. Biol. Chem.* **226**, 851

CHAPTER 9

THE ALKALOIDS

The alkaloids are nitrogenous bases, present in plants, which frequently cause physiological responses when administered to animals. The term is applied to a heterogeneous collection of bases, but purine and pyrimidine bases are usually excluded. However, because of their physiological activity in animals, some purine bases, e.g. caffeine, are classified as alkaloids. The existing classification of alkaloids employs a mixture of chemical and botanical nomenclature. Thus the pyrrolidine, pyridine and tropane alkaloids are classified on the nuclear structure of the bases. The senecio alkaloids are so called because the genus *Senecio* provides the greatest number of species containing alkaloids with a hydroxylated pyrrolizidine moiety.

The marked physiological responses to certain alkaloids and their use in medicine, led to the isolation of reasonably pure compounds. The structural complexity of these compounds intrigued many brilliant organic chemists and from a profound knowledge of structural relationships Robinson (1917 and 1955) developed theories of biogenesis which stimulated biochemical investigations. The isolation of reserpine from *Rauwolfia serpentina* and its wide use in medicine, led to major research efforts by large drug companies and an ever-increasing literature. The literature up to 1959 is covered in the seven volumes of *The Alkaloids* edited by Manske. In this short chapter we can only outline the principles of biogenesis developed by Sir Robert Robinson and give some examples of recent investigations using ^{14}C-labelled compounds.

BIOGENETIC SCHEMES

From a knowledge of the structure of alkaloids Robinson observed common structural features and relationships. Relationship implies a family, and in certain cases it was possible to place a series of compounds in an order of biogenesis. This approach however cannot give information about the mechanisms of biosynthetic reactions and Robinson attacked this problem by what he called laboratory analogies. For example he was able to demonstrate tropinone synthesis from succinic aldehyde, acetone dicarboxylic acid and methylamine.

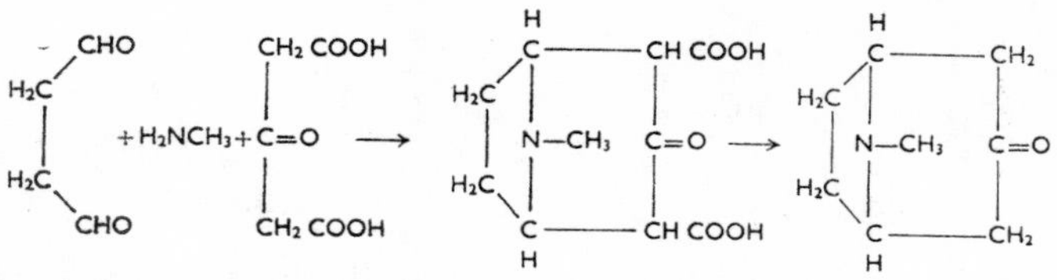

Robinson proposed that the biosynthesis of tropinone derivatives involved compounds *equivalent* to those used in his laboratory analogy. This point was not properly appreciated by some biochemists who argued that the postulated reactants had not been shown to exist in the plant.

Evidence in support of Robinson's biogenetic schemes has been sought by attempts to synthesize alkaloids under physiological conditions, i.e. at about room temperature in dilute aqueous solution close to neutrality and with reagents which could be derived from naturally occurring compounds. Schöpf (1937) has discussed possible reaction pathways by which postulated reactants may be formed, usually from amino acids, and has also provided examples of alkaloid synthesis under physiological conditions. Thus for example, tropinone was obtained in 70–85 per cent yield at pH 3–11 using the reactants employed by Robinson. Lobelanine (present in *Lobelia* sp.) was obtained in 50–80 per cent yield at pH 3–5 by the following reaction:

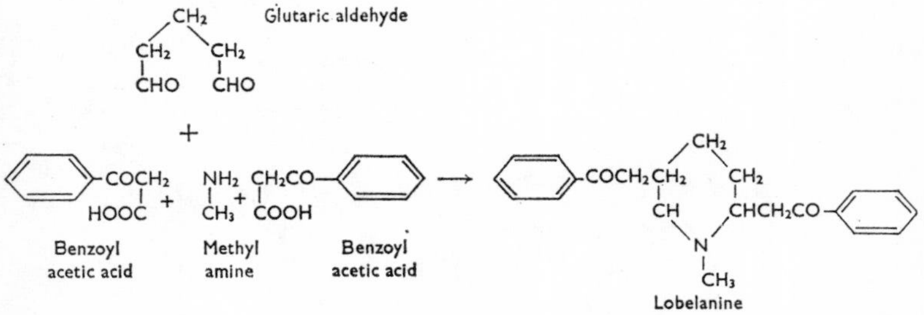

Following the success of Schöpf's synthesis of alkaloids under physiological conditions, similar experiments have been performed with enzyme preparations. Thus, it has been demonstrated that heterocyclic bases may be formed from compounds containing two amino groups by the action of diamino oxidases, e.g.

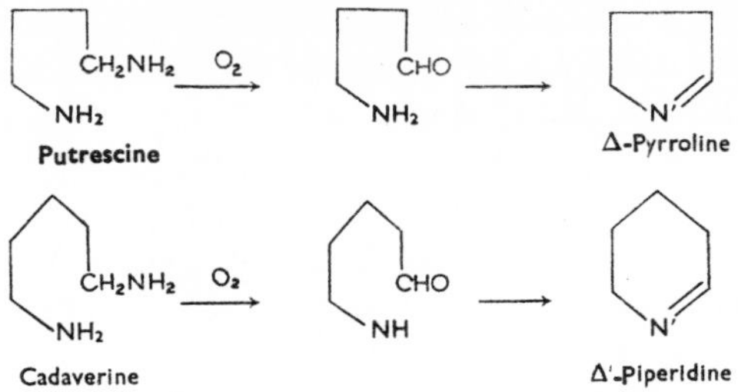

Preparations from peas cause dimerization of piperidine and oxidation to anabasine — the first alkaloid to be produced enzymically.

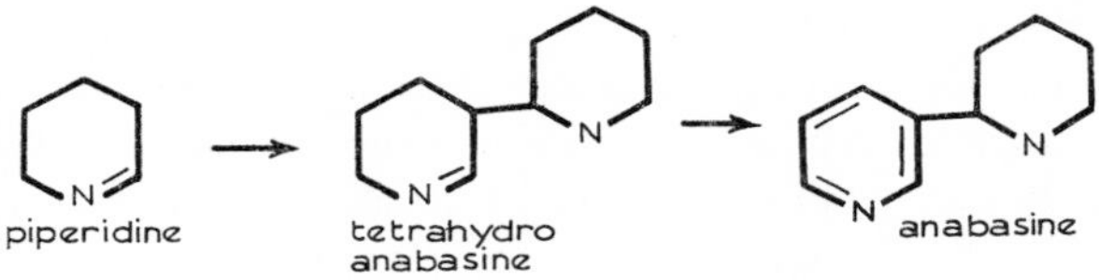

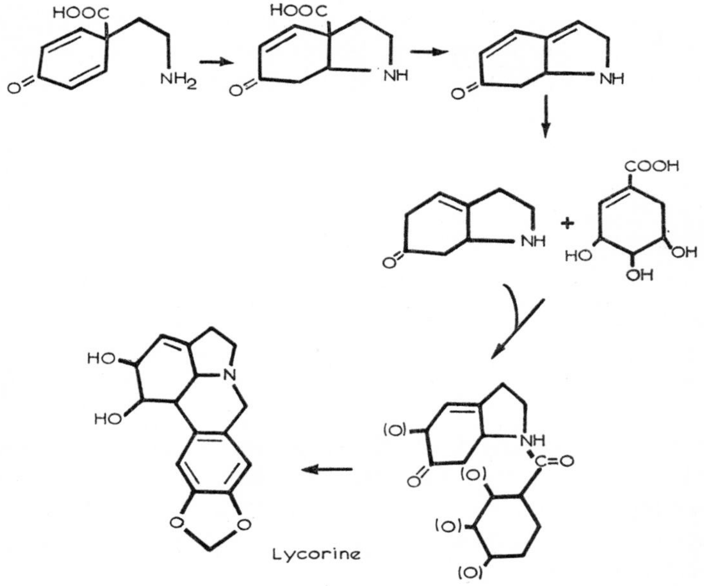

The biogenetic theories of Robinson are in large part based on the origin of alkaloids from amino acids and this thesis has been contested by Wenkert (1959). For example, Wenkert suggests that shikimic acid and prephenic acid are likely intermediates in alkaloid biosynthesis rather than tyrosine or phenylalanine. To take a specific example Wenkert suggests that the alkaloids of the Amaryllidaceae are formed from a shikimyl derivative of an aminated prephenate unit (scheme opposite).

However, feeding experiments have shown that when tyrosine is supplied to daffodils and *Narcissus* sp., it is incorporated into lycorine. If we assume that the conversion of prephenic acid to tyrosine is irreversible, then these results argue against the views of Wenkert.

THE USE OF LABELLED COMPOUNDS TO INVESTIGATE THE BIOSYNTHESIS OF ALKALOIDS

Alkaloids of the Amaryllidaceae

Feeding experiments with daffodils and *Narcissus* sp. have shown that tyrosine is incorporated into lycorine, norpluvine and galanthamine. The biogenetic scheme of Barton & Cohen (1957) proposes an oxidative coupling of phenolic intermediates derived from tyrosine. In support of this proposal it has been shown that norbelladine is incorporated into lycorine and norpluvine whilst a related phenol is incorporated into galanthamine.

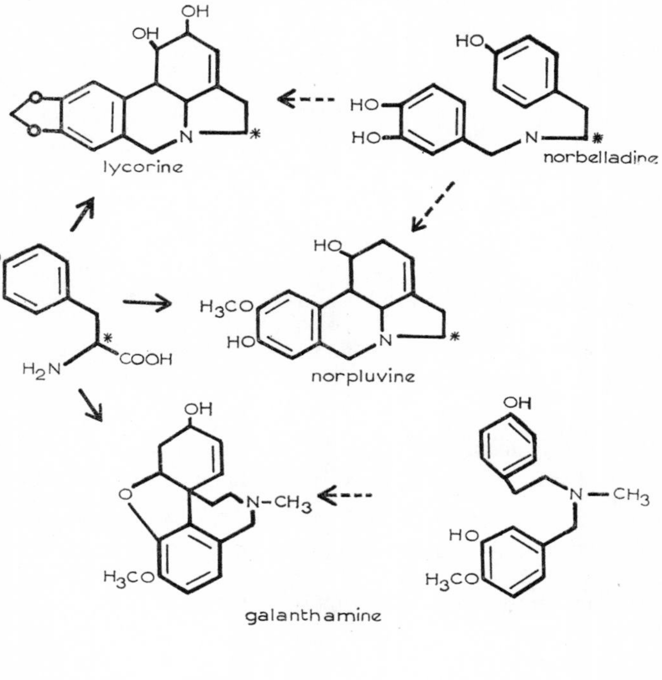

lycorine

norbelladine

norpluvine

galanthamine

The Tropane Alkaloids

The tropane alkaloids are found in solanaceous plants and possess the tropane nucleus:

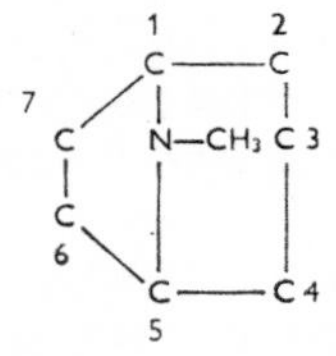

Examples are hyoscyamine and cocaine.

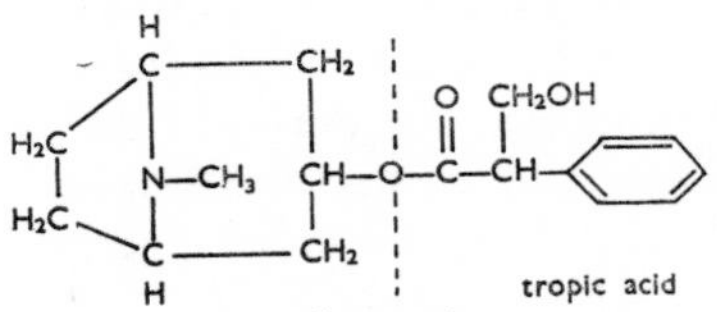

Hyoscyamine

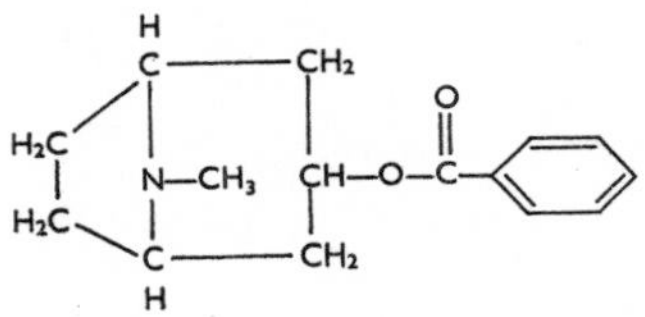

Cocaine

Feeding experiments have established the following facts:

(1) Ornithine-2-^{14}C supplied to *Datura stramonium* leads to the formation of hyoscyamine labelled in positions 1 and 5 of the tropane base.

(2) Feeding acetate-1-^{14}C to *Datura* labels the tropane base in carbon 3 whilst acetate-2-^{14}C introduces label into positions 2 and 5.

(3) Phenylalanine-3-^{14}C and formate-^{14}C are incorporated into the tropic acid moiety of hyoscyamine.

These facts support the following scheme:

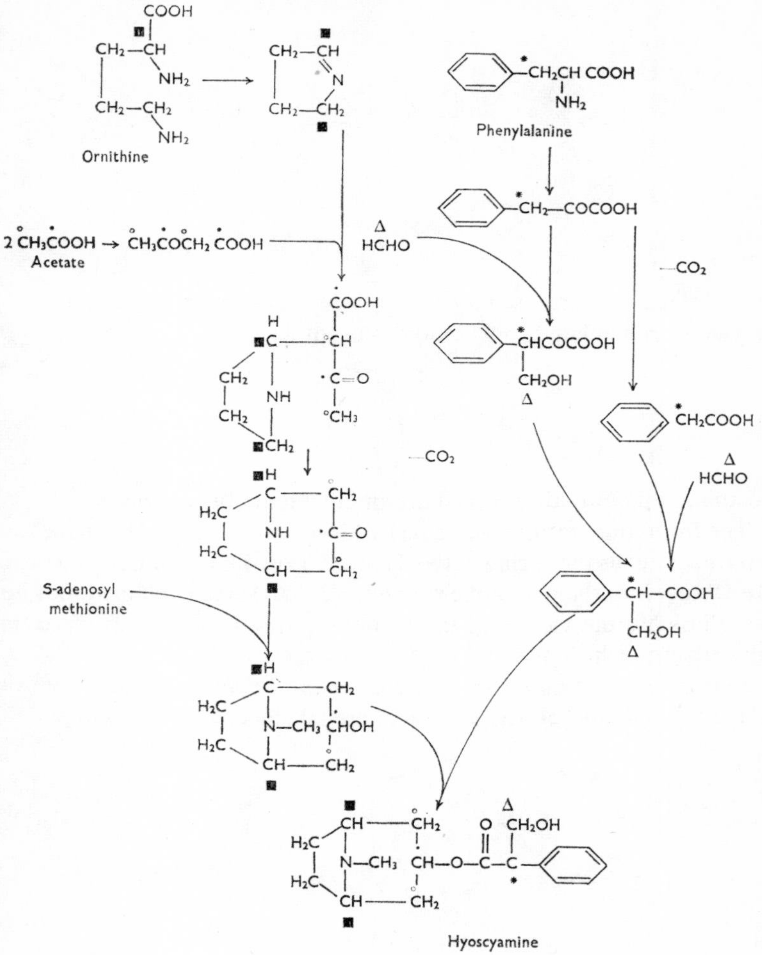

COOH
CH₂—CH
NH₂
CH₂—CH₂
NH₂
Ornithine

CH₂—CH
N
CH₂—CH₂

·CH₂CH COOH
NH₂
Phenylalanine

·CH₂—COCOOH

$-CO_2$

2 CH₃COOH → CH₃COCH₂ COOH
Acetate

Δ
HCHO

COOH
H
C——CH
CH₂   C=O
NH
CH₂   CH₃
CH₂

·CHCOCOOH
CH₂OH
Δ

·CH₂COOH

Δ
HCHO

H
C —— CH₂
H₂C
NH   C=O
H₂C
CH —— CH₂

$-CO_2$

CH—COOH
CH₂OH
Δ

S-adenosyl
methionine

H
C —— CH₂
H₂C
N—CH₃ CHOH
H₂C
CH —— CH₂

Δ
CH —— CH₂   O CH₂OH
H₂C
N—CH₃ CH—O—C—C
H₂C
CH —— CH₂
Hyoscyamine

Colchicine

Colchicine is present in members of the genus *Colchicum*.

Its structure was clarified in 1945 when a tropoloid structure for ring C was proposed. Much of the interest in colchicine biosynthesis turns about the formation of the tropolone ring. Feeding experiments with higher plants have produced the labelling pattern shown on p. 350:

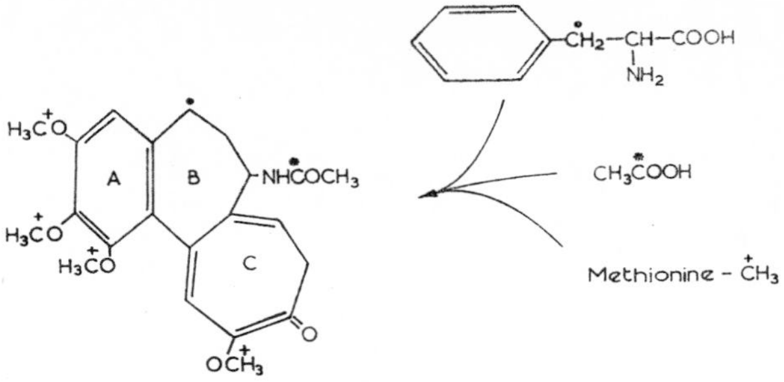

This data has been used to support schemes suggesting that colchicine biosynthesis is related to flavonoid biosynthesis.

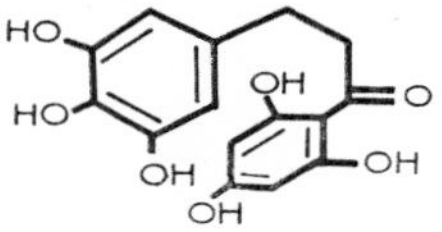

Postulated flavonoid intermediate in colchicine biosynthesis.

The tropolone ring of colchicine in this scheme is derived from the same intermediates as the A ring of the flavonoids (p. 406). Failure to incorporate acetate into the tropolone ring of colchicine is unexplained, but does not eliminate the view that the tropolone ring is derived from acetate equivalents such as malonyl CoA.

Feeding experiments with *Penicillium aurantiovirens* have shown that puberulic acid and puberulonic acid are labelled as shown below:

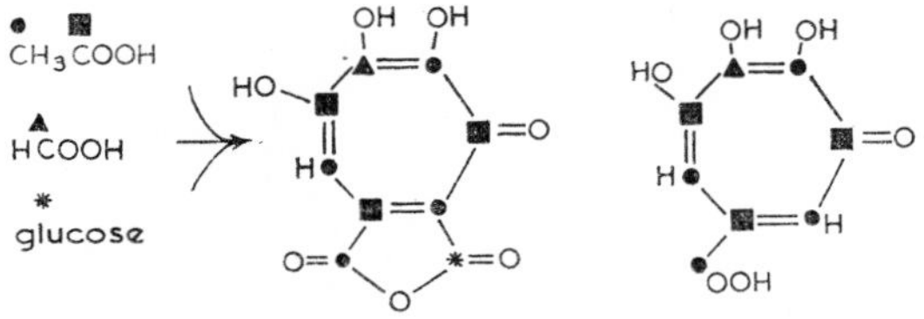

Puberulonic acid　　　　Puberulic acid

A postulated mechanism for the formation of the tropolone ring is shown below:

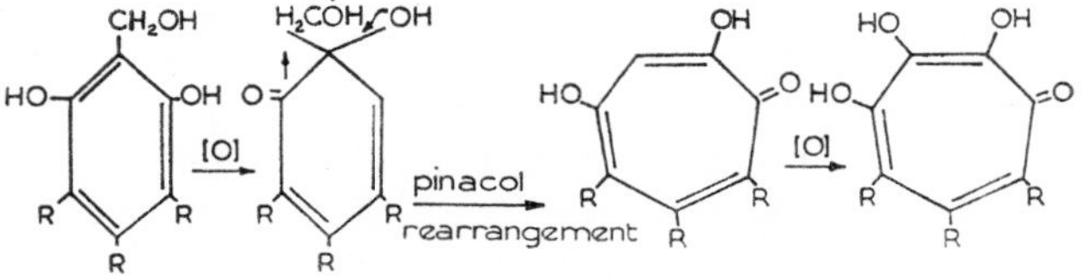

The Opium Alkaloids

The feeding of tyrosine-2-^{14}C to *Papaver somniferum* plants has established that 2 molecules of tyrosine (or equivalents) are incorporated into codeine, thebaine, morphine and papaverine. Thus papaverine formed from tyrosine-2-^{14}C has been shown to have equal radioactivity in the two carbons indicated below:

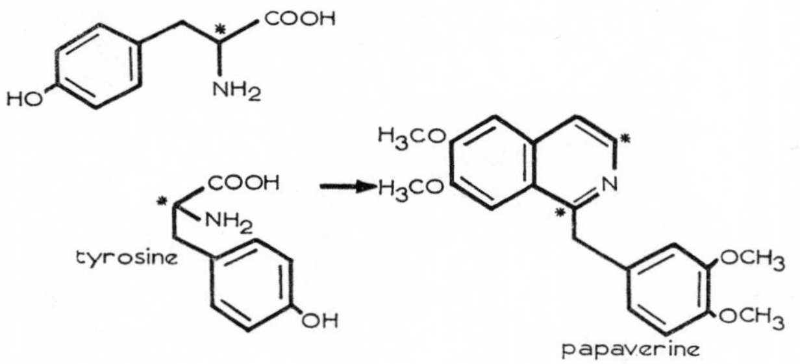

papaverine

The biogenetic scheme for morphine suggested by Robinson, proposes that norlaudansoline undergoes oxidative coupling between the two aromatic rings. ^{14}C-labelled norlaudanosoline has been synthesized and shown to be an efficient precursor of morphine, codeine, thebaine and papaverine.

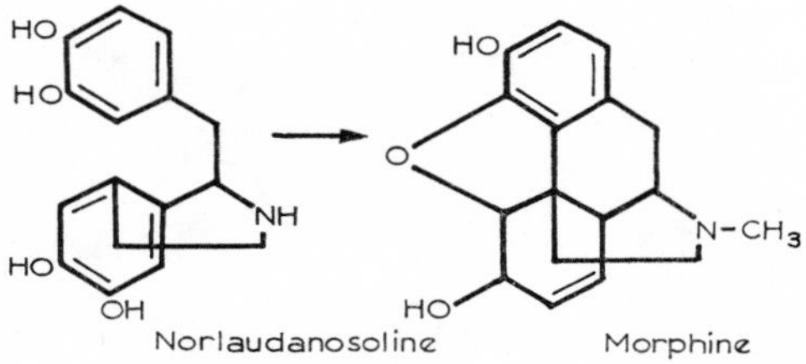

Norlaudanosoline   Morphine

It has generally been assumed that morphine is the precursor of codeine and thebaine which could be formed by successive methylation:

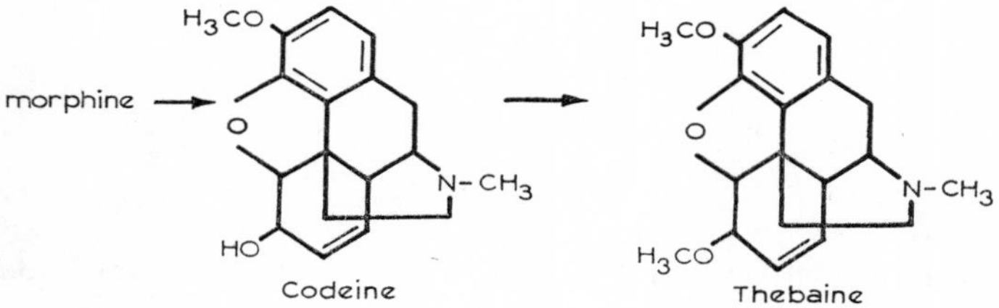

Codeine   Thebaine

23

The comparative rates of incorporation of ^{14}C-labelled carbon dioxide into these three alkaloids has led to the suggestion that thebaine is first formed, then by successive O-demethylation converted into codeine and morphine. When ^{14}C-labelled morphine was fed to *Papaver somniferum* via the roots, only ^{14}C-labelled morphine could be isolated. When codeine-^{14}C was supplied, ^{14}C-labelled morphine and codeine could be isolated and when thebaine-^{14}C was supplied label was detected in all three alkaloids.

Compounds Based on a C_6-C_2 Unit

Tracer and enzyme studies have established that hordenine is formed by the following reactions in barley seedlings:

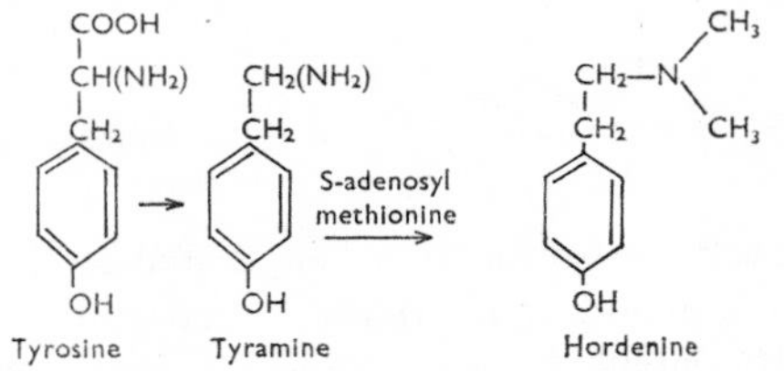

Ephedrine present in species of *Ephedra* has a C_6-C_3 structure, but tracer studies indicate that the C-methyl carbon is derived by methylation.

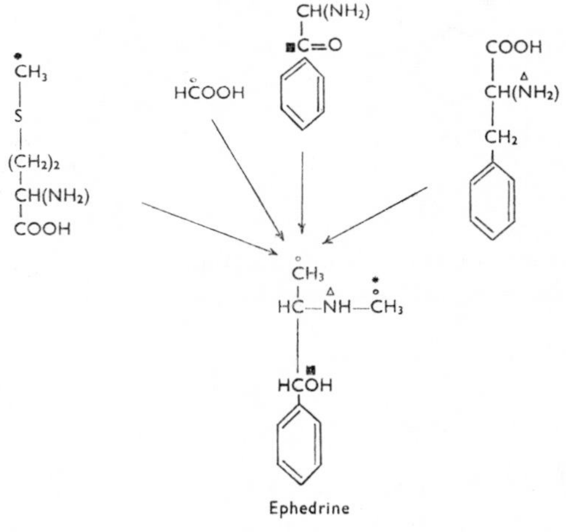

These results suggest that the N-methyl group is derived from S-adenosyl methionine whereas the C-methyl group is derived from some compound other than methionine (e.g. methyl THFA).

Nicotine, Anabasine and Ricinine

Nicotine, the major alkaloid of many *Nicotiana* species, is present in a wide range of plants. Anabasine is found in some *Nicotiana* species and ricinine is present in castor beans. The three alkaloids are discussed together because they all possess a pyridine nucleus:

Nicotine   Anabasine   Ricinine

Tracer experiments have established that nicotinic acid is a precursor of all three compounds. In the case of nicotine and anabasine the carboxyl group of nicotinic acid is lost, but in ricinine it becomes the cyano group. The route of synthesis of nicotinic acid has not been determined. However, it now seems clear that the route established in animals and *Neurospora*, tryptophane→kynurenine→3-hydroxyanthranilic acid→nicotinic acid, does not occur in plants. The following data have been obtained:

(1) The incorporation of labelled propionate into the pyridine ring of nicotine and ricinine occurs in the sequence propionate-2-^{14}C > propionate-3-^{14}C > propionate-1-^{14}C.

(2) Acetate-2-^{14}C but not acetate-1-^{14}C labels the pyridine ring.

(3) Glycerol-1,3-^{14}C is a good precursor of the pyridine ring of nicotinic acid in *E. coli*, of nicotine in tobacco, and ricinine in castor beans.

(4) Glycerol-2-^{14}C produces relatively little labelling of ricinine.

(5) Glycerol can supply all of the carbon atoms of nicotinic acid in *E. coli*.

(6) Succinate-2,3-^{14}C is a good precursor of ricinine whilst succinate-1,4-^{14}C is less effective.

The distribution of label in ricinine labelled by succinate-1,4-^{14}C is 25 per cent in the cyano group and 75 per cent in the pyridine ring.

(7) β-alanine-2-^{14}C labels ricinine.

It is not possible to determine the exact route of biosynthesis from this information.

The pyrrolidine ring of nicotine is labelled when ornithine-2-^{14}C is supplied, the label being found equally divided between positions 2' and

5'. This suggests a symmetrical intermediate and putrescine has been suggested. Labelled putrescine is incorporated into nicotine and, as noted on p. 346, diamino oxidase converts putrescine into Δ^1-pyrroline.

Similar feeding experiments with *Nicotiana glauca* have established that lysine and cadaverine (see pp. 346, 380) are precursors of the piperidine ring of anabasine. In contrast to the case of nicotine, the synthesis of anabasine appears not to involve a symmetrical intermediate such as cadaverine, since 90 per cent of the label from lysine-2-^{14}C was located in the 2' position of the piperidine ring.

READING LIST

JAMES W.O. (1948) Alkaloids in the Plant. *The Alkaloids* 1, 15. Ed. Manske R.H.F. Acad. Press, New York

MOTHES K. (1959) New Perspectives in the Biosynthesis of Alkaloids. *Symp. Soc. Exptl. Biol.* 13, 258

MOTHES K. (1960) Alkaloids in the Plant. *The Alkaloids* 6, 1. Ed. Manske R.H.F. Acad. Press, New York

BATTERSBY A.R. (1961) Alkaloid Biosynthesis. *Quart. Rev.* 15, 259

LITERATURE CITED

BARTON D.H.R. & COHEN T. (1957) *Festschrift Arthur Stole.* Birkhauser, Basel, p. 117

ROBINSON R. (1917) *J. Chem. Soc.* 111, 876

ROBINSON R. (1955) *The Structural Relations of Natural Products.* Clarendon Press, Oxford

SCHÖPF C. (1937) *Angew. Chem.* 50, 779, 797

WENKERT E. (1959) *Experientia* 15, 165

CHAPTER 10

THE METABOLISM OF AMINO ACIDS AND COMPOUNDS RELATED TO AROMATIC AMINO ACIDS

The amino acids present in proteins are shown in Table 1.1.
Examples of non-protein amino acids are given below (Table 10.1).

TABLE 10.1

Non-protein amino acids present in plants
(For further examples see Fowden, 1958)

Amino acid	Notes
β-Alanine $H_2N(CH_2)_2COOH$	Occurs as part of the molecule of CoA and free in a number of plants, e.g. apple. Its synthesis is discussed on p. 381.
Alliine $H_2C=CHCH_2S\,CH_2\,CH(NH_2)COOH$ $\parallel$ O	Present in garlic and converted to alliicine $(H_2C=CH\,CH_2SSCH_2CH=CH_2)$ $\parallel$ O and also to pyruvate and ammonia by the enzyme alliinase.
Allo-4-hydroxyproline 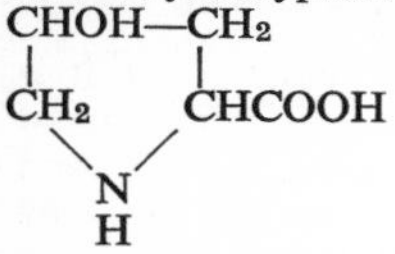 $CHOH-CH_2$ $\vert \qquad \vert$ $CH_2 \quad CHCOOH$ $\diagdown N \diagup$ $\quad H$	The toxic principle of *Amanita phalloides*.
2-Aminoadipic acid $HOOC(CH_2)_3CH(NH_2)COOH$	Occurs in pea and corn seeds. In the higher fungi is a precursor of lysine.
2-Aminobutyric acid $CH_3CH_2CH(NH_2)COOH$	Present in small amounts in a number of plants.
4-Aminobutyric acid $H_2N(CH_2)_3COOH$	Found in many plants, is probably formed by decarboxylation of glutamate.

TABLE 10.1—*contd.*

Amino acid	Notes
4-Amino-3-methylene butyric acid $H_2N(CH_2)_2C(CH_2)COOH$	Present in tulips and peanuts. May be formed by decarboxylation of 4-methylene glutamic acid.
2-Aminopimelic acid $HOOC(CH_2)_4CH(NH_2)COOH$	Found in *Asplenium septentrionale* together with 2-amino-4-hydroxypimelic acid.
Azetidine-2-carboxylic acid 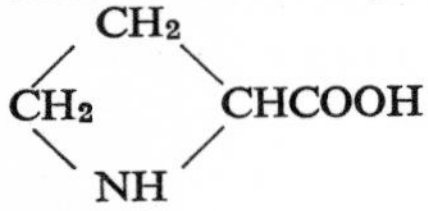 	Found in *Convallaria majalis.*
Baikiain 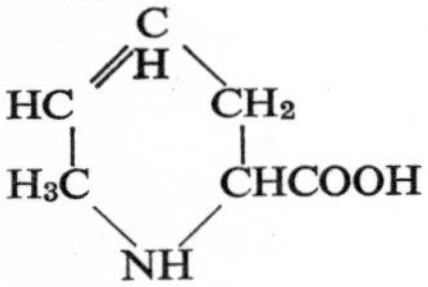 	Found in *Baikiaea plurijuga.*

Canavanine
$H_2NCNHO(CH_2)_2CH(NH_2)COOH$
   $\parallel$
   NH
	Present in soy bean and jack bean. Canavanosuccinic acid, the canavanine analogue of arginosuccinic acid (see p. 369) is present in *Chlorella*.

Citrulline $H_2NCONH(CH_2)_3CH(NH_2)COOH$	First discovered in water melon, frequently present in sap of trees. Metabolism discussed on p. 368.
Diaminobutyric acid $H_2N(CH_2)_2CH(NH_2)COOH$	Found in *Polygonatum multiflorum*. A possible intermediate in the formation of azetidine-2-carboxylic acid.
Dihydroxyphenylalanine 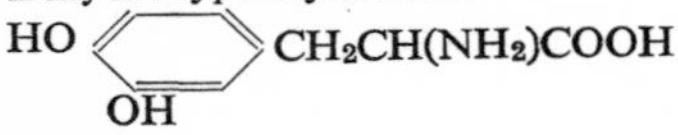	Present in various plants where it is probably formed by oxidation of phenylalanine or tyrosine. Oxidation leads to the formation of dopa melanin.
Djenkolic acid $HOOCCH(NH_2)CH_2SCH_2CH(NH_2)COOH$	The toxic principle of the Djenkol bean (*Pithecolobium lobatium*).
Homocysteine $HS(CH_2)_2CH(NH_2)COOH$	The postulated precursor of methionine, see p. 377.
Homoserine $HO(CH_2)_2CH(NH_2)COOH$	Produced in relatively large amounts by pea roots. It is an intermediate in the synthesis of threonine (see p. 379).

TABLE 10.1—contd.

Amino acid	Notes
4-Hydroxyglutamic acid HOOCCHOHCH₂CH(NH₂)COOH	Present in *Phlox decusata*. It is a substrate for glutamic-oxaloacetic transaminase.

4-Hydroxyglutamic acid
HOOCCHOHCH₂CH(NH₂)COOH

Present in *Phlox decusata*. It is a substrate for glutamic-oxaloacetic transaminase.

4-Hydroxypipecolic acid

$$\begin{array}{ccc} & CHOH & \\ H_2C & & CH_2 \\ H_2C & & CHCOOH \\ & NH & \end{array}$$

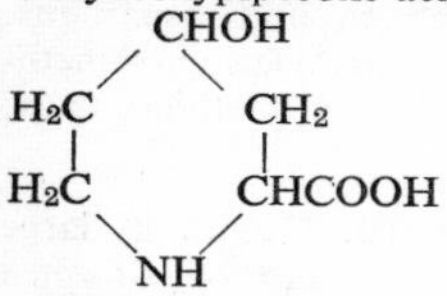

The hydroxypipecolic acid of *Acacia pentadena* was originally identified as 4-hydroxy. Evidence for the presence of 3-hydroxypipecolic acid in *Armeria maritima* is equivocal.

5-Hydroxypipecolic acid

$$\begin{array}{ccc} & CH_2 & \\ HOCH & & CH_2 \\ CH_2 & & CHCOOH \\ & NH & \end{array}$$

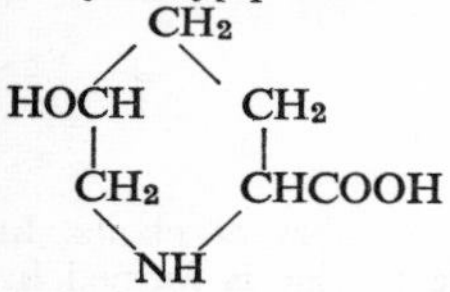

Found in leaves of *Rhapis excelsa* and fruit of *Phoenix dactylifera*.

4-Methyleneglutamic acid
HOOC—C—CH₂—CH(NH₂)COOH
$\quad\quad\; \|$
$\quad\quad CH_2$

4-Methyl-4-hydroxyglutamic acid
HOOC—C(OH)—CH₂—CH(NH₂)COOH
$\quad\quad\quad\; |$
$\quad\quad\quad CH_3$

4-Methylglutamic acid
HOOC—CHCH₂CH(NH₂)COOH
$\quad\quad\; |$
$\quad\quad CH_3$

All three are substrates for glutamic-oxaloacetic transaminase. The corresponding keto acids may be formed by the condensation of 2 moles of pyruvate or equivalents, e.g. phosphoenol pyruvate.

N-Methyltryptophane

[indole ring structure]—CH₂CH(NH₂)COOH
$\quad\quad\;$ N
$\quad\quad\; CH_3$

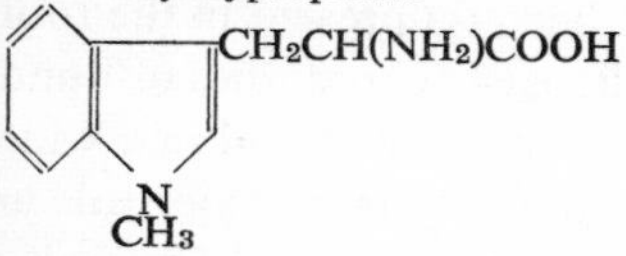

Present in seeds of *Abrus precatorius*.

Ornithine
H₂N(CH₂)₃CH(NH₂)COOH

Detected in a number of plants. α-Acetyl ornithine has been found in a number of species. α-Acetyl ornithine may be a precursor of ornithine (see p. 368).

Sarcosine
H₂NCH₂CH(NH₂)COOH

Generally considered to be formed by demethylation of glycine betaine.

S-Methylcysteine
H₃C—SCH₂CH(NH₂)COOH

Present in beans. In turnips it is formed by methylation of cysteine.

TABLE 10.1—*contd.*

Amino acid	Notes
S-Methylcysteinesulphoxide $H_3CSCH_2CH(NH_2)COOH$ $\parallel$ O	Present in a number of the Crucifereae. Probably formed by oxidation of methylcysteine.
S-Methylmethionine CH_3—S—CH_2—CH—$COOH$ $\mid +$ $\mid$ CH_3 NH_2	Found in cabbage and asparagus. Formed by the methylation of methionine by S-adenosyl methionine (p. 376).
Pipecolic acid 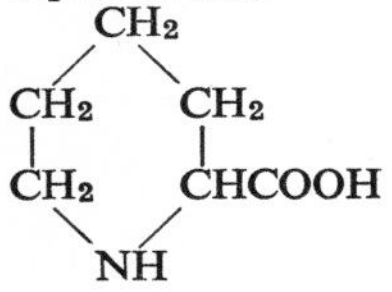 CH_2 CH_2 CH_2 CH_2 $CHCOOH$ NH	Widely distributed. Occurs in large concentration in bulb of *Dicentra eximia*. Formed from lysine (see p. 380).
Taurine $H_2N(CH_2)_2SO_3H$	Detected in a number of plants. In animals some taurine is formed by decarboxylation of cysteic acid, but most by decarboxylation of cysteine sulphinic acid.

The metabolism of amino acids can conveniently be divided into two sections: the entry of nitrogen into, and removal from, organic combination, and the formation and degradation of the carbon skeletons.

THE ENTRY OF NITROGEN INTO ORGANIC COMBINATION

Higher plants are unable to fix nitrogen, but bacteria present in the root nodules of the Leguminosae are able to fix nitrogen. The studies of Bond (1959) have established that a symbiotic relationship is found in a wide range of plants. In cultivated areas the Leguminosae play a major role in nitrogen economy, but in poor soils, plants such as *Alnus* and *Casuarina* may provide the main source of symbiotically fixed nitrogen. The biochemistry of nitrogen fixation, though of major importance, is considered outside the scope of this book, and the student is referred to the review articles by Bergersen (1960) and Yocum (1960).

The Utilization of Nitrate

Most plants utilize nitrate more readily than ammonia — possibly due to the toxicity of ammonia. In certain cases some of the enzymes involved in the utilization of nitrate are induced by the presence of nitrate. The reduction of nitrate to ammonia has been shown with cell-free extracts and the steps involved have been studied at the McCollum Pratt Institute in America and at Long Ashton in England.

NITRATE REDUCTASE

The reduction of nitrate to nitrite involves $NADH_2$ or $NADPH_2$ as the hydrogen donor. The enzyme nitrate reductase is a metalloflavoprotein containing FAD and molybdenum. The proposed mechanism of action is shown below.

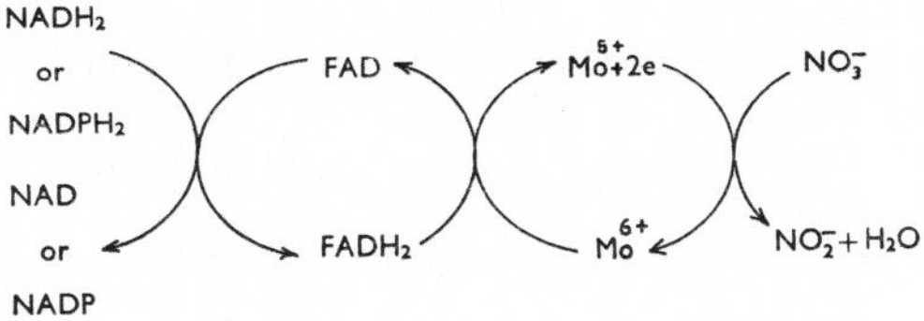

Preparations of nitrate reductase also show activity with cytochrome c in place of nitrate, but the question of enzyme specificity is unresolved.

NITRITE REDUCTASE

The nitrite reductase of *Neurospora* is an $NADH_2$-dependent flavoprotein containing FAD, Fe and Cu. Copper may be involved in the transfer of electrons from reduced FAD to nitrite — the role of iron is unknown. The enzyme in soy bean leaves appears to be stimulated by Mn^{++}. The product of the reaction is uncertain though it is presumably nitric oxide (NO) or hyponitrite $N_2O_2^=$. Hyponitrite is an inhibitor of purified nitrite reductase but crude preparations reduce nitrite to hydroxylamine. The hyponitrite reductase has not been purified from plants but studies with *Neurospora* extracts indicate that iron and copper are required for activity.

HYDROXYLAMINE REDUCTASE

Hydroxylamine is extremely toxic to plant tissues and presumably does not accumulate as an intermediate but is reduced to ammonia by the irreversible reaction

$$NH_2OH + NADH_2 \xrightarrow{Mn^{++}} NH_3 + NAD + H_2O$$

The enzyme has been demonstrated in plants but has not been highly purified.

The overall reduction of nitrate may be represented

$$\overset{\text{Mo}}{\underset{}{NO_3^-}} \to \overset{\text{Fe, Cu}}{\underset{}{NO_2^-}} \to NO \text{ or } N_2O_2^- \overset{\text{Fe, Cu}}{\to} NH_2OH \overset{\text{Mn}}{\to} NH_3$$

The Utilization of Ammonia

Ammonia enters into organic combination by three main reactions:

(a) as an α-amino group.

(b) as the amide groups of asparagine and glutamine.

(c) as carbamyl phosphate, an intermediate in the synthesis of citrulline (p. 369) and pyrimidines (p. 417).

In addition it should be noted that in some bacteria ammonia may be activated:

$$ATP + NH_3 \rightleftharpoons adenylamidate + PP$$

Aerobacter contains an enzyme which aminates xanthylic acid (see p. 416)

$$\text{xanthylic acid} + NH_3 + ATP \rightleftharpoons \text{guanylic acid} + AMP + PP$$

and *Clostridium propionicum* aminates acryl CoA to form β-alanyl CoA.

The Formation of α-Amino Groups

Three reactions have been proposed:

(a) $\text{fumarate} + NH_3 \rightleftharpoons \text{aspartate}$

(b) $\text{pyruvate} + NH_3 + NADH_2 \rightleftharpoons \text{alanine} + NAD + H_2O$

(c) $\alpha\text{-ketoglutarate} + NH_3 + NADH_2 \rightleftharpoons \text{glutamate} + NAD + H_2O$

Reaction (a) is catalysed by the enzyme aspartase which is present in bacteria, but its presence in higher plants is doubtful.

Reaction (b) has been demonstrated in bacteria and liver mitochondria but not in plants. It is of interest that studies on crystalline glutamic dehydrogenase from liver have shown that the enzyme catalyses a number of reversible oxidative deaminations of amino acids including the oxidative deamination of L-alanine. Glutamic dehydrogenase consists of 4 subunits which together catalyse the reaction with glutamate. The subunits are active with alanine but not with glutamate.

Reaction (c) is generally regarded as quantitatively the most important reaction. Evidence to support this view has been provided in the case of the food yeast *Torulopsis utilis* (Folkes, 1959). Kinetic data indicated that glutamate was formed by direct amination at a rate sufficient to account for over three-quarters of the synthesis of α-amino groups. The data also indicated a primary origin for the α-amino and amide groups of glutamine. Whilst this result is readily explained by the assumption that glutamine is formed from a pool of glutamate which is small compared with the general pool of glutamate, the possibility of other primary reactions should be considered. Thus it has been suggested (Smith, Bassham & Kirk, 1961) that the synthesis of alanine during photosynthesis does not involve transamination, because radioactivity (from $^{14}CO_2$) could not be detected in pyruvate even when the alanine was at isotopic equilibrium. These authors suggest the possibility that alanine is formed by the reductive amination of phosphoenolpyruvate.

THE TRANSFER OF AMINO GROUPS — TRANSAMINATION

Transamination is the transfer of the amino group from an amino acid to a keto acid.

$$R^1CH(NH_2)COOH + R^2COCOOH \leftrightharpoons$$
$$R^1COCOOH + R^2CH(NH_2)COOH$$

Enzymes catalysing such reactions are known as transaminases and are named by including both amino acid substrates. Thus glutamate-aspartate transaminase catalyses the reaction

$$\text{glutamate} + \text{oxaloacetate} \leftrightharpoons \alpha\text{-ketoglutarate} + \text{aspartate}$$

Other names are however used — thus the enzyme catalysing this reaction may be called glutamate-oxaloacetate transaminase or aminopherase. The number and specificity of the transaminases is uncertain but some idea of the extent of the reaction can be seen from the data of Table 10.2. Lupine mitochondria were incubated with various amino acids and α-

TABLE 10.2

Transaminase activity in lupine mitochondira

(Mitochondria were incubated with amino acid and α-ketoglutarate-^{14}C. Glutamate-^{14}C formed by transamination was isolated and counted. The values are corrected for a blank (16 c.p.m.) found when no amino acid was added. (Data from Wilson, King & Burris, 1954.))

Amino acid	Alanine	α-Aminobutyrate		γ-Amino-butyrate	Arginine
Counts in glutamate	276	92		9	133

Amino acid	Cysteate	Cysteine	Glycine	Histidine	Isoleucine
Counts in glutamate	131	23	8	4	22

Amino acid	Leucine	Lysine	Methionine	Ornithine	Valine
Counts in glutamate	59	15	10	21	6

ketoglutarate-[14]C. Glutamate-^{14}C formed by transamination was isolated and counted. Aspartate was not included in this particular experiment, but glutamate-aspartate transaminase is probably the most active transaminase in plants. The purified enzyme from cauliflowers has been shown to catalyse transamination between α-ketoglutarate or oxaloacetate and γ-hydroxyglutamate, γ-methyleneglutamate, β-hydroxyaspartate, cysteate and cysteinesulphinate.

The cofactor of transaminases is pyridoxal-5-phosphate or pyridoxamine-5-phosphate,

Pyridoxal phosphate   Pyridoxamine phosphate

which is usually tightly bound to the enzyme but may be, at least partly, removed during precipitation of the protein with ammonium sulphate. Such partially resolved preparations may be reactivated by the addition of pyridoxal phosphate or pyridoxamine phosphate. During transamination, the amino acid substrate and the enzyme bound pyridoxal phosphate condense to form a Schiff base. Subsequent electronic displacement dissociates the α-hydrogen atom and produces a tautomeric Schiff base which hydrolyses to give enzyme bound pyridoxamine phosphate and the keto acid product.

The reverse series of reactions starting with the keto acid substrate leads to the regeneration of pyridoxal phosphate and the formation of the amino acid product.

THE ROLE OF PYRIDOXAL PHOSPHATE IN AMINO ACID METABOLISM

The formation of a Schiff base between enzyme bound pyridoxal phosphate and an amino acid is the key to the participation of pyridoxal phosphate in a wide range of reactions involving amino acids.

Dissociation of the hydrogen atom at (1) leading to the formation of a tautomeric Schiff base is an essential step in transamination, racemisation, decarboxylation and in the activity of serine aldolase (p. 370). Cleavage at (2) is involved in decarboxylation and cleavage at (3) is involved in oxidative deamination as well as transamination.

The close association of pyridoxal phosphate with reactions of amino acid metabolism led to a widespread belief that an exclusive association was involved. However, the demonstration that each molecule of muscle phosphorylase a contained 4 molecules of pyridoxal phosphate dispelled this notion and subsequent work has shown that potato phosphorylase A has 2 moles of pyridoxal phosphate per mole of protein.

Despite the importance of pyridoxal phosphate, little is known about its biosynthesis, but a pyridoxal kinase present in yeast has been extensively purified.

$$\text{pyridoxal} + \text{ATP} \rightleftharpoons \text{pyridoxal phosphate} + \text{ADP}$$

THE FORMATION OF AMIDES

The synthesis of glutamine proceeds by the overall reaction

$$\text{glutamate} + \text{ATP} + \text{NH}_3 \xrightarrow{\text{Mg}^{++}} \text{glutamine} + \text{ADP} + \text{P}_i$$

The enzyme glutamine synthetase has been highly purified from pea seeds. The requirement for Mg^{++} can be replaced by other ions such as Co^{++} and Mn^{++}. In addition to the synthesis of glutamine, the enzyme catalyses glutamyl transfer reactions, e.g.

$$\text{glutamine} + \text{hydroxylamine} \rightarrow \gamma\text{-glutamyl hydroxamate} + \text{NH}_3$$

and the arsenolysis of glutamine

$$\text{glutamine} + H_2O \xrightarrow{\text{arsenate}} \text{glutamate} + NH_3.$$

Both reactions require ADP and arsenate, though phosphate can replace arsenate in the formation of γ-glutamyl hydroxamate. These results suggest that glutamyl phosphate is an intermediate, and recently evidence indicating the formation of an enzyme bound carboxyl activated glutamate has been obtained with preparations of glutamine synthetase from brain. Available evidence is in accord with the following reaction sequence:

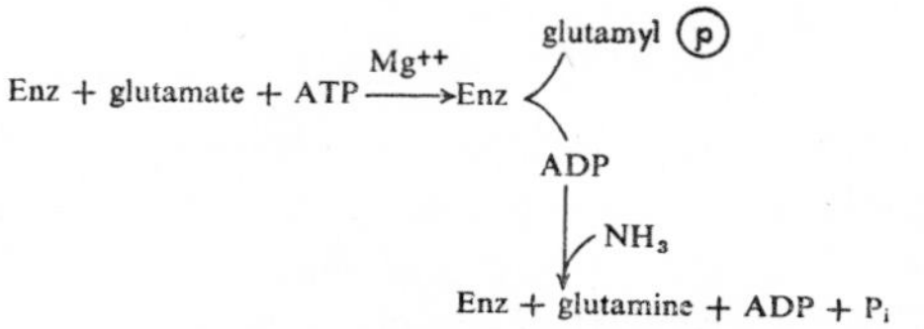

The synthesis of asparagine probably occurs by reactions similar to those involved in glutamine synthesis.

$$\text{aspartate} + NH_3 + ATP \rightleftharpoons \text{asparagine} + ADP + P_i$$

However, asparagine synthetase has not been highly purified so that only the overall reaction has been established.

CARBAMYL PHOSPHATE

Citrulline synthesis from ornithine involves a carbamylation reaction. In certain root nodules, e.g. alder, the carbamylation of ornithine represents a major pathway of nitrogen fixation. The active carbamylating compound is carbamyl phosphate which may be formed by the reaction

$$CO_2 + NH_3 + ATP \rightleftharpoons H_2N\!-\!\underset{\substack{\|\\O}}{C}\!-\!OPO_3 + ADP$$

or

$$CO_2 + NH_3 + 2ATP \rightleftharpoons H_2N\!-\!\underset{\substack{\|\\O}}{C}\!-\!OPO_3 + 2ADP + P_i$$

The reaction involving a single mole of ATP occurs in bacteria and the reaction involving 2 moles of ATP occurs in ureotelic animals. The latter reaction has a requirement for N-acetyl glutamate but its role is not known. Carbamyl phosphate formation has been demonstrated in preparations from mung bean seedlings but the stoichiometry of the reaction is unknown.

THE METABOLISM OF AMINO ACIDS

The various amino acids are conveniently discussed in groups or families in which the members of the group have a common origin or are interconvertible, though the oxidation of amino acids is first mentioned.

Animals and fungi possess D- and L-amino acid oxidases which are flavoproteins. Available evidence indicates that, if present in plants, these enzymes have little activity. Amino acids, however, are oxidized by the polyphenol oxidase system. The oxidation of glycine proceeds more rapidly than other amino acids and a probable sequence is shown below (Fig. 10.1).

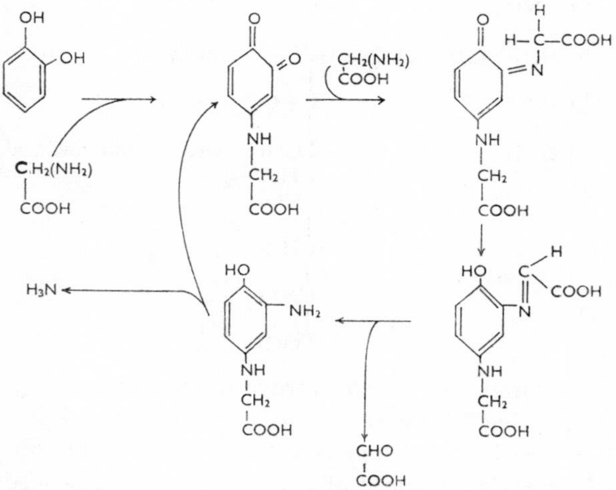

FIG. 10.1. Postulated reactions in the oxidation of glycine catalysed by polyphenol oxidase.

The Glutamate Family
(glutamate, glutamine, proline and hydroxyproline)

The first relationship between glutamate, ornithine and proline was observed in diabetic dogs where these amino acids were found to yield approximately equal quantities of glucose.

Glutamate and Glutamine

The reductive amination of α-ketoglutarate is important in bringing ammonia into organic combination. Glutamic dehydrogenase of plants is specific for NAD and is located in the mitochondria. The enzyme is usually assigned a dual role, i.e. reductive amination of α-ketoglutarate and oxidative deamination of glutamate — the product α-ketoglutarate being oxidized by the Krebs cycle. Evidence obtained with animal mitochondria indicates that only a small fraction of glutamate is oxidized by this pathway, most being oxidized to aspartate by the following reactions:

$$\text{glutamate} + \text{oxaloacetate} \rightleftharpoons \alpha\text{-ketoglutarate} + \text{aspartate}$$
$$\alpha\text{-ketoglutarate} + \tfrac{3}{2}O_2 \rightarrow \text{oxaloacetate} + H_2O + CO_2$$

Sum: $\text{glutamate} + \tfrac{3}{2}O_2 \rightarrow \text{aspartate} + CO_2 + H_2O$

The role of glutamate as an amino donor is discussed on p. 361. Glutamine may also play a role in transaminations of the type:

$$
\begin{array}{l}
\text{CONH}_2 \\
| \\
(\text{CH}_2)_2 \quad + \text{RCOCOOH} \rightarrow \\
| \\
\text{CH(NH}_2) \\
| \\
\text{COOH}
\end{array}
\quad
\begin{array}{l}
\text{CONH}_2 \\
| \\
(\text{CH}_2)_2 \quad + \text{RCH(NH}_2)\text{COOH} \\
| \\
\text{C}=\text{O} \\
| \\
\text{COOH} \quad \alpha\text{-Ketoglutaramic acid} \\
\downarrow H_2O \\
\text{COOH} \\
| \\
(\text{CH}_2)_2 \\
| \\
\text{C}=\text{O} \\
| \\
\text{COOH}
\end{array}
$$

In addition glutamine is a specific nitrogen donor of nitrogen atoms 3 and 9 in the purine ring, of the amine group in guanosine-5-phosphate and the amide group in NAD and NADP. These reactions involving the transfer of the amide nitrogen of glutamine can be classified into three groups depending on the participation of phosphorus compounds.

(1) Reactions not involving ATP.

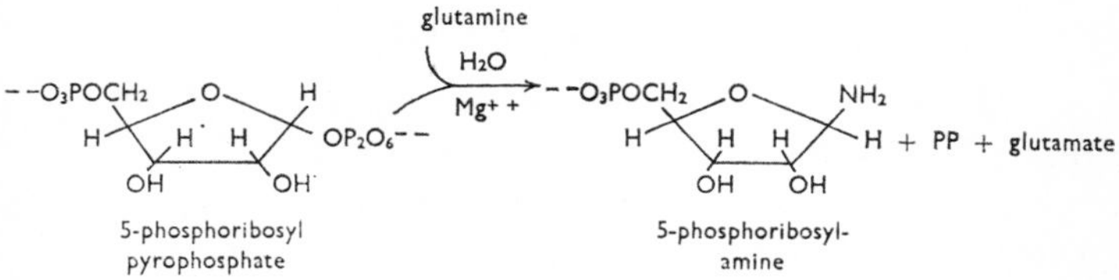

5-phosphoribosyl pyrophosphate → 5-phosphoribosyl-amine (glutamine, H_2O, Mg^{++}; $+ PP + $ glutamine)

(2) Reactions involving the splitting of the terminal phosphate of ATP

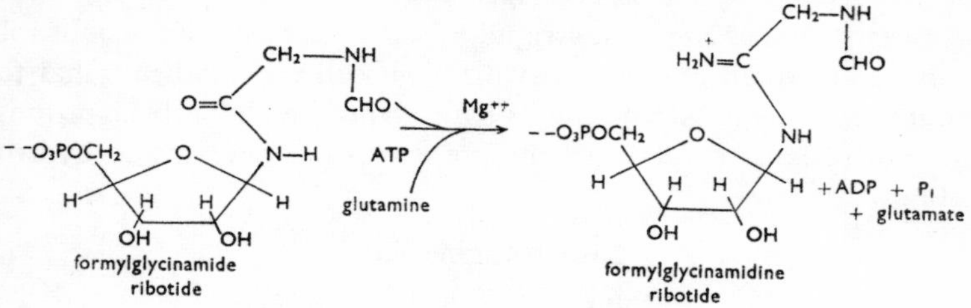

formylglycinamide
ribotide

formylglycinamidine
ribotide

(3) Reactions involving the release of pyrophosphate from ATP.

desamido NAD + glutamate + ATP ⇌ NAD + glutamate + AMP + PP

Only reaction (3) has been demonstrated in higher plants.

Most plants contain glutamic acid decarboxylase which produces γ-aminobutyrate from glutamate. This enzyme, which is particularly active in certain members of the Cucurbitaceae, has recently generated much interest since in animals it appears to have a special role in the central nervous system.

PROLINE

Tracer experiments have established that proline is formed from glutamate and the postulated intermediates are shown below.

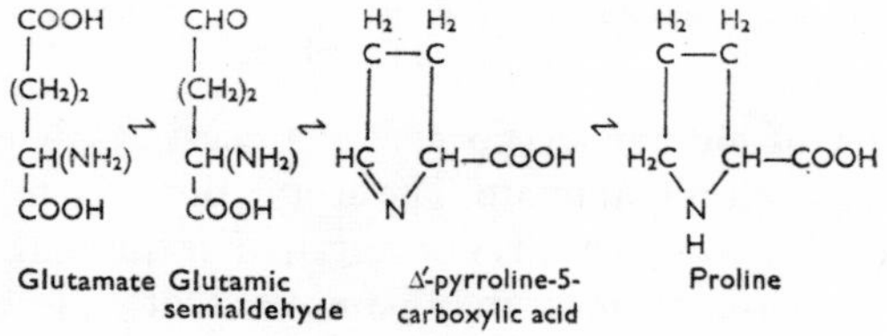

Glutamate   Glutamic
             semialdehyde

Δ'-pyrroline-5-
carboxylic acid

Proline

On thermodynamic grounds the reduction of glutamate to glutamic semialdehyde is not likely to be a single step reaction, but to require some form of activation of the carboxyl group (cf. the conversion of aspartate to aspartic semialdehyde). Glutamic semialdehyde undergoes spontaneous cyclization to equilibrate with pyrroline-5-carboxylic acid. The reduction of pyrroline-5-carboxylic acid to proline has been demonstrated in bacteria, fungi and animals. The oxidation of proline has been demonstrated with plant mitochondria but the mechanism is unknown.

24

HYDROXYPROLINE

Hydroxyproline is present in collagen and accumulates in protein formed when carrot tissue is growing rapidly in the presence of coconut milk. Analyses of proteins associated with plant cell walls indicate that they contain relatively large amounts of hydroxyproline. It has been proposed that proline must be activated before it can be converted to hydroxyproline.

The Ornithine Family

(ornithine, citrulline and arginine)

The members of this family, ornithine, arginine and citrulline are intermediates in the urea cycle proposed by Krebs and Henseleit in 1932. Whilst there is little evidence to support the view that a urea cycle functions in plants, there is ample evidence for the interconversion of these amino acids.

ORNITHINE

In *E. coli*, ornithine is formed from glutamate by the following reactions:

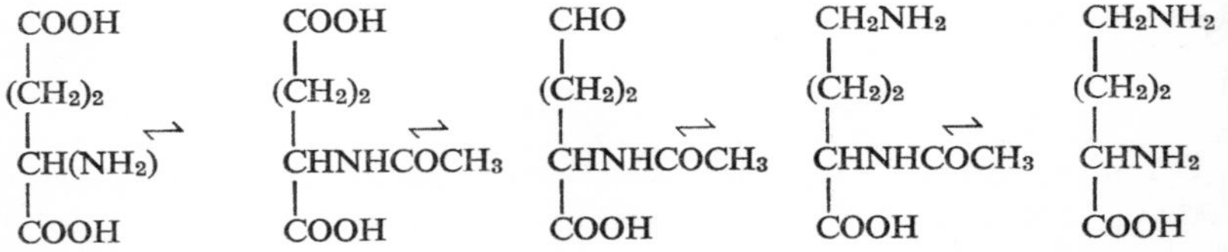

COOH	COOH	CHO	CH_2NH_2	CH_2NH_2
$(CH_2)_2$	$(CH_2)_2$	$(CH_2)_2$	$(CH_2)_2$	$(CH_2)_2$
$CH(NH_2)$ $\rightharpoonup$	CHNHCOCH$_3$ $\rightharpoonup$	CHNHCOCH$_3$ $\rightharpoonup$	CHNHCOCH$_3$ $\rightharpoonup$	CHNH$_2$
COOH	COOH	COOH	COOH	COOH
Glutamate	N-Acetyl-glutamate	N-Acetyl-glutamic semialdehyde	α-N-Acetyl ornithine	Ornithine

The acetylation of glutamate proceeds via acetyl CoA and the transamination step requires glutamate. The acetylation step prevents cyclization of the semialdehyde, but it is not certain that this pathway functions in plants; in this connection it may be noted that α-N-acetyl ornithine has been found in plants. Transamination between glutamate and glutamic semialdehyde yielding ornithine has been demonstrated with plant extracts, and the rapid formation of glutamate from ornithine suggests interconversion without acetylation.

CITRULLINE

In a number of species, citrulline appears as a quantitatively important product of carbon dioxide fixation and in certain root nodules appears as an early product of nitrogen fixation. The final reaction involved in the synthesis of citrulline is the transcarbamylation of ornithine which has been demonstrated with plant mitochondria.

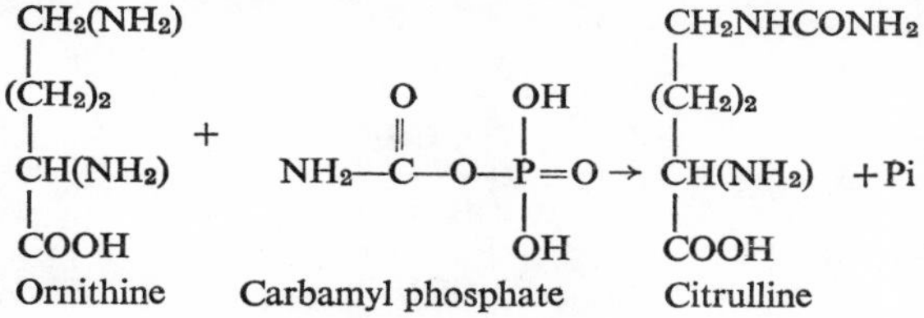

$$
\begin{array}{c}
CH_2(NH_2) \\
| \\
(CH_2)_2 \\
| \\
CH(NH_2) \\
| \\
COOH \\
\text{Ornithine}
\end{array}
+
\begin{array}{c}
\quad\quad O \quad\quad OH \\
\quad\quad \| \quad\quad | \\
NH_2-C-O-P=O \\
\quad\quad\quad\quad\quad | \\
\quad\quad\quad\quad\quad OH \\
\text{Carbamyl phosphate}
\end{array}
\rightarrow
\begin{array}{c}
CH_2NHCONH_2 \\
| \\
(CH_2)_2 \\
| \\
CH(NH_2) \\
| \\
COOH \\
\text{Citrulline}
\end{array}
+ Pi
$$

ARGININE

The studies of Ratner and her co-workers have shown that in liver and kidney, arginine is formed by the following reactions:

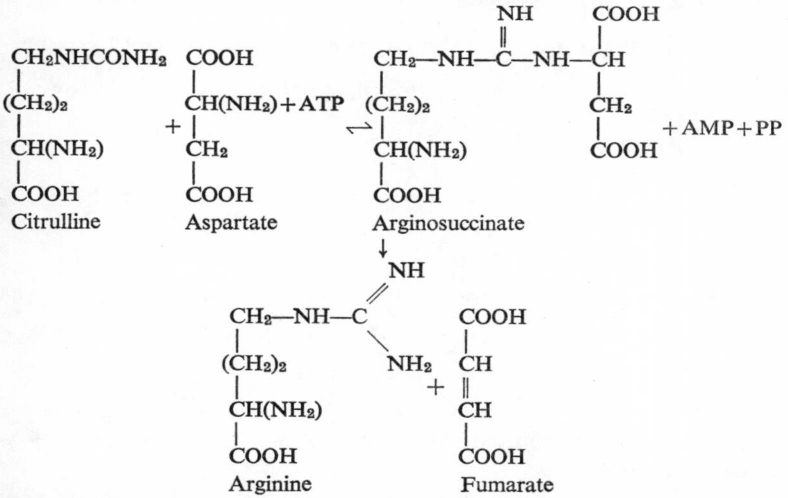

$$
\begin{array}{c}
CH_2NHCONH_2 \\
| \\
(CH_2)_2 \\
| \\
CH(NH_2) \\
| \\
COOH \\
\text{Citrulline}
\end{array}
+
\begin{array}{c}
COOH \\
| \\
CH(NH_2) \\
| \\
CH_2 \\
| \\
COOH \\
\text{Aspartate}
\end{array}
+ ATP
\rightleftharpoons
\begin{array}{c}
\quad\quad NH \quad\quad COOH \\
\quad\quad \| \quad\quad | \\
CH_2-NH-C-NH-CH \\
| \quad\quad\quad\quad\quad | \\
(CH_2)_2 \quad\quad\quad CH_2 \\
| \quad\quad\quad\quad\quad | \\
CH(NH_2) \quad\quad COOH \\
| \\
COOH \\
\text{Arginosuccinate}
\end{array}
+ AMP + PP
$$

$$
\downarrow
$$

$$
\begin{array}{c}
\quad\quad NH \\
\quad\quad \nearrow \\
CH_2-NH-C \\
| \quad\quad\quad\quad \searrow \\
(CH_2)_2 \quad\quad NH_2 \\
| \\
CH(NH_2) \\
| \\
COOH \\
\text{Arginine}
\end{array}
+
\begin{array}{c}
COOH \\
| \\
CH \\
\| \\
CH \\
| \\
COOH \\
\text{Fumarate}
\end{array}
$$

The arginosuccinate cleavage enzyme has been demonstrated in jack beans and peas. Arginine appears to be a quantitatively important amino acid in a number of species, e.g. tulips and pea seeds, and participates in a transamidination reaction with glycine.

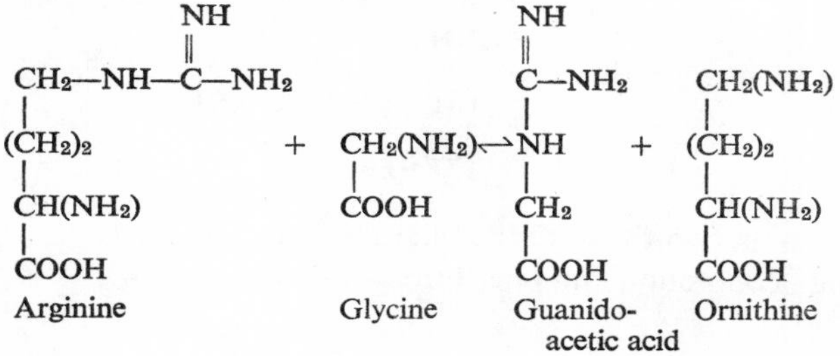

$$
\begin{array}{c}
\quad\quad NH \\
\quad\quad \| \\
CH_2-NH-C-NH_2 \\
| \\
(CH_2)_2 \\
| \\
CH(NH_2) \\
| \\
COOH \\
\text{Arginine}
\end{array}
+
\begin{array}{c}
CH_2(NH_2) \\
| \\
COOH \\
\text{Glycine}
\end{array}
\rightarrow
\begin{array}{c}
\quad\quad NH \\
\quad\quad \| \\
C-NH_2 \\
| \\
NH \\
| \\
CH_2 \\
| \\
COOH \\
\text{Guanido-} \\
\text{acetic acid}
\end{array}
+
\begin{array}{c}
CH_2(NH_2) \\
| \\
(CH_2)_2 \\
| \\
CH(NH_2) \\
| \\
COOH \\
\text{Ornithine}
\end{array}
$$

Methylation of guanidoacetic acid yields creatine:

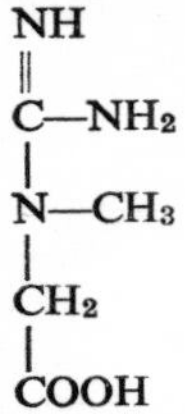

$$
\begin{array}{c}
\text{NH} \\
\parallel \\
\text{C—NH}_2 \\
\mid \\
\text{N—CH}_3 \\
\mid \\
\text{CH}_2 \\
\mid \\
\text{COOH}
\end{array}
$$

The Serine, Glycine Family

Serine and glycine are interconvertible by the pyridoxal phosphate requiring enzyme serine aldolase.

serine + tetrahydrofolate ⇌ hydroxymethyltetrahydrofolate + glycine

The structure of 5, 6, 7, 8 tetrahydrofolate (THFA) is shown below:

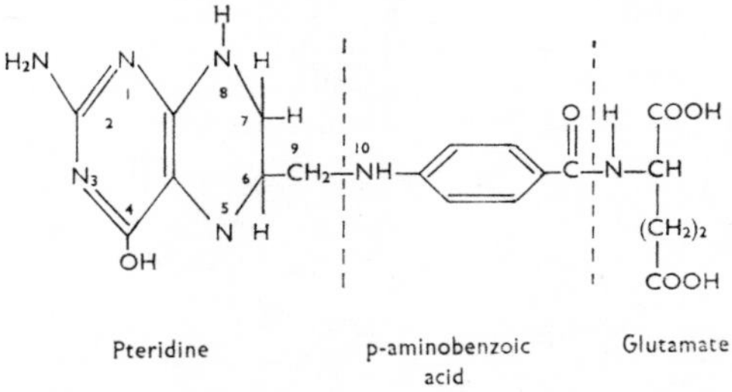

Pteridine   p-aminobenzoic   Glutamate
                        acid

Related compounds contain extra glutamic acid residues linked by γ-glutamyl bonds.

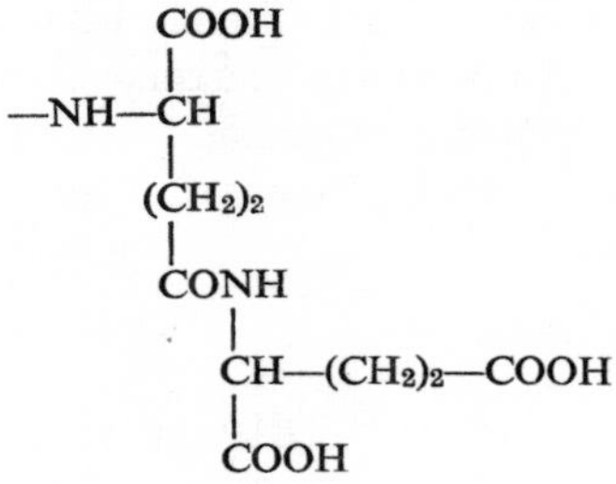

$$
\begin{array}{c}
\text{COOH} \\
\mid \\
\text{—NH—CH} \\
\mid \\
\text{(CH}_2)_2 \\
\mid \\
\text{CONH} \\
\mid \\
\text{CH—(CH}_2)_2\text{—COOH} \\
\mid \\
\text{COOH}
\end{array}
$$

In leaves about two-thirds of the folic acid group exists as the diglutamyl conjugated compound and one-third as monoglutamates.

The biosynthesis of pteridine is related to that of purines and riboflavin (see p. 184). Thus glycine, formate and carbon dioxide, provide the carbon atoms indicated in Fig. 10.2.

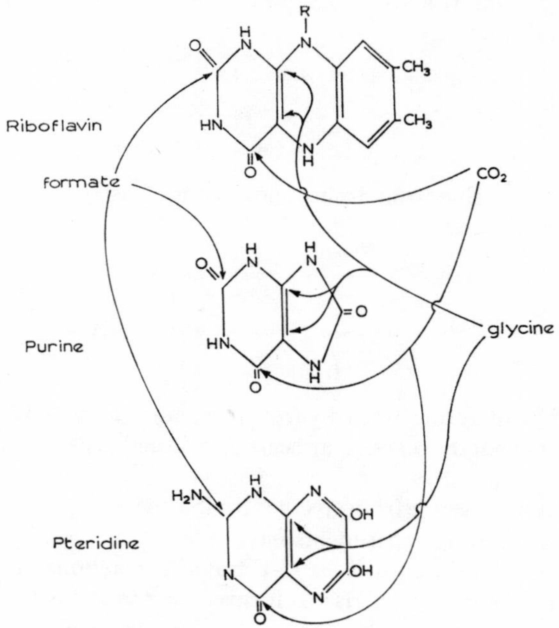

FIG. 10.2. Incorporation of various labelled compounds into riboflavin, purines and pteridines.

Hydroxymethyltetrahydrofolic acid is synonymous with N^5,N^{10}-methyl-enetetrahydrofolic acid

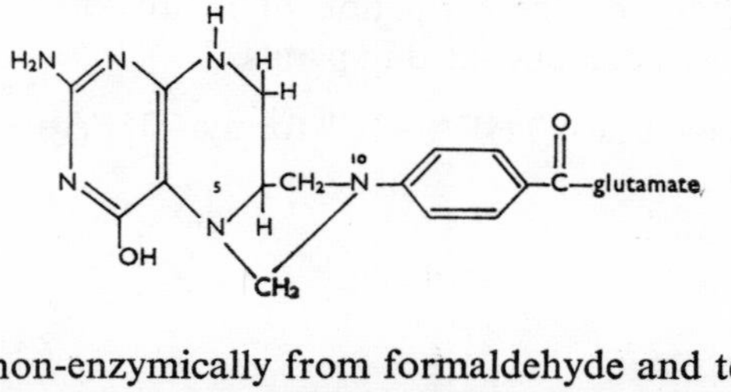

and is formed non-enzymically from formaldehyde and tetrahydrofolic acid. Liver contains an enzyme which catalyses the binding of formaldehyde by tetrahydrofolate.

A number of experiments with ^{14}C compounds have been taken to mean that in plants, serine is formed from glycine, whilst other experiments have indicated that glycine is formed from serine. The formation of glycine-2-^{14}C from ribose-5-phosphate-1-^{14}C has been demonstrated with spinach extracts.

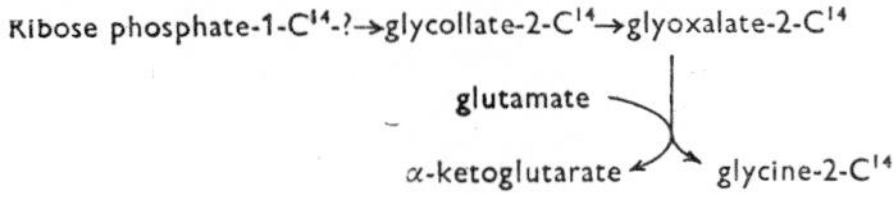

Ribose phosphate-1-C^{14}-?→glycollate-2-C^{14}→glyoxalate-2-C^{14}

glutamate

α-ketoglutarate ← glycine-2-C^{14}

The synthesis of serine from 3-phosphoglycerate has been demonstrated in extracts of pea seedlings.

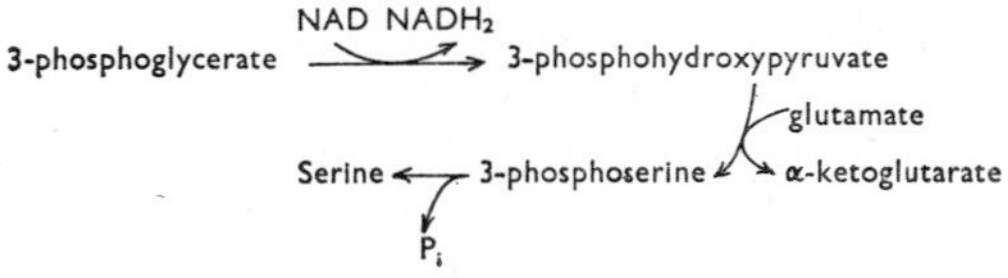

NAD NADH₂

3-phosphoglycerate ⟶ 3-phosphohydroxypyruvate

glutamate

Serine ← 3-phosphoserine ← α-ketoglutarate

Pᵢ

The formation of serine from hydroxypyruvate has not been demonstrated in plants but the reaction appears as a probable pathway for serine synthesis.

The formation of serine from glycine requires the addition of a hydroxymethyl group. Feeding experiments have shown that formate and the α-carbon of glycolate are used in C-1 transfer reactions. It is widely assumed that glycolate gives rise to formate by the following reactions.

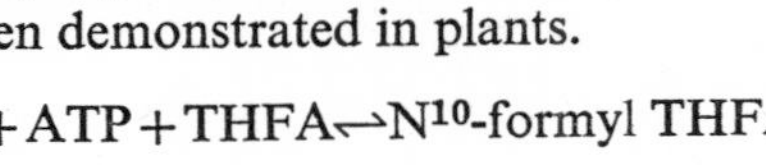

glycolate   glyoxalate   formate + CO_2

$\frac{1}{2}O_2$ H_2O_2 H_2O

The second reaction is non-enzymic and its physiological significance may be questioned.

Enzymes catalysing the formation of hydroxymethyl THFA from formate have been demonstrated in plants.

$$\text{formate} + \text{ATP} + \text{THFA} \rightleftharpoons \text{N}^{10}\text{-formyl THFA} + \text{ADP} + P_i$$

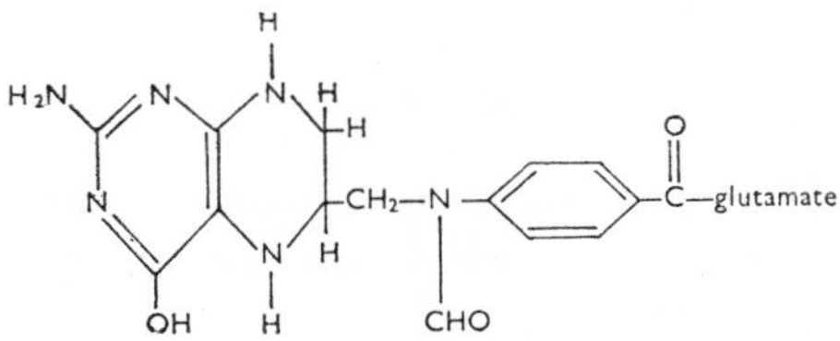

$$N^{10}\text{-formyl THFA} + NADPH_2 \rightleftharpoons \text{hydroxymethyl THFA} + NADP + H_2O$$

Many of the various forms of 'active C_1' units involved in metabolism are tetrahydrofolic acid derivatives — e.g. formyl, hydroxymethyl and formamino. N^{10}-formyl THFA is formed spontaneously by the hydrolysis of N^5, N^{10}-methenyl THFA,

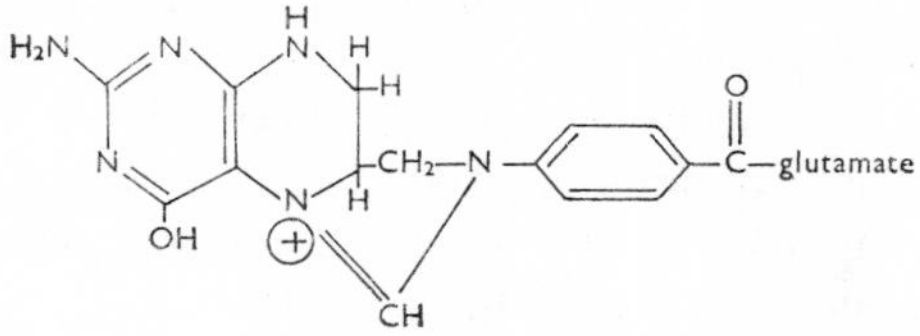

and it is frequently difficult to determine which form is the active intermediate in formylations.

A formimino transfer from formiminoglycine (a product of purine breakdown) to tetrahydrofolate occurs in bacteria, and in animals the formimino group of formiminoglutamic acid (a degradation product of histidine) is transferred to THFA to form N^5-formimino THFA.

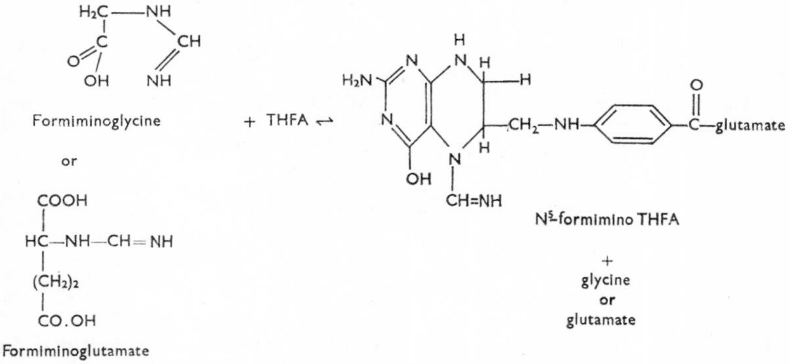

METHIONINE AND METHYLATION

Perhaps more interest is associated with the active form of methyl transfer. The transfer of the hydroxymethyl group of serine to homocysteine forming methionine has been demonstrated with slices of storage tissue but not with cell free extracts. In bacteria and animals the synthesis of methionine has been shown to involve at least two enzymes and the following cofactors — hydroxymethyl THFA, ATP, $NADH_2$ and flavin adenine dinucleotide or flavin mononucleotide.

$$
\begin{array}{llll}
\mathrm{CH_2SH} & & \mathrm{CH_3-S-CH_2} & \\
| & & | & \\
\mathrm{CH_2} & +\text{hydroxymethyl THFA} & \mathrm{CH_2} & +\mathrm{THFA}+\mathrm{H_2O} \\
| & \rightleftharpoons & | & \\
\mathrm{CH(NH_2)} & +\mathrm{NADH_2} & \mathrm{CH(NH_2)} & +\mathrm{NAD} \\
| & & | & \\
\mathrm{COOH} & & \mathrm{COOH} &
\end{array}
$$

One of the two enzymes is a cobamide-containing protein, though the identity of the active form of vitamin B_{12} is not yet known. It appears that one enzyme reduces hydroxymethyl THFA to N^5-methyl THFA. The second, cobamide-containing, enzyme is involved in the transfer of the methyl group to an 'active' form of homocysteine which may be S-adenosyl homocysteine or S-acetylhomocysteine.

The involvement of a B_{12} vitamin in methionine biosynthesis is of special interest in plant biochemistry because attempts to demonstrate B_{12} have given negative results, and with the exception of plants possessing root nodules, it has not been possible to show a cobalt requirement.

Whilst 5-methyl THFA may be involved in the transfer of a methyl group to homocysteine, the intermediate which is generally involved in methyl transfer is S-adenosyl methionine which is formed by the reaction:

$$
\begin{array}{llll}
& \mathrm{CH_3} & \mathrm{CH_3} & \\
& | & | & \\
\text{Adenosyl-P-P-P} \;+ & \mathrm{S} & \quad\text{Adenosyl-S}+ & +\mathrm{PP}+\mathrm{P_i} \\
& | & | & \\
& \mathrm{(CH_2)_2} \;\rightarrow & \mathrm{(CH_2)_2} & \\
& | & | & \\
& \mathrm{CH(NH_2)} & \mathrm{CH(NH_2)} & \\
& | & | & \\
& \mathrm{COOH} & \mathrm{COOH} & \\
\text{ATP} & \text{Methionine} & \text{S-Adenosyl methionine}
\end{array}
$$

This reaction has been demonstrated in plant extracts and the transfer of the methyl group to a variety of compounds has also been established.

It was thought for some time that two of the three methyl groups of choline were transferred via a folic acid intermediate, the third methyl group being derived from methionine. Recent investigations with liver preparations have shown that all three methyl groups are derived from methionine, but the methyl group acceptor is not ethanolamine but rather phosphatidylethanolamine. The product of methylation is lecithin, which subsequently releases choline (Fig. 10.3).

Choline is widely distributed in plants and phosphorylcholine may play

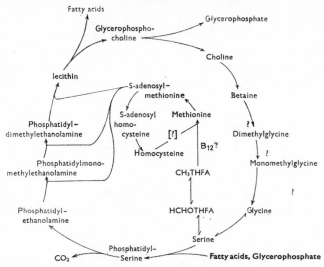

FIG. 10.3. Metabolism of lecithin in relation to methyl groups.

a role in the transport of phosphate. Glycine betaine is a simple example of a number of betaines (shown below) found in plants.

Glycine betaine   Stachydrine   Hypophorine   Trigonelline

Available evidence indicates that the methyl donor is in all cases S-adenosyl methionine, but glycine betaine can itself act as a methyl donor. In tobacco, methyl groups from betaine are incorporated into nicotine, and in barley betaine transfers methyl groups to tyramine to form hordenine. It should be noted that betaines are onium compounds and all known transmethylations involve a methyl group or groups directly linked to an onium pole. Transmethylations involving betaine have been demonstrated with cell free preparations from animals, but not from plants. The formation of hordenine and trigonelline by methylation from S-adenosyl methionine has been demonstrated in plant extracts.

Five types of methylation may be distinguished.

(a) C—CH₃

Direct evidence for C-methylation is available in only a few cases. Extracts of yeast incorporate the methyl group of methionine (presumably as S-adenosyl methionine) into the side chain (as carbon 28) of ergosterol. A case of special importance is the methyl group of thymine.

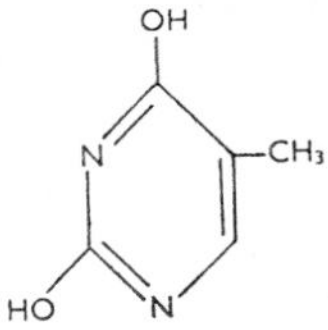

Thymine

Experiments with animals and bacteria indicate that methionine does not donate the methyl group of thymine but that a form of C_1 THFA is involved.

(b) O—CH₃

Methoxyl groups are common in plants and available evidence indicates that O-methylation is involved rather than C-methoxylation. Methionine furnishes the methoxy groups of lignin and ricinine.

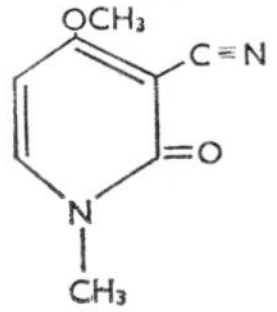

Ricinine

(c) S—CH₃

Many plants contain S-methylmethionine,

$$CH_3 - \overset{+}{\underset{\underset{CH_3}{|}}{S}} - CH_2 - \underset{\underset{NH_2}{|}}{CH} - COOH$$

and its synthesis from S-adenosyl methionine and methionine has been demonstrated in cell-free extracts.

(d) $\overset{—O}{\underset{—O}{>}} CH_2$

The methylenedioxy group is peculiar to plants and feeding experiments with *Dicentra* hybrids indicate that the methylenedioxy groups of the alkaloid protopine are derived from methionine.

(e) N—CH₃

Choline and the betaines are examples of N-methyl compounds. As noted on p. 375 all methyl groups of choline can be formed by transmethylation from methionine. Most alkaloids contain N-methyl groups. Thus in protopine the methylenedioxy groups and the N-methyl group are formed from methionine.

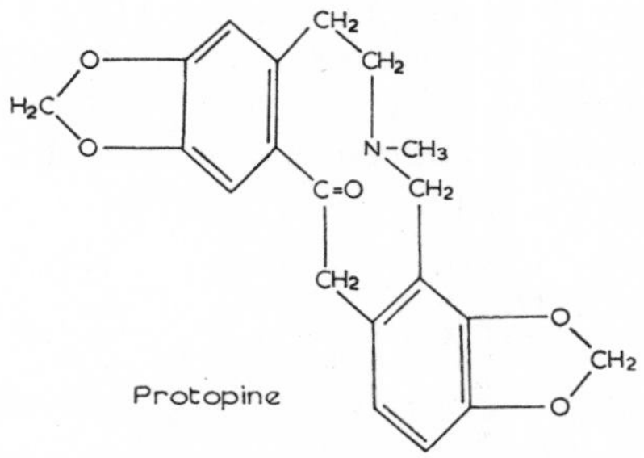

Protopine

The Sulphur-containing Amino Acids

(cysteine, homocysteine and methionine)

The form of sulphur most available to plants is the sulphate ion which is reduced to sulphite. Thermodynamically, the reduction of sulphate

$$SO_4^{--} + H_2 \rightarrow SO_3^{--} + H_2O \qquad \Delta G^\circ = 14 \text{ kcal}$$

is extremely unfavourable, and an active form of sulphate (3'-phospho-adenosine-5'-phosphosulphate) is the probable substrate for the NADPH₂ linked reduction.

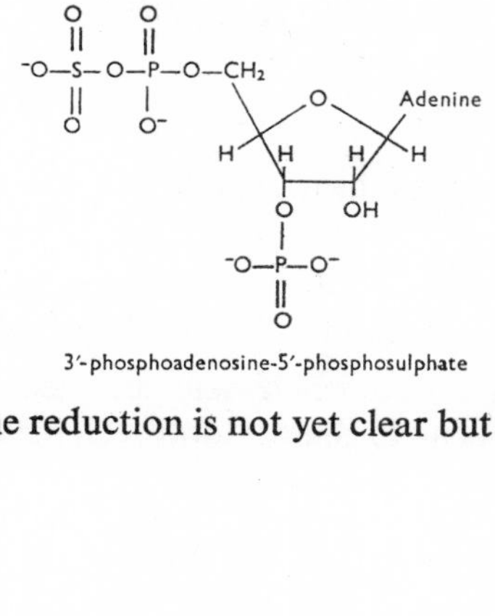

3'-phosphoadenosine-5'-phosphosulphate

The mechanism of the reduction is not yet clear but further reduction of sulphite by $NADPH_2$ has been demonstrated in yeast, resulting in the production of hydrogen sulphide.

$$SO_3^{--} + 3NADPH_2 + 2H^+ \rightarrow H_2S + 3NADP + 3H_2O$$

An enzyme present in yeast incorporates hydrogen sulphide into cysteine by the reaction

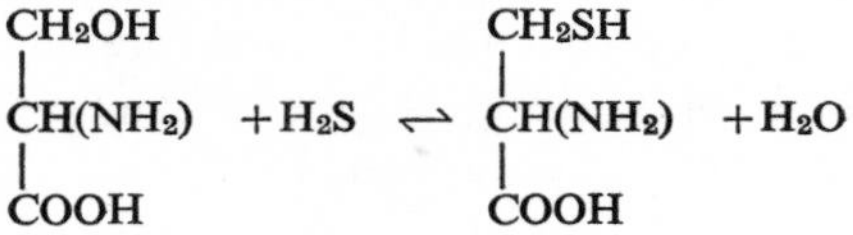

$$\begin{array}{ccc}
CH_2OH & & CH_2SH \\
| & & | \\
CH(NH_2) & +H_2S \rightleftharpoons & CH(NH_2) & +H_2O \\
| & & | \\
COOH & & COOH
\end{array}$$

This reaction has not yet been demonstrated in plants and there remains the important question whether cysteine is the only port of entry of sulphur or whether an analogous reaction between hydrogen sulphide and homoserine results in the production of homocysteine. Homocysteine and cysteine are interconvertible by the reactions:

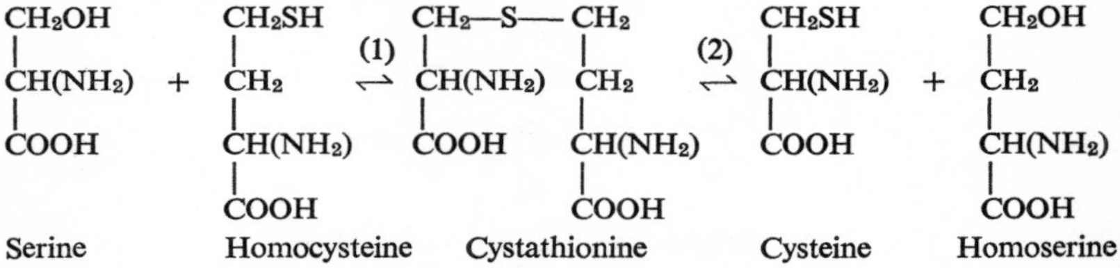

$$\begin{array}{ccccccccc}
CH_2OH & & CH_2SH & & CH_2-S-CH_2 & & CH_2SH & & CH_2OH \\
| & & | & (1) & | & | & (2) & | & & | \\
CH(NH_2) & + & CH_2 & \rightleftharpoons & CH(NH_2) & CH_2 & \rightleftharpoons & CH(NH_2) & + & CH_2 \\
| & & | & & | & | & & | & & | \\
COOH & & CH(NH_2) & & COOH & CH(NH_2) & & COOH & & CH(NH_2) \\
& & | & & & | & & & & | \\
& & COOH & & & COOH & & & & COOH \\
\text{Serine} & & \text{Homocysteine} & & \text{Cystathionine} & & & \text{Cysteine} & & \text{Homoserine}
\end{array}$$

Separate enzymes are involved; the enzyme catalysing reaction 1 also deaminates serine and the enzyme catalysing reaction 2 deaminates homoserine. These activities have not yet been demonstrated in higher plants.

Fragmentary evidence permits the following tentative scheme for the metabolism of the sulphur amino acids.

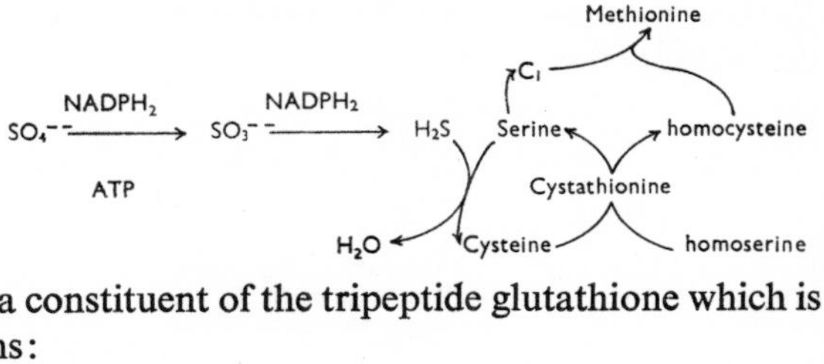

Cysteine is a constituent of the tripeptide glutathione which is formed by the reactions:

(1) glutamate + cysteine + ATP $\rightleftharpoons$ γ-glutamylcysteine + ADP + P_i
(2) γ-glutamylcysteine + glycine + ATP $\rightleftharpoons$ glutathione + ADP + P_i

A report that soluble ribonucleic acid was necessary for glutathione synthesis has subsequently been withdrawn (Lane & Lipmann, 1961).

The Aspartate Family
(aspartate, asparagine, homoserine, threonine and lysine)

It is possible that some aspartic acid may be formed by the direct amination of fumarate. However, it is probable that most aspartic acid is formed from oxaloacetate by transamination with glutamate. Oxaloacetate is a participant in the Krebs cycle, but as pointed out on p. 171, intermediates cannot be removed from the cycle if it is to fulfil its respiratory function. Consequently, the generally accepted pathway for aspartate formation via oxaloacetate is by carbon dioxide fixation (p. 172). In some plants oxaloacetate may be formed from malate produced by the action of malate synthetase (p. 303). Aspartate is the specific donor of nitrogen atom 1 in the purine ring and of the amino group attached to C-6 in adenylic acid. Aspartate combines with carbamyl phosphate to yield carbamyl aspartate — the precursor of the pyrimidines.

HOMOSERINE

The formation of homoserine by the following reactions has been demonstrated in yeast extracts.

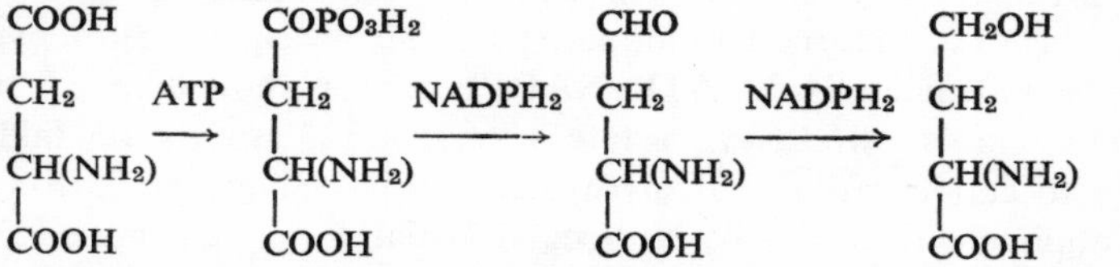

$$
\begin{array}{ccccccc}
\text{COOH} & & \text{COPO}_3\text{H}_2 & & \text{CHO} & & \text{CH}_2\text{OH} \\
| & & | & & | & & | \\
\text{CH}_2 & \xrightarrow{\text{ATP}} & \text{CH}_2 & \xrightarrow{\text{NADPH}_2} & \text{CH}_2 & \xrightarrow{\text{NADPH}_2} & \text{CH}_2 \\
| & & | & & | & & | \\
\text{CH(NH}_2) & & \text{CH(NH}_2) & & \text{CH(NH}_2) & & \text{CH(NH}_2) \\
| & & | & & | & & | \\
\text{COOH} & & \text{COOH} & & \text{COOH} & & \text{COOH} \\
\text{Aspartate} & & \text{\textit{β}-Aspartyl-} & & \text{Aspartic-\textit{β}-semi-} & & \text{Homoserine} \\
& & \text{phosphate} & & \text{aldehyde} & &
\end{array}
$$

Homoserine is formed rapidly in germinating peas and tracer studies indicate that homoserine is formed from aspartate in higher plants. Both dehydrogenases shown in the above scheme have been isolated from pea seeds.

THREONINE

Threonine formation in fungi and bacteria proceeds by the reactions:

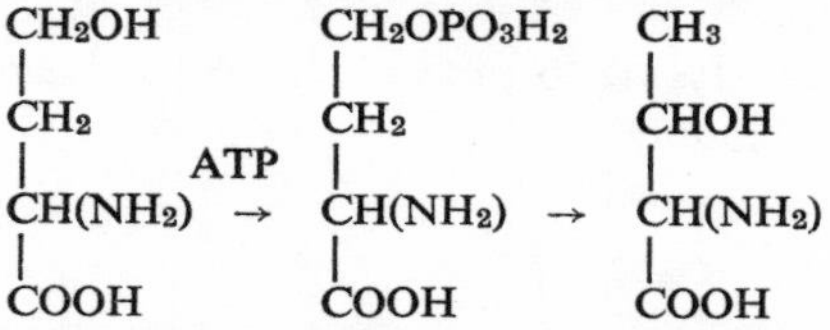

$$
\begin{array}{ccccc}
\text{CH}_2\text{OH} & & \text{CH}_2\text{OPO}_3\text{H}_2 & & \text{CH}_3 \\
| & & | & & | \\
\text{CH}_2 & & \text{CH}_2 & & \text{CHOH} \\
| & \xrightarrow{\text{ATP}} & | & \rightarrow & | \\
\text{CH(NH}_2) & & \text{CH(NH}_2) & & \text{CH(NH}_2) \\
| & & | & & | \\
\text{COOH} & & \text{COOH} & & \text{COOH} \\
\text{Homoserine} & & \text{Homoserine} & & \text{Threonine} \\
& & \text{phosphate} & &
\end{array}
$$

Tracer experiments indicate that these reactions occur in higher plants.

LYSINE

Tracer studies have shown that higher fungi and some phycomycetes form lysine by a pathway involving α-aminoadipic acid.

$$COOH—(CH_2)_3CH(NH_2)COOH$$

Bacteria, blue green and green algae, some phycomycetes and higher plants form lysine by a pathway involving α-diaminopimelic acid. A decarboxylase has been found in extracts of maize seedlings which forms L-lysine from *meso*-diaminopimelic acid:

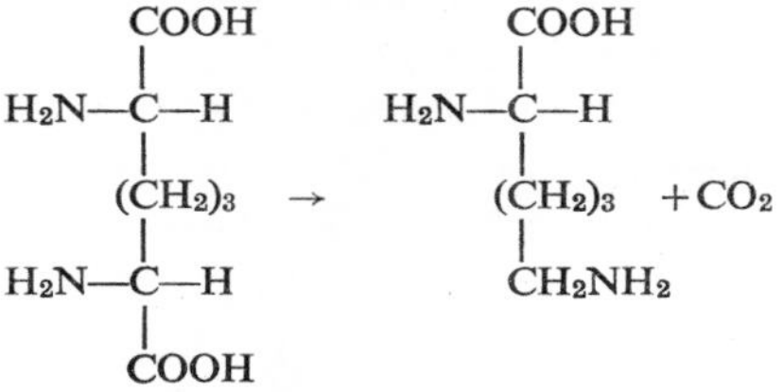

Meso-Diaminopimelic acid   L-Lysine

The formation of diaminopimelic acid has been studied in bacteria; thus extracts of *E. coli* form diaminopimelic acid from aspartate and pyruvate when supplemented with ATP, NADPH$_2$ and glutamate. Further fractionation has shown that aspartate is converted to aspartyl semialdehyde prior to condensation with pyruvate. The immediate precursor of diaminopimelic acid may be N-succinyl-L-diaminopimelic acid. Here the function of the succinyl group might be to prevent cyclization before the addition of the second amino group in the same way as in N-acetylornithine. If this reaction is involved in lysine synthesis, then a racemase is necessary to convert L-diaminopimelic acid to the *meso* form. The finding that maize seedlings slowly decarboxylate L-diaminopimelic acid suggests the existence of this racemase. Studies with *E. coli* suggest that the immediate precursor of N-succinyl diaminopimelic acid is N-succinyl-α-aminoketopimelic acid which is a substrate for a fairly specific transaminase.

The conversion of lysine to pipecolic acid has been demonstrated in plants and in *Neurospora*.

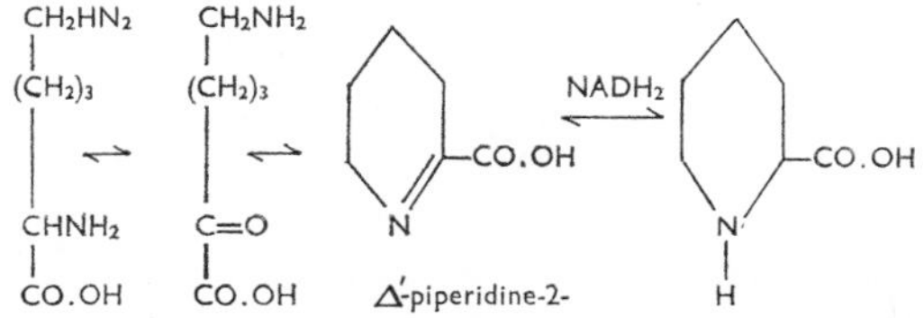

α-keto-ϵ-amino-caproic acid Δ^1-piperidine-2-carboxylic acid   Pipecolic acid

Considerable quantities of pipecolic acid are found in legumes, and the reduction of $\triangle^1$-piperidine-2-carboxylic acid to pipecolic acid by extracts of pea seedlings has been shown to require $NADH_2$.

Alanine
(α- and β-alanine)

Higher plants contain a highly active transaminase which transfers the amino group from glutamate to pyruvate. Suggestions that alanine is formed by the reductive amination of pyruvate are unconfirmed, though an alanine dehydrogenase has been purified from *Mycobacterium tuberculosis*, and purified glutamic dehydrogenase from liver has alanine dehydrogenase activity (see p. 360).

β-ALANINE

β-Alanine is the only known naturally occurring β-amino acid and is a constituent of coenzyme A. In bacteria it is formed by decarboxylation of aspartic acid.

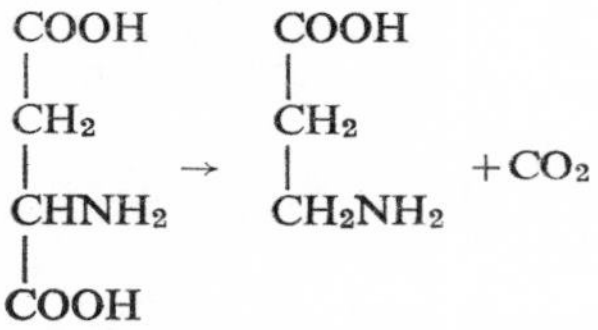

$$
\begin{array}{ccc}
COOH & COOH \\
| & | \\
CH_2 & CH_2 \\
| & \rightarrow \quad | \quad +CO_2 \\
CHNH_2 & CH_2NH_2 \\
| \\
COOH
\end{array}
$$

Aspartic acid is decarboxylated by extracts of squash fruit.

An alternative pathway is by transamination of malonic semialdehyde (p. 284).

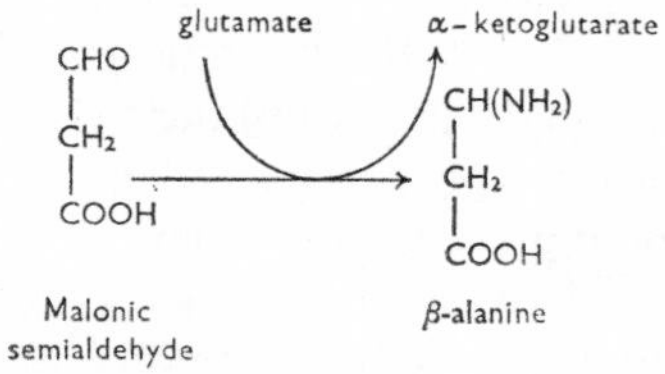

$$
\begin{array}{ccc}
 & \text{glutamate} & \alpha\text{- ketoglutarate} \\
CHO & & \\
| & & CH(NH_2) \\
CH_2 & & | \\
| & \longrightarrow & CH_2 \\
COOH & & | \\
 & & COOH \\
\text{Malonic} & & \beta\text{-alanine} \\
\text{semialdehyde} & &
\end{array}
$$

Evidence for this pathway has been obtained with slices of plant tissues, which convert propionate-^{14}C into β-alanine-^{14}C.

The Branched Chain Amino Acids
(valine, isoleucine and leucine)

VALINE

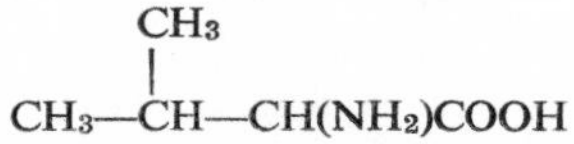

$$
\begin{array}{c}
CH_3 \\
| \\
CH_3\!-\!CH\!-\!CH(NH_2)COOH
\end{array}
$$

Studies with bacteria and fungi have shown that valine is formed from acetaldehyde and pyruvate.

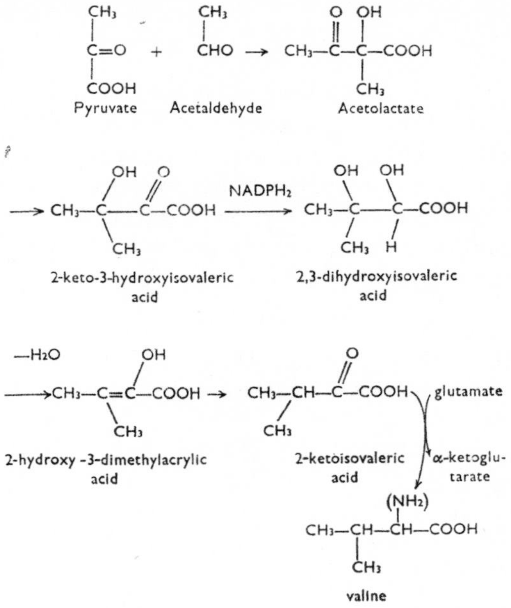

$$
\begin{array}{ccccc}
CH_3 & & CH_3 & & O\ \ OH \\
| & & | & & \|\ \ | \\
C{=}O & + & CHO & \rightarrow & CH_3{-}C{-}C{-}COOH \\
| & & & & | \\
COOH & & & & CH_3 \\
\text{Pyruvate} & & \text{Acetaldehyde} & & \text{Acetolactate}
\end{array}
$$

$$
\xrightarrow{\hphantom{xx}}
\underset{\substack{\text{2-keto-3-hydroxyisovaleric}\\\text{acid}}}{CH_3{-}\overset{OH}{\underset{CH_3}{C}}{-}\overset{O}{C}{-}COOH}
\xrightarrow{\text{NADPH}_2}
\underset{\substack{\text{2,3-dihydroxyisovaleric}\\\text{acid}}}{CH_3{-}\overset{OH}{\underset{CH_3}{C}}{-}\overset{OH}{\underset{H}{C}}{-}COOH}
$$

$$
\xrightarrow{-H_2O}
\underset{\substack{\text{2-hydroxy-3-dimethylacrylic}\\\text{acid}}}{CH_3{-}C{=}\underset{CH_3}{C}{-}COOH}
\rightarrow
\underset{\substack{\text{2-ketoisovaleric}\\\text{acid}}}{CH_3{-}\underset{CH_3}{CH}{-}\overset{O}{C}{-}COOH}
\underset{\alpha\text{-ketoglutarate}}{\overset{\text{glutamate}}{\big\rbrace}}
$$

$$
\underset{\text{valine}}{CH_3{-}CH{-}\overset{(NH_2)}{CH}{-}COOH}
\quad \underset{CH_3}{}
$$

A dihydroxy acid dehydrase has been found in a number of plants and purified from spinach. The enzyme requires Mn^{++} or Mg^{++} and dehydrates 2,3-dihydroxyisovaleric acid to 2-ketoisovaleric acid.

In the scheme shown above, the migration of the α-methyl group of acetolactate to the carbonyl carbon and the reduction of the carbonyl to a hydroxyl group is shown as proceeding via an isomerase and a reduction. The reduction step could precede the isomerase step and in *E. coli* and *N. crassa* both 2-keto-3-hydroxy acid reductase and 2-hydroxy-3-keto acid reductoisomerase activities have been demonstrated.

ISOLEUCINE

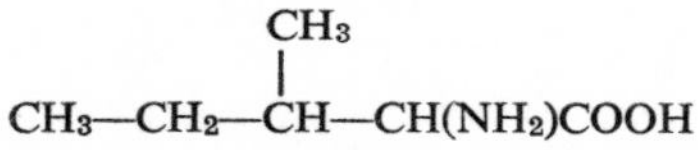

$$
\underset{}{CH_3{-}CH_2{-}\overset{CH_3}{CH}{-}CH(NH_2)COOH}
$$

Studies with bacteria and fungi indicate that isoleucine is formed from acetaldehyde and 2-ketobutyrate by reactions similar to those involved in valine synthesis.

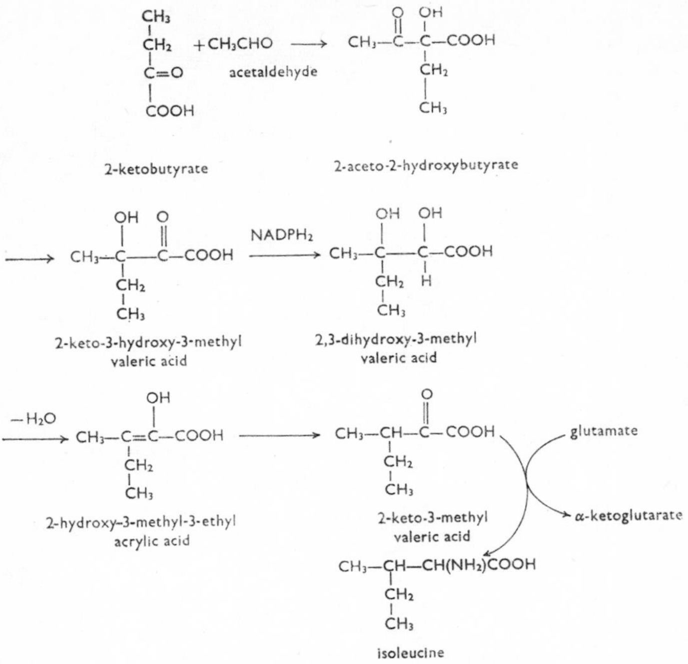

CH₃—CH₂—C(=O)—COOH +CH₃CHO ⟶ CH₃—C(=O)—C(OH)—COOH with CH₂, CH₃

2-ketobutyrate   acetaldehyde   2-aceto-2-hydroxybutyrate

⟶ CH₃—C(OH)—C(=O)—COOH (CH₂, CH₃)   —NADPH₂→ CH₃—C(OH)—C(OH,H)—COOH (CH₂, CH₃)

2-keto-3-hydroxy-3-methyl   2,3-dihydroxy-3-methyl
valeric acid   valeric acid

—H₂O→ CH₃—C=C(OH)—COOH (CH₂, CH₃) ⟶ CH₃—CH—C(=O)—COOH (CH₂, CH₃) — glutamate / α-ketoglutarate

2-hydroxy-3-methyl-3-ethyl   2-keto-3-methyl
acrylic acid   valeric acid

CH₃—CH—CH(NH₂)COOH (CH₂, CH₃)

isoleucine

With the exception of the dehydrase these reactions have not been demonstrated in plants. Preparations from spinach leaves which dehydrate dihydroxyisovaleric acid also dehydrate dihydroxymethylvalerate. As in the case of valine the migration of the α-alkyl group to the carbonyl carbon and the reduction of the carbonyl to a hydroxyl group may proceed as shown or by a reduction followed by an isomerization.

LEUCINE

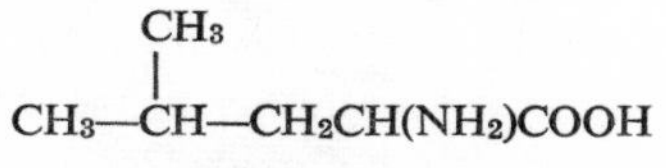

CH₃
|
CH₃—CH—CH₂CH(NH₂)COOH

Details of the biosynthesis of leucine are unknown. In *E. coli* leucine synthesis may involve a condensation between α-keto isovaleric acid and acetyl CoA. In *Torulopsis utilis* synthesis may occur from acetate and the isobutyryl moiety of valine. The situation in plants is unknown.

The degradation of isoleucine, leucine and valine has been studied in animal tissues and appears to follow a similar pattern (Fig. 10.4):

25

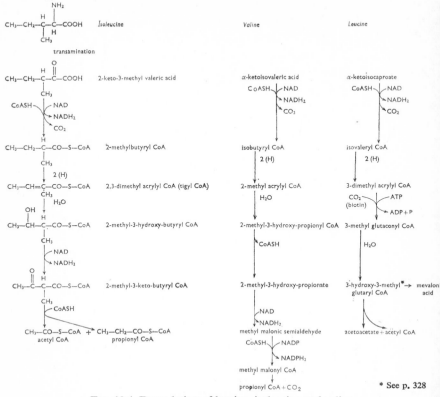

FIG. 10.4. Degradation of leucine, isoleucine and valine.

Evidence supporting the operation of the above schemes in plants is as follows:

(a) Leucine is degraded by guayule seedlings to α-ketoisocaproate, isovalerate and 3-dimethylacrylate. An enzyme from flax seedlings, in the presence of ATP and CoA, catalyses the activation of 3-dimethyl-acrylate and the uptake of carbon dioxide to form 3-hydroxy-3-methyl glutarate, which is further degraded to acetoacetate and acetyl CoA.

(b) An enzyme system has been demonstrated in extracts of acetone powders of a number of plants which decarboxylates methyl malonyl CoA to propionyl CoA (final step in the degradation of valine).

(c) 3-Methylbutyrate-1-^{14}C, isobutyrate-1-^{14}C and isovalerate-1-[14]C (the products of oxidative decarboxylation of isoleucine, valine and leucine, respectively) are converted to $^{14}CO_2$ under conditions described for the β-oxidation of fatty acids by peanut mitochondria (p. 276).

Feeding experiments have shown that the synthesis of the cyanogenetic glucosides, lotaustralin and linamarin, in *Trifolium repens* is related to the metabolism of isoleucine and valine.

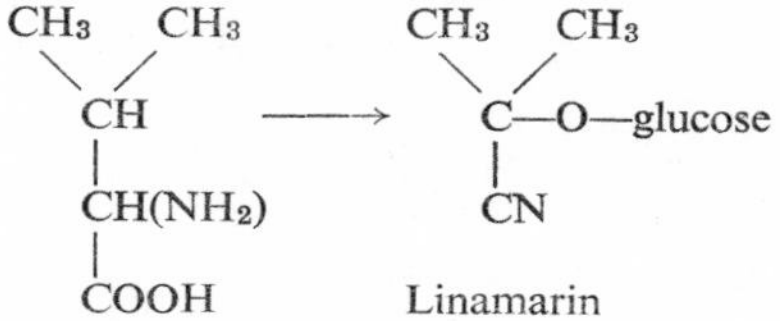

CH3 CH3
CH
CH(NH2)
COOH
CH3 CH3
C—O—glucose
CN
Valine → Linamarin

CH3 C2H5
CH
CH(NH2)
COOH
CH3 C2H5
C—O—glucose
CN
Isoleucine → Lotaustralin

Histidine

The biosynthesis of histidine is closely related to the metabolism of purines (see p. 414) and very little work has been undertaken with higher plants. Experiments with micro-organisms indicate the pathway of biosynthesis shown in Fig. 10.5.

The Aromatic Amino Acids

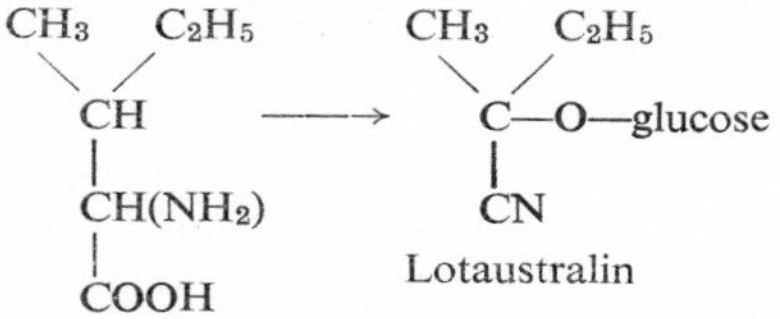

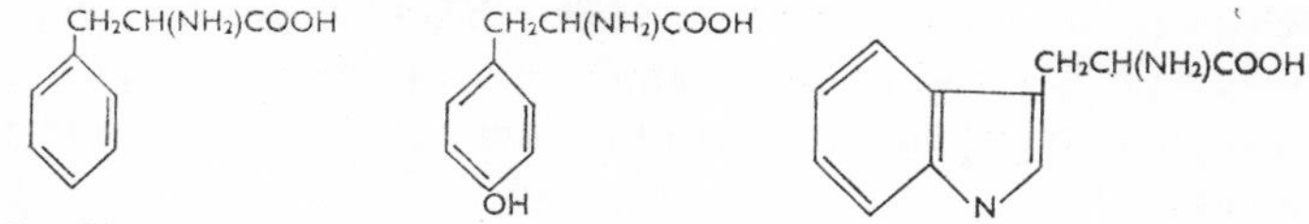

CH2CH(NH2)COOH
CH2CH(NH2)COOH
OH
CH2CH(NH2)COOH
N
Phenylalanine Tyrosine Tryptophane

The pathway of synthesis of aromatic amino acids has largely been elucidated by the use of bacterial mutants. Bacterial cultures are irradiated with X-rays or ultraviolet light to induce mutation and then placed on a basal medium to which penicillin is added. Penicillin kills only bacteria which are actively growing and is innocuous to resting bacteria. The wild type bacteria start to grow but are killed by the penicillin. Since penicillin

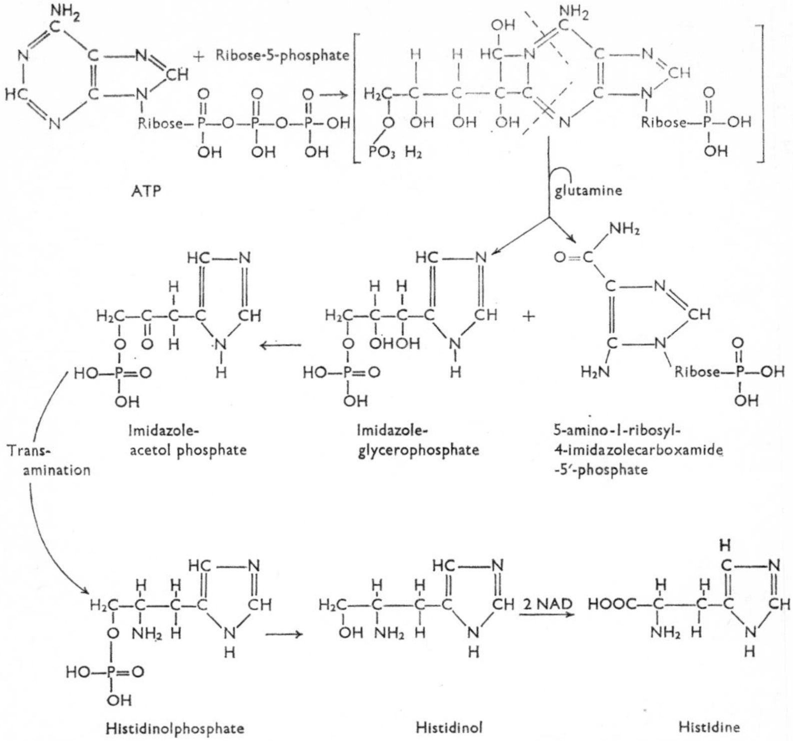

FIG. 10.5. Reactions involved in the biosynthesis of histidine.

kills only growing bacteria, mutants which require supplements for growth are not killed. Penicillin is removed, then the mutants are plated on a medium supplemented with aromatic amino acids.

Using these mutants a systematic search was started for intermediates between glucose and aromatic amino acids (Davis, 1955). Success was finally achieved when a sample of shikimic acid was tested as an intermediate:

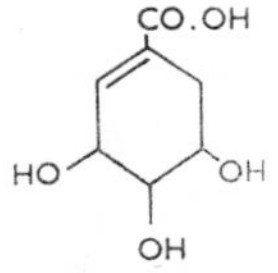

Shikimic acid was thought at this time to be a rare plant acid, but is now known to be widely distributed in plants and serves as a growth supplement for a number of bacterial mutants. Using mutants which grew when supplemented with shikimic acid, two products which accumulated in the medium were isolated and identified as:

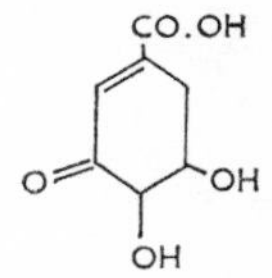

CO.OH

O=   OH

OH

5-dehydroshikimic
acid

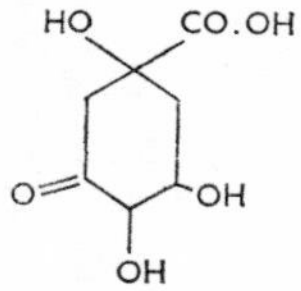

HO   CO.OH

O=   OH

OH

Dehydroquinic
acid

An enzyme catalysing the reaction

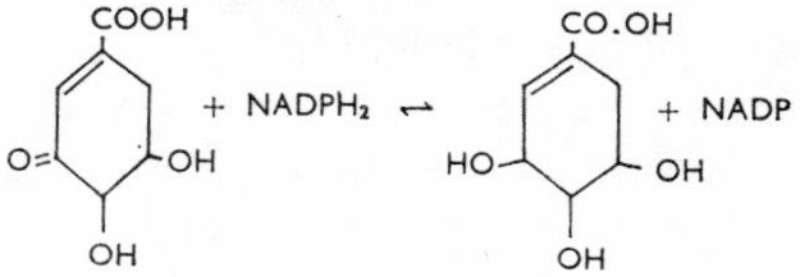

COOH
+ NADPH$_2$ ⇌
O=   OH

OH

CO.OH
+ NADP
HO   OH

OH

has been isolated from *E. coli* and a number of higher plants. Mutants of *E. coli* which accumulate dehydroshikimic acid do not possess this enzyme which has been named dehydroshikimic reductase.

The reaction

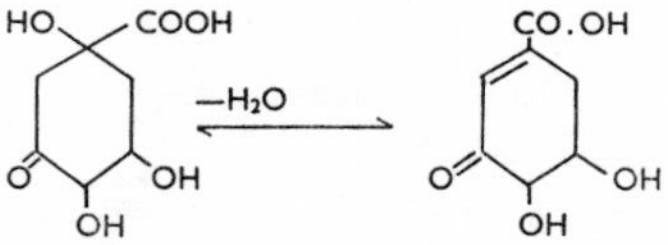

HO   COOH
—H$_2$O →
O   OH

OH

CO.OH

O=   OH

OH

has been demonstrated in *E. coli* and a number of plants, but is absent from mutants that accumulate dehydroquinic acid.

Quinic acid, which is widely distributed in plants, is a growth factor for *Aerobacter* but not for *E. coli* and is considered to be formed by a side reaction:

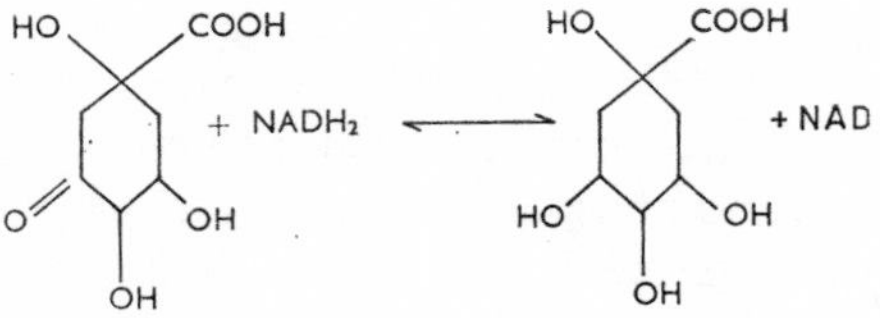

HO   COOH
+ NADH$_2$ ⇌
O=   OH

OH

HO   COOH
+ NAD
HO   OH

OH

Young rose buds convert quinic acid to shikimic acid.

Bacterial mutants gave no indication of the nature of the precursors of dehydroquinic acid and the reaction sequence was determined by means of ^{14}C-labelled compounds. Glucose, labelled in specific positions, was supplied to mutants accumulating shikimic acid. The distribution of isotope found in shikimic acid is shown below:

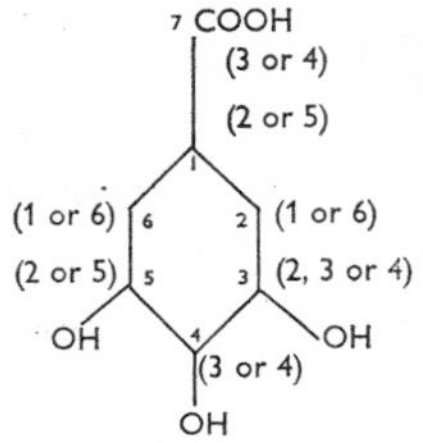

The numbers in brackets refer to the carbon atoms of glucose. It is clear that carbons 1, 2 and 7 of shikimic acid come from 2, 1 and 3 or 5, 6 and 4, respectively, of glucose, suggesting a 3-carbon intermediate. Feeding experiments with pyruvate showed little incorporation, hence a phosphorylated 3-carbon intermediate was assumed. The remaining labelling of shikimate was more difficult to interpret, but it was observed that sedoheptulose phosphate was a good precursor of dehydroquinic acid and erythrose-4-phosphate was suggested as an intermediate. Subsequently, it was shown that dehydroquinic acid was formed by the reactions:

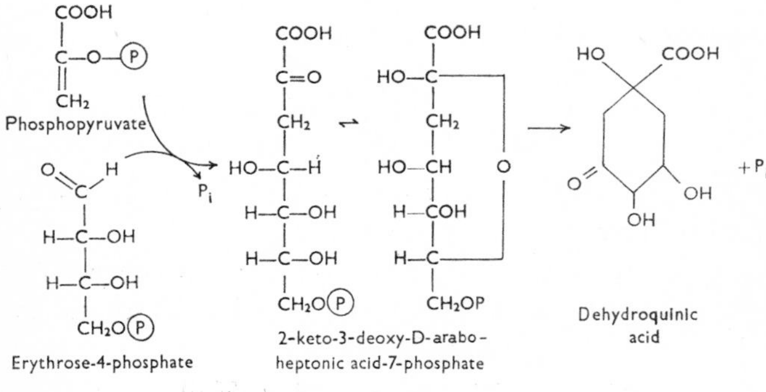

Whilst the individual reactions of this sequence have not been demonstrated in plants, cell free extracts are able to convert a mixture of erythrose-4-phosphate and phosphopyruvate to dehydroquinic acid.

The existence of intermediates between shikimic acid and aromatic compounds was established with the isolation of a compound — prephenic acid — which accumulates in certain mutants provided the medium is alkaline. Under acid conditions prephenic acid decarboxylates to give the aromatic compound phenylpyruvate.

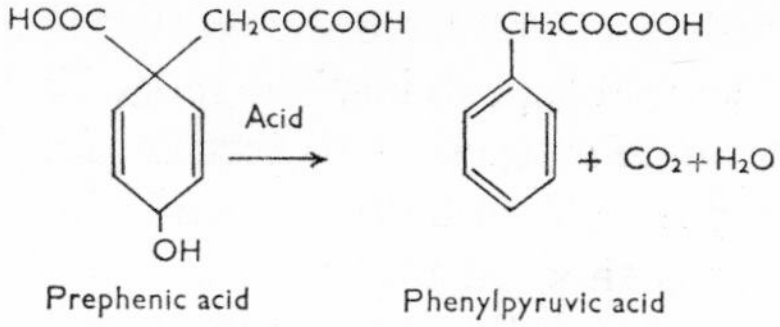

Prephenic acid   Phenylpyruvic acid

Prephenic acid is probably formed from shikimic acid by the reactions:

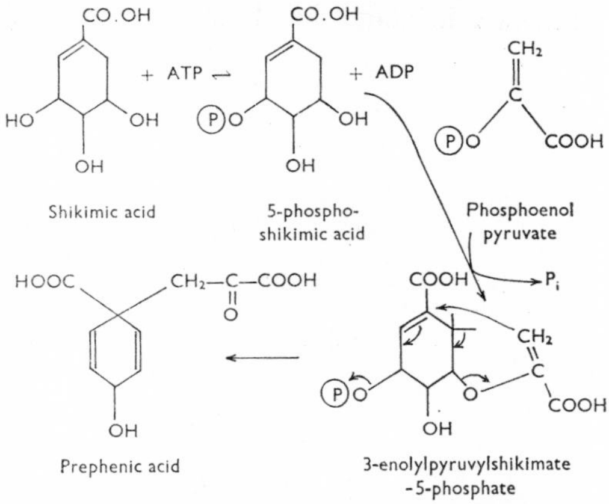

Shikimic acid   5-phospho-   Phosphoenol
                       shikimic acid   pyruvate

Prephenic acid   3-enolylpyruvylshikimate
                              -5-phosphate

Prephenic acid appears to be the immediate precursor of the aromatic ring and is a branching point for the formation of phenylalanine and tyrosine. Animals hydroxylate phenylalanine to obtain tyrosine, and individuals unable to effect this conversion suffer from phenyl-ketonuria in which the urine contains products derived from phenylalanine and the individual is mentally retarded.

Plants, on the other hand, have separate pathways for the formation of phenylalanine and tyrosine. Thus prephenic acid is converted either to phenylpyruvic acid or to hydroxyphenylpyruvic acid and the corresponding amino acids are formed by transamination.

Whilst there is little direct evidence to support the view that plants form tryptophane from shikimic acid, there is ample evidence that microorganisms form tryptophane by the pathway shown in Fig. 10.6.

Cell-free preparations from E. coli are able to form anthranilic acid from 5-phosphoshikimic acid and glutamine, but the details of the reaction are not known. The enzyme tryptophane synthetase catalyses three reactions:

(1) indole + serine⇌tryptophane
(2) indoleglycerol phosphate⇌indole + triosephosphate
(3) indoleglycerol phosphate + serine⇌tryptophane + triosephosphate

The studies of Yanofsky (1960) have shown that these reactions require two associated but separable proteins. The rate of indole formation from indoleglycerol phosphate is too slow to account for the observed rate of formation of tryptophane from indoleglycerol phosphate if indole is an intermediate. It is thus thought that reaction (3) represents the *in vivo* tryptophane synthetase reaction. However, it should be noted that reaction (1) is more rapid than the other two reactions. The presence of tryptophane synthetase in plants has been inferred by demonstrating reaction (1).

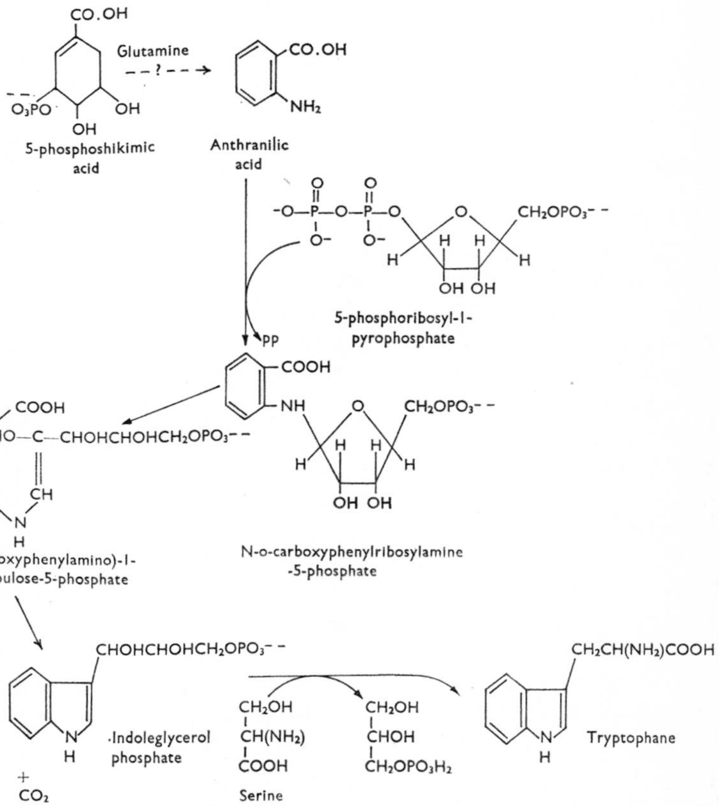

FIG. 10.6. Reactions involved in the biosynthesis of tryptophane.

The Formation of Amino Acids During Photosynthesis

It is generally held that the photosynthetic pathway to amino acids involves the reactions described in the previous pages. However, kinetic studies have indicated that special reactions may be involved. Thus Smith, Bassham & Kirk (1961) have proposed that alanine is formed by the reductive amination of phosphoenolpyruvate, and serine by amination of 2-phosphoglycerate.

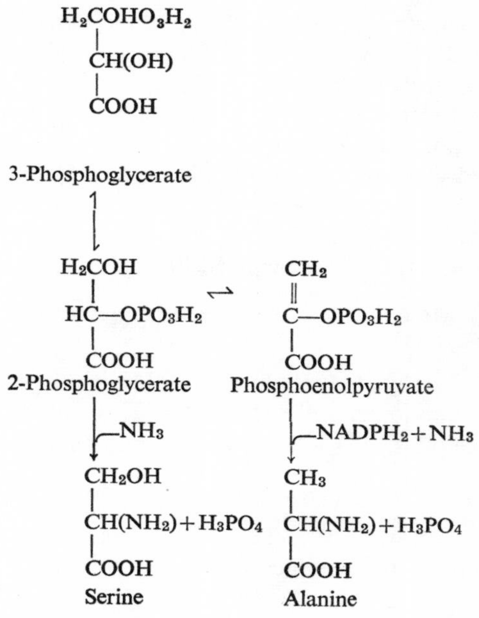

$$
\begin{array}{l}
H_2COHO_3H_2 \\
| \\
CH(OH) \\
| \\
COOH
\end{array}
$$

3-Phosphoglycerate

$$
\begin{array}{ll}
H_2COH & CH_2 \\
| & \| \\
HC-OPO_3H_2 \quad\rightleftharpoons\quad & C-OPO_3H_2 \\
| & | \\
COOH & COOH \\
\text{2-Phosphoglycerate} & \text{Phosphoenolpyruvate}
\end{array}
$$

$$
\begin{array}{ll}
\quad\llcorner-NH_3 & \quad\llcorner-NADPH_2+NH_3 \\
CH_2OH & CH_3 \\
| & | \\
CH(NH_2)+H_3PO_4 & CH(NH_2)+H_3PO_4 \\
| & | \\
COOH & COOH \\
\text{Serine} & \text{Alanine}
\end{array}
$$

THE METABOLISM OF COMPOUNDS RELATED TO THE AROMATIC AMINO ACIDS

Lignin

Lignin occurs between the microfibrils of certain cells where its packing resists compression. This contrasts with the resistance to tension which is due to the orientation of cellulose fibrils. Lignin is recognized in sections by colour reactions which are facilitated by sunlight — thus phenol and hydrochloric acid stain lignin blue green, phloroglucinol and hydrochloric acid give a bright red and aniline sulphate a yellow. A number of colour reactions are given by hardwoods but not by softwoods. These tests (e.g. the Mäule reaction), which involve some method of chlorinating a section and subsequently treating it with ammonium hydroxide, indicate the presence of syringyl units.

The isolation of native lignin is technically difficult. Some 5–10 per cent may be extracted by first removing gums with ether then extracting with 95 per cent ethanol. Alternatively, cellulose may be removed by inoculating wood with a 'brown rot' fungus and when decay is complete the lignin is extracted with alcohol. Because of this difficulty, much work has been performed on preparations obtained by more drastic methods. The most important method of removing lignin is in the commercial pulping of wood with sulphite and sulphurous acid at 135°, but this method is seldom used on a small scale.

The nature of the association of lignin with cellulose is unknown. Evidence suggesting a chemical linkage may be summarized:

(1) Methylation of lignin can be increased after the wood has been hydrolysed.

(2) Methylated cellulose is soluble in chloroform, methylated lignin is insoluble, but when wood is treated with dimethyl sulphate, lignin and cellulose dissolve in chloroform without separation.

Evidence suggesting a mechanical incrustation may be summarized:

(1) Up to 10 per cent of lignin can be extracted with 95 per cent alcohol at room temperature.

(2) Electron micrographs of wood taken before and after removal of lignin show no change in the structural arrangement of cellulose.

CHEMICAL STRUCTURE

Oxidation of lignin with nitrobenzene gives a number of products depending on the origin of the lignin. Thus softwood lignin yields vanillin, hardwood lignin yields vanillin and syringaldehyde whilst lignin from monocotyledons yields vanillin, syringaldehyde and p-hydroxybenzaldehyde.

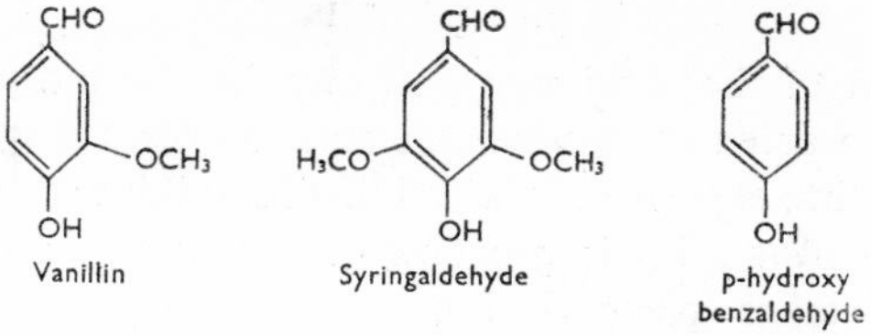

Vanillin   Syringaldehyde   p-hydroxy
                                          benzaldehyde

Prolonged heating with ethanol and hydrochloric acid produces small amounts of the following products.

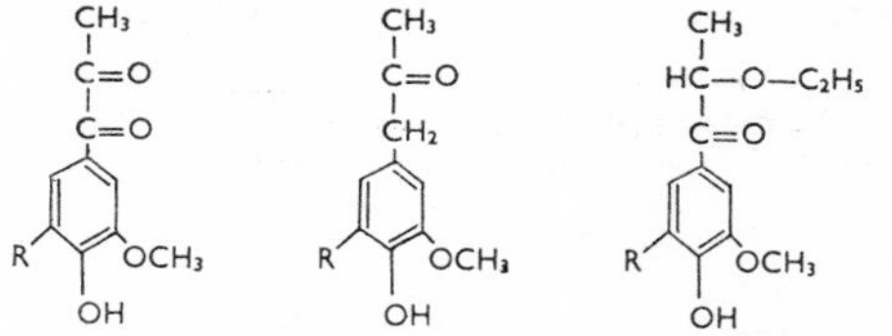

In the case of softwood lignin R = H and for hardwood lignin R = H or OCH$_3$.

The products of ethanolysis are phenylpropanoid compounds and it is generally held that lignin is a polymer consisting predominantly of substituted phenylpropanoid units. The structure of the polymer is unknown, but any simple repeating unit formula is inadequate. A formula due to Adler (1957) is shown below which illustrates the types of linkage involved but the formula should not be taken literally.

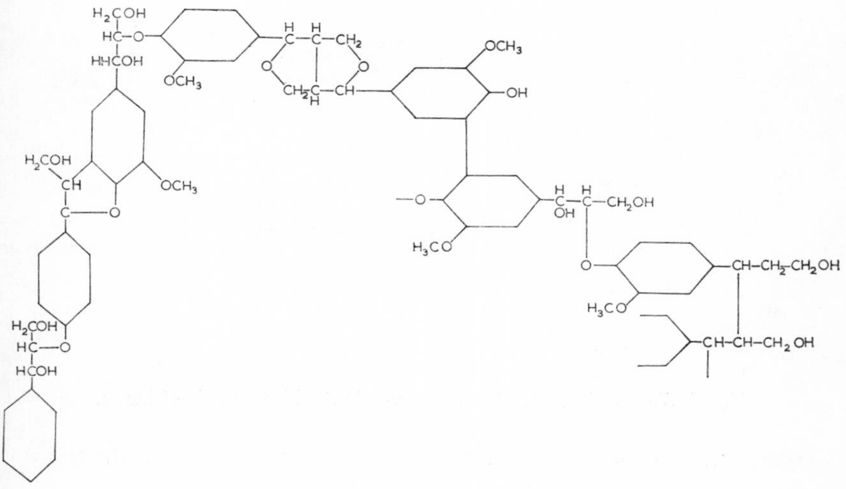

BIOSYNTHESIS

The elucidation of the shikimate pathway for the biosynthesis of the aromatic amino acids suggested that shikimic acid might be a lignin precursor. Feeding experiments with labelled shikimic acid have shown that shikimic acid is a lignin precursor and that no re-arrangement of carbon atoms takes place during the conversion. Further feeding experiments have shown that phenylalanine is a good precursor of lignin in gymnosperms and angiosperms, and that in addition tyrosine is a precursor of lignin in grasses and Compositae. An enzyme which deaminates phenylalanine has been found in legumes,

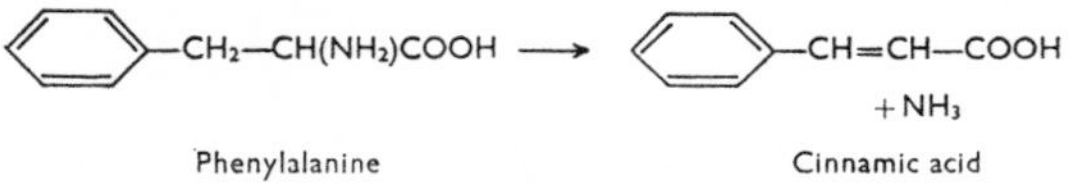

Phenylalanine → Cinnamic acid + NH₃

and an enzyme deaminating tyrosine has been found in grasses.

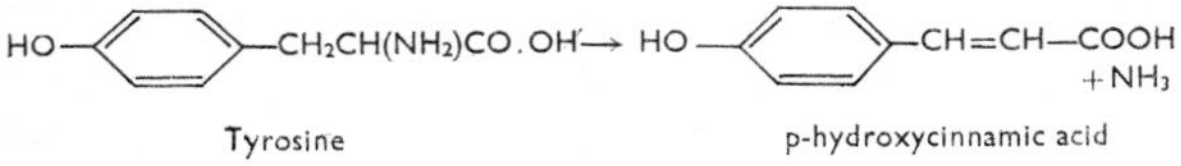

Tyrosine → p-hydroxycinnamic acid + NH₃

Other feeding experiments have shown that cinnamic, p-hydroxycinnamic, caffeic, ferulic and sinapic acids are efficient lignin precursors. Accordingly, the following scheme (Fig. 10.7) has been suggested for lignin formation.

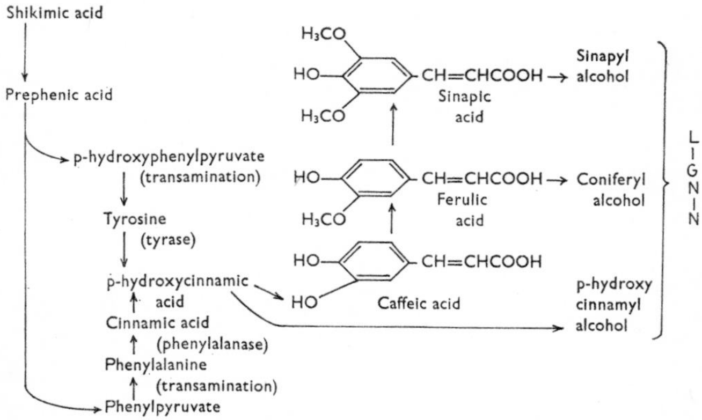

FIG. 10.7. Postulated reactions involved in the biosynthesis of lignin.

Hydroxylation is discussed on p. 398. It is possible that some hydroxy lation and methoxylation may take place after polymerization of lignin. The alcohols are considered to be lignin precursors on the basis of model experiments. Press juice from the mushroom *Psalliota campestris* causes coniferyl alcohol to polymerize to a compound resembling conifer lignin; the active enzyme in the juice is the phenol oxidase, laccase.

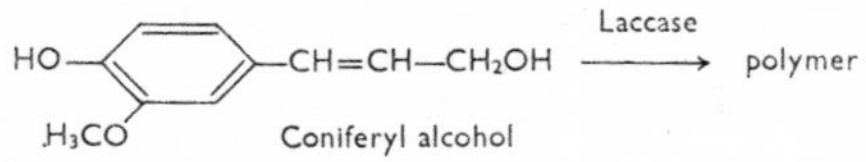

Coniferyl alcohol

The addition of both coniferyl alcohol and sinapyl alcohol to the mushroom extract leads to the formation of a compound resembling angiosperm lignin. The key compound in these model experiments – coniferyl alcohol – does not occur in the free form, but its β-glucoside, coniferin, is found in coniferous species. It has been suggested that the soluble coniferin is translocated to the site of lignin synthesis, where coniferyl alcohol is liberated by the action of β-glucosidase.

Whilst Freudenberg's group have concentrated on an oxidase as the enzyme responsible for lignification, Siegel (1956) has considered the possibility that peroxidase is involved. When filter paper is added to eugenol, hydrogen peroxide and peroxidase, a lignin-like polymer is formed on the paper. Other studies have indicated that purified eugenol

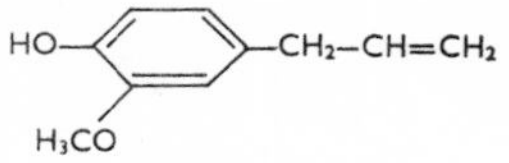

Eugenol

does not undergo polymerization, and that coniferaldehyde, which is a product of spontaneous oxidation, is the true

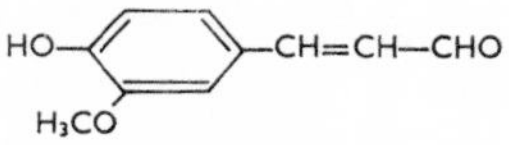

Coniferaldehyde

substrate for polymerization. Nevertheless, the studies of Siegel raise two important points:

(1) There is good evidence that lignin is chemically associated with cellulose, and filter paper was essential for the polymerization reaction observed by Siegel. Subsequent experiments by Freudenberg's group have shown that the laccase system can form ethers with sorbitol or sucrose.

(2) Peroxidase is proposed as an alternative to the oxidase system, for the polymerization. The following evidence supports the role of peroxidase:

(a) Hydrogen peroxide greatly increases the deposition of lignin in sections and in tissue cultures.

(b) There is a correlation between the sites of lignin deposition and the sites of greatest peroxidase activity.

(c) Peroxidase inhibitors inhibit the formation of lignin.

Indole Compounds

Many derivatives of indole are found in plants, ranging from the relatively complex indole alkaloids to indole itself, which is present in orange blossom. The most important indole compounds are the indole auxins — and in particular, indoleacetic acid (IAA) and indoleacetonitrile. Despite their importance in plant physiology, little is known about their metabolism. It is generally assumed that IAA is formed from tryptophane and a number of pathways have been suggested (Fig. 10.8).

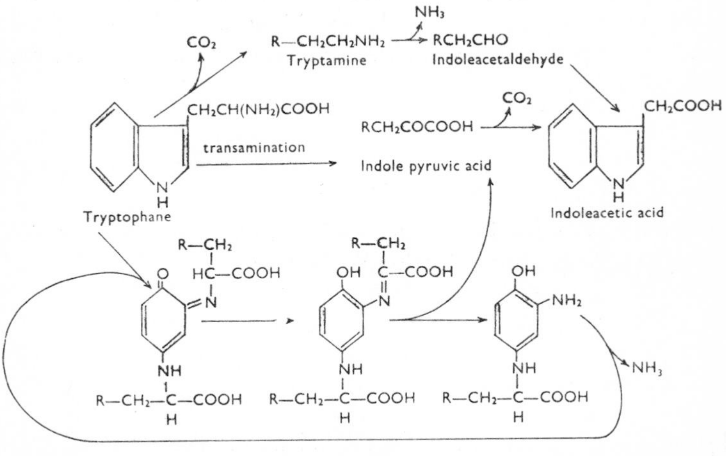

FIG. 10.8. Possible reactions involved in the biosynthesis of indoleacetic acid.

The pathway involving tryptamine is supported by the finding that a number of plants (e.g. pineapple, oats and carrots) can form IAA from tryptamine. The presence of the decarboxylase which converts tryptophane to tryptamine has been demonstrated in melon. However, a number of plants (e.g. spinach and mung beans) are unable to convert tryptamine to IAA. The decarboxylation of indolepyruvic acid to form IAA has been demonstrated in many plants, though the identity of the enzyme system has not been established. The formation of indolepyruvic acid by transamination has not been demonstrated in plants. Evidence for the formation of indolepyruvic acid via the phenolase complex has been presented (Gordon & Paleg, 1961).

Plant preparations give low rates of conversion of tryptophane to IAA and other reactions have been proposed, e.g. the combination of indole and glyoxylate to from indoleglycolate which subsequently yields IAA. The possibility that indoleglycerol phosphate is an auxin precursor should also be considered. The interconversions of various indole compounds have been discussed by Fawcett (1961).

Phenolic Compounds

Phenolic substances occur throughout the plant kingdom, largely in the form of glycosides or esters. They may be classified into three groups based on the number of aromatic rings in the molecule.

PHENOLS WITH ONE AROMATIC RING

A simple example is gallic acid which is widely distributed in plants. Its biosynthesis has been investigated in *Geranium pyrenaicum* by feeding ^{14}C-labelled glucose, acetate and phenylalanine. Glucose was the best precursor of gallic acid, suggesting a biosynthetic origin from shikimic acid, rather than by β-oxidation of a trihydroxylated C9 molecule derived from phenylalanine. The related compound protocatechuic acid is formed in relatively large amounts by *Neurospora* mutants blocked in the conversion of dehydroshikimic acid to shikimic acid. Protocatechuic acid is formed from dehydroshikimic acid by dehydration and it is possible that gallic acid is formed from protocatechuic acid by hydroxylation. Alternatively gallic acid may be formed by dehydrogenation of dehydroshikimic acid.

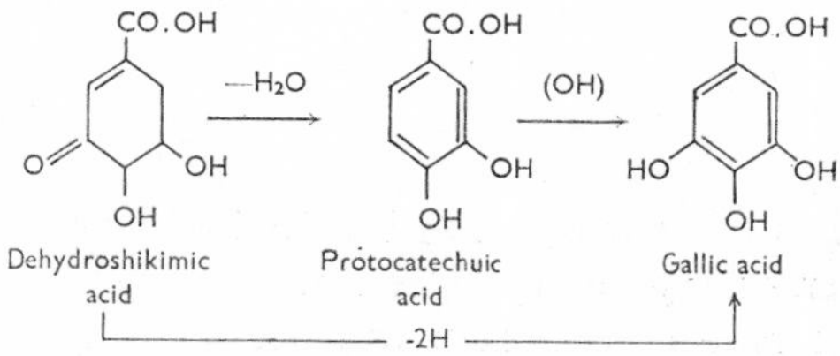

Gallic acid is an inhibitor of dehydroshikimic acid reductase from pea seedlings and it is possible that the production of gallic acid inhibits the formation of shikimic acid and derivatives.

Phenols with 9 carbon atoms are common and may be divided into the cinnamic acids and the coumarins. Examples of common cinnamic acids are p-coumaric, caffeic and the methylated derivatives ferulic acid and sinapic acid:

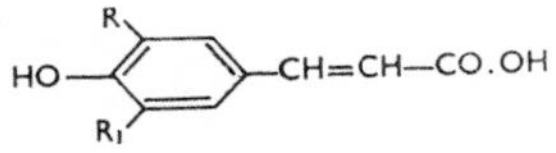

$$HO-\underset{R_1}{\overset{R}{\bigcirc}}-CH=CH-CO.OH$$

$R = R' = H$ p-Coumaric acid
$R = H, R' = OH$ Caffeic acid
$R = H, R' = OCH_3$ Ferulic acid
$R = R' = OCH_3$ Sinapic acid

Caffeic acid occurs chiefly in combination with quinic acid as the depside chlorogenic acid:

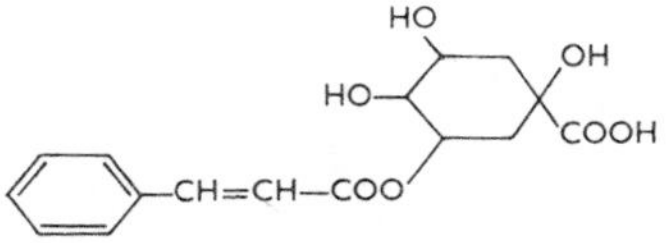

In *Salvia splendins* all the above cinnamic acids occur as depsides and are readily formed from phenylalanine but not from tyrosine. Feeding experiments (Neish, 1960) were consistent with the following sequence in which compounds are converted to more highly substituted members, by reactions which are not readily reversible:

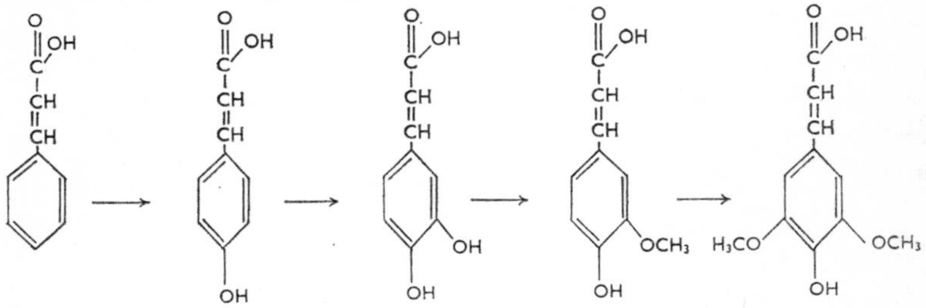

trans-cinnamic ⟶ p-coumaric ⟶ caffeic ⟶ ferulic ⟶ sinapic
acid   acid   acid   acid   acid

The mechanism of hydroxylation involved in these reactions is unknown. However, a few general points about hydroxylation may be noted. Crystalline horseradish peroxidase can act as a hydroxylase in the presence of dihydroxyfumaric acid, though the mechanism is uncertain (see p. 205). The polyphenol oxidase system which is widely distributed in plants is a specific phenol o-hydroxylase. Purified preparations of polyphenol oxidase show an induction period which can be removed specifically by o-diphenols or non-specifically by reducing agents. These requirements suggest the reduction of cupric enzyme which is thus the o-hydroxylase of the phenolase complex.

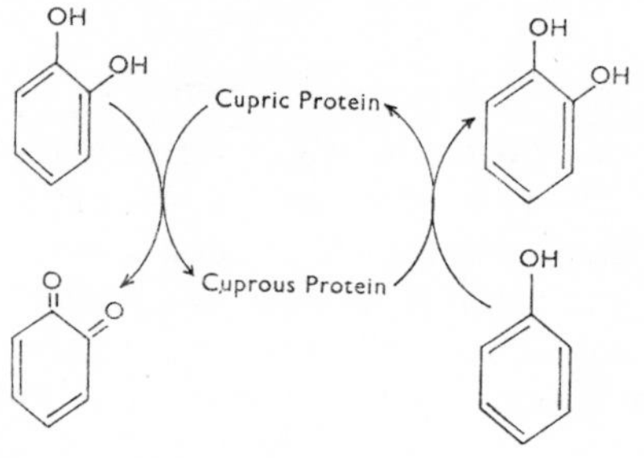

The phenolase complex could be the mechanisms for the formation of the o-dihydroxybenzenoid pattern found in caffeic acid and frequently in the flavonoids.

A number of specific hydroxylases have been demonstrated in animals. Thus the hydroxylation of phenylalanine to tyrosine involves a compound closely related to or identical with THFA. Liver microsomes contain a hydroxylase which is active with certain non-polar substances (e.g. naphthalene) and requires $NADPH_2$ for activity.

A number of non-enzymic systems hydroxylate aromatic compounds. Thus Fenton's reagent hydroxylates phenol to catechol, and a mixture of ferrous iron, ascorbic acid and a chelating agent catalyses a number of hydroxylations in the presence of oxygen.

The coumarins can be regarded as lactones of cinnamic acids. Thus coumarin is the lactone of o-hydroxycinnamic acid and scopoletin is the lactone of o-hydroxyferulic acid. Since the coumarins are phenyl propane derivatives, their synthesis from cinnamic acids is to be expected. Thus tracer studies have shown that *trans*-cinnamic acid is converted to coumarin by *Melilotus alba*, whilst scopoletin is formed from ferulic acid by *Helianthus annuus*, *Triticum vulgare* and *Zea mays*, where it occurs as the D-glucoside (scopolin). *Trans*-cinnamic acid is probably formed from phenylalanine by the action of the enzyme phenylalanase, which has been demonstrated in clover and partially purified from barley.

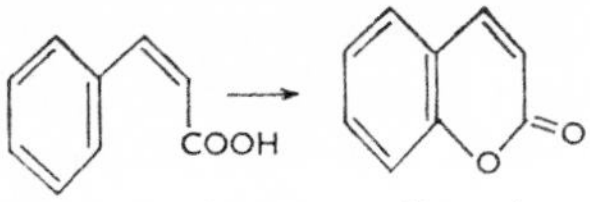

Cinnamic acid   Coumarin

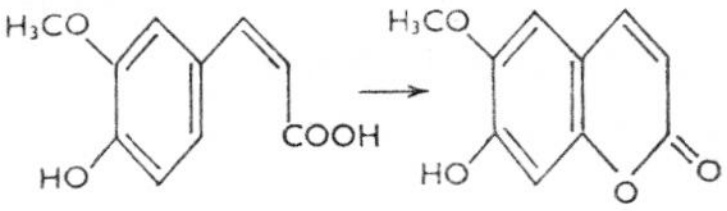

Ferulic acid   Scopoletin

The mechanism of ring closure remains uncertain. Hydroxylation at the ortho position would allow cyclization to produce the coumarin. In support of this mechanism is the observation that in *Melilotus alba* the formation of coumarin from *trans*-cinnamic acid is accompanied by the formation of *o*-coumaric acid, which is also converted into coumarin. An alternative mechanism involves oxidative cyclization:

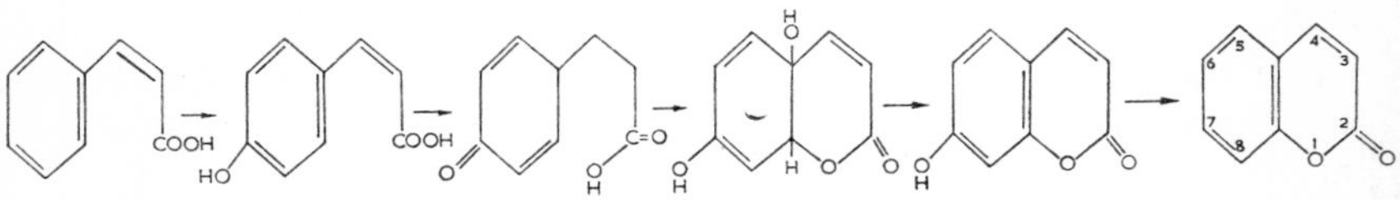

In the case of coumarin, this mechanism requires the para-hydroxylation of cinnamic acid, followed by the removal of this hydroxyl group after cyclization. The main support for this mechanism comes from the observation that almost all the natural coumarins have an oxygen atom at position 7, i.e. they may be derived from *p*-hydroxycinnamic acid.

A third mechanism is suggested by the cyclization of diphenyl-2-carboxylic acid to 3,4-benzocoumarin:

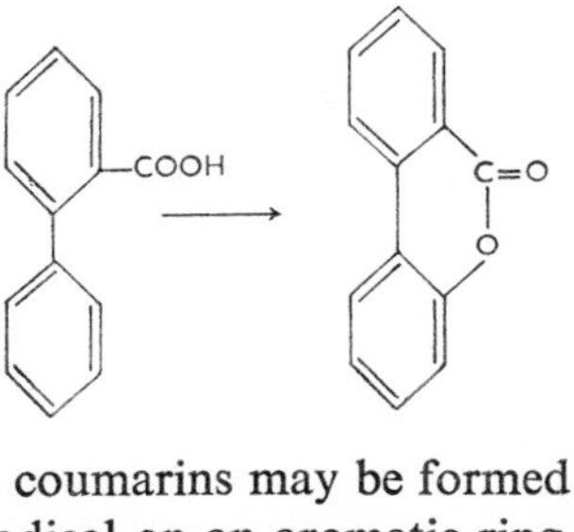

It is thus possible that coumarins may be formed by an intramolecular attack of a carboxyl radical on an aromatic ring. Feeding experiments with *Hierochloë odorata* have shown that *p*-coumaric acid is 1/70th as efficient as cinnamic acid as a precursor of coumarin. Similarly tyrosine is only 1/60th as efficient as phenylalanine. It has been suggested that an activated form of cinnamic acid is the precursor of all the coumarins and ortho- or para-hydroxylation of this intermediate leads to coumarin or 7-hydroxycoumarins.

PHENOLS WITH TWO AROMATIC RINGS

This group includes the flavonoids, isoflavonoids and rotenoids.

The flavonoids all contain a diarylpropane unit (C_6-C_3-C_6) and are classified on the structure of the connecting C_3 portion of the molecule. The benzene rings are designated A and B; the A ring, which usually has the hydroxyl pattern of phloroglucinol, forms a pyran ring with the C_3 unit in the anthocyanidins and a pyrone ring in the flavones, etc. A variety of systems for numbering the carbon atoms are in use:

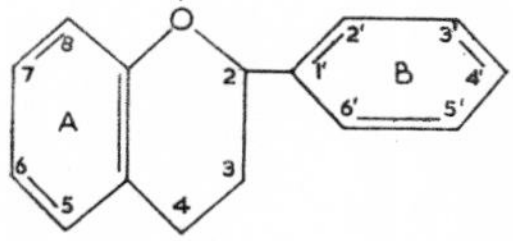

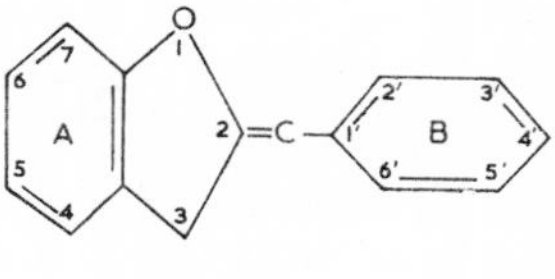

In this book we use the numbering given in II and retain it for flavonoids lacking an oxygen ring. The numbering of the benzalcoumaranones is given in III and retains the numbering in the A and B rings. The more widely used numbering of benzalcoumaranones is given in IV.

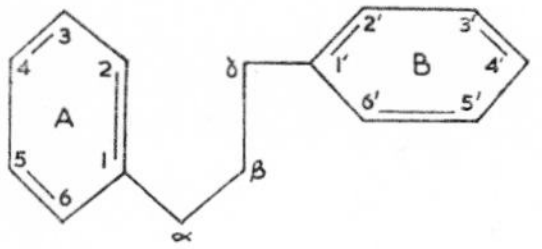

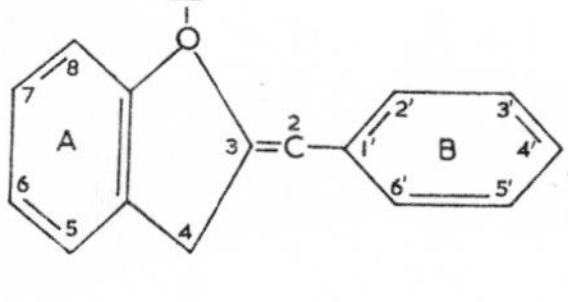

The two benzene rings are drawn in the same plane; in the case of flavones, flavonols, chalcones and anthocyanidins, the rings may be in the same plane, but in the leucoanthocyanidins, flavononols and flavanones, the oxygen ring probably has the almost strainless half-chain configuration and the benzene rings are not in the same plane. The various types of flavonoids are shown in Table 10.3.

TABLE 10.3

Types of Flavonoid Compounds

Class	Examples	Notes
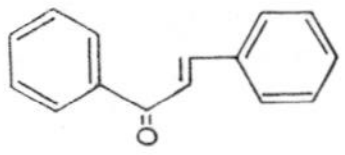 Chalcone	7,9,3',4'-Tetrahydroxychalcone (butein) in Douglas fir and other *Coreopsis* sp. 7,8,-Dihydroxy,-3,4,6-methoxylchalcone (pedicin) 7,8,9,3',4'-Pentahydroxychalcone (stillopsidin) in *Coreopsis stillmanii*.	The chalcones are relatively uncommon. Butein is oxidized by an enzyme present in *Coreopsis sulphureus* to the corresponding benzalcoumarone (aurone). The enzyme is not specific for butein and attacks other hydroxychalcones.
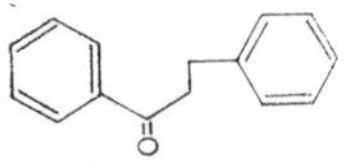 Dihydrochalcone	7,9,6',4'-Tetrahydroxydihydrochalcone (phloretin) as phloridzin in the root bark of some rosaceous fruit trees. 5,9,6'-Trihydroxy-7-methoxy dihydrochalcone (Asebotin) as the 2-glucoside in *Andromeda japonica*.	
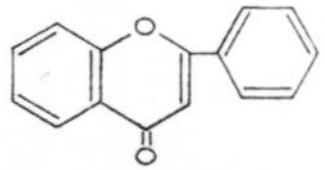 Flavone	5,7,-Dihydroxyflavone (chrysin) in *Populus* buds. 5,7,4'-trihydroxyflavone (apigenin) in yellow *Dahlia* and as 7-glucoside in *Cosmos* flowers. 5,7,3',4'-Tetrahydroxyflavone (luteolin) in *Reseda luteola* and *Genista tinctoria*. 5,7,4'-Trihydroxy-3',5'-dimethoxyflavone (tricin) in wheat.	Flavones and flavonols react with ammonia to produce brighter yellow colours. The unsubstituted flavone occurs as a dust on *Primula* species. Methoxylation is infrequent and flavones frequently occur free.

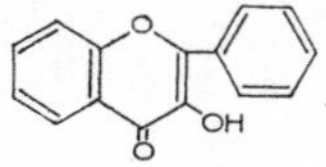

Flavonols possessing a free hydroxy group in the 5-position give a yellow colour and yellow green fluorescence when treated with boric acid and organic acids. Glycosidation is frequent. The leaves of *Vaccinium myrtillus* contain 5 glycosides of quercitin. Rutin, the 3 rutinoside (glucose and rhamnose) of quercitin constitutes 3–5 per cent of the dry weight of *Fagopyrum esculentum* when about to flower. Rutin is used medicinally for cases with capillary fragility.

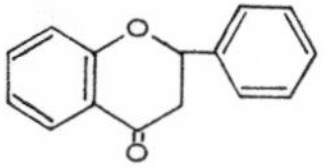

5,7-Dihydroxyflavonol (galangin) in rhizomes of *Alpinia*.
5,7,4′-Trihydroxyflavonol (kaempferol) in *Delphinium* flowers, as 3-rhamnoside in *Rosa*.
5,7,3′,4′-Tetrahydroxyflavonol (quercitin) as the 3-rhamnoside in oak bark, the 3-glucoside in *Lea*.
5,7,2′,4′-Tetrahydroxyflavonol (morin) in *Morus tinctoria*.
5,7,3′,4′,5′-Pentahydroxyflavonol (myricetin) as the 3-rhamnoside in Myricaceae.

Flavonol

Flavanones containing phenolic groups have a characteristic absorption peak at 320 mμ when in neutral solution. Flavanones may be present in bagasse lignin. Each citrus species may contain a different flavanone glycoside.

5,7,4′-Trihydroxyflavanone (naringenin) as naringin, a glycoside with rhamnose and glucose, in fruits of *Citrus paradisi*.
5,7,-Dihydroxy-2′-methoxyflavanone (citronetin) as glycoside in citrus peel.
5,7,3′-Trihydroxy-4′-methoxylflavanone (hesperetin) as hesperidin, a glucoside with rhamnose and glucose, in fruits of *Citrus sinensis*.
5,7-Dihydroxy-6,8-dimethyl-4′-methoxylflavanone (Mattecinol) in leaves of *Matteucia orientalis*.

Flavanone

TABLE 10.3—contd.

Class	Examples	Notes
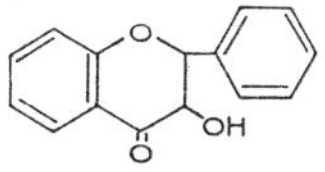 Flavanonol	5,7-Dihydroxyflavanonol (pinobanksin) in *Pinus* sp. 5-Hydroxy-7-methoxyflavanonol (alpinone) in *Alpinia japonica*. 5,7-Dihydroxy-6-methylflavanonol (strobokanksin) in *Pinus* sp. 5,7,4'-Trihydroxyflavanonol (aromadendrin) the most widely distributed flavanonol. 5,7,3',4'-Tetrahydroxyflavanonol (taxifolin) in heartwood of Douglas fir.	Flavanones and flavanonols can be detected on chromatograms by fuming in ammonia to produce grey-brown to red-brown colours. The flavanonols are of limited distribution and usually occur free.
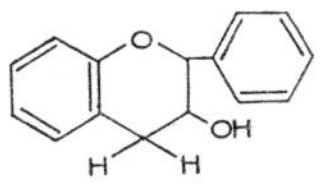 Catechin	5,7,3',4'-Tetrahydroxycatechin (catechin and epicatechin) in *Acacia* wood and tea leaves; also as the 3-galloyl ester. 5,7,3',4',5'-Pentahydroxycatechin (pyrogallolcatechin). 5,7,4'-Trihydroxy-3'-methoxycatechin (Arachidose) as glucoside (arachidoside) in seeds of *Arachis* sp.	Catechin has the *trans*-configuration and epicatechin the *cis*-configuration at C-3. The catechins have a marked tendency to polymerize and are widely distributed.
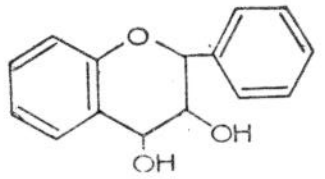 Leucoanthocyanidin	5,7,2,3',4'-Pentahydroxyleucoanthocyanidin in peanuts. 7,8,3',4'-Tetrahydroxyleucoanthocyanidin (melacidin) in heartwood of *Acacia melanoxylon*.	In dicotyledons the distribution of leucoanthocyanidins is strongly correlated with woodiness. They are present in ferns but not in lower plants. The leucoanthocyanins have tannin-like properties, e.g. they are strongly adsorbed on hide powder; give precipitates with gelatin and alkaloids and are astringent to the taste. The structure of leucoanthocyanidins has been established in very few cases, and the 3,5 diol structure is assumed.

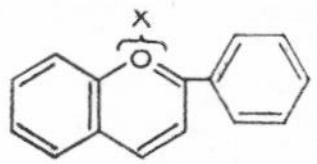

3,5,7,4'-Tetrahydroxyanthocyanidin (pelargonidin).
3,5,7,3',4'-Pentahydroxyanthocyanidin (cyanidin).
3,5,7,3',4',5'-Hexahydroxyanthocyanidin (delphinidin).
3,5,7,4'-Tetrahydroxy-3-methoxyanthocyanidin (peonidin).
3,5,7,4',5'-Pentahydroxy-3'-methoxyanthocyanidin (petunidin).
3,5,7,4'-Tetrahydroxy-3',5'-dimethoxyanthocyanidin (malvidin).
3,5,7,4'-Tetrahydroxy-4,3'-dimethoxyanthocyanidin (rosinidin).
3,5,4-Trihydroxy-7,3',5'-trimethoxyanthocyanidin (hirsutidin).
5,7,4'-Trihydroxyanthocyanidin (gesneridin).
6,7-Dihydroxy-5,4'-dimethoxyanthocyanidin (carajuridin).

Anthocyanidin
(× = monovalent
anion)

7-Hydroxy-4'-methoxyisoflavone (formononetin) in *Trifolium pratense.*
5,7-Dihydroxy-4'-methoxyisoflavone (biochanin A) *Cicer arietinum.*
5,7,4'-Trihydroxyisoflavone (genistein) in *Genista tinctoria* and *Soja hispida.*
6,4'-Dihydroxy-5,7-methoxyisoflavone (muningin) in *Pterocarpus angolensis.*
5,4-Dihydroxy-7-methoxyisoflavone (prunetin) in *Pterocarpus angolensis.*
5,7,3'-Trihydroxy-6,4',5'-trimethoxyisoflavone (iridin) as the 7-glucoside in *Iris florentina.*

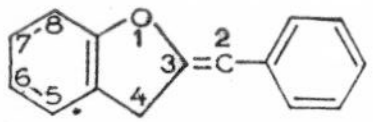

Isoflavone

5,7,3',4'-Tetrahydroxy benzalcoumaranone (aureusin) as the glycoside in yellow *Antirrhinium majus.*

Benzalcoumaranone

Anthocyanins are common; those based on the structure of cyanidin are the more numerous. Pelargonidin occurs frequently in tropical plants and delphinidin at higher altitudes. Gesneridin and carajuridin are rare. Hydroxylation is the main factor determining anthocyanin colour. Anthocyanidins are usually (perhaps always) present as glycosides.

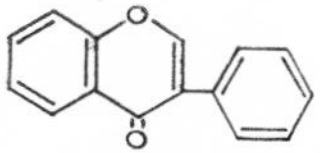

The rotenoids are closely related to the isoflavonoids.

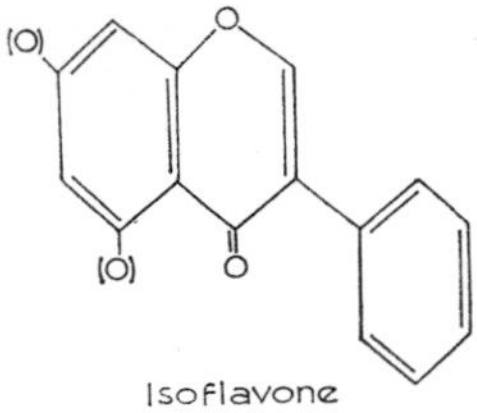

Isoflavone

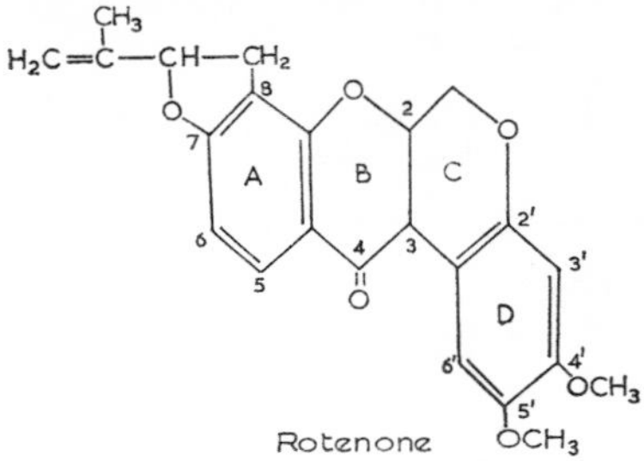

Rotenone

Rotenone is present in *Pachyrrhizus erosus* and *Derris malaccensis*. The rotenoids possess a tetracyclic C_{16}-nucleus comprising rings A, B, C and D with introduction of various groups such as a C_5 unit in rotenone, a C_2 unit in elliptone and a C_1 unit in munduserone.

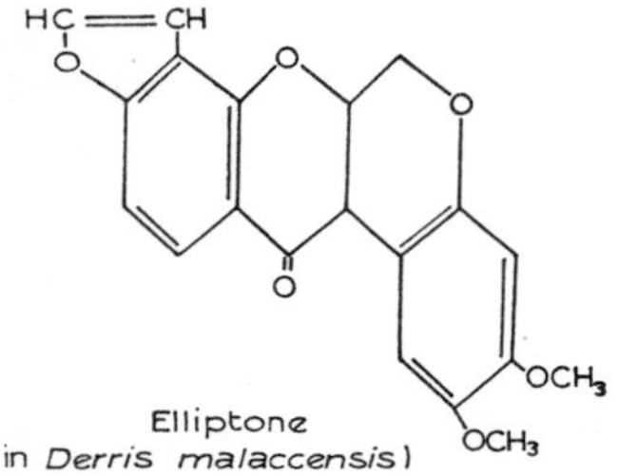

Elliptone
(in *Derris malaccensis*)

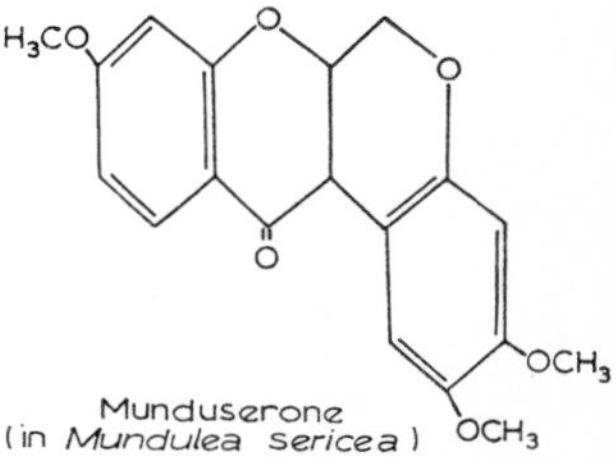

Munduserone
(in *Mundulea sericea*)

Feeding experiments have shown that acetate is an effective carbon source for the A ring whilst shikimic acid is a precursor of the B ring. Various phenyl propane derivatives such as phenylalanine and cinnamic acid, which are known to be formed by the shikimic pathway, are precursors of the C_3-interaryl unit. It follows that flavonoid synthesis involves condensation of an active C_9 unit with a C_6 unit derived from acetate.

Experiments with fungi have shown that acetate enters benzene rings via malonic acid. Thus the synthesis of 6-methyl salicylic acid involves the condensation of 3 moles of malonyl CoA and 1 mole of acetyl CoA. In flavonoid biosynthesis, it seems probable that a 'cinnamyl' CoA unit replaces acetyl CoA.

$$3\text{-malonyl CoA} + \text{'cinnamyl' CoA} \rightarrow$$
$$3\ CO_2 + \text{flavonoid}$$

The question of nuclear hydroxylation and methoxylation has not been resolved. Assuming that hydroxylation occurs prior to condensation, the hydroxylation pattern of the various cinnamyl CoA compounds would determine the position of hydroxyl groups on the B ring. Evidence to support this view is as follows:

(1) Hydroxylation patterns of cinnamic acids should be similar to that of the B ring of the flavonoid. Thus feeding phenylalanine-2-^{14}C to *Fagopyrum esculentium* yields labelled quercitin and caffeic acid.

(2) A single species may have a number of flavonoids with the same hydroxylation pattern. For example *Coreopsis maritima* contains esters of caffeic acid and seven flavonoids all with the 3′,4′hydroxylation.

(3) As noted on p. 398, the reactions whereby the cinnamic acids are hydroxylated are not readily reversible. Nevertheless hydroxylated cinnamic acids are readily incorporated into flavonoids. Thus, ferulic acid is incorporated into tricin (5,7,4′-trihydroxy-3′,5′-dimethoxyflavone) when supplied to wheat. On the other hand when similar data are examined quantitatively, it weakens the above argument. Thus the relative effectiveness of the following compounds as precursors of quercitin in *Fagopyrum tatarcium* is given by the order: shikimic acid > phenylalanine > cinnamic acid > caffeic acid > sinapic acid > ferulic acid.

The view that hydroxylation precedes condensation leads to the expectation that caffeic acid should be the most effective precursor of quercitin. However, if caffeic acid takes part in condensation as the CoA derivative, the effectiveness of caffeic acid may be limited by the rate at which it is activated.

(4) Much genetic information has been obtained concerning the anthocyanidins, which is equivocal, though generally consistent with the view that hydroxylation precedes condensation. For example, a homozygous recessive variety (mm) of *Antirrhinium majus* contains five 4′-hydroxyflavonoids, whereas flowers with the gene M contain four 4′,5′-dihydroxyflavonoids and only one 4′-hydroxyflavonoid. Flowers of the genotype (mm nn) do not form flavonoids, but contain 4- and 3,4-hydroxycinnamic acids.

The origin of the hydroxyl groups on the A ring remains uncertain.

The structure of the C_3 unit connecting the two aryl units is the basis for classifying the various flavonoids (Table 10.3). It is not yet clear whether there is a particular C_3 structure from which all others are formed or whether the structure of the C_3 unit is determined (whilst part of the phenylpropane unit) prior to condensation. Available evidence indicates that the above possibilities represent extremes and that modification of the C_3 unit takes place before and after condensation. General schemes of biosynthesis have been reviewed by Seshardi (1951 and 1959), Geissman & Hinreiner (1952) and Bogorad (1958). Here we present Figure 10.9 giving possible reactions involved in biosynthesis and restrict discussion to the limited amount of experimental evidence available.

Isoflavones. Feeding specifically labelled phenylalanine to *Trifolium pratense* leads to the formation of specifically labelled formononetin. The labelling pattern observed requires an aryl migration:

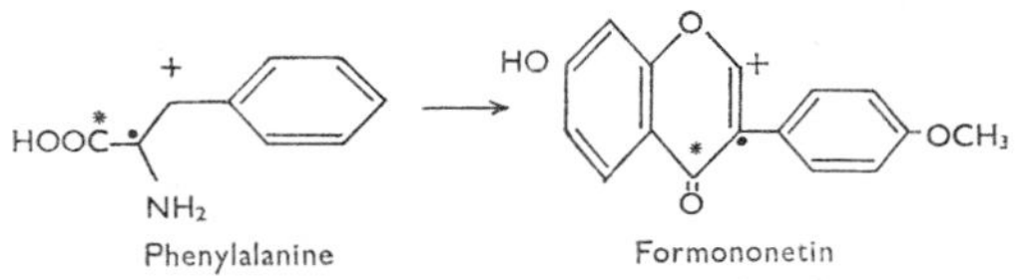

Phenylalanine   Formononetin

The mechanism of this conversion is unknown, but the demonstration that feeding labelled chalcone to *Trifolium pratense* produces labelled formononetin, suggests the possible sequence:

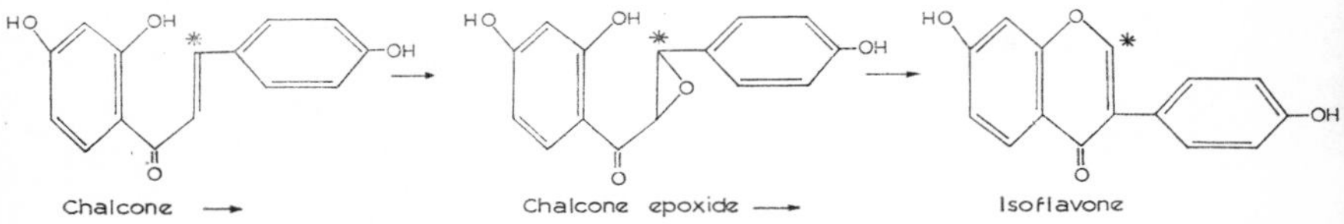

Chalcone ⟶   Chalcone epoxide ⟶   Isoflavone

Benzalcoumaranones. Enzymes have been isolated from ray cells of *Cosmos sulphureus* and *Coreopsis lanceolata* which catalyse the oxidation of hydroxychalcones to the corresponding benzalcoumaranone.

Anthocyanidins. The young colourless bracts of the banana flower contain leuco-cyanidin (i.e. the leucoanthocyanin which yields cyanidin after treatment with hot acid) and leucodelphinidin. As the flower ages the bracts become pigmented with glycosides of peonidin (3'-methoxy-cyanidin), cyanidin, malvidin (3',5'-dimethoxydelphinidin) and delphinidin, whilst the leucoanthocyanidins disappear. Maize kernels of the genetic constitution a_2a_2 prpr contain leucopelargonidin. Similarly kernels of the constitution a_2a_2 Pr contain leucocyanidin while A_2 Pr kernels contain a glycoside of cyanidin.

Much work has been done on the stimulation of anthocyanin synthesis by light, but it is probable that light has a general effect on flavonoid synthesis. The wavelengths which are effective in promoting anthocyanin

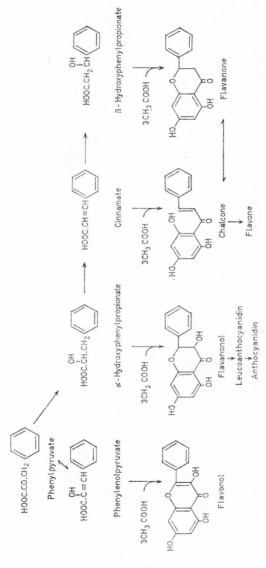

Fig, 10.9. Possible biosynthesis of flavonoides.

synthesis are not those involved in photosynthesis. The loci of light action is unknown. It has been suggested that light stimulates the production of the A ring and alternatively that it stimulates the production of the phenylpropane unit. The topic has been reviewed by Bogorad (1958).

POLYMERIC PHENOLIC COMPOUNDS — THE TANNINS

The tannins are a heterogeneous group of polyhydoxy phenolic compounds with molecular weights in the range 600–2000, and which combine with hide to form leather. Two main groups may be differentiated.

(A) Hydrolysable tannins which yield carbohydrates, usually glucose, and phenolic acids (e.g. gallic acid) by hydrolysis.

(B) Condensed or non-hydrolysable tannins which contain little carbohydrate and are converted into insoluble, amorphous phlobaphenes by the action of mineral acids.

The hydrolysable tannins may be subdivided into (1) the gallotannins, e.g. Turkish (*Quercus infectoria*, galls) and Sumach tannins (*Rhus coriaria*) in which gallic acid is the main phenolic compound produced by hydrolysis, and (2) the ellagitannins, e.g. myrobalans (*Terminitia chebula*) which yield ellagic acid as well as gallic acid on hydrolysis.

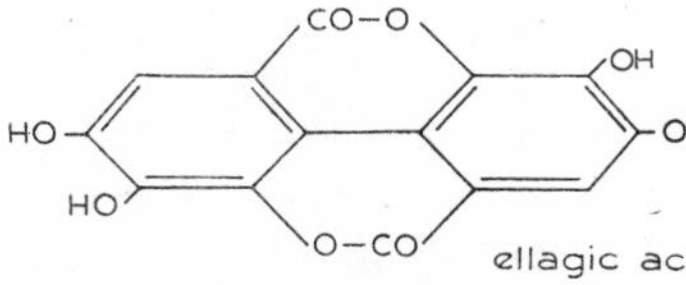

ellagic acid

The main constituent of Turkish gallotannin possesses a β-penta-*o*-galloylglucose nucleus to which additional galloyl residues are attached by depside links.

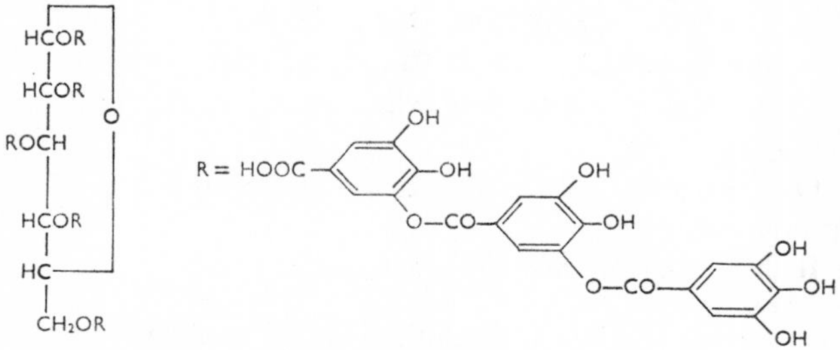

The main component of gallotannin

The main component of Tara tannin (*Caesalpinia spinosa*) does not contain glucose but is a galloylated quinic acid.

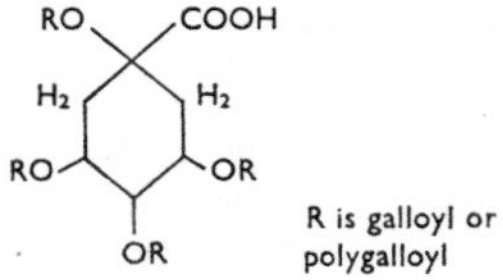

R is galloyl or
polygalloyl

The condensed tannins may be polymers of leucoanthocyanins or catechins or mixed polymers of flavonoids. A synthetic catechin polymer has been shown to have 8,6′ linkages.

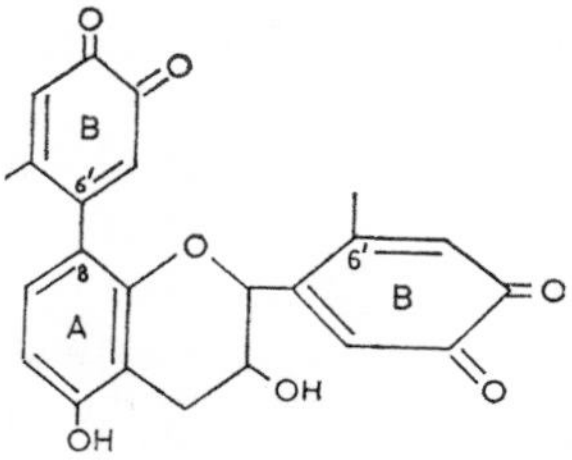

Similar structures have been demonstrated in tannins from *Acacia catechin* and *Uncaria gamper*.

This definition of tannins is in agreement with the views of White (1956) and defines the tannins used in industry. When used in a botanical context, the term tannin has a somewhat different meaning. The following tests have been taken as criteria for the presence of tannins in plants:

(1) The compound should form precipitates with gelatin, alkaloids, and formaldehyde plus hydrochloric acid.

(2) It should adsorb strongly to hide powder.

(3) It should give a red colour when treated with vanillin and strong acid.

(4) On treatment with hot acid the compound should give a red precipitate and

(5) It should have a markedly astringent taste.

Following these criteria leucoanthocyanins could be responsible for many 'tannin' reactions. In the case of *Eucalyptus* species it is probable that the leucoanthocyanins are the precursors of condensed tannins. Thus in *Eucalyptus marginata*, the sapwood contains leucoanthocyanins and the concentration increases at the sapwood heartwood boundary, where they are changed into insoluble condensed tannins.

The phenolic compounds have long been considered as end products of metabolism and much discussion given to their physiological significance. However, evidence is appearing which indicates that in certain cases these compounds are not metabolically inert. For example many leaves contain an anthocyanin decolorizing enzyme, but the product of the reaction has not been identified. Buckwheat seedlings incorporate carboxyl-labelled phenylalanine into rutin and cyanidin; after reaching a maximum, the specific activity of rutin and cyanidin declines, suggesting that both substances are metabolized. The benzalcoumarin scopoletin and its glycoside appear to be in equilibrium within tobacco tissue, but the equilibrium value is affected by auxin, kinetin levels. It has been suggested that scopoletin and its glycoside are involved in cell wall synthesis (Skoog & Montaldi, 1961).

READING LIST

CHIBNALL A.C. (1939) *Protein Metabolism in the Plant*. Yale Univ. Press

McELROY W.D. & GLASS B. (Ed.) (1955) *A Symposium on Amino Acid Metabolism*. Johns Hopkins Press, Baltimore

DAVIS B.D. (1955) Intermediates in Amino Acid Biosynthesis. *Adv. Enz.* **16**, 247

The Chemistry of Vegetable Tannins. A Symposium (1956). Geo. Marshall & Co., London

MEISTER A. (1957) *Biochemistry of the Amino Acids*. Acad. Press

BOGORAD L. (1958) The Biogenesis of Flavonoids. *Ann. Rev. Pl. Physiol.* **9**, 417

YEMM E.W. & FOLKES B.F. (1958) The Metabolism of Amino Acids and Proteins in Plants. *Ann. Rev. Pl. Physiol.* **9**, 245

WEBSTER G.C. (1959) *Nitrogen Metabolism in Plants*. Row-Peterson & Co., White Plains, New York

PORTER H.K. (Ed.) (1959) Utilisation of Nitrogen and its Compounds by Plants. *Symposia of the Society for Experimental Biology* **13**. Cambridge Univ. Press

HUENNEKENS F.M. & OSBORN M.J. (1959) Folic Acid Coenzymes and One-Carbon Metabolism. *Adv. Enz.* **21**, 369

NEISH A.C. (1960) Biosynthetic Pathways of Aromatic Compounds. *Ann. Rev. Pl. Physiol.* **11**, 81

BRAUNSTEIN A.E. (1960) Pyridoxal Phosphate. In *The Enzymes*. **2** Chapter 6. Ed. Boyer P.D., Lardy H. & Myrbäck K. Acad. Press, New York

PRIDHAM J.B. (Ed.) (1960) *Phenolics in Plants in Health and Disease*. Pergamon Press, Oxford

JAENICKE L. (1961) Die Folsaure im Staffwechsel der Einkohlenstoff-Einheiten. *Angewandte Chemie* **73**, 449

GRISEBACK H. & OLLIS W.D. (1961) Biogenetic Relationships between Coumarins, Isoflavonoids and Rotenoids. *Experientia* **17**, 4

LITERATURE CITED

ADLER E. (1957) *Tappi* **40**, 294

BERGERSEN F.J. (1960) *Bact. Rev.* **24**, 246

BOGORAD L. (1958) *Ann. Rev. Pl. Physiol.* **9**, 417

BOND G. (1959) *Symposia of the Society for Experimental Biology* **13**, 59

DAVIS B.D. (1955) *Adv. Enz.* **16**, 247

FAWCETT C.H. (1961) *Ann. Rev. Pl. Physiol.* **12**, 345

FOLKES B.F. (1959) *Symp. Soc. Exptl. Biol.* **13**, 126

FOWDEN L. (1958) *Biol. Rev.* **33**, 393

GEISSMAN T. A. & HINREINER E. (1952) *Bot. Rev.* **18**, 77

GORDON S.A. & PALEG L.G. (1961) *Pl. Physiol.* **36**, 838

KREBS H.A. & HENSELEIT K. (1932) *Z. Physiol. Chem.* **210**, 33

LANE B.G. & LIPMANN F. (1961) *J. Biol. Chem.* **236**, PC80

NEISH A.C. (1960) *Ann. Rev. Pl. Physiol.* **11**, 55.

SESHARDI R. (1959) *Tetrahedron* **6**, 169

SESHARDI T.R. (1951) *Ann. Rev. Biochem.* **20**, 487

SIEGEL S.M. (1956) *Quart. Rev. Biol.* **31**, 1

SKOOG F. & MONTALDI E. (1961) *Proc. Natl. Acad. Sci.* **47**, 36

SMITH D.C., BASSHAM J.A. & KIRK M. (1961) *Biochim. et Biophys. Acta* **48**, 299

WHITE T. (1956) *The Chemistry of the Vegetable Tannins. A Symposium.* Geo. Marshall
     & Co., London

WILSON D.G., KING K.W. & BURRIS R.H. (1954) *J. Biol. Chem.* **208**, 863

YANOFSKY C. (1960) *Bact. Rev.* **24**, 221

YOCUM C.S. (1960) *Ann. Rev. Pl. Physiol.* **11**, 25

CHAPTER 11

NUCLEIC ACIDS AND THE SYNTHESIS OF PROTEINS

Nucleic acid appears to be the universal and probably the sole genetic material. Present evidence indicates that genes function by controlling the specificity of protein synthesis. The inter-relationship between nucleic acids and proteins in the transmission of genetic information is a rapidly developing borderline subject involving both biochemistry and genetics. The relative simplicity of bacteria and viruses has made them the favourite choice for much of the work in this field. By contrast, the amount of data available for higher plants is limited.

Nucleic acids are high polymers of nucleotides. A nucleotide is a phosphate ester of a nucleoside, which is a purine or pyrimidine glycoside. The metabolism of the purines and pyrimidines is considered first.

PURINE BASES

The four purine bases are shown below:

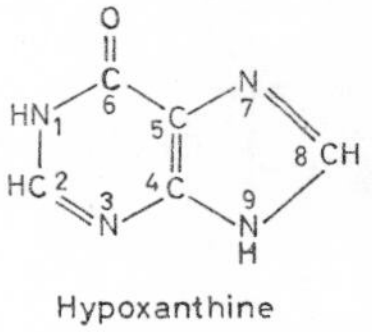

Hypoxanthine 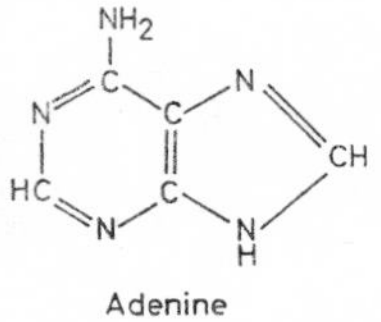   Adenine

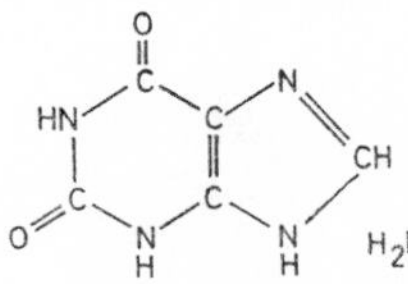

Xanthine 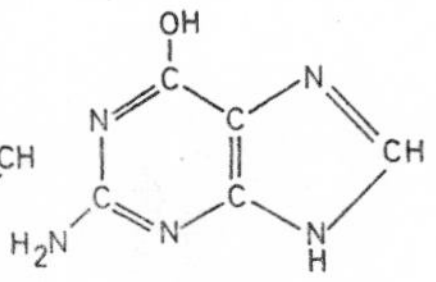   Guanine

Their biosynthesis has been extensively studied in animals and bacteria, but little work has been done with plants. The bases are formed as 5-phosphoribosyl compounds known as ribotides or ribonucleotides.

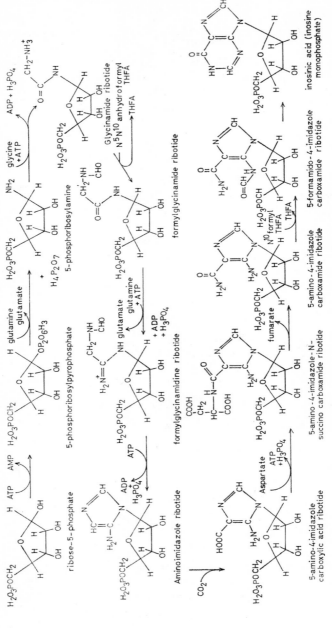

Fig. 11.1. Scheme for the biosynthesis of inosinic acid.

Inosinic acid is the parent nucleotide in the sense that the other nucleotides are formed from it. Tracer studies of inosine biosynthesis have shown its origin from the compounds shown below:

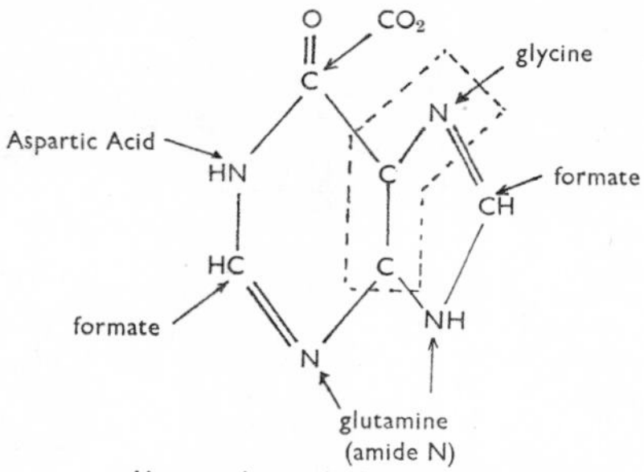

Hypoxanthine—the base of Inosine

The biosynthesis of inosinic acid is shown in Fig. 11.1.

The formation of 5-phosphoribosylpyrophosphate has been demonstrated with preparations of mitochondria from a number of plants. 5-Amino-4-imidazolecarboxamide-2-^{14}C has been shown to be an efficient precursor of purines in wheat embryos.

The reactions involved in the synthesis of xanthylic, guanylic and adenylic acid are shown in Fig. 11.2

Inosine-5-phosphate dehydrogenase has been demonstrated in pea seeds. Evidence has been presented that adenylosuccinase from yeast is identical with the succinocarboxamide ribotide-cleaving enzyme (Fig. 11.1).

The degradation of purines leads in many plants to the accumulation of the ureides, allantoin and allantoic acid.

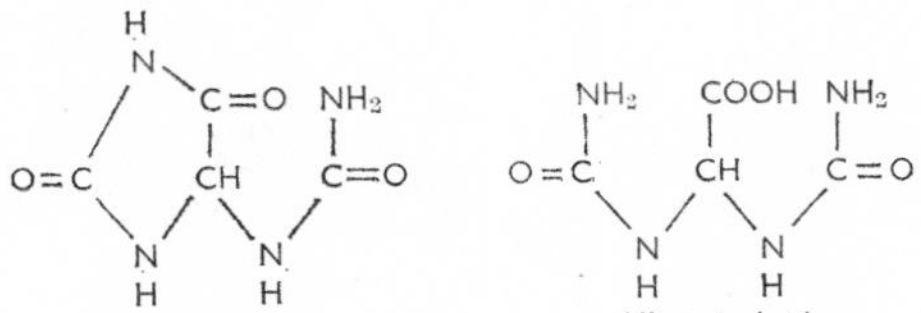

Allantoin Allantoic Acid

In certain plants these ureides seem to play a role in storage and translocation (Bollard, 1959). Adenine-8-^{14}C labels allantoic acid, allantoin and urea when supplied to leaves of *Acer saccharinum*. Hypoxanthine-

27

8-^{14}C and glycine-2-^{14}C label allantoin when supplied to sterile root cultures of *Symphytum uplandicum*, but little or no label is found in

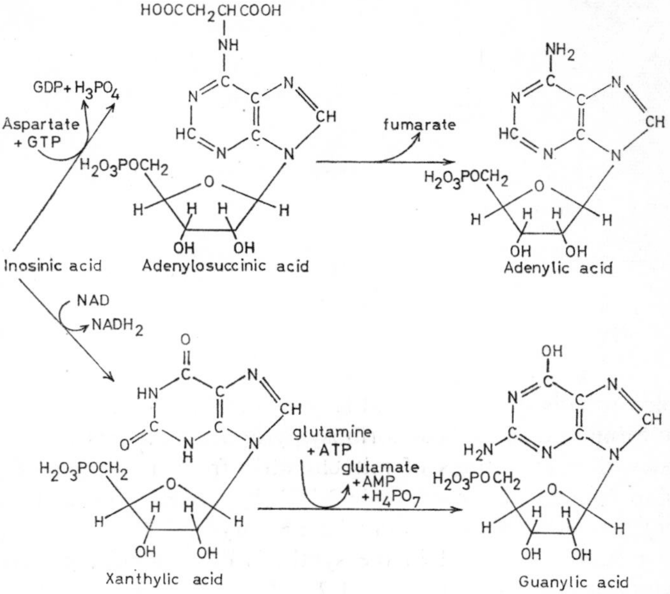

Fig. 11.2. Reactions involved in the biosynthesis of adenylic, xanthylic and guanylic acids.

allantoic acid or urea. These results suggest that glycine is incorporated into purine bases which are subsequently converted to allantoin. The distribution of label (derived from glycine-2-^{14}C) in allantoin is in agreement with a pathway involving purines, labelled as shown below:

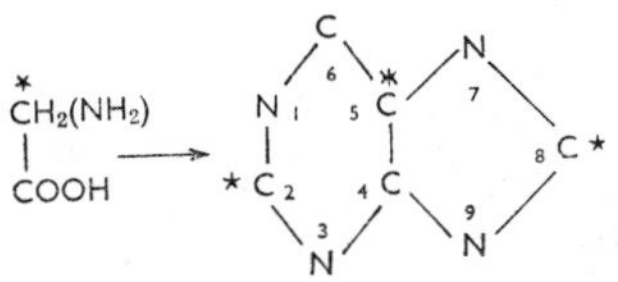

Label in positions C2 and C8 reflects the conversion of glycine-2-^{14}C to an active Cl unit. Label in C5 is in agreement with the reactions shown in Fig. 11.1.

The formation of allantoic acid is thought to proceed by the reaction:

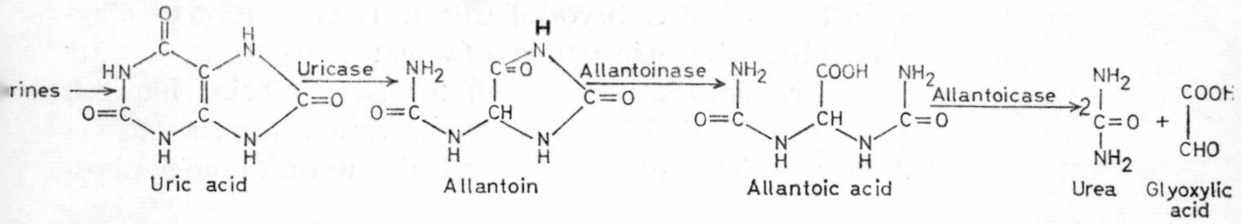

Uricase has been demonstrated in a number of seeds and allantoinase has been found in many growing plants. Allantoicase has been found only in seedlings of soya bean.

PYRIMIDINE BASES

The four most important pyrimidine bases are shown below:

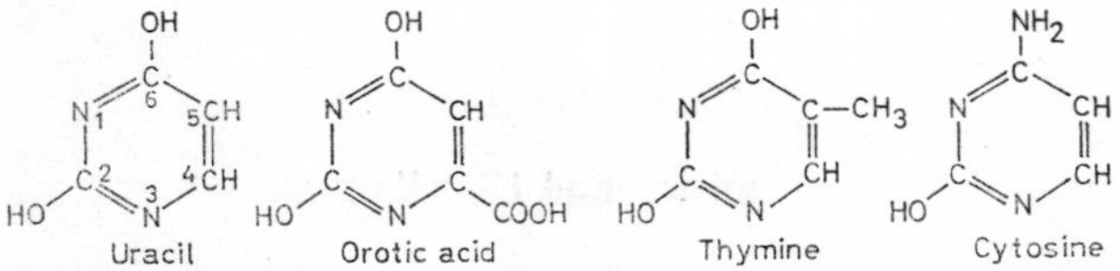

Reactions involved in the biosynthesis of orotic acid are shown in Fig. 11.3.

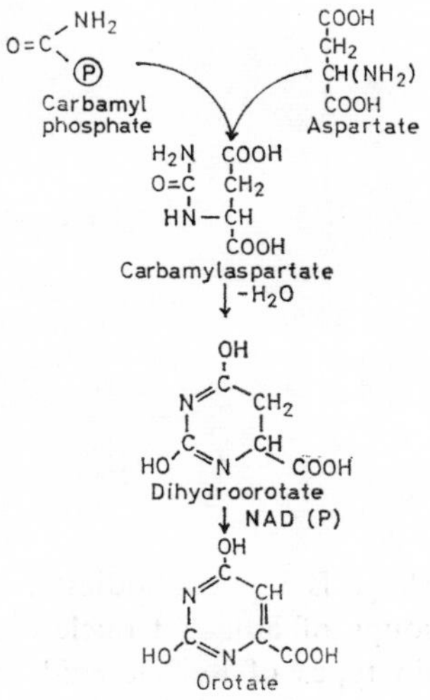

Fig. 11.3. Biosynthesis of orotic acid.

The incorporation of aspartate-2-^{14}C into pyrimidines has been demonstrated in leaves and embryos of wheat. The oxidation of dihydro-orotic acid has been shown in extracts of wheat embryos, and appears to involve a flavoprotein, the requirement for NADP being indirect. The formation of other pyrimidine bases from orotic acid proceeds via the ribosyl derivative. Thus orotic acid gives rise to orotidine-5'-phosphate.

orotate + 5-phosphoribosylpyrophosphate⇌orotidine-5'-
$$\text{phosphate} + \text{pyrophosphate}$$

The enzyme orotidine-5'-phosphate pyrophosphorylase has been demonstrated in wheat embryos. The reactions involved in the synthesis of uridylic, cytidylic and thymidylic acids are shown in Fig. 11.4.

NUCLEIC ACIDS

Chemistry and Distribution

Nucleic acids have the general structure:

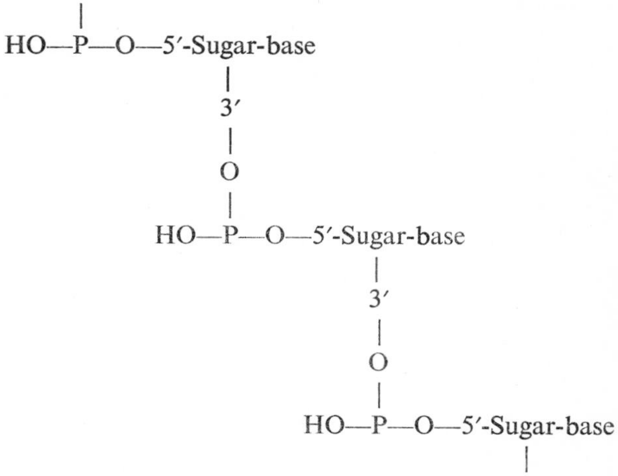

$$
\begin{array}{c}
| \\
\text{HO—P—O—5'-Sugar-base} \\
| \\
3' \\
| \\
O \\
| \\
\text{HO—P—O—5'-Sugar-base} \\
| \\
3' \\
| \\
O \\
| \\
\text{HO—P—O—5'-Sugar-base} \\
|
\end{array}
$$

The internucleotide linkage is a phosphodiester bond formed between the sugar hydroxyl groups of adjacent nucleosides. According to the sugar present two main types of nucleic acid are recognized, deoxyribonucleic acid (DNA) and ribonucleic acid (RNA). Both DNA and RNA occur in all living cells. Extracts of nucleic acids show consider-

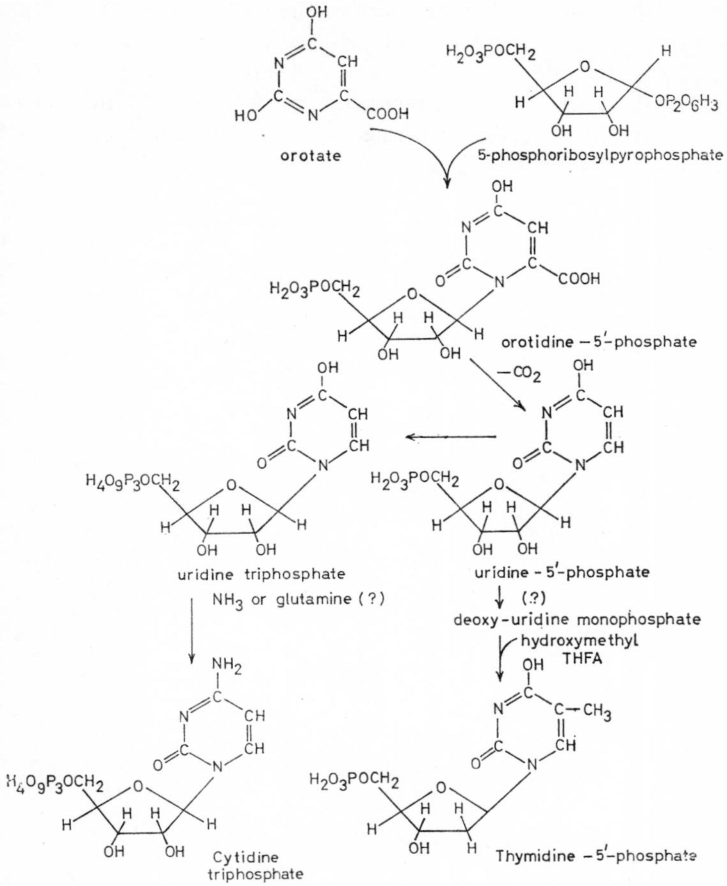

Fig. 11.4. Biosynthesis of uridine triphosphate, cytidine triphosphate and thymidine phosphate.

able heterogeneity, which is particularly marked with RNA. The lack of pure preparations of homogeneous nucleic acid has prevented the elucidation of their detailed structures.

DEOXYRIBONUCLEIC ACID

Analyses of DNA from many sources indicate that deoxyribose is the only sugar present in appreciable amounts and that guanine, adenine, thymine and cytosine comprise most of the bases. DNA from higher plants generally contains 5-methyl cytosine in addition to the above bases. The purine and pyrimidine nucleosides found in plant DNA are 9- and 3- β-D-(2'-deoxy) ribofuranosides respectively. The internucleotide bonds are almost certainly formed between carbons 3' and 5' of the deoxyribose moieties of adjacent nucleotides (Fig. 11.5).

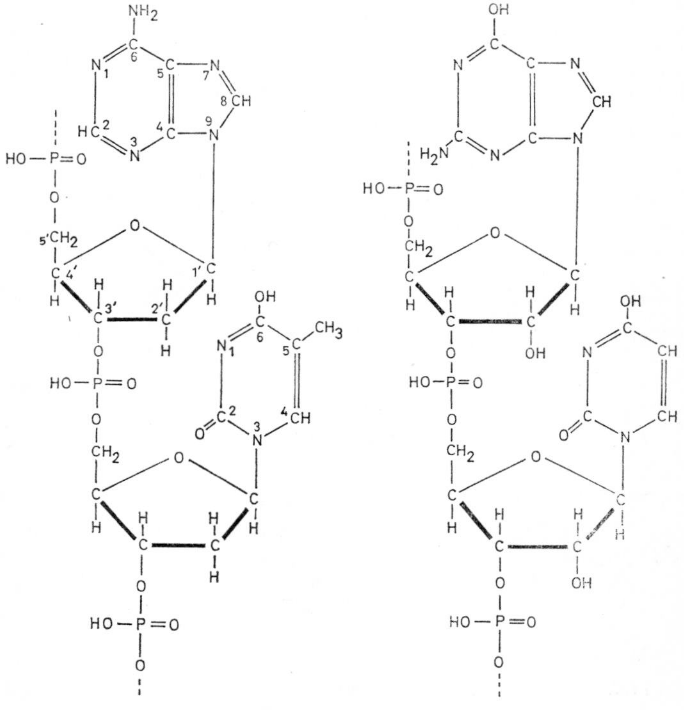

Deoxyadenylyl - (3'→5')-thymidylyl   Guanylyl - (3'→5') - uridylyl

Fig. 11.5. Internucleotide bonds of nucleic acids.

Estimates of the number of nucleotides in DNA vary considerably. Molecular weights of $5–7 \times 10^6$ are frequently reported but there is evidence that the true molecular weights are in the region of 50×10^6.

The relative proportions of the different bases have been determined for DNA from a wide range of organisms. Data from plants are given in Table 11.1.

TABLE 11.1

Base ratios of plant DNA

Proportion of bases as molar percentages

Origin	Guanine	Adenine	Cytosine	5-Methyl cytosine	Thymine
Daucus carota (leaf)	23·2	26·7	17·3	6·0	26·8
Pinus siberica (seed)	20·8	29·2	14·6	4·9	30·5
Cucurbita pepo (seed)	21·0	30·2	16·1	3·7	29·0
Phaseolus vulgaris (seed)	20·6	29·7	14·9	5·2	29·6
Gossypium hirsutum (embryos)	16·9	32·8	12·7	4·6	32·9
Zea mays (germ)	22·8	26·8	17·0	6·2	27·2
Allium cepa (seed)	18·4	31·8	12·8	5·4	31·3
			Cytosine + 5-Methyl cytosine		
Scenedesmus accuminatus	32·9	18·7	30·9		17·5
Rhabdonema adriaticum	18·6	31·4	18·3		31·7

Similar data have been obtained from animals and micro-organisms. DNA is characterized by equivalence between adenine and thymine and between guanine and cytosine+methyl cytosine. The base pairing between purines and pyrimidines is the result of limitations imposed by hydrogen bonding in the Watson and Crick model for DNA (p. 422). No differences have been detected in the base ratios of DNA from different tissues of the same organism.

An immense number of different DNA molecules can result from variation in the sequence in which the bases are arranged along the sugar phosphate backbone. As yet it has not been possible to determine the complete base sequence for any molecule of DNA. However, there is sufficient experimental data from a number of sources, including rye germ, to show that the bases in DNA are not randomly arranged and to indicate strongly that DNA from a given species is characterized by a unique sequence of bases.

The configuration of the DNA molecule has been extensively studied. Watson and Crick proposed a model structure which, with few modifications, has been generally accepted as representing the basic arrangement of the nucleotides in DNA.

The most important features of this model are:

(i) The molecule consists of two polynucleotide chains held in a double helix. The two chains both follow a right-handed helix around the same axis but the carbon atoms in the two sugar phosphate chains run in opposite directions.

(ii) The two chains are held together by hydrogen bonding between the bases which are arranged on the inside of each chain.

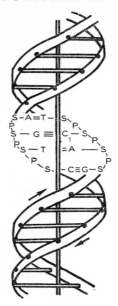

(iii) The sugar phosphate helix is regular, thus the glycosidic bonds bearing opposing bases will always occur at the same distance apart. This limits the possible base pairs. Two purines would not fit into the available space and two pyrimidines would be too far apart for hydrogen bonding to occur between them. The hydrogen bond distances restrict the possible base pairs to adenine with thymine and guanine with cytosine or 5-methyl cytosine (Fig. 11.6). Such an arrangement explains the equivalence found in the base ratios of DNA.

This structure for DNA places no restriction upon the base sequence in a given chain. However, the sequence in one chain determines that in the other, so that one chain is always the complement of the other. For example, if one chain is T—G—G—A—C—T the other will be A—C—C—T—G—A.

Studies with isolated DNA indicate that it can exist in a number of closely related forms which differ mainly in the pitch of the helix.

With the exception of a number of viruses, particularly those from plants, DNA is regarded as the major and possibly the sole genetic material. DNA appears to be a universal constituent of chromosomes and the content per nucleus of a particular species is, with few excep-

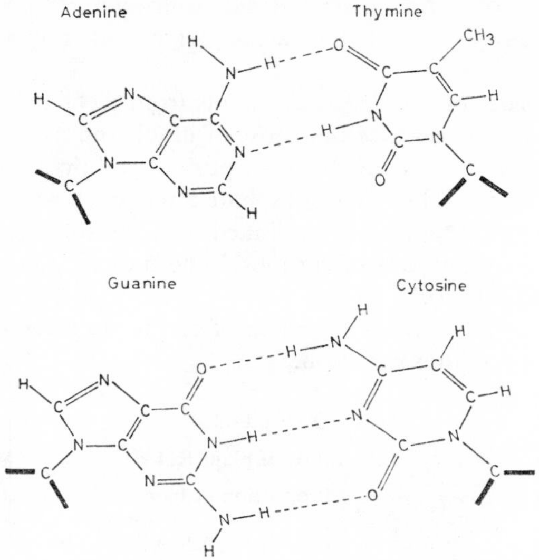

Fig. 11.6. Postulated base pairing between two strands of DNA.

tions, constant for a given level of ploidy. Most of the DNA of plants is found in the chromosomes in close association with proteins. The characteristic proteins of plant nuclei are histones which are low molecular weight basic proteins. Increases in the level of histones coincide with DNA synthesis in a variety of plant tissues.

DNA is not universally confined to the nucleus. Large quantities are found in the cytoplasm of the eggs of some animals, and there are a number of reports of the extranuclear occurrence of DNA in plants.

Little is known of the way in which DNA is arranged within the chromosome. Genetical and cytological studies imply a longitudinal arrangement of DNA which is specific and constant for a given chromosome. Chromosomes are multistranded structures and it is conceivable that a single molecule of DNA extends along the whole length of each strand.

RIBONUCLEIC ACID

Most, if not all, of the sugar of RNA is D-ribose. Adenine, guanine, cytosine and uracil were thought to be the only bases in RNA, but more recent analyses have revealed the presence of small amounts of a number of other bases. There is evidence that RNA from higher plants contains small amounts of 5-ribosyluracil (pseudo-uridine), thymine, 5-methyl cytosine, 1-methyl guanine and a number of other methylated base derivatives.

The nucleosides of adenine and guanine from RNA have been shown to be 9-β-D-ribofuranosides and those of uracil and cytosine to be 3-β-D-ribofuranosides. Probably the other purines and pyrimidines of RNA are similarly linked. The monophosphate esters of these nucleosides are the monomers of RNA. They are linked by a phosphodiester bond between the hydroxyl groups of carbons 3 and 5 of the ribose of adjacent nucleotides (Fig. 11.5).

Base ratios of RNA from a number of plants are given in Table 11.2. These ratios show little variation.

TABLE 11.2

Base ratios of plant RNA

Origin	Proportion of bases as molar percentages			
	Guanine	Adenine	Cytosine	Uracil
Xanthium sp. (vegetative and flowering shoots)	30·8	22·8	23·9	22·5
Pinus sibirica (seeds)	31·3	25·1	24·3	19·3
Papaver somniferum (seeds)	30·3	25·3	25·1	19·3
Cucurbita pepo (seeds)	30·6	25·2	24·8	19·4
Phaseolus vulgaris (seeds)	31·4	24·9	24·1	19·6
Allium cepa (seeds)	29·8	24·9	24·7	20·6
Scenedesmus accuminatus	32·9	18·7	30·9	17·5

The purine and pyrimidine contents are not equal. In contrast to DNA there is no general equivalence between 6-amino purines and 6-keto pyrimidines, or 6-keto purines and 6-amino pyrimidines. This pattern conforms to that found in RNA from animals and bacteria with the exception of soluble RNA (s-RNA).

s-RNA has a helical structure similar to that of DNA. The molecule is envisaged as being folded back upon itself so that the order of the atoms in one half of the molecule runs in the opposite direction to that in the other. The halves of the molecule are regarded as being equivalent to the two chains of DNA. The molecular configuration of other types of RNA is not yet known, largely because they have not been crystallized. The order in which the bases occur in RNA molecules has not yet been determined, but available evidence shows that it is not random.

At least two types of RNA occur in plant cells, ribosomal RNA and soluble or transfer RNA. Ribosomes are ribonucleoprotein particles which appear to be the site of protein synthesis. Ribosomes from different sources show similarities in composition and structure. Preparations of ribosomes consist almost entirely of RNA and protein and have a relatively high content of divalent cations. Ribosomes from pea seedlings are reported to contain 40 per cent RNA, 60 per cent protein and 4 moles of divalent cation per mole of base. Ribosomal RNA contains only very small quantities of unusual bases, and has a molecular weight in the region 5×10^5–1×10^6.

Preparations of ribosomes from peas and other organisms contain particles which differ in molecular weight and shape. There appear to be two basic particles which become reversibly aggregated with increasing concentrations of magnesium. The different particles are often described by their sedimentation coefficients (S) in the ultracentrifuge. The following inter-relationship has been proposed for particles from *E. coli*.

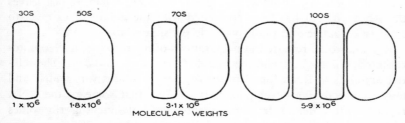

The values for the molecular weights agree closely with theoretical expectations. There is some evidence that the different particles all contain RNA and protein in the same proportion.

The manner in which the RNA and protein are arranged in ribosomes is not known. Pea ribosomal protein has been degraded into twelve sub-units.

Most of the ribosomes of plant cells appear to occur free in the cytoplasm or attached to the outside of the endoplasmic reticulum (a network of lipoprotein membranes found in the cytoplasm). Ribosomes are frequently isolated still attached to, or otherwise contaminated with, varying amounts of these membranes. Such particles are termed microsomes.

Soluble RNA (s-RNA) is composed of relatively small molecules containing from 75–100 nucleotides. s-RNA from plants appears to be similar to that described from animals and bacteria. There is evidence that the s-RNA of wheat germ is characterized by a much higher proportion of unusual bases than the ribosomal RNA. The base ratios of s-RNA from *Vigna sesquipedalis* differ from those of ribosomal RNA of the same tissue. Plant s-RNA has not yet been shown to possess the base equivalence reported for s-RNA from other organisms. Evidence from animals and micro-organisms suggests that there are specific types of s-RNA for each of the protein amino acids. s-RNA molecules are terminated by guanosine-5'-monophosphate at one end and by the sequence

adenyl-5'→3'- cytidyl-5'→3'- cytidyl-5'→3'—

at the other. The latter sequence is essential for attachment to amino acids and the specificity is probably determined by the nucleotide sequence within the molecule.

The amount of RNA present in plant cells varies considerably. During the development of pea roots the amount of RNA increases proportionally with the amount of protein. In general, RNA is present in greatest amounts in cells which are synthesizing protein. In pea leaves the RNA content has been correlated with the ability of extracts to catalyse oxidative and photosynthetic phosphorylation.

RNA has been reported in preparations of microsomes, nuclei, mitochondria, chloroplasts and the soluble fraction of plant cells. The relative amounts of RNA found in the different fractions vary widely and may change during development. It is likely that some of the RNA reported for different fractions represents contaminating ribosomes which probably contain the bulk of the RNA. Whether the proportion of RNA found in the ribosomes is as high as the 90 per cent reported for animals and micro-organisms is not yet clear. RNA occurs in plant nuclei, both in the nucleolus and in close association with the chromosomes. At least some of the nuclear RNA is present in the form of ribosomes. That RNA is normally associated with plant mitochondria is indicated by electron micrographs which show the presence of electron dense particles with the appearance of ribosomes. Further, purified RNase has been shown to lower the oxidative and phosphorylative activities of plant mitochondria. It has been suggested that some of the RNA reported present in chloroplasts is located in ribosomes within the chloroplast.

Metabolism

DNA

Most of the DNA in plants appears to be synthesized between the telophase of one division and the prophase of the next. There is little data available on the mechanism of DNA synthesis in plants but an enzyme which catalyses the formation of DNA from deoxyribonucleoside-5′-triphosphates has been demonstrated in bacteria and animals. This enzyme, DNA polymerase, has been purified and catalyses the following reaction:

$$
\begin{array}{l}
\text{n (dATP)} \\
\qquad + \\
\text{n (dGTP)} \\
\qquad + \qquad + \text{DNA} \rightharpoonup \text{DNA} \\
\text{n (dCTP)} \\
\qquad + \\
\text{n (TTP)}
\end{array}
\quad
\left[
\begin{array}{c}
\text{dAP} \\
| \\
\text{dGP} \\
| \\
\text{dCP} \\
| \\
\text{TP}
\end{array}
\right]_n
\quad + 4n\text{PP}
$$

dATP, dGTP etc. = deoxyribonucleoside triphosphate

Magnesium, primer DNA and the 5′-triphosphates of all four deoxyribonucleosides are essential. Under these conditions a net synthesis of polynucleotide corresponding to 2–20 times the amount of primer added can be demonstrated. An enzyme from a given species is active with primer DNA from a wide range of organisms. There is evidence that primer DNA must be in a single stranded form before it is effective. The enzyme from calf thymus is inactive with native DNA but active with single stranded DNA from 'phage ϕX–174 or native DNA which has been heated.

The synthesis of DNA *in vivo* may be presumed to be normally an exact duplication of existing DNA. It is therefore important to establish whether the product of DNA polymerase is a precise replica of the primer DNA. Comparison of the product with the primer has not revealed any significant differences between the two. They are alike in sedimentation coefficient, viscosity, molecular weight, internucleotide linkage and base ratios.

Evidence of a closer similarity between primer and product DNA has been obtained from Kornberg's laboratory. The four nucleotides of DNA can be linked 5'→3' to form only 16 different dinucleotides. These dinucleotides have been called nearest neighbour base pairs. The frequency with which these different dinucleotides occur in DNA synthesized by cell free preparations can be determined. DNA polymerase catalyses the esterification of the phosphate attached to C5' of the deoxyribose of the nucleoside triphosphates. This phosphate is esterified with C3' of the deoxyribose of another nucleotide. If DNA polymerase acts upon TPP, dATP, dCTP and dGT^{32}P and the resulting DNA is hydrolysed to nucleoside-3'-phosphates, the ^{32}P will be transferred from the dGT^{32}P to all the nucleotides with which it was linked 5'→3'. By measuring the ^{32}P content of each of the four nucleoside-3'-phosphates it is possible to determine the frequency of the different nearest neighbour base pairs for guanine. Similar data can be obtained for the other bases.

Studies of the pattern of nearest neighbour base frequencies in the product of DNA polymerase show:

(i) The pattern varies with the source of the primer, each different primer giving rise to DNA in which the pattern is non random and apparently unique.

(ii) In all instances studied the formation of the pattern involved base pairing between adenine and thymine and between guanine and cytosine.

There is thus strong evidence that DNA polymerase catalyses the synthesis of DNA which is an exact copy of the primer. This property and the evidence that the deoxyribonucleoside-5'-triphosphates are the only compounds known to serve as precursors for DNA indicate that DNA polymerase may catalyse the synthesis of DNA *in vivo*. It is probable that a double helix of DNA splits or unwinds into two single strands which act as primers to give two new double stranded DNA molecules of identical structure.

DNA is considered to be metabolically stable. There is evidence that its rate of turnover is slow in rapidly growing bacterial and animal cells. Autoradiographic evidence indicates that the chromosomal material of plants does not extensively break down and reform between divisions.

A number of plants have been shown to contain enzymes which appear similar to the DNases studied in animals and micro-organisms. DNases are phosphodiesterases which hydrolyse the internucleotide links within the DNA chain. The exact products of the reaction are not known. A DNase from barley catalyses the partial degradation of DNA leaving a residue noticeably rich in thymine. Rye grass DNase has been shown to form 5′-monoesters and to have little preference for linkages between different nucleotides.

RNA

There is evidence that plants contain two enzymes capable of synthesizing polyribonucleotides. A fraction containing most of the DNA of pea seedlings appears to catalyse the formation of RNA according to the following reaction:

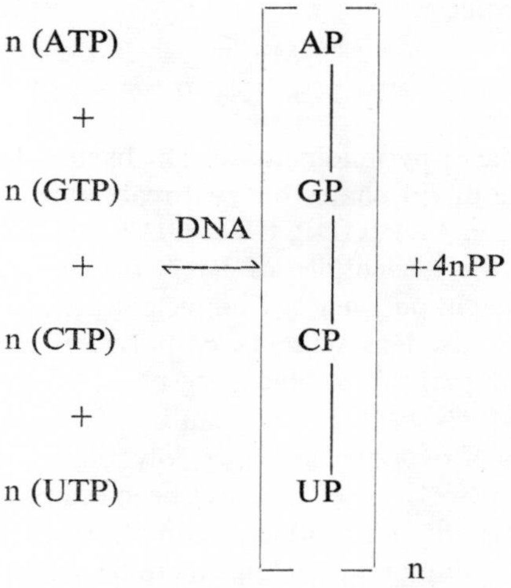

$$
\begin{array}{c}
n\,(\text{ATP}) \\
+ \\
n\,(\text{GTP}) \\
+ \\
n\,(\text{CTP}) \\
+ \\
n\,(\text{UTP})
\end{array}
\quad\xrightarrow{\text{DNA}}\quad
\left[\begin{array}{c}
\text{AP} \\
| \\
\text{GP} \\
| \\
\text{CP} \\
| \\
\text{UP}
\end{array}\right]_n
\;+\;4n\text{PP}
$$

All four ribonucleoside triphosphates are required. A similar enzyme, RNA polymerase, has been demonstrated in animals and bacteria. Studies with preparations from bacteria have established that all four ribonucleosides are incorporated into RNA, mostly in non terminal positions. Both the animal and bacterial enzymes have an absolute requirement for DNA. It is likely that this is also true of the plant enzyme since partial removal of DNA results in partial inhibition of RNA synthesis. There is evidence that the DNA required by this enzyme acts as a template which orders the base sequence in the newly formed RNA. The enzyme from *Micrococcus lysodeikticus* functions equally effectively with DNA from a range of different organisms. The base ratios (equating thymine with uracil) and the pattern of nearest neighbour base frequencies of the product RNA are identical with those of the primer DNA. Studies with the pea enzyme indicate a close relationship between the DNA primer and the newly synthesized RNA. The two nucleic acids form an association with protein in which the structure is unknown except that the ratio of RNA to DNA is 1 : 2. There is evidence of naturally occurring DNA–RNA complexes.

These observations are consistent with the hypothesis that plants contain an RNA polymerase which synthesizes RNA in which the base sequence is directly determined by DNA.

There is evidence that spinach leaves contain a polynucleotide phosphorylase, which catalyses the polymerization of ribonucleoside diphosphates according to:

$$\text{n(X—R—PP)} \overset{\text{Mg}}{\rightleftharpoons} \text{(X—R—P)n} + \text{nP}$$

where X is a purine or pyrimidine base. The bacterial enzyme is specific for ribonucleoside diphosphates but will react with those containing a variety of bases, e.g. ADP, GDP, CDP, UDP and IDP. In the presence of a mixture of the nucleotides of RNA the enzyme forms a linear high molecular weight polymer of ribonucleotides linked $5' \rightarrow 3'$ through phosphodiester bonds. This synthetic co-polymer resembles RNA.

With a partially purified enzyme a lag phase precedes the formation of polymer. Although this lag phase can be eliminated by the addition of small amounts of oligonucleotide or polynucleotide, an absolute dependence upon such a "primer" has not been established. The relationship between "primer" and product is complicated. The effect of oligonucleotides in overcoming the lag appears to be unspecific. For example, a compound composed of adenylic acid units will prime the polymerization of UDP as well as that of ADP.

Limited specificity has been noted with the polynucleotide primers. RNA from a variety of sources is effective in promoting the synthesis of the RNA like copolymer. Comparison of the base ratios of primer RNA and the synthetic polymer revealed that the composition of the product was determined by the relative concentrations of the substrates and not by the composition of the primer.

The polynucleotide phosphorylase reaction is readily reversible and the enzyme will degrade RNA from a variety of sources, though s-RNA appears to be resistant.

The "pH 5" fraction of animal and bacterial cells catalyses the terminal addition of cytidine-5'-phosphate and adenine-5'-phosphate from the corresponding triphosphates to the 3' OH ends of s-RNA. Nuclear and ribosomal RNA do not serve as substrates. Only three nucleotide residues appear to be added. The order cytidine, cytidine, terminating with adenine appears to be the same for all s-RNA molecules. The reaction requires magnesium, is reversible and is a prerequisite for the formation of amino acyl—RNA compounds. The importance of the latter in protein synthesis (p. 435) makes it likely that similar enzymes are present in plants.

The mechanism of RNA synthesis *in vivo* in plants has not been established. The properties of RNA polymerase make it likely that at least some of the cellular RNA is synthesized by this enzyme. The role of polynucleotide phosphorylase is not apparent. The lack of means to ensure exact replication and its limited distribution (apparently absent from animals and some plants) argue against the synthesis of RNA by polynucleotide phosphorylase. It is possible that the main role of this enzyme is degradative.

The site of RNA synthesis in plant and animal cells is not known. The nucleolus is often regarded as the site of synthesis. In fact recent studies with isolated pea nuclei suggest that RNA is synthesized in the chromosome fraction.

The degradation of RNA in plants could be catalysed by polynucleotide phosphorylase or the widely distributed RNase. RNase is a phosphodiesterase which cleaves the internucleotide bonds of RNA (Fig. 11.7).

All known plant RNases can hydrolyse RNA completely to ribonucleoside-2′,3′-cyclic phosphates. The plant enzymes differ from those from animals in that they catalyse the cleavage of bonds between any of the different nucleotides. However, there is evidence that plant RNase shows a preference for links involving guanosine. RNase from rye grass and the purified enzyme from spinach also catalyse the hydrolysis of both pyrimidine and purine nucleoside cyclic phosphates to the corresponding nucleoside-3′-phosphates. RNase from tobacco and pea plants hydrolyses the cyclic phosphates of purine nucleosides slowly and no activity was detected with those of the pyrimidine nucleosides.

PROTEIN SYNTHESIS

The Site of Protein Synthesis

Subcellular particles from plants and animals catalyse the incorporation of amino acids into polypeptides. This incorporation represents the addition or exchange of amino acids to the ends of peptide chains. A net synthesis of protein has been reported with pea ribosomes

28

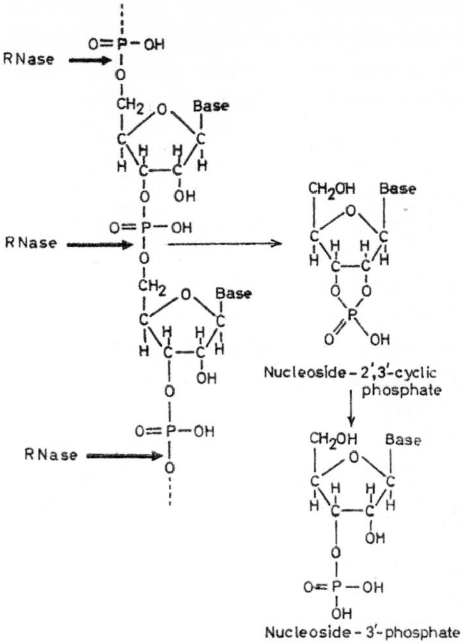

Fig. 11.7. Action of RNase.

supplied with the 20 amino acids and amides usually found in protein, together with ATP, GTP, $MnCl_2$, $MgCl_2$, s-RNA and a system for re-generating ATP. The ability of pea ribosomes to catalyse protein synthesis *in vitro*, and the correlation between the level of RNA and protein synthesis, strongly suggest that ribosomes are the site of protein synthesis *in vivo*. This view is supported by the finding that when leucine-^{14}C is supplied to discs of tobacco leaves, the greatest initial incorporation of label is found in the microsomal fraction.

Plant nuclei, mitochondria and chloroplasts have also been reported to synthesize protein. Carefully isolated nuclei from peas incorporate labelled leucine into protein in the presence of the other protein amino acids and ATP. Protein synthesis in plant mitochondria does not seem to have been conclusively demonstrated since contamination by ribosomes has not been excluded. The incorporation of amino acids into protein has been shown to be catalysed by chloroplast preparations.

It has been proposed that all protein synthesis takes place in ribosomes. There is insufficient data to decide whether this is true for plants. The reports that protein synthesis may occur in nuclei, mitochondria and chloroplasts are not necessarily at variance with this hypothesis, since there is evidence that these organelles contain ribosomes.

The Precursors of Proteins

Amino acids are generally regarded as the precursors of proteins. The chief evidence for this view is:

(i) Protein synthesis by isolated pea ribosomes is almost totally inhibited in the absence of any one of the protein amino acids.

(ii) Certain amino acid analogues are incorporated into specific proteins.

(iii) The kinetics of incorporation of ammonia-^{15}N into the amino acids and protein of yeast in log phase are consistent with the view that the protein was formed from the amino acids and that any intermediate must occur in very small amounts.

An alternative hypothesis has been proposed. It argues that plant proteins are formed by a condensation of compounds derived from carbohydrate with amino donors like glutamine. This hypothesis has not been generally accepted (Yemm and Folkes, 1958).

The Reactions of Protein Synthesis

Thermodynamic considerations and the demonstration that ATP is necessary for the *in vitro* synthesis of protein establish that proteins cannot be synthesized by the reversal of proteolysis.

The current scheme for protein synthesis may be summarized:

(1) Activation of amino acids
  Enz + AA + ATP ⇌ Enz—AMP—AA + PP
(2) Formation of amino acyl-RNA compounds
  Enz—AMP—AA + s-RNA ⇌ AA—s-RNA + AMP + Enz
(3) Formation of peptide bonds
  n(AA—s-RNA) + ribosome ⇌ polypeptide on ribosome + n(s-RNA)
(4) Release of polypeptide
  Polypeptide on ribosome → polypeptide + ribosome

Much more data is available for the first two steps than the remaining reactions.

Cell free preparations from plants catalyse an amino acid dependent incorporation of pyrophosphate into ATP. The same preparations also form amino acid hydroxamic acids in the presence of ATP. These observations suggest that the amino acids are activated by formation of amino acid-adenylate compounds. Studies with animal and microbial preparations support this hypothesis. ATP is formed when pyrophosphate and synthetic amino acid-adenylate compounds are incubated with preparations from yeast and animals.

In the absence of s-RNA no exchange can be demonstrated between ATP and AMP. With catalytic quantities of enzyme the proposed amino acid-adenylates cannot be detected. If large amounts of enzyme are used, amino acid-adenylates can be found in amounts equivalent to the quantity of enzyme. These data strongly suggest that the amino acid-adenylates are firmly bound to the enzyme. Studies with preparations from animals show that ^{18}O is transferred from the carboxyl group of the amino acid to the AMP phosphate. This indicates that it is the carboxyl group which is activated. The reaction may be represented:

$$
\text{Enz} + \text{ATP} + \text{R—CH—COOH} \rightarrow \text{E—AMP—O—C—CH—R} + \text{PP}
$$

with the $\overset{\text{O}}{\overset{\|}{\text{C}}}$ group, and NH$_2$ groups below the respective CH carbons.

The formation of amino acid hydroxamates involves the following reaction:

$$
\text{E—AMP—O—C—CH—R} + \text{NH}_2\text{OH} \rightarrow \text{R—CH—C—NHOH} + \text{E} + \text{AMP}
$$

with $\overset{\text{O}}{\overset{\|}{\text{C}}}$ groups, NH$_2$ below CH carbons, and Hydroxylamine labelled below NH$_2$OH.

Extracts of peas which catalyse the above reactions also catalyse the formation of amino acid-polynucleotide compounds in the presence of a fraction containing s-RNA. Studies with preparations from animals and micro-organisms have revealed that in the presence of activating enzyme, ATP, s-RNA and magnesium the amino acids become linked to the s-RNA. There is strong evidence that the linkage is an ester bond formed with the 2′ or 3′ hydroxyl group of the terminal adenosine of the s-RNA (see p. 426). In the presence of s-RNA, synthetic amino acyl-adenylates give rise to amino acyl-RNA compounds. It thus appears that s-RNA is the acceptor for the activated amino acids. Attempts to separate the activating and transferring activities have been unsuccessful and it is probable that a single enzyme catalyses both reactions. The overall reaction,

$$\text{ATP} + \text{amino acid} + \text{s-RNA} \rightleftharpoons \text{amino acid-s-RNA} + \text{AMP} + \text{PP}$$

is reversible and studies with partially purified enzymes give equilibrium constants for amino acid-s-RNA synthesis of 0·3 to 0·7. The enzyme is referred to as an activating enzyme or an amino acyl-RNA synthetase.

Extracts of peas may form amino acid-s-RNA compounds with all the protein amino acids. A number of activating enzymes have been partially purified from animals and micro-organisms. Specificity studies indicate a high degree of specificity for the s-RNA and also for the amino acid. Thus the transfer of amino acids to s-RNA is additive not competitive, and partial purification of s-RNA specific for single amino acids has been reported.

Evidence for the participation of amino acid-s-RNA compounds in protein synthesis may be summarized:

(i) Pea preparations incorporate amino acid-s-RNA compounds of all the protein amino acids into ribosomal protein.

(ii) Synthesis of protein by pea ribosomes *in vitro* requires the presence of the fraction containing the activating enzymes.

(iii) Amino acids bound to s-RNA are more readily incorporated into protein by cell free extracts of peas than an equivalent concentration of free amino acids.

(iv) When valine-^{14}C was supplied to ascites cells the distribution of activity in s-RNA and ribosomal protein changed in a manner which was consistent with the view that valine was converted to valine-s-RNA and then incorporated into protein.

Knowledge of the remaining reactions of protein synthesis is limited. During protein synthesis by isolated pea ribosomes there is a rapid turnover of at least some of the ribosomal protein but the net accumulation of protein is reported to occur in the incubation medium.

The transfer of amino acids from amino acid-s-RNA to peptide linkage in isolated ribosomes of peas requires a divalent cation, GTP, glutathione and an uncharacterized enzyme extractable from ribosomes. There is evidence that this transfer is directed to the N-terminal end of polypeptide chains.

28§

It appears that once this polypeptide chain is completed it is released from the ribosomes in a reaction which requires a divalent cation, ATP and 'release enzymes'.

Protein synthesis in plant nuclei and that reported for mitochondria and chloroplasts has not been studied enough to determine whether it proceeds by the same mechanism which operates in the ribosomes. There is little data which is not consistent with the hypothesis that all protein in the plant cell is synthesized by the same mechanism. Amino acid activating enzymes have been reported present in chloroplasts.

Protein Turnover

In the 1940's it was shown that ammonia ^{15}N was rapidly incorporated into protein in intact plants. It was proposed that plant protein existed in a dynamic state. This hypothesis was consistent with the observation of a close connection between protein metabolism and respiration in plants. It is accepted that in the plant as a whole, concomitant synthesis and degradation of protein occur. However, it is not clear whether there is turnover of the proteins of an individual resting cell in the plant. In the absence of conclusive data from plants, opinion has largely been determined by work with micro-organisms and animals. Until the last three or four years there was little proof of protein turnover, and a number of workers believed that proteins did not turnover. More recently definitive evdence of protein turnover has been obtained from animals and micro-organisms.

Specificity of Protein Synthesis

The one gene one enzyme hypothesis proposed by Beadle and Tatum has led to an acceptance of the view that the specific structure of proteins is genetically controlled. It is suggested that genetic information is coded by a specific sequence of nucleotides on DNA and that these sequences control the linear arrangement of amino acids in proteins.

The close connection between RNA and protein synthesis has led to the hypothesis that the genetic information of DNA is transferred to RNA which acts as a template for protein synthesis. It is, however, conceivable that in certain cases DNA may act directly as a template for protein synthesis. It follows that RNA can carry genetic information and that there is a mechanism which will permit the specific selection and arrangement of amino acids along RNA. Studies with tobacco mosaic virus show that almost pure preparations of viral RNA can transmit the genotype of the virus. Studies on the specificity of the amino acid-s-RNA synthetases strongly indicate that these enzymes can catalyse the formation of specific amino acid-s-RNA compounds for each protein amino acid. The specificity of these compounds would ensure that they would fit only into the appropriate place on the template. Since there is evidence that this specificity is due to the nucleotide sequences in the s-RNA, it has been postulated that each amino acid-s-RNA compound is attached to an RNA template by hydrogen bonding.

Also implicit in the general hypothesis is a mechanism whereby the base sequence of DNA can be copied in RNA. Present evidence indicates that RNA polymerase could fulfil this requirement.

Since proteins are formed on the ribosomes it has been proposed that ribosomes originate in the nucleus and that ribosomal RNA is the template. Recently this view has been questioned. Studies with 'phage infected *E. coli* have shown that, although 'phage specific protein is synthesized after infection, it is formed in ribosomes which existed before the 'phage entered the cell. In fact no new ribosomes could be detected after infection. Further experiments with bacteria have provided evidence for a hitherto unrecognized type of RNA termed messenger RNA. There is evidence that messenger RNA constitutes a small proportion of the total RNA, is labile, turns over rapidly, has the same base ratio as DNA and can become reversibly associated with ribosomes. It has been proposed that messenger RNA, formed in the nucleus, acts as the template for protein synthesis in the ribosome. The rapid turnover of messenger RNA has been taken to indicate that a given template has a short life. If these hypotheses are correct then the ribosome must be viewed as a non-specific structure which can synthesize a variety of proteins according to the messenger RNA present.

Support for the view that messenger RNA is the template has been obtained with cell free systems. The incorporation of amino acids by well washed ribosomes from *E. coli* is greatly stimulated by the addition of purified RNA. Evidence that the added RNA determines the specificity of the protein formed in this system comes from experiments in which the RNA was replaced by synthetic polyribonucleotides of known composition. These polymers were prepared by incubating the appropriate substrates with polynucleotide phosphorylase. Nirenberg and Matthaei found that the addition of polyuridylic acid instead of RNA led to a marked stimulation of phenylalanine incorporation. No other amino acids were incorporated to anything like the same extent. Further study indicated that the phenylalanine was incorporated into polyphenylalanine by reactions similar to those which catalyse the incorporation of amino acids into protein. Subsequently it has been shown that by varying the composition of the added polyribonucleotide the incorporation of other protein amino acids can be specifically stimulated. For example a co-polymer of cytidylic and guanylic acids stimulates the incorporation of proline, whilst a co-polymer of adenylic and guanylic acids stimulates the incorporation of lysine. From these experiments it appears that the composition of the added RNA determines the composition of the product.

It seems probable that genetic information is coded as a specific sequence of bases in DNA and that this code is replicated in RNA templates and then translated into a specific sequence of amino acids. The way in which a sequence of four different bases determines a sequence of twenty different amino acids is known as the coding problem.

A variety of codes has been suggested. Recently it has become possible to study this problem experimentally. The observation that polyuridylic acid stimulated the incorporation of phenylalanine indicated that a sequence of uridylic acid residues coded for phenylalanine. Attempts to decipher the code have been made by comparing the ability of different synthetic polyribonucleotides to stimulate the incorporation of protein amino acids.

A second approach has involved the use of artificially produced mutants of tobacco mosaic virus. Treatment of the viral RNA with nitrous acid changes cytosine to uracil and adenine to guanine. The protein of viruses derived from RNA which has been treated with nitrous acid differs from the protein of untreated virus in that certain amino acids have been replaced by others. An indication of the code can be obtained by comparing the changes of amino acids with the changes in the nucleotides known to have been caused by nitrous acid.

Genetic experiments with 'phage have also contributed to our knowledge of the code.

Evidence available at present indicates that the code probably has the following features:—

(i) 3 bases code one amino acid.
(ii) The code is non-overlapping and is "read" from a fixed starting point.
(iii) The code is degenerate—at least some amino acids are coded by more than one triplet of bases.

READING LIST

On Protein Synthesis, Crick, F. H. C. (1958) *Symp. Soc. Exptl. Biol.* 12, 138.
Enzymic Reactions in the Synthesis of the Purines, Buchanan, J. M. & Hartman, S. C. (1959) *Adv. Enz.* 21, 199.
The Enzymic Synthesis of Pyrimidines, Reichard, P. (1959) *Adv. Enz.* 21, 263.
The Relationship of Nucleic Acid and Protein Synthesis as Revealed by Studies with Cell-Free Systems, Hoagland, M. B., in The Nucleic Acids 3, Chapter 37. Ed. Chargaff, E. & Davidson, J. N. Acad. Press, New York, 1960.
The Biosynthesis of Protein, Ed. Harris, R. J. C. (1960) Acad. Press, New York.
The Chemistry of Nucleic Acids, Jordan, D. O. (1960) Butterworths, London.
The Intracellular Turnover of Proteins and Nucleic Acids and Its Role in Biochemical Differentiation, Mandelstam, J. (1960) *Bact. Rev.* 24, 289.
Protein Synthesis, Webster, G. C. (1961) *Ann. Rev. Pl. Physiol.* 12, 113.

LITERATURE CITED

BOLLARD E. G. (1959) *Symp. Soc. Exptl. Biol.* 13, 304.
YEMM E. W. & FOLKES B. F. (1958) *Ann. Rev. Pl. Physiol.* 9, 245.

SUBJECT INDEX

Names of specific enzymes are not included in the index. Specific enzymes mentioned in the text may be found by referring to the substrate(s) on which the enzyme acts. For example, information on alcohol dehydrogenase is listed in the index under 'alcohol'.